STARCH:
Chemistry and Technology

VOLUME II
INDUSTRIAL ASPECTS

STARCH:

Chemistry and Technology

EDITED BY

ROY L. WHISTLER

DEPARTMENT OF BIOCHEMISTRY
PURDUE UNIVERSITY
LAFAYETTE, INDIANA

EUGENE F. PASCHALL

MOFFETT TECHNICAL CENTER
CORN PRODUCTS CO.
ARGO, ILLINOIS

ASSISTANT EDITORS

J. N. BEMILLER
DEPARTMENT OF CHEMISTRY
SOUTHERN ILLINOIS UNIVERSITY
CARBONDALE, ILLINOIS

HUGH J. ROBERTS
KRAUSE MILLING COMPANY
MILWAUKEE, WISCONSIN

VOLUME II

INDUSTRIAL ASPECTS

1967

Academic Press   New York and London

ACADEMIC PRESS INC.
111 Fifth Avenue, New York, New York 10003

United Kingdom Edition published by
ACADEMIC PRESS INC. (LONDON) LTD.
Berkeley Square House, London W.1

LIBRARY OF CONGRESS CATALOG CARD NUMBER: 65-21330

PRINTED IN THE UNITED STATES OF AMERICA.

LIST OF CONTRIBUTORS

Numbers in parentheses indicate the pages on which the authors' contributions begin.

ANDERSON, ROY A. (53), Northern Regional Research Laboratory, Peoria, Illinois

ARMBRUSTER, F. C. (553), George M. Moffett Technical Center, Corn Products Co., Argo, Illinois

COMPTON, JACK (147), Institute of Textile Technology, Charlottesville, Virginia

DUX, ERIC F. W.[1] (537), Sichel Adhesives Ltd., The Adhesives Division of Corn Products (Sales) Ltd., London, England

EVANS, R. B. (253), National Starch and Chemical Corporation, Plainfield, New Jersey

HAMILTON, R. M. (351), Moffett Technical Center, Corn Products Co., Argo, Illinois

HJERMSTAD, ERLING T. (423), Penick & Ford Ltd., Cedar Rapids, Iowa

HOGAN, J. T. (65), Southern Regional Research Laboratory, New Orleans, Louisiana

HULLINGER, CLIFFORD H. (445), American Maize-Products Company, Roby, Indiana

KNIGHT, J. W. (279), Corn Products Company, Ltd., Trafford Park, Manchester, England

KOOI, E. R. (553), George M. Moffett Technical Center, Corn Products Co., Argo, Illinois

KRUGER, L. H. (369), Research Department, National Starch and Chemical Corporation, Plainfield, New Jersey

LANGLOIS, DAVID P. (451), A. E. Staley Mfg. Co., Decatur, Illinois

MARTIN, W. H. (147), Institute of Textile Technology, Charlottesville, Virginia

MAYWALD, EILEEN C. (637, 649), Moffett Research Center, Corn Products Co., Argo, Illinois

[1] Present address: J. Lyons and Co., Ltd., London, England.

v

MEHLTRETTER, C. L. (433), Northern Regional Research Laboratory, Peoria, Illinois

NISSEN, EDWARD K. (121), Technical Service, Union Starch & Refining Co., Inc., Granite City, Illinois

OSMAN, ELIZABETH M. (1963), State University of Iowa, Iowa City, Iowa

PASCHALL, E. F. (351, 403), Moffett Technical Center, Corn Products Co., Argo, Illinois

POWELL, EUGENE L. (523), American Maize-Products Company, Roby, Indiana

ROBERTS, HUGH J. (293), Krause Milling Company, Milwaukee, Wisconsin

RUTENBERG, M. W. (369), Research Department, National Starch and Chemical Corporation, Plainfield, New Jersey

SCALLET, BARRETT L. (237), Central Research Department, Anheuser-Busch, Inc., St. Louis, Missouri

SCHOCH, T. J. (79, 637), Moffett Technical Center, Corn Products Co., Argo, Illinois

SENTI, F. R. (499), Northern Regional Research Laboratory, Peoria, Illinois

SCHILDNECK, PAUL (217), A. E. Staley Mfg. Co., Decatur, Illinois

SHIPMAN, LEE (103), General Foods Corporation, Dover, Delaware

SMITH, C. E.[2] (217), A. E. Staley Mfg. Co., Decatur, Illinois

SMITH, ROBERT J. (569), Moffett Technical Center, Corn Products Co., Argo, Illinois

SOWELL, ERNEST A. (237), Central Research Department, Anheuser-Busch, Inc., St. Louis, Missouri

TREADWAY, R. H. (87), Eastern Regional Research Laboratory, Philadelphia, Pennsylvania

WAGONER, JOHN A. (451), A. E. Staley Mfg. Co., Decatur, Illinois

WATSON, STANLEY A. (1), Moffett Technical Center, Corn Products Co., Argo, Illinois

WIVINIS, GERALD P. (649), Moffett Technical Center, Corn Products Co., Argo, Illinois

WURZBURG, O. B. (253), National Starch and Chemical Corporation, Plainfield, New Jersey

[2] Deceased 1964.

PREFACE

The second volume of this treatise presents a comprehensive survey of the practical aspects of starch chemistry. It is written primarily for those who are concerned with the manufacture and uses of starches and of starch-derived products, but it will be of interest to all chemists concerned with starch reactions.

In the preparation of this volume, the editors faced, even more than in the preparation of Volume I, the difficult task of compressing into a single volume the vast amount of useful, practical information on the manufacture and uses of starches. It is hoped that a uniform condensation has been achieved by division of the chapters into four major categories: manufacture of commercially important starches; uses for starches in the paper, textile, and food industries; manufacture and uses of starch derivatives; and selected chapters on the analysis, identification, and microscopy of starches. Although some minor topics have not been discussed, all significant practical matters are presented.

Over thirty recognized authorities in the wet-milling, food, paper, and textile industries, in government laboratories, and one from a university have contributed to Volume II. Some minor duplication of subject matter occurs because of the nature of the format. Wherever possible, cross references are made to additional discussion. In many cases, the authors have been unable to give precise details on manufacturing processes because of the confidential nature of the information. Usually, sufficient literature references are cited to enable the reader to pursue the subject further.

Although documentation of material presented is quite complete, descriptions should not be construed as indicating that the use of the procedures or processes described are free from patent restrictions.

The editors express their sincere thanks to the many collaborators for their time and patience in making this volume possible.

ROY L. WHISTLER
EUGENE F. PASCHALL

March, 1967

CONTENTS

Chapter I

Manufacture of Corn and Milo Starches

Stanley A. Watson

Chapter II

Manufacture of Wheat Starch

Roy A. Anderson

Chapter III

The Manufacture of Rice Starch

J. T. Hogan

Chapter IIIa

Properties and Uses of Rice Starch

T. J. Schoch

Chapter IV

Manufacture of Potato Starch

R. H. Treadway

Chapter V

Manufacture of Tapioca, Arrowroot, and Sago Starches

Lee Shipman

Chapter VI

Starch in the Paper Industry

Edward K. Nissen

Chapter VII
Starch in the Textile Industry
Jack Compton and W. H. Martin

Chapter VIII
Starch in the Food Industry
Elizabeth M. Osman

Chapter IX
Production and Uses of Acid-Modified Starch
Paul Shildneck and C. E. Smith

Chapter X
Production and Use of Hypochlorite-Oxidized Starches
Barrett L. Scallet and Ernest A. Sowell

Chapter XI

Production and Use of Starch Dextrins

R. B. Evans and O. B. Wurzburg

Chapter XII

Modification and Uses of Wheat Starch

J. W. Knight

Chapter XIII

Starch Derivatives

Hugh J. Roberts

Chapter XIV

Production and Uses of Starch Phosphates

R. M. Hamilton and E. F. Paschall

Chapter XV

Production and Uses of Starch Acetates

L. H. Kruger and M. W. Rutenberg

Chapter XVI

Production and Uses of Cationic Starches

E. F. Paschall

Chapter XVII

Production and Uses of Hydroxyethylstarch

Erling T. Hjermstad

Chapter XVIII

Production and Use of Dialdehyde Starch

C. L. Mehltretter

Chapter XIX

Production and Use of Cross-Linked Starch

Clifford H. Hullinger

Chapter XX

Production and Use of Amylose

David P. Langlois and John A. Wagoner

Chapter XXI

High-Amylose Corn Starch: Its Production, Properties, and Uses

F. R. Senti

Chapter XXII

Production and Use of Pregelatinized Starch

Eugene L. Powell

Chapter XXIII

Production and Uses of Starch Adhesives

Eric F. W. Dux

Chapter XXIV

Production and Use of Dextrose

E. R. Kooi and F. C. Armbruster

Chapter XXV

Characterization and Analysis of Starches

Robert J. Smith

Chapter XXVI

Industrial Microscopy of Starches

Thomas J. Schoch and Eileen C. Maywald

Chapter XXVII

Photographs of Starches

Gerald P. Wivinis (Technical Photographer) and Eileen C. Maywald

Contents of Volume I
Fundamental Aspects

Errata for Volume I

Page 505, lines 16 and 17—*for* increases *read* decreases

Page 508, line 29—*for* increased *read* decreased

CHAPTER I

MANUFACTURE OF CORN AND MILO STARCHES

By Stanley A. Watson

Moffett Technical Center, Corn Products Co., Argo, Illinois

I. Introduction

Mechanical innovations developed by trial and error during full-scale operations stimulated much of the early growth of the corn starch industry (1). Today, process and product improvements more commonly follow research and engineering studies and thorough pilot plant evaluation. In the 15 years since the publication of Kerr's well-documented description of the wet milling process (2), many changes have taken place. Most wet milling plants have been completely redesigned for continuous automatic operation. Such installations now require much less space than the units they replaced; working conditions and plant sanitation have vastly improved; and continuous operation and product monitoring have improved product quality and uniformity. A typical modern wet milling process is described at the end of this chapter.

1

The major part of the chapter, however, is concerned with the structure and composition of corn and milo kernels, the fundamentals of steeping, and the factors involved in the physical separation of the component parts of the kernels. Although continued improvement in the mechanical aspects of the wet milling process can be expected, the future progress of the industry depends upon increased knowledge of grain structure and composition, on genetics and breeding to produce corn and milo types of specialized value, and on a better understanding of the mechanical and colloidal behavior of grain components in aqueous systems.

II. CORN: ITS ORIGIN, STRUCTURE, AND COMPOSITION

1. Origin

The word "corn" is used in the United States as the common name for the cultivated member of the grass family (Gramineae) known to botanists as *Zea mays* L. More specifically, "corn" here means the seed produced by *Zea mays;* it is not a general term for grains as in Europe. Maize is the common name generally used outside of the United States.

The genus *Zea* has only one species, but a number of types are recognized which differ primarily in structure of the seed. Examples are popcorn, sweet corn, dent corn, flint corn, and flour corn. Corn, as we now know it, is a captive of civilization. It has been grown under cultivation for so many thousands of years that it is now incapable of growing in competition with wild plants. This fact, along with much cytological and morphological evidence, led Weatherwax and Randolph (*3*) to hypothesize that corn may have originated by mutation from a now extinct ancestor that also produced its close relatives *Tripsacum* (gamma grass) and *Euchlena* (teosinte). Recent archeological evidence (*4*) has reinforced the idea that the wild ancestor of corn was corn, not one of its relatives, and that it was well established by about 5600 B.C. Corn has reached its present state of development through continued mutations, hybridizations, segregations, and selections in the gardens of man. It has been the staple item of food for countless generations of Indians of both North and South America. These early agriculturalists developed, by chance or by design, many forms of the plant through breeding methods now known as mass selection, preservation of mutations, and hybridization. The American Indians gave to the rest of the world a plant of economic worth greater than all the gold plundered by the early Spanish explorers. Corn has continuously improved; at first by the same haphazard methods employed by the Indians, but more recently by the application of scientific corn breeding methods aided by a growing knowledge of the morphology, physiology, and biochemistry of this amazing plant (5).

2. Culture

Corn has spread from the Americas to other parts of the world and is today established as a crop of importance on every continent. Corn production by continents is given in Table I (6). Diverse types of corn

Table I

World Corn Production Average, 1960–1963 (6)

	Acreage (1000 acres)	Production (1000 bushels[c])
North America	82,817	4,133,750
United States only	61,835	3,162,917
South America	30,018	666,250
Western Europe[a]	8,280	336,250
Eastern Europe[b]	20,423	625,000
U.S.S.R.	16,200	392,500
Asia	54,213	905,000
Africa	30,885	595,000
Oceania	211	—
Estimated total	243,047	7,661,100

[a] Austria, France, Greece, Italy, and Spain.

[b] Albania, Bulgaria, Czechoslovakia, Hungary, Rumania, and Yugoslavia.

[c] One standard bushel is 56 pounds at 15.5 percent moisture.

have been developed that will grow under many climatic and soil conditions. The region of greatest productivity in the United States has a frost-free season of over 140 days and an annual precipitation of 24–40 inches (except where irrigated) with 8 inches or more falling from June through August. The corn plant utilizes about one-half its seasonal water requirement during the 5 weeks following attainment of maximum leaf area (tasseling stage). A mean summer temperature of 70° to 80°F and a mean night temperature of 58°F are best (7). The typical hybrid corn grown in the central United States is 7 to 10 feet tall, has 10 to 14 leaves, and one ear borne at about the center of the stalk.

A favorable climate, large areas of good soil, and a free enterprise system have enabled the United States to remain the largest producer of corn. Corn that is used for starch manufacture in the United States is grown in the area of most intensive corn culture—the corn belt, an area comprising about 725 counties in 12 north central states. Yields of corn in this area have steadily risen to the present level of 100 to

150 bushels an acre through use of improved hybrids, intensive fertilization, and retirement of the least productive land.

3. Utilization

In the United States corn is classed as a feed grain. Of the corn grown in the United States for grain, 55 to 60% is retained on the farm for animal feeding. About half the corn sold from the farm also goes into manufactured animal feeds which are chiefly composed of ground corn; about one-fourth is used in industry, and the remainder is exported. The dry milling industry uses more than 120 million bushels of corn annually in the manufacture of corn meal and breakfast foods. The distilling industry uses 25–35 million bushels a year. The amount of corn used for starch manufacture in the United States has increased almost every year since the industry began. In 1964 corn wet millers used 193.9 million bushels of corn or about 5% of the corn raised by farmers. From this corn they produced 2495 million pounds of starch, 1049 million pounds of corn sugar, 2800 million pounds of corn syrup, and 367 million pounds of corn oil. Production of by-product feeds amounted to 1.35 million tons (6). Use of corn by the wet milling industry slightly exceeded 200 million bushels in 1965; it has increased about 5% annually over the past 5 years.

Corn wet milling plants have been established in almost every corn producing country of the world. Corn starch and corn syrup are important items of world commerce and are vital constituents of manufactured goods of many kinds.

4. Development of the Kernel

The corn kernel is a caryopsis or berry, a one seeded fruit, borne on a female inflorescence commonly known as the ear. Each ear bears upon its central stem, the cob, up to 1000 individual and seemingly indentical kernels (Figs. 1 and 2). An understanding of the growth of corn kernels and development of their contained structures is helpful when considering problems of corn quality and wet milling. Therefore, a brief description of kernel ontogeny is appropriate.

Each corn kernel develops from a single male-sterile flower upon fertilization by a pollen grain. The pollen grains are produced in the male inflorescence, commonly known as the tassel. They are carried by wind and are lodged on the hairy ends of the elongate stigmas (silks) of female flowers. Each silk grows from a single female flower (later the crown of the kernel) until it protrudes from the end of the husk that surrounds and protects the ear. Pollen grains germinate on the silk and send a slender tube down through it to deposit three sperm nuclei in the ovule. One nucleus fuses with the egg nucleus to form the embryo which later develops into the germ of the kernel. The other two nuclei fuse with a second nucleus in the ovule to begin the development of the endosperm part of the mature kernel (8). The ovary wall develops into the pericarp (hull) which continues to expand for as long as the kernel increases in size during maturation (8, 9).

Growth and development of the plant up to the time of pollination requires 50–80 days from planting, depending upon the inherited earliness of the variety and the climatic conditions, especially the temperature and soil moisture (10). About 16–24 hr. after pollination, the

FIG. 1.—Ear and shelled grain of United States hybrid dent corn, 0.5 actual size. United States dent hybrids have been successfully introduced onto other continents where the growing season is similar to that of the United States.

fertilized nuclei begin to divide to form their respective tissues. The embryo begins to differentiate at about 8 days, grows rapidly in size for about 25 days, and finally reaches full development in 45–55 days (9, 11–13). Groszmann and Sprague (12) observed that the weight of embryo and weight of oil in the embryo increased continuously to full kernel maturity. Wang demonstrated that embryo development in hybrid corn is more rapid than in inbred lines (13).

Endosperm differentiation begins 6–8 days after fertilization (9). The endosperm grows rapidly for about the first 30 days and dry matter continues to be deposited up to about 50 days after pollination (12). Cells in the upper central endosperm are the first to be formed and therefore are the first in which starch granules are deposited (*14*). Starch appears in this region 10–12 days after fertilization (*14, 15*), and subsequently its deposition spreads downward and outward. New endosperm cells are formed at the periphery of the endosperm, and, as new layers are formed, starch synthesis occurs in waves from top to bottom of the kernel. Duvick (*14*) visually observed in living endosperm cells the formation of starch granules in knobs on "mitochondria-like" filaments. These knobs exhibited phosphorylase activity just prior to the appearance of starch (*16*). The greater detail revealed by the electron microscope indicates that starch granules develop in proplastids (*17*; see also Vol. I, Chapter 5) instead of in mitochondria.

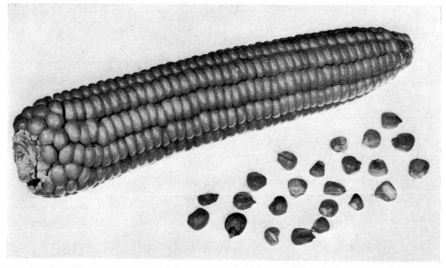

Fig. 2.—Ear and shelled grain of Argentine flint corn, 0.6 actual size. Many open pollinated varieties of flint corn are grown commercially in several South American countries. They are used for starch manufacture in Argentina and Brazil and in some European countries on import.

About a week after the first appearance of starch granules in the central endosperm cells, some of the minute cytoplasmic granules begin to enlarge into protein granules (*18*). Development of the protein granules progresses through the endosperm in waves following starch formation. In a mature kernel, the central endosperm contains the largest starch granules (10–30 μ) and the smallest protein granules ($< 1.0 \mu$). Starch granules occupy a much greater volume of these large central cells than do protein granules. Cells successively closer to the periphery are successively smaller and contain smaller starch granules (1–10 μ) and larger protein granules (1–3 μ). Duvick (*14*) has clearly described the arrangement of components in a mature endosperm cell: ". . . a section through a horny endosperm cell had somewhat the appearance of a section through a box of white marbles (starch grains) in which buckshot (protein granules) has been used as packing between the marbles; the whole boxfull is then filled with a transparent glue (clear viscous cytoplasm) which surrounds marbles and buckshot and makes the ensemble, when dry, a rigid conglomerate." The protein granules contain the alcohol-soluble protein, zein (18), and the clear matrix apparently contains the alkali-soluble protein, glutelin, as well as the globulins and other remnants of cytoplasm. Mature endosperm cells are shown in Figure 3 (upper plate).

Protein extraction data obtained on maturing kernels (19–21) show that the percentages of protein as zein and glutelin increase as the kernel matures, but globulin content decreases, probably as a result of dilution. Chemical changes in maturing whole corn kernels have been the subject of many studies (19–26) which are of interest with respect to differences in composition and maturity of corn harvested for grain. Because of varietal, cultural, and climatic variables, the data in different reports are obviously not identical, but the same general patterns may be seen in all. The best available data have been combined into a plot of normal changes in weight and composition of whole corn kernels during their development (Fig. 4).

Analytical values for starch, fat, protein, and sugar are obviously not reliable indicators for the stage of maturity in corn because net synthesis continues for 20–25 days after these components have reached relatively static proportions. The long-used descriptive terms—milk, dough, and dent stages—are merely qualitative measures of kernel moisture content and are useful for field observations only. Moisture content is an important criterion of maturity (27), but obviously, at some point, moisture loss becomes unrelated to maturation and becomes merely a function of drying. This stage is generally recognized as occurring when the kernel moisture has dropped to 35–30%, but the exact value differs among different inbreds and hybrids. Therefore, most authorities agree that maturity is reached when kernels no longer show an increase in dry weight. Early, medium, and late varieties in Iowa showed nearly the same number of days, 49–52, from silking to maturity (27). Again, this value is not easy to determine and is useful only in field studies. The detection of immature corn in commercial lots is, therefore, difficult. Fully mature corn kernels develop a characteristic sheen and sound appearance that experts can detect, but which may be modified during harvesting and storage. Practical methods of maturity detection will be discussed in Section II,7.

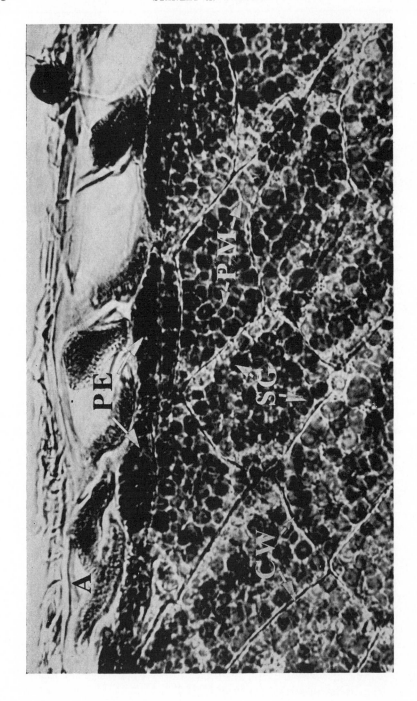

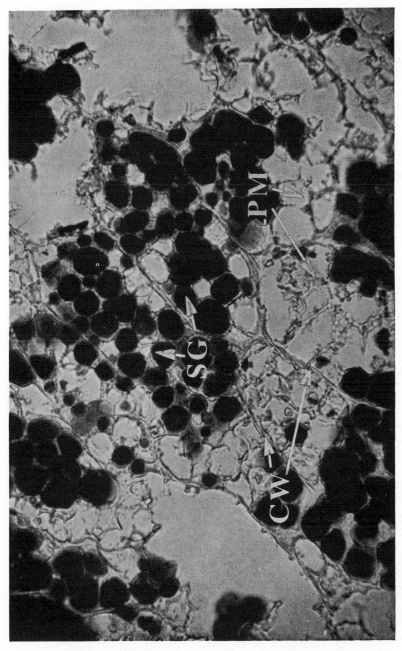

Fig. 3.—(Upper) Section of corn horny endosperm region, 10 microns thick, before steeping: Mag. 720×. (Lower) After steeping (iodine stained). A, aleurone layer; PE, dense peripheral endosperm cells; CW, cell walls; SG, starch granules; PM, protein matrix.

5. Structure of the Mature Kernel

Kernels of ordinary dent corn weigh about 350 mg. each, with an extreme range of 150 to 600 mg. An average kernel from the center of an ear of corn is a flattened ovoid measuring about 4 mm. thick, 8 mm. wide and 12 mm. long. Kernels at the ends of the ears are round owing to absence of pressure from neighboring kernels. About 75% of the kernels in an ordinary lot of dent corn are classified as flat kernels and 20% are classified as round kernels. The remaining 5% are very small kernels

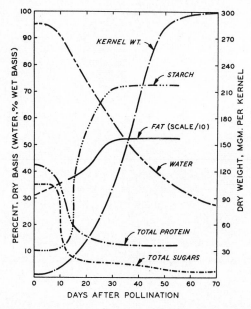

Fig. 4.—Plot of changes in dry weight of corn kernels and changes in chemical components during kernel growth period following fertilization of the ovules (pollination) (19–26).

from the ear tip. Seed corn is usually separated into about eight size grades for use in mechanical planters (28).

The mature corn kernel is composed of four principle parts: tip cap, pericarp (hull or bran), germ, and endosperm (Fig. 5). The relative proportions of these components is similar for most standard corn belt hybrids (29), but special types such as high- and low-oil strains may deviate considerably from the average (30, 31).

The proportions of component parts determined by hand dissection of typical dent corn kernels (29) are summarized in Table II. The average composition in Table II conforms very closely to analysis of average commercial dent corn. The wet milling process of corn for starch recovery is designed to obtain practically complete separation of the kernel components. Computations from these data show that germ contains 84.3% of the fat, 83.5% of the ash, 65.3% of the sugar, and 22.2% of

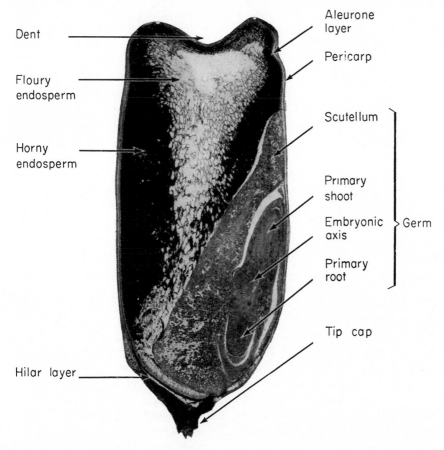

FIG. 5.—Longitudinal 10-micron bisection of a mature dent corn kernel: Mag. 10×. Iodine stained. Note how starch has been lost from floury endosperm cells because of the softening action of sulfur dioxide.

the protein in an average whole kernel; endosperm contains 98.5% of the starch and 73.6% of the protein contained in the whole kernel.

The structural relationship of these parts is shown in Figure 5. The corn kernel is a seed organized for germination and nourishment of the embryo. The tip cap is the remnant of the organ for attachment of kernel to cob. It is composed of star-shaped cells arranged in a spongy structure well adapted for rapid moisture absorption (32). Between the tip cap and the base of the germ is a black tissue, known as the hilar layer (*32, 33*) which apparently functions as a sealing mechanism upon maturation of the kernel.

The smooth outer covering of the kernel, the pericarp, is composed of an outer layer of dead, hollow, elongate cells packed into a tough, rather dense tissue. Beneath the dense layer is a spongy layer of cross and tube cells that is continuous with the tip cap and functions to absorb water. Directly beneath the spongy layer is a very thin suberized membrane known as the seed coat or testa. Next beneath the testa is a tough tissue, one cell in thickness, known as the aleurone cell layer which comprises about 3% of the kernel weight (*32, 34*). Although the aleurone layer is morphologically part of the endosperm, it is largely included in bran or fiber fractions in both wet and dry milling. In hand peeling, the aleurone and part of the pericarp remain with the endosperm (Table II).

The mature endosperm of average dent corn is composed of two major regions: floury or soft endosperm, 34% by weight; and horny or hard endosperm, 66% by weight (*30*). This ratio varies considerably, however, depending on the protein content of the kernel and the variety. Flour corns contain little or no horny regions. Although the dividing line between horny and floury endosperm is morphologically indistinct, the floury region is characterized (*35*) by large cells, large round starch granules, and a relatively thin protein matrix which ruptures during drying to form voids. These voids give the region its floury white appearance (*14*). In the horny endosperm, the intact protein matrix is thicker and does not rupture upon drying. The resulting pressure on the starch granules causes them to assume the angular surfaces characteristic of a closely packed solid. The horny endosperm contains only 1.5 to 2.0% higher protein content than the floury endosperm (*30, 34*); but, just under the aleurone layer, there is a denser row of cells known as sub-aleurone or dense peripheral endosperm (*36*) containing as much as 28% protein (*34*). These small cells contain very small starch granules and a very thick protein matrix, but comprise probably less than 5% of the endosperm. The sub-aleurone region of the endosperm can cause considerable difficulty in starch purification (*36*). The horny endosperm in flint corn extends over the entire crown; but, in dent corn, a failure of starch synthesis in the crown region results in eventual collapse of cells and inward shrinkage on drying (*14*). Starch can be recovered with ease from the floury endosperm by grinding corn after simple water soaking. Maximum starch recovery from horny endosperm requires the use of softening agents, which will be discussed in Section IV,2.

Table II

Component Parts of Mature Dent Corn Kernels and Their Chemical Compositions (29)

Part		Percent dry weight of whole kernel	Composition of kernel parts (% d.b.)[a]				
			Starch	Fat	Protein	Ash	Sugar
Germ	Range	10.5–13.1	5.1–10.0	31.1–38.9	17.3–20.0	9.38–11.3	10.0–12.5
	Mean	11.5	8.3	34.4	18.5	10.3	11.0
Endosperm	Range	80.3–83.5	83.9–88.9	0.7–1.1	6.7–11.1	0.22–0.46	0.47–0.82
	Mean	82.3	86.6	0.86	8.6	0.31	0.61
Tip-cap	Range	0.8–1.1	—	3.7–3.9	9.1–10.7	1.4–2.0	—
	Mean	0.8	5.3[b]	3.8	9.7	1.7	1.5
Pericarp[c]	Range	4.4–6.2	3.5–10.4	0.7–1.2	2.9–3.9	0.29–1.0	0.19–0.52
	Mean	5.3	7.3	0.98	3.5	0.67	0.34
Whole kernels	Range	—	67.8–74.0	3.9–5.8	8.1–11.5	1.27–1.52	1.61–2.22
	Mean	100	72.4	4.7	9.6	1.43	1.94

[a] d.b. = dry basis.   [b] Composite from nine different corn-belt hybrids.   [c] Also known as hull or bran.

The germ or embryo in average dent corn constitutes 11.5% of the kernel weight (Table II), but in high oil types of corn the germ percentage is higher (*31, 37*). The variety with the highest known oil content, Illinois High Oil Line (13–14% of oil), has a germ that comprises 22.3% of the kernel weight (*38*). Oil content of the germ also increases slightly with increase in germ size (*37*). The germ is composed of two major parts, the scutellum and the embryonic axis (Fig. 5). The embryonic axis which is the structure that grows into a seedling upon germination, makes up only about 10% of the germ (*39*). The larger scutellum stores nutrients which are quickly mobilized during initial seedling growth. The surface of the scutellum, in close contact with the endosperm, is covered by the secretory epithelium, a layer deeply furrowed by canals or glands lined with elongated secretory cells (*40*). The function of the cells is to secrete enzymes, largely alpha-amylase (*41*), which diffuse into the endosperm where they digest starch and other constituents to provide nourishment for the embryo.

The scutellar epithelium adheres to the endosperm by an insoluble cementing substance apparently consisting of degradation products of crushed cells and largely composed of pentoglycans and protein (*42*). This layer provides a strong bond that resists many chemical and physical means of separating germ and endosperm and requires prolonged steeping for an effective separation of whole intact germ from endosperm in wet milling. The major portion of the scutellum is composed of thick-walled isodiametric cells densely packed with cytoplasm. Oil droplets may be seen in sections of such cells, but a recent observation of lipid–protein particulates in cottonseed cotyledon (*43*) suggests that the state of oil in the scutellum should be reinvestigated.

During wet milling of corn, the objective is to obtain complete separation of endosperm and hull from the germ, but at the same time to avoid breaking germ cells. Any germ cells that are cut open during milling lose oil into the surrounding medium where recovery is not practical.

6. Chemical Components of Corn

The proximate analysis of corn for starch, oil, protein, fiber, and ash (Table III) is useful for evaluating corn for industrial fractionation and for animal feeding and human food. Many data have been published detailing the proximate analyses of various hybrids and of corn grown under various cultural regimes (*21, 25, 44, 45*). Table III gives ranges from published values; the averages are values obtained on corn received at two large wet milling plants in Illinois during the 5 year period from 1958–1962.

Although proximate analyses are broadly useful, they do not reveal the true chemical make-up of corn from a molecular and biological viewpoint. An increasing flow of knowledge of the chemistry of corn components helps the industry develop new and specific uses for products produced by corn wet milling.

Table III
Proximate Analysis of Corn Grain

	Range (45)	Average
Moisture, % (wet basis)	7–23	16.7
Starch, % (d.b.)[a]	64–78	71.5
Protein, (N × 6.25), % (d.b.)	8–14	9.91
Fat, % (d.b.)	3.1–5.7	4.78
Ash (oxide), % (d.b.)	1.1–3.9	1.42
Fiber (crude), % (d.b.)	1.8–3.5	2.66
Sugars, total, % (d.b.)	1.0–3.0	2.58
Total carotenoids, mg./kg.	5–40	30

[a] d.b. = dry basis.

a. *Starch*

As described in Volume I, Chapter X, the starch in ordinary dent corn is composed of 27% amylose and 73% amylopectin. Corn breeders have produced varieties with starch containing 100% of amylopectin (waxy maize) and other varieties containing up to 70–80% of amylose (see Vol. I, Chapter IV and this Volume, Chapter XXI). Both types are presently being used for commercial starch production.

b. *Fiber*

The pericarp of the corn kernel is comprised of about 40% cellulose and 40% pentoglycan (46). Both substances are cell-wall components in the pericarp and other fibrous tissues. The pentoglycan component is extractable from corn pericarps (or wet-milled coarse fiber) with dilute sodium hydroxide and may be recovered by dehydration in alcohol. Sometimes called corn fiber gum, it dissolves in water to form viscous pastes at 3–10% concentration (46, 47). It is a highly branched molecule(s) made up of 65% D-xylose, 35% L-arabinose, 8% DL-galactose, 8% D-glucose, and 7% glucuronic acid residues (46, 48).

c. *Sugars*

The major sugar in corn is sucrose. Its concentration in the whole kernel is 0.9–1.9% (26, 49); approximately three-fourths of the total resides in the embryo and only one-fourth in the endosperm (49).

D-Glucose makes up 0.2–0.5% of the whole kernel and D-fructose 0.1–0.4%. Only about one-fifth of each of these sugars is in the embryo; the remainder is in the endosperm. The embryo contains about two-thirds of the total sugar, and the endosperm contains about one-third. A small amount of raffinose (0.1–0.3%, whole kernel basis) is located entirely in the embryo. The raffinose disappears within about 2 days after the beginning of seed germination; maltose appears 2–4 days after initiation of germination, but is detected in the endosperm only after the initiation of amylase activity (*49*).

d. *Fat*

The germ contains 84% of the total kernel fat. Approximately 98% of the fat is in the form of glycerides of several fatty acids. The fatty acid distribution of corn oil as commercially produced in the United States is linoleic, 56%; oleic, 30%; linolenic, 0.7%; total saturated acids, 14% (*50*). The iodine number of average corn oil is 124. However, individual commercially grown corn hybrids give oils with iodine numbers that vary between 114 and 130. Iodine numbers of oils from corn belt inbred lines vary between 111 and 151 (*51*). Oil from equatorial regions averages 110–115 (*50*). These variations in iodine numbers are largely a reflection of differences among the proportions of linoleic, oleic, and stearic fatty acids in the glycerides (*52*). Iodine numbers of oils from individual corn varieties are relatively constant from year to year in the United States.

Minor constituents of crude corn oil include sitosterol, 1.0%; phosphatides, 1.0–1.5%; and tocopherols, 0.10%. Although total fat in commercial corn hybrids ranges from 3.5 to 5.7%, hybrids containing up to 9% oil (*52*) and one special line containing up to 14% oil (*53*) have been developed.

The composition of the fat in isolated endosperm has not been studied in detail. Fat isolated from the gluten fraction derived from wet milling is similar to germ oil, but has a higher content of unsaponifiables (*54*). A minor component of endosperm fat, the carotenoid group of pigments, is of considerable economic importance. These pigments, which are responsible for the color of yellow corn, are associated with the endosperm protein. Therefore, their concentration is greatest in the horny endosperm (*55*), and they are concentrated entirely in the gluten fraction during wet milling of corn (*56*). Fresh, commercial yellow dent corn contains 20–35 mg./kg. of total carotenoids. Quackenbush and co-workers (*51*) found a range of 5.7 to 57.9 mg./kg. in fresh grain of 125 inbred lines widely used as parents for corn belt hybrids. The major carotenoid pigments of yellow corn endosperm are beta-carotene (the major vitamin A precursor), lutein, and zeaxanthin. The last two pigments, classed as xanthophylls, have no known metabolic activity in animals but are absorbed and deposited in the adipose fat of poultry and in the yolk of eggs. The feeding of yellow corn or corn gluten meal contributes to the pleasing yellow color of poultry meat and of egg yolks (56). The carotenoid pigments in corn are gradually destroyed by oxidation, especially if the corn is exposed to light, high temperatures, or both (57). Thus, market corn loses one-fourth to one-half of its carotenoid content each year between February and September (56), making the production of a corn gluten meal of constant xanthophyll content virtually impossible.

e. *Proteins*

The proteins of corn have received much attention because of their importance in the animal and human diet. Many studies have utilized

Table IV

Typical Distribution of Major Proteins Among
Component Parts of the Corn Kernel (63)

Part	Part as % of kernel (d.b.)	Total protein in part (% d.b.)	Distribution of Protein (%)			
			Globulin (salt- or acid-sol.)	Zein (ethanol-sol.)	Glutelin (alkali-sol.)	Insoluble
Whole grain	100	11.4	25	48	25	2
Germ	11	18.4	37	5	51	7
Endosperm	82	12.0	20	52	17	11
Hull	7	4.2	—	—	—	—

the classic isolation technique of Osborne and Mendel (58) employing successive extractions of ground corn with water, 5% sodium sulfate, 70% aqueous ethanol, and 0.5N sodium hydroxide (19, 20, 38). More recently, Mertz and co-workers (59–61) adapted the alkaline copper sulfite reagent of Swan (62) to provide a nearly complete solution of corn proteins with a resultant improvement in fractionation and characterization.

Corn protein is a mixture of several distinct protein types: salt-soluble globulins; the alcohol-soluble prolamin, zein; and the alkali-soluble protein, glutelin. These proteins are distributed differently between germ and endosperm. Table IV gives data, recalculated from Bressani and Mertz (63), for a typical corn of relatively high protein content. The amounts of several proteins in germ are nearly the same in divergent types of corn, but in endosperm the proportion of zein increases with increasing protein content of the kernel (38, 63, 64) up to a maximum of about 60% of the endosperm protein. The alcohol-soluble and alkali-soluble fractions are essentially single protein types, but the globulin fraction contains a number of components, many of which are probably enzymes (60). Most of the globulins are dissolved during steeping or wet milling. The proteins occurring in germ and endosperm, although similar in solubility, may differ in structure (61). Zein is prepared industrially by extraction of gluten with 70% isopropyl alcohol (65) at a yield of about 2% of the corn dry substance.

Mertz and co-workers (65a, 65b) recently found that two mutant corn varieties, opaque-2 and floury-2, have endosperms in which glutelin is the predominant protein. One sample of opaque-2 endosperm contained 26% zein and 39% glutelin compared with 34% zein and 29% glutelin for a comparable normal corn containing 8.7% protein in the whole kernel. Lysine content was 3.4% (protein basis) for the opaque-2 endosperm compared with 2.0% for normal; tryptophan content was also proportionately higher in the opaque-2 and floury-2 mutants (65b). When fed to rats as the sole source of protein, the opaque-2 corn produced growth rates equivalent to casein which were almost 3-fold greater than those obtained with normal corn (65c). Yahl and Watson (65d) reported that on wet milling, the opaque-2 corn gave a high yield of steepwater and a lower yield of starch and gluten than normal corn. The steepwaters had equal lysine contents, but the opaque-2 gluten contained 2- to 3-fold greater lysine and tryptophan content than normal gluten.

f. *Mineral Components*

The corn kernel contains all the elements necessary for plant growth in easily mobilizable form. Phytin (hexaphosphoinositol) apparently plays a central role in mobilization of cations and is the primary storage form of phosphorus. Phytin phosphorus occurs in corn germ at a concentration of about 1.7%. Nearly all phytin in corn is located in the germ (66), probably as a mixed potassium magnesium salt. It is rapidly hydrolyzed during germination. The mineral components of corn (44, 45) expressed as percentage of the grain are potassium, 0.35%; magnesium, 0.12%; calcium, 0.02%; phosphorus, 0.28%; sulfur, 0.17%. Approximately 80% of the total ash is located in the germ (29). The mineral components are almost completely leached from the kernels during steeping in preparation for wet milling.

g. *Minor Organic Constituents*

Corn contains all the known water-soluble vitamins (45, 67). Niacin is present as a bound complex which can be released upon alkaline degradation (*68*). The corn gluten fraction from wet milling contains a high concentration of this substance. The four heterocyclic nitrogen compounds, niacin, trigonelline (*N*-methylnicotinamide), tryptophan, and the plant growth substance, indoleacetic acid, are chemically and physiologically related in corn (*69*). Indoleacetic acid occurs in relatively high concentrations in corn and wet milled fractions (*70*), especially in the steepwater in which its concentration is of the order of 200 micrograms per gram of dry substance. The nonprotein nitrogeneous (N.P.N.) substance constitutes 0.03% of the total nitrogen in the germ and 0.01% in the endosperm (*70a*). About 50% of the N.P.N. is free amino acids. The germ contains most of the quaternary nitrogen compounds, betaine, trigonelline, and choline, as well as purine and pyrimidine bases and their nucleosides.

7. Corn Quality

Much that has been discussed above relates to corn quality with respect to differences in composition that may have important effects on wet milling properties. Physical and biological properties are also important in corn wet milling. Sound, fully matured kernels that have high germinative viability are generally preferred for starch manufacture. Various degrees of damage, both physical and biological, may be inflicted on the corn kernel during maturation, in harvesting, and in subsequent handling or storage. Early killing frosts may delay maturation with resultant low kernel density and often low oil content and low starch yield in wet milling. So-called "soft corn," which is usually caused by a particularly early freeze, seldom enters the commercial trade because storability is poor. Laboratory experiments indicate that soft corn also gives poor wet milling results (*71*).

Until recently, most corn was picked at about 18–22% moisture. It was stored on the ear in slatted buildings called cribs for several months before shelling at moisture contents of 14–20%. In recent years, an increasing volume of corn has been harvested with machines that pick and shell the grain in the field. Optimum moisture for the combine harvesting operation is 22–28%, which requires that the corn be subjected to immediate artificial drying (*72*). Such corn may be of poorer quality for wet milling because dryer operators tend to use elevated temperatures to speed the rate of drying. Abusively dried grain exhibits stress cracks in the endosperm, which cause it to shatter upon handling (*73*). Grain that has been heated in excess of 60° generally exhibits lowered starch yield on wet milling and produces starch of reduced quality (*74, 75*). In addition, corn dried at excessive temperature becomes infected with mold at lower moisture levels than sound corn. Overheating apparently causes some physical change in the endosperm that results in a supernormal relative humidity equilibrium condition as noted by Tuite and Foster (76).

Corn is also rendered more susceptible to growth of storage fungi if it is damaged by shelling at high moisture content. Corn that is to be stored through summer must be dried to 13% moisture to prevent mold development in the kernels (77). Fungal growth on corn always lowers the quality for wet milling purposes. Whether the organisms are the cob-rotting types, such as *Diplodia zeae*, that infect corn in the field during periods of wet weather, or the more xerophytic organisms, such as *Aspergillus* sp. and *Penicillium* sp., that invade corn stored in bulk (78), an initial effect is the hydrolysis of fat to free fatty acids (78, 79). More severe infection successively causes darkening of the germ, loss of dry matter, complete rotting of the germ, and finally microbial invasion of the endosperm. A secondary effect of fungal infection in a grain mass is heating that may become so intense as to cause darkening of the entire kernel and, on some occasions, may cause spontaneous combustion (80).

Laboratory experiments have shown that oil yield is reduced when mold infected corn is wet milled. This effect is due to loss of fat through respiration, to fragmentation of severely damaged germs during milling, and to removal of free fatty acids during oil refining. Starch recovery is adversely affected when fungal growth has resulted in severe heating.

Insect infested corn is undesirable for wet milling because of actual loss of dry substance, contamination by insect body parts, and mold damage that may accompany insect activity. Because of the many deleterious effects caused by mold and insects, corn which is appreciably damaged by either is unfit for wet milling and is summarily rejected by the entire wet milling industry.

Measurement of quality in corn for wet milling is important in purchasing, process control, and research. Determination of market grade is the usual starting point and is of primary utility in trading. The grade requirements for corn on the United States market are given in Table V (81). The grade is determined by the factor having the highest rating. The wet milling industry uses principally corn of grades 2 and 3. Sample grade is not suitable for use in starch manufacture. Sound corn at a moisture content above 20% may be used during harvest season if it is moved quickly and used promptly.

The importance of moisture control in relation to corn storage has already been mentioned. Kempf (82) found no significant difference in yield of wet milling products from corn at 10, 15, or 19% moisture.

Mold damage is determined in market corn by visually counting the number of kernels with discolored germs (81). Heat-damaged corn is detected by the presence of discolored kernels. In each instance, however, significant damage with respect to wet milling properties may occur before kernels become visibly discolored. Such subvisible change may be detected in several ways. One of the most sensitive tests is the viability count, determined by sprouting. This method discloses the number of damaged kernels, but 3–5 days are required to make the determination. A more rapid procedure for viability testing utilizes

Table V
United States, Grading Standards for Corn[a] (81)

| | | | Maximum Limits | | |
| | | | | Damaged kernels | |
Grade	Minimum test weight per bushel (lb.)	Moisture (%)	Broken corn and foreign material (%)	Total (%)	Heat-damaged kernels (%)
1	56	14.0	2.0	3.0	0.1
2	54	15.5	3.0	5.0	0.2
3	52	17.5	4.0	7.0	0.5
4	49	20.0	5.0	10.0	1.0
5	46	23.0	7.0	15.0	3.0
Sample grade[b]	—	—	—	—	—

[a] Grades and grade requirements for the classes Yellow Corn, White Corn, and Mixed Corn.

[b] Sample grade shall be corn which does not meet the requirements for any of the grades from No. 1 to No. 5, inclusive; or which contains stones; or which is musty, or sour, or heating; or which has any commercially objectionable foreign odor; or which is otherwise of distinctly low quality.

2,3,5-triphenyltetrazolium chloride. A red coloration develops in viable germs on incubation with the chemical. This method provides a valid viability estimate in 1 hour (74, 83, 84). Although the procedure is rather laborious, because each kernel must first be cut through the embryonic axis before staining, it is particularly useful in diagnosing causes and extent of deterioration (84).

An equally rapid procedure that may be more useful for bulk samples is based upon a simple manometric estimation of the level of the enzyme L-glutamic acid decarboxylase (85) in the ground corn sample. This enzyme is apparently very easily destroyed when corn is dried or stored under adverse conditions. Results are said to be more closely correlated with viability than in the long-used rapid method for estimating free fat acidity (86).

No sure way of quickly measuring the extent of damage caused by excessive heating during artificial drying was known until the observations of Tuite and Foster (76). Their data indicate that deviation from expected values for equilibrium relative humidity of grain is correlated with heat damage and with adverse effects on wet milling properties (87).

A somewhat similar, but still more rapid, method of detecting heat damaged corn has recently been presented (88). The ratio of electrical resistance to conductance of a sample of corn deviates from normal values in proportion to the temperature at which the corn was dried.

Several procedures for conducting small scale laboratory wet millings have been developed (36, 89–91) which correlate well with manufacturing practice. These procedures are time-consuming but useful in correlating wet milling properties with other grain characteristics. Kempf and Tegge (92) used the complete wet milling method of Pelshenke and Lindemann (91) to show how starch and protein contents of various types of corn relate to the yield of starch and gluten. Refinements of the corn wet milling technology can be materially aided by development of new and rapid techniques for measuring quality attributes of corn.

III. Milo: Its Culture, Structure, and Composition

1. Origin and Culture

"Milo" is a popular name for the cereal most generally known as grain sorghum. The scientific name is *Sorghum vulgare* (family *Gramineae*) which covers many diverse plant forms. They include the sorgos (sweet sorghums) used for forage, silage, and syrup; Sudan grass grown for pasture, hay, and silage; broomcorn used in household brooms; and the grain sorghums (93). The grain sorghum varieties originally introduced into the United States from Africa and India included kafir, milo, durra, shallu, and others. Presently grown varieties and hybrids were derived largely from milo-kafir crosses (7). Nevertheless, the local terms, such as "milo maize" or "milo," "kafir corn," and "gyp corn," are still applied to whatever variety of grain sorghum is grown in a particular locality. The term "milo" has most generally been applied to the grain of commerce and to the industrial and food products derived therefrom. The terms milo and grain sorghum are, therefore, used interchangeably here.

Although most people in the United States are unfamiliar with grain sorghums, they are a food and feed grain of world-wide importance.

They are grown extensively in Pakistan, central India, north and central Africa, and China, or almost anywhere that limited rainfall precludes the culture of corn or rice (94). World production of grain sorghum in 1938–1940 was estimated to be over 24 million short tons of which 18 million tons was consumed as human food (95).

The major grain sorghum producing areas in the United States are South Dakota, Nebraska, eastern Colorado and New Mexico, western Texas, Oklahoma, Kansas, Missouri, Arizona, and California. Grain sorghum production has risen in the United States from under 50 million bushels in 1930 to 500–600 million bushels (56 lb./bu.) in 1958 to 1963. Production increases were spurred in the 1930's by the development of earlier maturing varieties and of plant types adapted to mechanical harvesting, and in the late 1950's by the development of hybrids. Practical hybrids resulted from the discovery of male-sterile types that could be cross-pollinated on a large scale (93). Use of hybrid grain sorghums increased grain yields by as much as 25%, thus making possible the production of 100–150 bushels of grain per acre under favorable conditions. Hybrid grain sorghums now account for practically all the acreage in commercial grain areas. Only about 25% of the milo crop is fed to livestock on the farm where it is grown. However, about 95% of the entire crop is used for animal feeding, with 8–10 million bushels used annually for wet and dry milling.

The sorghum plant resembles corn in vegetative appearance. Mature plants of American grain sorghum varieties range from 2 to 15 feet tall with 10 to 16 broad leaves on a stiff stalk. Stalks of mature plants may be juicy or quite dry, but the juice is usually only slightly sweet. Seeds and heads are larger for grain sorghums than for the sorgos. The buckshot size grains are borne on a terminal head, or rachis, containing 800–3000 kernels (Fig. 6). The flowers carry both male and female organs and are self pollinated; therefore, commercial hybrid seed production requires male-sterile types. Fertilization occurs in 50–75 days after emergence, depending on the inherited maturity. Grain matures about 40 days after pollination. Mature seeds thresh free of the glume. The grain is harvested at 14–18% moisture with standard combine harvesting machines.

Grain sorghum can be grown wherever the summer temperature averages 65° F or higher with a frost-free period of 120 days or more. Sorghums are grown most widely in semi-arid regions because they withstand extreme heat better than other plants. They are well adapted to regions that have 17–25 inches of annual rainfall, but they produce highest grain yields in the arid regions when irrigated. Unlike corn, the sorghum plant becomes practically dormant during periods of drought and resumes normal growth when moisture again becomes available (7). Milo is resistant to grasshopper and corn rootworm injury, and some

FIG. 6.—Mature hybrid milo inflorescence (head), 0.5 actual size; and threshed kernels, Mag. 4×.

varieties are resistant to corn borers and cinch bugs; it is subject to head mold, foliar diseases, and weather damage to kernels when grown in regions of high rainfall.

2. Structure and Composition

Milo kernels are flattened spheres measuring 4.0 mm. long by 3.5 mm. wide by 2.5 mm. thick (Fig. 6). The weight of individual sorghum kernels ranges from 8 to 50 mg. with an average of 28 mg., and there are 12,000 to 18,000 kernels to a pound. Seed coat colors of the prehybrid varieties ranged from white through pale orange, tan and red, to dark red-brown (*96*). Most grain now in commercial channels is a brownish red color, primarily because one or both parent lines of most hybrids are of that color.

Fertilization and development of the milo caryopsis follows a pattern similar to that of corn (*97*), but kernel development proceeds at a some-what faster pace. Starch granules begin to develop in the central crown region of the endosperm 7–9 days after fertilization, and oil synthesis in the germ begins at about the same time. Kernel expansion is pro-duced by endosperm cell production from a peripheral layer of meristem cells. This meristem tissue eventually matures to form the aleurone layer. Dry substance deposition in the milo grain ceases about 30 to 40 days after fertilization (*98*). Endosperm cells formed during the final wave of cell division usually fail to enlarge as do other endosperm cells. Thus, the mature milo kernel contains a sub-aleurone layer of peripheral cells that are distinguished by small dimensions, small starch granules, and a thick protein matrix (*36*). The milo kernel has a much greater proportion of horny endosperm than is found in. dent corn. Although some varieties have a high proportion of floury endosperm, true floury and dent types are not readily distinguished; and dent types are rare. Waxy starch endosperm and sweet endosperm milos are known (*93*), but high amylose types have not been found to date.

The pericarp of milo is similar in structure to that of corn, except that it is coated with a thick layer of wax and includes many very small starch granules in the mesocarp layer (*97, 98*). These tiny starch granules are not recoverable with the endosperm starch in wet milling.

The principal parts of the milo kernel are shown in Figure 7. The relative weight proportions and compositions of these respective parts are given in Table VI (*99*). Milo, like corn, contains about 94% of its total starch together with 81% of its protein in the endosperm. The germ contains 76% of the total fat. The morphological structure of milo germ and endosperm is almost identical with that of corn.

The proximate analysis of milo is given in Table VII. The range of values (*45*) include some extremes not commonly encountered, such as high fiber values which are undoubtedly the result of retention of the glume or kernel husk that in some varieties is not readily removed during threshing. The average values for moisture, starch, protein, fat, ash, and fiber are averages for milo received at Corpus Christi, Texas, for use in starch manufacture during 1959 to 1962. Most of this grain was produced from hybrid milos which produce slightly larger seeds with slightly higher starch and lower protein content than the regular

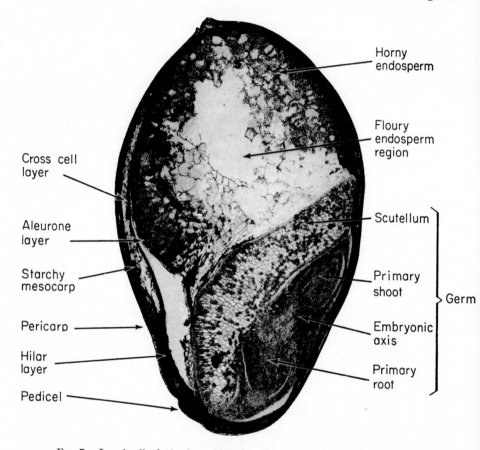

FIG. 7.—Longitudinal 10 micron bisection of mature milo kernel, Mag. 30×. Iodine stained. Note that practically all of the floury endosperm was lost on sectioning because of the softening action of sulfur dioxide.

vareties. Milo differs from corn in that it has lower fat content, but slightly higher protein and starch contents. It also seems to be more variable in protein content than corn. This fact has caused problems in mixed feed formulation (100). One reason for this variability may be that the milo entering commercial channels is grown under a wider range of soil fertility and moisture conditions than is cash market corn.

Wax content is measured by extraction of whole kernels with hot benzene (*99, 101*). Milo wax is similar to carnauba wax.

All varieties contain some tannin, but the dark brown varieties are

Table VI

Component Parts of Mature Milo Kernels and Their Chemical Compositions (99)[a]

		Parts dry weight (% of whole kernel)	Composition of kernel parts (%, dry basis)			
			Starch	Protein	Fat	Ash
Germ	Range	7.8–12.1	—	18.0–19.2	26.9–30.6	—
	Mean	9.8	13.4[b]	18.9	28.1	10.36[a]
Endosperm	Range	80.0–84.6	81.3–83.0	11.2–13.0	0.4–0.8	0.30–0.44
	Mean	82.3	82.5	12.3	0.6	0.37
Bran	Range	7.3–9.3	—	5.2–7.6	3.7–6.0[c]	—
	Mean	7.9	34.6[b]	6.7	4.9	2.02[b]
Whole kernel	Range	—	72.3–75.1	11.5–13.2	3.2–3.9[c]	1.57–1.68
	Mean	—	73.8	12.3	3.6	1.65

[a] Includes five varieties.
[b] Composite.
[c] Includes wax. Wax content of whole kernel is range, 0.29–0.44%; mean, 0.32% d.b.

Table VII

Proximate Analysis of Milo Grain

	Range (%, dry basis) (45)	Average (%, dry basis)
Water (% wet basis)	8–20	15.5
Starch	60–77	74.1
Protein (N × 6.25)	6.6–16	11.2
Fat (CCl$_4$ extract)[a]	1.4–6.1	3.7
Ash	1.2–7.1	1.5
Fiber (crude)	0.4–13.4	2.6
Pentoglycans	1.8–4.9	2.5
Sugars (as dextrose)	0.5–2.5	1.8
Tannin	0.003–0.17	0.1
Wax	0.2–0.5	0.3

[a] Includes wax.

particularly high in tannin content. Most varieties carry only traces of carotenoid pigments, but yellow endosperm types from Africa have been used to breed varieties which contain up to 15 mg./kg. of total carotenoids (*102*). The exposed seeds, however, are subject to severe losses of carotenoids in the field (*103*).

Milo germ oil is similar to corn oil in chemical and physical properties (54). Average iodine number is 122, and major fatty acid components are palmitic, 10%; stearic, 4%; oleic, 32%; linoleic, 56%. The oil extractable from milo gluten with hexane (7% d.b.) is more saturated than germ oil, having an iodine value of 98.

The proteins of milo endosperm and germ have received very little attention. A zein-like protein known as kafirin is extractable from the endosperm, or from the wet milling gluten fraction, with 60% aqueous ethanol or isopropanol at 40°–60°. Kafirin represents about 83% of the endosperm protein and contains a high proportion of glutamic acid (104). Bressani and Rios (105) have reported the amino acid composition of grain sorghum.

The mineral components of milo ash approximate the following proportions: 18% potassium; 8% magnesium, 0.9% calcium, 0.02% iron; 16% phosphorus; 0.3% sulfur. The phosphorus is largely present in the germ as phytin.

The sugars of whole milo kernels are also much like those of corn (106). Both regular and waxy types average 1.20% total sugars: 0.85% sucrose, 0.09% D-glucose, 0.09% D-fructose, and 0.11% raffinose. Sugary varieties contain 2.8% total sugar with a distribution of component sugars similar to that in regular varieties.

3. Milo Quality

Commercial lots of milo are graded No. 1 to No. 4 and Sample Grade (Table VIII) (81). Basis for grading is moisture content, test weight, foreign material, damage, and percentage of other grains. The excessively high allowance for broken kernels and foreign material is based on the concept that milo in the United States is a feed grain and that the foreign material has feed value. This material must be removed completely before the grain is usable for starch manufacture. Milo often shows surface darkening or weathering caused by growth of *Alternaria* sp. on the pericarp when the heads are subjected to high humidity before harvest. However, weathering does not adversely affect wet milling unless damage is severe. Storage of milo grain in bulk at moisture contents over 14% can result in mold growth and severe damage (107). Milo intended for long storage must be artificially dried to 12.0% moisture for safe storage. Because milo generally dries rapidly in the field (98), moisture content at harvest is ordinarily 14–18%. For this reason, milo lots damaged by high temperature drying are infrequently encountered. However, excessive drying temperatures can cause adverse effects on the wet milling properties of milo (108).

In general, milo is similar to corn in wet milling properties. The harder nature of the milo kernel makes starch recovery more difficult, resulting in slightly lower starch recoveries than with corn (109). The commercial starch manufacturing process for milo is almost identical to that of corn; therefore, the process described in Section IV applies to both.

A study of the milling properties of five waxy varieties and seven regular grain sorghum varieties (110) demonstrates the individual differences in milling characteristics. The regular varieties gave starch

Table VIII
U.S. Grading Standards for Grain Sorghum (81)[a]

| | | | Maximum limits of | | |
| | | | | | |
Grade	Minimum test weight per bushel (lb.)	Moisture (%)	Damaged kernels — Total (%) ·	Heat-damaged kernels (%)	Broken kernels, foreign material, and other grains (%)
1	57	13.0	2.0	0.2	4.0
2	55	14.0	5.0	0.5	8.0
3[b]	53	15.0	10.0	1.0	12.0
4	51	18.0	15.0	3.0	15.0
Sample Grade[c]	—	—	—	—	—

[a] Grades and grade requirements for the classes Yellow Grain Sorghum, White Grain Sorghum, Brown Grain Sorghum, and Mixed Grain Sorghum.
[b] Grain sorghum which is distinctly discolored shall not be graded higher than No. 3.
[c] Sample grade shall be grain sorghum which does not meet the requirements of any of the grades from No. 1 to No. 4, inclusive; or which contains stones; or which is musty, or sour, or heating; or which is badly weathered; or which has any commercially objectionable foreign odor except of smut; or which is otherwise of distinctly low quality.

yields of 60.7–65.4%, and the waxy varieties gave starch yields of from 56.2 to 59.3% (grain, dry basis). Protein content of the starches averaged 0.47% for the regular varieties and 0.26% for the waxy varieties. Colors of the starches, although almost white, were affected by the intensity of pigments in the pericarp or remnants of pigmented nucellar layer. Varieties having a complete pigmented nucellar layer, for example, Hegari (96), produce starches of such high color that they are unsuited for commercial use.

Microscopically both regular and waxy milo starches are almost identical to corn starches (111), but average granule diameter is a little larger: 15.0 μ on a number basis and 17.4 μ on a weight basis compared with respective values of 9.2 μ and 14.1 μ for corn starch (*112*). A more significant difference between these two starches is that milo starch has a gelatinization temperature range of 67°–75°, which is about 3° higher than the 62°–72° range observed with corn starch (*112*). Waxy milo

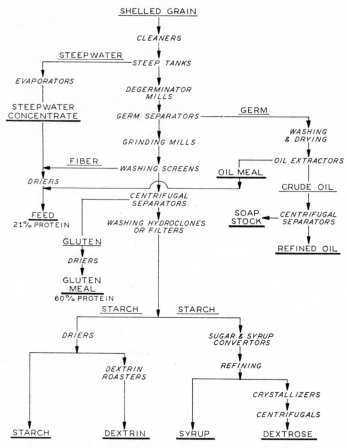

Fig. 8.—Flow diagram of the wet milling process.

starch gelatinizes at a temperature about 5° higher than nonwaxy milo starch, a characteristic of all waxy starches relative to their nonwaxy counterparts. Paste properties of milo starches are similar to those of corn starches (*111, 113*).

IV. The Wet Milling Process

Wet milling of corn and milo for starch manufacture is more than simple grinding of water soaked grain. It is a highly specfic and completely integrated system developed to separate the major components of the kernel as completely as possible. A simplified flow sheet of the process is given in Figure 8. Table IX gives the composition of the major products

Table IX
Average Compositions of the Major Products Obtained from the Corn Wet Milling Process[a]

Starch	%	Gluten	%
Moisture	10–11	Moisture	10
Protein	0.25–0.30	Protein	65
Ash	0.08	Starch	20
Fat (total, acid hyd.)	0.65	Fat	7
Oil (CCl$_4$ extr.)	0.02	Fiber	2
Starch	99.0	Ash	1
		Carotenoids, ppm.	100–300

Steepwater	%	Corn gluten feed	%
Moisture	50	Moisture	10–12
Protein N	7.5	Protein	24
Peptide and amino N	35.0	Fiber	8
Ammonia and amide N	7.5	Starch	4
Lactic acid	26	Ash	8
Carbohydrates (as dextrose)	2.5	Fat	2
Phytic acid	7.5	Pentoglycans	18
Ash (total)	18		
Potassium[b]	4.5		
Magnesium[b]	2.0		
Phosphorus[b,c]	3.3		

Germ meal, extracted	%	Crude oil	%
Moisture	7	Glycerides[d]	96.1
Protein	24	Free fatty acids	1.5
Fat	1–2	Sitosterol	1.0
Starch	16	Tocopherols	0.1
Fiber	10	Phospholipids	1.0
Pentoglycans	22		

[a] All percentages other than moisture are expressed on a dry basis.
[b] Included in total ash.
[c] About 75% is phytin phosphorus.
[d] Major fatty acids are linoleic, 56%; oleic, 30%; and saturated fatty acids, 13%.

obtained from the wet milling of corn. Composition of milo fractions are similar, except that milo gluten contains no carotenoid pigments. Gluten feed is a mixture of steepwater, fiber, and defatted germ meal.

It normally contains no gluten. Each manufacturing step leading to these products is described in this section.

1. Cleaning the Grain

Shelled grain is received at the wet milling plants in bulk. It is prepared for milling by screening to remove all large and small pieces of cob, chaff, sand, and other undesirable foreign material. Dust and light chaff are removed by aspiration. Cleaning the corn is an important first step in the wet milling process (Fig. 8).

2. Steeping

a. *Principles*

Prior to wet milling, the corn must be softened by a steeping process developed specifically to produce optimum milling and separation of corn components. Steeping is more than simple water soaking of corn. It involves maintaining the correct balance of water flow, temperature, sulfur dioxide concentration, and an adequate population of lactic acid bacteria. Corn is normally steeped 30 to 50 hr. at a temperature of 48° to 52°. By the end of the steeping period, the corn should have (a) absorbed water to about 45% (wet basis), (b) released about 6.0–6.5% of its dry substance as solubles into the steepwater, (c) absorbed about 0.2 to 0.4 g. of sulfur dioxide per kilogram, and (d) become sufficiently soft to yield when squeezed between the fingers. A wet milling test (89) will then reveal that the germ is easily liberated intact and free of adhering endosperm or hull. The starch will be readily freed from fiber by fine milling and screening and will settle free of gluten in a properly diluted slurry (8°–12° Baumé).

b. *Mechanics of Commercial Steeping*

Steeps are large tanks that may be constructed of any material resistant to the corrosive action of solutions of sulfur dioxide and lactic acid at pH 3–4. Wooden stave construction is most common. Steep tanks usually hold 2000 to 3500 bushels of grain.

The tanks are filled with raw grain from an overhead conveyor and are emptied through an orifice at the apex of the conical bottom. The inside surface of the cone bottom is usually covered with a strainer (slatted wood or stainless steel) for drainage. Each steep is equipped with piping to move steepwater from one steep to another, to pass it through a heat exchanger, or to withdraw it from the system. Water movements may be conducted entirely by gravity from a head tank, in which case all steeps must be closed except for filling or emptying. More commonly, the water is moved by either a small pump for each steep tank or one large pump for an entire battery.

To prevent the loss of valuable organic matter, and to avoid sewage disposal problems, careful management in the re-use of water is essential. For this reason the entire milling and steeping installation is operated as a countercurrent washing unit. Fresh water, usually a mixture of steam condensate and softened tap water, is introduced at the final starch washing step just prior to drying or conversion. Water of low hardness must be used to prevent the formation of calcium sulfate haze in starch hydrolyzates. The filtrate from the final starch washing is used to slurry the starch for the next to last washing operation. Water works its way from starch washing to steeps, gradually increasing in solubles content during passage through a series of dilution and reconcentration steps, and finally attaining a solubles level of 0.10–0.20%. It is then ready to be used in steeping the corn.

Steeps are normally operated as countercurrent batteries of 8 to 12 tanks, although much longer batteries are sometimes used. Starch wash water containing 0.1–0.2% of sulfur dioxide is placed on corn that has been in the steeps longest and, therefore, has lowest residual solubles content. As the steepwater moves over the corn kernels in successive steeps, sulfur dioxide and water are gradually absorbed by the corn and leaches the solubles. Changes in water and corn at successive steeps through a battery are shown in Figure 9. Residence time for corn in the steeps is normally 30–50 hr. Corn enters the steeps containing 12 to 20% water and leaves containing 45% water. Steepwater withdrawn from the system contains from about 40 to 80 g./liter of total solubles, depending on the ratio of water to corn. The steepwater is concentrated to 35–55% dry substance for addition to fibrous milling residues in the preparation of by-product animal feeds. If it is to be sold as a fermentation nutrient or for use in mixed feeds, steepwater is evaporated to 50–55% solids. The components of steepwater solids are given in Table IX. If the steeping has been properly conducted, the steepwater will have a pH of 3.9–4.1. The steeped corn should contain less than 2% solubles.

c. *Water Absorption*

Water absorption by kernels of corn or milo is not normally a limiting factor in steeping because maximum absorption is achieved early in the steeping time. Water enters the kernel through the porous tip cap and moves quickly into voids in the pericarp by capillary action (*32, 114*). Diffusion of water into endosperm and germ follows standard diffusivity laws that apply equally to corn or milo (*114*). The rate of diffusion increases with increase in temperature but is not appreciably affected by sulfur dioxide (115). Maximum moisture content is reached in about 6 hr. at 60° (114). Apparently no one has studied the effect of gas discharge from the kernel on water absorption. Kernels immersed in water or steep acid continue to discharge gas, probably air plus carbon dioxide from decarboxylation of glutamic acid (85), for many hours after initial immersion. Corn that has been artificially dried at an excessive temperature attains a lower final water content during steeping than unheated corn (75).

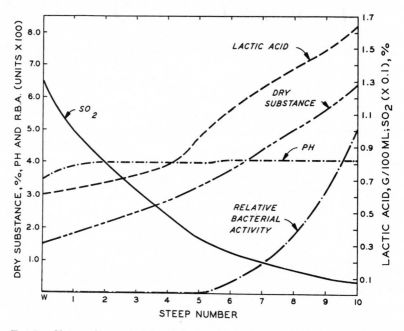

FIG. 9.—Changes in composition of steepwater flowing over grain in successive steeps of a commercial countercurrent corn steep battery. Steepwater samples were obtained for analysis simultaneously from each steep of a battery. "W" under Steep Number is composition of input water; No. 1 contains fully steeped corn; No. 10 contains new corn. Water flow is left to right; corn flow is right to left.

Entry of water and exit of dissolved substances is believed to be restricted by the hilar layer and the aleurone layers, but the seed coat may be the layer most restrictive to moisture entry as it is in wheat (116). Once inside the endosperm or germ, the water probably moves rapidly into areas of crushed cells (dent) and intercellular spaces (40, 83). Initially, the germ can absorb more water than the endosperm (117). As steeping proceeds, however, the extensive leaching of solubles and the sustained hyperphysiologic temperature of 50°–60° probably cause the germ cells to die and lose their semipermeability. The germ then tends to become flacid and rubbery. This condition aids in the recovery of intact germ in the initial milling step. Whole steeped kernels are usually turgid suggesting that the kernel as a whole retains its semipermeable character. Small organic molecules, such as sugars, phytate, and amino acids, pass freely through the membranes into the water but some dissolved protein is retained inside the intact kernel.

The free volume increases of corn and of milo kernels in water are similar and are directly related to water absorption (118). However, the volume expansion of the two grains in a large bulk is different because of differences in shape of the kernels. Corn in a large steep does not appear to increase in volume because the weight of grain forces the swelling kernels to reorient to fill the irregular voids between kernels. The spherical milo kernels, being initially closely packed, do exhibit a volume increase during the water absorption phase of steeping.

d. *Effect of Sulfur Dioxide*

Sulfur dioxide was first used in corn steeping probably to prevent growth of putrefactive organisms. Eventually this chemical was found indispensible to maximum starch yield. Cox, MacMasters, and Hilbert (119) were the first to study the effects of steeping agents by microscopic observations of thin sections of corn kernels. They demonstrated that, during steeping with sulfur dioxide over a 24-hr. period at 50°, the protein matrix gradually swells, becomes globular, and finally disperses. The degree of globulation of the protein was shown to be directly related to the ease of starch recovery on grinding or on agitation of the thin sections of the endosperm from the steeped kernels. Protein dispersion was faster as the sulfur dioxide concentration was increased to 0.4%. The presence of lactic acid produced some apparent softening action, but other acids had little effect. Other reducing agents can replace sulfur dioxide (119). Rate of protein swelling is faster and dispersion more complete with new fresh corn than with old dry corn (120).

Sulfur dioxide dissolved in water forms an equilibrium mixture:

$$H_2SO_3 \rightleftharpoons H^+ + HSO_3^-$$

The bisulfite ion is the active agent in steeping.

The reaction of bisulfite ion with endosperm protein is completed in 4 to 6 hr. when diffusion of bisulfite into the kernel is not a limiting factor. Thus, sections of unsteeped horny endosperm (10 μ thick) bathed in a solution of constant bisulfite ion concentration exhibited rapid loss of starch granules from the protein matrix on gentle agitation (121). Under these conditions, the rate and extent of starch release increased with increasing bisulfite concentration (0.05 to 0.02%) and with increasing temperature (52° to 60°). At pH levels below 9, the pH of the medium did not have a significant effect on starch release in steeping thin endosperm sections. Other acids, including lactic, did not effect starch release from thin endosperm sections even on agitation for 24 hr. at 52° to 60°, which emphasizes the unique role of sulfur dioxide in starch release. Figure 3 (lower) shows protein of horny endosperm from which starch has been released by action of sulfur dioxide.

Similar effects were observed on steeping isolated corn endosperm (degerminated corn meal) in bisulfite solutions buffered at pH 4 with lactic acid–sodium lactate (106). During the first 2 hours of contact with the bisulfite solution at 50°, the endosperm lost more nitrogenous material than control endosperm steeped in lactate buffer alone. The bulk of the dissolved nitrogen was precipitated when the steepwater was adjusted to pH 7 and heated to boiling. This information indicates that a relatively high-molecular-weight protein is dissolved from the endosperm by the action of bisulfite. The appearance of this protein in solution coincided with the release of starch from the endosperm cells.

A probable explanation of the action of bisulfite ion on corn protein is provided by studies with other proteins (62, 122). By reacting with the sulfhydryl radical, bisulfite ion reduces the disulfide bonds that cross-link protein strands.

$$RS\text{—}SR + SO_3^- \rightarrow RSSO_3^- + RS^-$$

The resulting protein thiosulfate is more soluble in water. The reaction rate is greatest at pH 5.0.

The protein liberated by bisulfite action on corn endosperm is zein-like in nature. Furthermore, aqueous ethanol extraction of bisulfite-steeped endosperm yielded less zein than hydrated unsteeped endosperm (106). However, unsteeped endosperm extracted first with aqueous ethanol, either before or after a water soak to hydrate the protein, yielded less starch upon milling than endosperm steeped with bisulfite at pH 4.0. This suggests that zein as such is not the primary cementing substance. Since Duvick (18) has indicated that zein granules are embedded in a cytoplasmic protein matrix composed largely of glutelin and globulin, it appears that bisulfite may be reacting with glutelin. Globulins are not implicated because extraction of endosperm with salt solutions does not liberate starch (106). A study of the reaction of bisulfite with wheat glutenin (M.W. 2–3 × 10^6) has revealed that a protein fraction (M.W. 25,000) is liberated that is electrophoretically identical with gliadin (123). Woychick postulates that glutenin is a polymer of gliadin, the gliadin molecules being associated through disulfide linkages. In studies with whole ground corn, Turner and co-workers (124) observed that native protein dissolved in $8M$ urea showed several electrophoretically mobile components and some material that did not migrate. The latter fraction became mobile when disulfide bonds were cleaved by the action of cupric sulfite or mercaptoethanol.

Corn that has been artificially dried at an excessive temperature yields lower amounts of soluble protein during bisulfite steeping (75, 125). Presumably, hydrogen bonds formed during heating restrict solubility of protein thiosulfates.

e. Role of the Lactic Acid Bacteria

Although corn can be adequately steeped in pure water solutions of sulfur dioxide in the laboratory, commercial steeping inevitably involves microorganisms. Raw corn carries a natural population of bacteria, yeasts, and molds which, although normally small, is capable of rapid multiplication in aqueous systems. Practical men learned early that corn steeped at temperatures of 45°–55° was "sweet," but that putrefaction and butyric acid or alcohol production occurred at lower temperatures. Steeping at 45°–55° is now known to favor development of lactic acid bacteria. The lactic acid produced lowers the pH of the medium and restricts growth of most other organisms. Substrate for the bacteria is the sugar that early leaches from the corn. Sucrose is quickly inverted to D-glucose and D-fructose, each of which is converted almost completely to 2 moles of lactic acid with release of energy needed for bacterial development. About one-half of the lactic acid formed is neutralized by bases leaching from the corn. The system is buffered at about pH 3.9–4.1. The amino acids required by these bacteria for protein synthesis are also supplied by the corn, although some protein or peptide hydrolysis does occur in steepwater during lactic acid formation. About 85% of the nitrogen in well incubated steepwater is in the form of amino acids or simple peptides (Table IX).

The microbiology of steeping has not been studied in detail to the author's knowledge. However, major organisms are thermophilic lactobacilli, including species resembling *Lactobacillus bulgaricus*. Spore formers related to "flat sours" also appear to be active components of the system (126, 127).

Although the grain is the primary source of the lactic acid bacterial inoculation, the process water used is a major source of inoculum in commercial steeping. Corn incubated at 50° with fresh milling process water develops a vigorous culture of lactic acid bacteria in about 32 hr., but corn immersed in sterilized process water or tap water requires about 3 days for development of fermentation (128). Data obtained from a commercial sized steep filled with 3200 bushels of corn and covered with process water freshly charged with 0.125% of sulfur dioxide dramatically illustrate the biological events in steeping (Fig. 10). Sulfur dioxide concentration in the water quickly drops to a very low level as the bisulfite ion is absorbed by the corn. The increase in steep-water pH is the result of both absorption of sulfurous acid and leaching of bases from the corn (Fig. 10, Upper). Sugar concentration increases to a peak, and relative bacterial activity (RBA) begins to enter the log phase at 16 hr. (Fig. 10, Lower). As the sugar concentration declines, the lactic acid concentration increases concomitantly. When the sugar supply has been exhausted, the bacterial activity declines rapidly. Total dry substance and total protein (not shown) increase steadily during the entire steeping period.

Although all these events occur in commercial countercurrent steep batteries, their sequence is different and often masked by the continuous flow of water. All absorption of bisulfite ion occurs in the 3–4 steeps at the grain discharge end of the battery, and all the fermentation occurs in the 3–4 steeps at the water discharge end. Operating variables in a countercurrent battery are restricted to the following conditions that promote growth of the lactic acid bacteria: (a) temperature between 47° and 55°; (b) sulfur dioxide concentration in steep acid such that water entering the fermentation steeps (grain inlet end) will contain less than 0.01%; (c) water withdrawal rate slow enough to allow time for bacterial development.

No clear evidence has ever been presented to indicate the essential nature of lactic acid in corn or milo steeping, except for possible soften-ing of cell walls (119, 121). However, personal observation indicates that fermentation-steeped corn is softer than corn steeped in pure solu-tions of sulfur dioxide and lactic acid.

3. Milling and Fraction Separation

The object of the milling process is to provide for as complete separa-tion of component parts of the corn kernel as is possible and practical. While commercial yield figures are not available, a laboratory procedure (129) gives results close to those obtained in commercial wet milling (Table X). Data are given for regular dent hybrid corn, a special high-oil hybrid corn and regular red milo. All three grains were steeped 48 hr. at 52° in a 0.1% sulfur dioxide solution at pH 4. The starch separation was conducted by tabling. In tabling, the denser starch settles on the table, but the lighter gluten containing many of the small starch granules flows off the end of the table. The surface of the starch is then gently hosed or "squeegeed" to remove traces of gluten. The

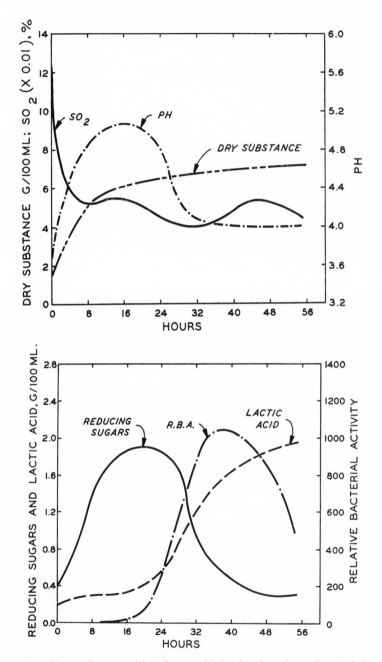

Fig. 10.—Changes in composition of steepacid circulated continuously at 49° through a single steep of raw corn over a 56-hour period. Both corn and SO$_2$-water were added at 0 hours.

Table X

Laboratory Wet Milling Results Obtained with Regular and High-oil Dent Corn and Regular Red Milo[a]

Fraction	Regular dent corn (%)	High-oil dent corn (%)	Red milo (%)
Whole grain analysis			
Moisture	14.3	13.6	14.9
Starch	71.5	67.0	73.1
Protein	10.5	10.4	13.0
Fat	5.10	7.96	3.6
Wax	Trace	Trace	0.32
Solubles			
Yield[b]	7.6	10.8	7.20
Protein[c]	46.1	46.9	41.5
Starch			
Yield	63.7	59.7	60.17
Protein	0.30	0.26	0.32
Fat	0.02	0.03	0.03
Germ			
Yield	7.3	10.9	6.17
Starch	7.6	7.2	19.1
Protein	10.7	7.2	11.9
Fat	58.9	65.5	39.6
Oil Yield[b]	4.30	7.14	2.44
Fiber			
Yield	9.5	9.8	9.30
Starch	11.4	12.3	36.7
Protein	11.3	11.0	19.7
Fat	1.8	2.7	3.8
Gluten			
Yield	7.4	6.3	9.57
Starch	25.8	32.0	39.9
Protein	50.7	42.3	47.2
Fat	3.7	4.4	5.4
Squeegee			
Yield	3.9	3.6	5.57
Starch	91.7	93.8	74.8
Protein	6.1	3.6	20.7
Fat	0.3	0.4	1.6
Total dry substance	99.4	101.0	98.0
Recalculation to Expected Centrifugal Results			
Starch			
Yield	68.5	65.7	67.2
Gluten			
Yield	5.76	4.0	8.1
Protein	70.0	70.0	70.0

[a] All percentages other than moisture are expressed on a dry basis.
[b] Percent of original grain.   [c] Analytical values expressed as percent of the fraction.

material, high in starch content, washed off the table is termed the "squeegee" fraction.

Gluten obtained by tabling seldom contains more than 50% protein. To approximate the results obtained by continuous commercial centrifugation, the gluten and squeegee data were recalculated to 70% protein, which increases starch yield (Table X). The data reported for wet milling of high-oil corn show that the additional oil in the kernel is recoverable in germ, but starch and gluten yields are reduced accordingly. The higher protein and lower fat content of the milo grain is reflected in lower oil yield in germ and higher gluten yield.

After steeping, the grain is coarsely ground or "pulped" with water

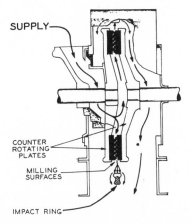

Fig. 11.—Cutaway diagram of attrition mill with impact ring. (Courtesy of the Bauer Brothers Company, Springfield, Ohio.)

in an attrition (cracking) mill. The most commonly used mill has one stationary and one rotating milling surface as shown in Figure 11. When used for degermination, the plates are covered with pyramidal knobs and the impact ring is absent. The bulk of the germ is freed in the first pass, but a second pass is usually provided after free germ has been removed. The mill gap is adjusted to give the most free germ with minimum breakage. Oil liberated in this step is absorbed by gluten and is not recovered. Over half of the original starch and gluten is also freed in this first milling step. The large difference in density between the oil-rich germ and the other kernel components provides easy separation. Formerly separation was effected in large U shaped vats. Germ was continuously skimmed off the top of the vat as it floated on a 7° Baumé starch suspension while the starch, endosperm, and hull were continuously discharged from the bottom. Most wet milling plants are currently being converted to the liquid cyclone method of germ recovery. The liquid cyclone, or hydroclone, is a conical tube about 6 in. in diameter at the top of its 3-ft. length (Fig. 12). Pulped corn adjusted to 7°–8° Baumé with suspended starch is forced into the tube under pressure. The orifice angle and aperture are chosen to produce a rotational velocity sufficient to cause a separation of the particles of differing density (130). The heavier endosperm and fiber particles pass out the bottom of the tube while the lighter germ is drawn off the top of the

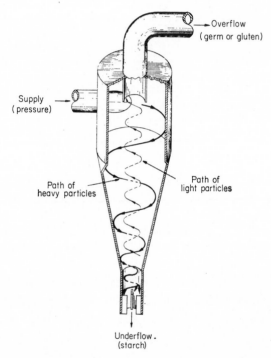

FIG. 12.—Cutaway diagram of hydroclone separator. (Courtesy of Dorr–Oliver Incorporated, Stamford, Connecticut.)

vortex. A bank of germ hydroclones is shown in Figure 13. Recovered germ is washed to recover occluded starch and is then dried in preparation for oil recovery by expelling or extracting. The cyclone type of germ recovery equipment occupies less floor space, is easier to maintain and clean, and is more responsive to changes in operating conditions than the trough flotation equipment due to less slurry holdup.

Following germ separation, the bulk of the free starch and gluten is screened from the coarser particles to reduce the solids load to the subsequent milling operation. Starch remaining in endosperm chunks (horny endosperm) is released by a more thorough milling procedure. Conventionally, this milling step has been accomplished with Buhr stone mills (2). Newer types of mills with greatly increased capacity and lower maintenance costs are gradually replacing Buhr mills. One type of mill employs vertically oriented, counter-rotating grooved plates made of hardened steel alloys (131) (Fig. 11). An outer impact ring (132) increases milling efficiency. Production rate for one of these mills is equal to several Buhr mills, and maintenance costs are low.

Fig. 13.—Battery of hydroclones used for separation of germ from milled, steeped corn. (Courtesy of Dorr–Oliver Incorporated, Stamford, Connecticut.)

An impact type mill known as the Entoleter is preferred by many millers (133) (Fig. 14). Endosperm slurry dropped onto the rotating horizontal disk is flung with great force against both rotating and stationary pins. Rapid and complete starch release is obtained with minimum fiber attrition. The larger pieces of fiber permit occluded starch to be more efficiently recovered by washing. High throughput rate, low maintenance cost, uniform operation, and improved quality and yield of starch are advantages of these machines. These machines remove the art from milling because there is no mill gap adjustment and no speed control.

The starch released by milling must be separated from fiber. This separation was formerly made by passing the mixture over screens and finally over silk or nylon bolting cloth affixed to open shakers and reels constructed of wood (2). Enclosed stainless steel reels are still popular for washing fiber. The milled corn is passed into the center of the rotating, slightly inclined reel covered with perforated metal sheets having holes 0.027 in. in diameter. The coarse fiber particles passing out the end of the reel are rewashed and pressed to dewater prior to drying. The fine fiber passing through the holes is separated from the starch and gluten by screening on nylon bolting cloth (mesh size about 75 μ). The fine fiber is reslurried and rescreened 3 or 4 times to recover

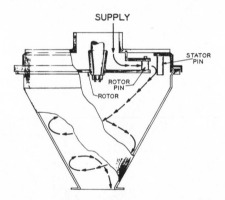

FIG. 14.—Cutaway diagram of Entoleter impact mill.

free starch. Enclosed gyratory stainless steel shakers (Rotex) have largely replaced open reels and shakers with only slightly improved washing efficiency, but much improved cleanliness and working conditions. The water used in fiber washing is usually heavily charged with sulfur dioxide to prevent growth of microorganisms on the screens. Closed shakers and reels are vented to the outside.

New fiber washing techniques are being developed which are expected to greatly improve screening efficiency and reduce floor space. One such machine known as the "screen pump" has recently been introduced (134, 135). The slurry of fiber and loose starch resulting from milling is pumped into a helically formed bar-screen such that the starch granules and water pass through the perforations and the fiber passes continually out of the unit in the form of a mat. Several units are operated in series, each interrupted by reslurrying the fiber mat in water.

After fiber has been adequately washed, it is squeezed or filtered to reduce content of free moisture. It is then usually mixed with concentrated steepwater and dried for use in animal feed. Several types of high volume continuous presses are now widely used for fiber dewatering.

The defibered mixture of starch and protein is known as "mill starch." Protein content varies between 5 and 8% depending on the endosperm protein content of the original corn or milo. The mill starch streams from both the degermination and fiber washing steps are combined and filtered or centrifugally concentrated to remove solubles and to adjust the concentration of solids in preparation for the final step of starch recovery. The low density of gluten particles (1.1) as compared

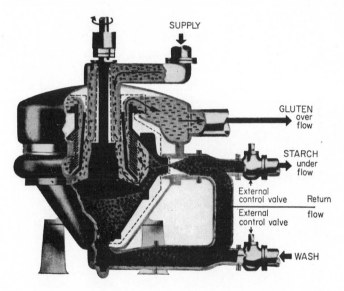

Fig. 15.—Cutaway diagram of Merco centrifugal starch separation machine. (Courtesy of Dorr–Oliver Incorporated, Stamford, Connecticut.)

with starch (1.5) permits their ready separation by settling or centrifugation. A container of mill starch obtained from adequately steeped corn will, in about 10 min., deposit a layer of white starch on the bottom and a layer of yellow gluten on the top. In about 1 hr. the gluten layer will have further settled to leave a layer of supernatant liquid. The historic method of settling starch on long inclined wooden troughs called tables (2) has virtually disappeared. Tables have been replaced in most starch factories by continuous centrifuges. These machines operate on the principle of a cream separator (Fig. 15). The heavier starch granules are thrown to the periphery of the centrifuge bowl and are ejected through nozzles, while the lighter gluten particles are swept up by a countercurrent stream of water between angled separator plates and out along the central axis (*136*). The gluten is delivered at a protein concentration of 60–70% (d.b.) but at a very low solids concentration. It is next concentrated by further centrifugation in a machine that permits only water to be passed into the overflow. The heavy gluten is then filtered and dried in rotary or flash dryers.

FIG. 16.—Interior (foreground) and exterior views (background) of hydroclone starch separation units. Each white circle in open unit is one hydroclone tube. (Courtesy of the Dorr–Oliver Company, Stamford, Connecticut.)

The starch stream discharging from the centrifuge must be further purified by passing through a second centrifuge or through hydroclones to reduce the protein content to the minimum level of about 0.3%. The construction of the starch separation hydroclone tubes and the principle of their operation is identical with the larger germ hydroclones (Fig. 12). The hydroclone apparatus used for starch-protein separation is composed of numerous conical tubes, each 6 in. long by 0.75 in. in diameter and usually made of plastic. Several hundred of these small hydroclone tubes are housed in a partitioned chamber (Fig. 16). The starch-protein mixture enters the center section of the unit and is forced by means of a hydrostatic head simultaneously into each of the individual tubes. The starch granules discharge from the heavy-particle end of the tubes (underflow) into one side of the chamber; the gluten particles discharge through the vortex finder into the overflow side of the chamber (*137*). The starch stream is rediluted with water overflow from a succeeding hydroclone and passes into a second set of hydroclones. Six to ten sets of hydroclones arranged in countercurrent sequence provide for final removal of insoluble protein and give a complete washing operation that replaces two or three drum filters (*134*).

As previously described, the only fresh water entering the milling operation contacts the starch in the last hydroclone stage. From there it works forward through the process, finally emerging at the steeps carrying with it substances dissolved from the corn. Product starch emerges from the hydroclones at a concentration suitable for direct use in conversion to sugar or syrup.

The history of starch drying has been one of continued reduction in drying time. New drying procedures with reduced product retention time have given improved quality. Refined starch slurry from the hydroclones is first dewatered on a moving belt filter or in a basket centrifuge prior to drying. One popular starch dryer employs a moving belt of metal fabric that carries the starch cake through chambers of circulated air heated to a desired temperature and finally through a cooling chamber (*138*). The entire cycle requires 20 to 60 min., depending on the nature of the product to be dried. The large number of modified starches now being made in most starch factories require the flexibility of drying time and temperature obtainable with the moving belt dryer but not with the old kiln dryers (*2*). The most rapid starch drying is provided by a flash dryer. Starch filter cake is injected into the bottom of a stream of rapidly moving heated air. The starch particles are dried instantly and are collected in dust cyclones. Baunack (*139*) has described several flash dryer arrangements. He reports that drying conditions can be varied to control patricle size and bulk density of starch, gluten, and fiber products dried in flash dryers.

The new continuous processes used in modern starch factories are particularly suited to operation through remote control. Instrumentation has added a new dimension of control over many phases of these operations. Central control panels record tank levels, flow rates, temperatures, and slurry densities and provide instant and precise control through remote control valves and other devices (*140*). The combination of continuous material flow in closed equipment and remote control of the process has raised the modern corn starch factory from a corn grinding plant to the level of sanitation and control required in a food processing plant.

V. References

(1) F. L. Jeffries, "Corn Grinding as I Have Seen It," Corn Products Co., New York, N.Y., 1942.

(2) R. W. Kerr, "Chemistry and Industry of Starch," Academic Press Inc., New N.Y., 2nd Ed., 1950.

(3) P. Weatherwax and L. F. Randolph, "Corn and Corn Improvement," G. F. Sprague, ed., Academic Press Inc., New York, N.Y., 1955, pp. 1–61.

(4) P. C. Manglesdorf, R. S. MacNeish, and W. C. Galinat, Science. **143**, 538 (1964).

(5) G. F. Sprague, "Corn and Corn Improvement," Academic Press Inc., New York, N.Y., 1955, pp. 221–292.

(6) U.S. Dept. Agr., Agr. Stat. 1965, pp. 30–57.

(7) J. H. Martin and W. H. Leonard, "Principles of Field Crop Production," The MacMillan Co., New York, N.Y., 1949, pp. 331–436.

(8) E. C. Miller, J. Agr. Res., **18**, 255 (1919).

(9) L. F. Randolph, J. Agr. Res., **53**, 881 (1936).

(10) R. H. Shaw and H. C. S. Thom, Agron. J., **43**, 9 (1951).

(11) B. Brimhall and G. F. Sprague, Cereal Chem., **28**, 225 (1951).

(12) A. Groszmann and G. F. Sprague, J. Am. Soc. Agron., **40**, 88 (1948).

(13) F-H. Wang, Am. J. Botany, **34**, 113 (1947).

(14) D. N. Duvick, Am. J. Botany, **42**, 717 (1955).

(15) L. Bernstein, Am. J. Botany, **30**, 517 (1943).

(16) D. Duvick, Botan. Gaz., **115**, 82 (1953).

(17) M. S. Buttrose, J. Ultrastruct. Res., **4**, 231 (1960).

(18) D. Duvick, Cereal Chem., **38**, 374 (1961).

(19) L. Zeleny, Cereal Chem., **12**, 536 (1935).

(20) S. A. Watson, Ph.D. Thesis, University of Illinois, Urbana, Ill., 1948.

(21) R. Bressani and R. Conde, Cereal Chem., **38**, 76 (1961).

(22) E. B. Earley and E. E. DeTurk, J. Am. Soc. Agron., **36**, 803 (1944).

(23) E. B. Earley, Plant Physiol., **27**, 184 (1952).

(24) J. W. Evans, Cereal Chem., **18**, 468 (1941).

(25) M. J. Wolf, M. M. MacMasters, J. E. Hubbard, and C. E. Rist, Cereal Chem., **25**, 312 (1948).

(26) R. L. Whistler, H. H. Kramer, and R. D. Smith, Arch. Biochem. Biophys., **66**, 374 (1957).

(27) R. H. Shaw and H. C. S. Thom, Agron. J., **43**, 542 (1951).

(28) J. M. Airy, "Corn and Corn Improvement," G. F. Sprague, ed., Academic Press Inc., New York, N.Y., 1955, p. 405.

(29) F. R. Earle, J. J. Curtis, and J. E. Hubbard, Cereal Chem., **23**, 504 (1946).

(30) C. G. Hopkins, L. H. Smith, and E. M. East, Illinois, Univ., Agr. Expt. Sta. Bull. No. **87** (1903).

(31) A. M. Brunson, F. R. Earle, and J. J. Curtis, J. Am. Soc. Agron., **41**, 30 (1949).

(32) M. J. Wolf, C. L. Buzan, M. M. MacMasters, and C. E. Rist, Cereal Chem., **29**, 334 (1952).

(33) D. Bradbury, M. J. Wolf, and R. J. Dimler, Cereal Chem., **39**, 72 (1962).

(34) J. J. C. Hinton, Cereal Chem., **30**, 441 (1953).

(35) M. J. Wolf, C. L. Buzan, M. M. MacMasters, and C. E. Rist, Cereal Chem., **29**, 349 (1952).

(*36*) S. A. Watson, E. H. Sanders, R. D. Wakely, and C. B. Williams, *Cereal Chem.*, **32**, 165 (1955).

(*37*) G. F. Sprague and B. Brimhall, *Agron. J.*, **41**, 30 (1949).

(*38*) E. O. Schneider, E. B. Earley, and E. E. DeTurk, *Agron. J.*, **44**, 161 (1952).

(*39*) M. J. Wolf, C. L. Buzan, M. M. MacMasters, and C. E. Rist, *Cereal Chem.*, **29**, 321 (1952).

(*40*) M. J. Wolf, C. L. Buzan, M. M. MacMasters, and C. E. Rist, *Cereal Chem.*, **29**, 362 (1952).

(*41*) L. S. Dure, *Plant Physiol.*, **35**, 925 (1960).

(*42*) H. L. Seckinger, M. J. Wolf, and M. M. MacMasters, *Cereal Chem.*, **37**, 121 (1960).

(*43*) L. Yatsu and A. Altschul, *Science*, **142**, 1062 (1963).

(*44*) J. J. Curtis and F. R. Earle, *Cereal Chem.*, **23**, 88 (1946).

(*45*) D. F. Miller, "Composition of Cereal Grains and Forages," Publ. No. 585, National Academy of Sci., National Res. Council, Washington, D.C., 1958.

(*46*) M. J. Wolf, M. M. MacMasters, J. A. Cannon, E. C. Rosewall, and C. E. Rist, *Cereal Chem.*, **30**, 451 (1953).

(*47*) S. A. Watson, in "Industrial Gums," R. L. Whistler, ed., Academic Press Inc., New York, N.Y., 1959, p. 299.

(*48*) R. L. Whistler and J. N. BeMiller, *J. Am. Chem. Soc.*, **78**, 1163 (1956).

(*49*) K. Taüfel, K. J. Steinbach, and B. Hartman, *Nahrung*, **4**, 452 (1960).

(*50*) J. B. Beadle, D. E. Just, R. E. Morgan, and R. A. Reiners, *J. Am. Oil Chemists' Soc.*, **42**, 90 (1965).

(*51*) F. W. Quackenbush, J. G. Firch, A. M. Brunson, and L. R. House, *Cereal Chem* , **40**, 250 (1963).

(*52*) A. R. Baldwin and M. S. Sniegowski, *J. Am. Oil Chemists' Soc.*, **31**, 414 (1954).

(*53*) C. M. Woodworth, E. R. Leng, and R. W. Jugenheimer, *Agron. J.*, **44**, 60 (1952).

(*54*) A. R. Baldwin and M. S. Sniegowski, *J. Am. Oil Chemists' Soc.*, **28**, 24 (1951).

(*55*) C. W. Blessin, J. D. Brecher, and R. J. Dimler, *Cereal Chem.*, **40**, 582 (1963).

(*56*) S. A. Watson, *Proc. Ann. Hybrid Corn Res. Conference, 17th.* American Seed Trade Assoc., Washington, D.C., 1962, p. 92.

(*57*) F. W. Quackenbush, *Cereal Chem.*, **40**, 266 (1963).

(*58*) T. B. Osborne and B. L. Mendel, *J. Biol. Chem.*, **18**, 1 (1914).

(*59*) E. T. Mertz and R. Bressani, *Cereal Chem.*, **34**, 63 (1957).

(*60*) E. T. Mertz, N. E. Lloyd, and R. Bressani, *Cereal Chem.*, **35**, 146 (1958).

(*61*) N. E. Lloyd and E. T. Mertz, *Cereal Chem.*, **35**, 156 (1958).

(*62*) J. M. Swan, *Nature*, **180**, 643 (1957).

(*63*) R. Bressani and E. T. Mertz, *Cereal Chem.*, **35**, 227 (1958).

(*64*) D. W. Hansen, B. Brimhall, and G. F. Sprague, *Cereal Chem.*, **23**, 329 (1949).

(*65*) L. C. Swallen, *Ind. Eng. Chem.*, **33**, 394 (1941).

(*65a*) E. T. Mertz, L. S. Bates, and O. E. Nelson, *Science*, **145**, 279 (1964).

(*65b*) O. E. Nelson, E. T. Mertz, and L. S. Bates, *Science*, **150**, 1469 (1965).

(*65c*) E. T. Mertz, O. A. Veron, L. S. Bates, and O. E. Nelson, *Science*, **148**, 1741 (1965).

(*65d*) K. R. Yahl and S. A. Watson, *Am. Assoc. Cereal Chemists, 51st Ann. Meeting*, New York, N.Y., 1966.

(*66*) T. H. Hamilton, B. C. Hamilton, B. C. Johnson, and H. H. Mitchell, *Cereal Chem.*, **28**, 163 (1951).

(*67*) J. A. Cannon, M. M. MacMasters, M. J. Wolf, and C. E. Rist, *Trans. Ann. Assoc. Cereal Chemists*, **10**, 74 (1952).

(*68*) J. S. Wall, R. J. Dimler, and F. R. Senti, Proc. Symp., "What's New In Corn," Midwest Sect., Am. Assoc. Cereal Chemists, Chicago, Illinois, 1961.

(69) M. L. Stechsel and S. G. Wildman, *Am. J. Botany,* **37,** 682 (1950).

(70) G. S. Avery, Jr., J. Berger, and B. Shalucha, *Am. J. Botany,* **28,** 596 (1941).

(70a) D. D. Christman, J. S. Wall, and J. F. Cavins, *J. Agr. Food Chem.,* **13,** 272 (1965).

(71) M. J. Cox, M. M. MacMasters, and C. E. Rist, *Am. Assoc. Cereal Chemists, 32nd Ann. Meeting,* Kansas City, Missouri, 1947.

(72) V. W. Davis, R. N. Van Arsdall, and J. E. Willis, *Illinois, Univ., Agr. Expt. Sta. Bull.* No. **638,** 1959.

(73) R. A. Thompson and G. H. Foster, *U.S. Dept. Agr., Marketing Res. Rept.* No. **631,** Agricultural Marketing Service (1963).

(74) M. M. MacMasters, M. D. Finkner, M. M. Holtzapfel, J. H. Ramser, and G. H. Dungan, *Cereal Chem.,* **36,** 247 (1959).

(75) S. A. Watson and Y. Hirata, *Cereal Chem.,* **39,** 35 (1962).

(76) J. Tuite and G. H. Foster, *Cereal Chem.,* **40,** 630 (1963).

(77) R. A. Bottomley, C. M. Christensen, and W. F. Geddes, *Cereal Chem.,* **27,** 271 (1950).

(78) G. Semeniuk, "Storage of Cereal Grains and their Products," J. A. Anderson and A. W. Alcock, ed., Am. Assoc. of Cereal Chemists, St. Paul, Minn., 1954, p. 77.

(79) L. Zeleny, reference *78,* p. 46.

(80) M. Milner and W. F. Geddes, reference *78,* p. 152.

(81) "Official Grain Standards of the United States," *U.S. Dept. Agr. SRA-AMS* **177,** Rev. May 1964.

(82) W. Kempf, *Staerke,* **13,** 404 (1961).

(83) P. D. Baird, M. M. MacMasters, and C. E. Rist, *Cereal Chem.,* **27,** 508 (1950).

(84) R. P. Moore, *Crops Soils,* **15,** No. 1, 10 (1962).

(85) G. M. Bautista and P. Linko, *Cereal Chem.,* **39,** 445 (1962).

(86) L. Zeleny, *Cereal Chem.,* **17,** 29 (1940).

(87) G. F. Foster, *Proc. Am. Hybrid Corn Res. Conf., 20th.* American Seed Trade Assoc., Washington, D.C., 1965, p. 75.

(88) C. E. Holaday, *Cereal Chem.,* **41,** 533 (1964).

(89) S. A. Watson, C. B. Williams, and R. D. Wakely, *Cereal Chem.,* **28,** 105 (1951).

(90) M. M. MacMasters, F. R. Earle, H. H. Hall, J. H. Ramser, and G. H. Dungan, *Cereal Chem.,* **31,** 451 (1954).

(91) P. F. Pelshenke and E. Lindemann, *Staerke,* **6,** 177 (1954).

(92) W. Kempf and C. Tegge, *Staerke,* **13,** 363 (1961).

(93) J. R. Quinby and J. H. Martin, *Advan. Agron.,* **6,** 305 (1954).

(94) R. E. Karper and J. R. Quinby, *Econ. Botany,* **1,** 355 (1947).

(95) E. Anderson and J. H. Martin, *Econ. Botany,* **3,** 265 (1949).

(96) A. F. Swanson, *J. Agr. Res.,* **37,** 577 (1928).

(97) E. H. Sanders, *Cereal Chem.,* **32,** 12 (1955).

(98) J. W. Collier, *Crop Sci.,* **3,** 419 (1963).

(99) J. E. Hubbard, H. H. Hall, and F. R. Earle, *Cereal Chem.,* **27,** 415 (1950).

(100) G. D. Miller, C. W. Deyoe, T. L. Walter, and F. W. Smith, *Agron. J.,* **56,** 302 (1964).

(101) F. A. Kummerow, *Oil & Soap,* **23,** 167, 273 (1946).

(102) C. W. Blessin, C. H. Van Etten, and R. Wiebe, *Cereal Chem.,* **35,** 359 (1959).

(103) C. W. Blessin, R. J. Dimler, and O. J. Webster, *Cereal Chem.,* **39,** 389 (1962).

(104) L. Unger, *Am. Assoc. Cereal Chemists, 45th Ann. Meeting,* Chicago, Ill., 1960.

(105) R. Bressani and B. J. Rios, *Cereal Chem.,* **39,** 50 (1962).

(106) Y. Hirata and S. A. Watson, unpublished data.

(107) J. W. Sorenson and M. G. Davenport, *Agr. Eng.,* **33,** 220 (1952).

(108) J. W. Sorenson, H. P. Smith, J. P. Hollingsworth, P. T. Montfort, F. E. Horan, R. A. Anderson, and R. L. Zipf, *Texas Agr. Expt. Sta. Bull.* **710,** College Station, Texas, 1940.

(109) R. L. Zipf, R. A. Anderson, and R. L. Slotter, *Cereal Chem.,* **27,** 463 (1950).

(110) S. A. Watson and Y. Hirata, *Agron. J.,* **47,** 11 (1955).

(111) M. M. MacMasters, M. J. Wolf, and H. L. Seckinger, *J. Agr. Food Chem.,* **5,** 455 (1957).

(112) T. J. Schoch and E. Maywald, *Anal. Chem.,* **28,** 382 (1956).

(113) F. E. Kite, T. J. Schoch, and H. W. Leach, *Bakers' Dig.,* **31,** No. 4, 42 (1957).

(114) L.-T. Fan, P. S. Chu, and J. A. Shellenberger, *Cereal Chem.,* **40,** 303 (1963).

(115) L.-T. Fan, H.-C. Chen, J. A. Shellenberger, and D. S. Chung, *Cereal Chem.,* **42,** 385 (1965).

(116) J. J. C. Hinton, *Cereal Chem.,* **32,** 296 (1955).

(117) E. H. Toole, *Am. J. Botany,* **11,** 325 (1924).

(118) L.-T. Fan, P. S. Chu, and J. A. Shellenberger, *Biotechnol. Bioeng.,* **4,** 311 (1962).

(119) M. J. Cox, M. M. MacMasters, and G. E. Hilbert, *Cereal Chem.,* **21,** 447 (1944).

(120) J. A. Wagoner, *Cereal Chem.,* **25,** 354 (1948).

(121) S. A. Watson and E. H. Sanders, *Cereal Chem.,* **38,** 22 (1961).

(122) I. M. Kolthoff, A. Anastasi, and B. H. Tan, *J. Am. Chem. Soc.,* **82,** 4147 (1960).

(123) J. H. Woychick, F. R. Huebner, and R. J. Dimler, *Archiv. Biochem. Biophys.,* **105,** 151 (1964).

(124) J. E. Turner, J. Boundy, and R. J. Dimler, *Cereal Chem.,* **42,** 452 (1965).

(125) T. A. McGuire and F. R. Earle, *Cereal Chem.,* **35,** 179 (1958).

(126) R. L. Bruner, unpublished data.

(127) R. W. Liggett and H. Hoffler, *Bacteriol. Rev.,* **12,** 297 (1948).

(128) S. A. Watson, Y. Hirata, and C. B. Williams, *Cereal Chem.,* **32,** 382 (1955).

(129) S. A. Watson, in "Methods in Carbohydrate Chemistry," R. L. Whistler, ed., Academic Press Inc., New York, N.Y., Vol. 4, 1964, p. 3.

(130) P. L. Stavenger and D. E. Wuth, U.S. Patent 2,913,112 (1959); *Chem. Abstr.,* **54,** 2844 (1960).

(131) M. E. Ginaven, U.S. Patent 3,040,996 (1962).

(132) R. R. Dill and M. E. Ginaven, U.S. Patent 3,118,624 (1964).

(133) D. W. Dowie and D. Martin, U.S. Patent 3,029,169 (1962); *Chem. Abstr.,* **57,** 3684 (1962).

(134) J. W. Power and R. F. Huehner, *Food Eng.,* **31,** No. 2, 66 (1959).

(135) M. L. E. Von Titeleboom, U.S. Patent 2,995,246 (1961).

(136) A. Peltzer, Sr., U.S. Patent 2,973,896 (1961).

(137) H. J. Vegter, U.S. Patent 2,778,752 (1957); *Chem. Abstr.,* **51,** 4745 (1957).

(138) S. Bogaty, U.S. Patent 2,338,619 (1944); *Chem. Abstr.,* **38,** 3841 (1944).

(139) F. Baunack, *Staerke,* **15,** 299 (1963).

(140) W. E. Carlson, *Food Eng.,* **30,** No. 12, 76 (1958).

CHAPTER II

MANUFACTURE OF WHEAT STARCH

By Roy A. Anderson
Northern Regional Research Laboratory,[1] *Peoria, Illinois*

I. Introduction

Although corn is the major source of starch in the United States, wheat also plays an important role as a raw material for the production of starch. This is particularly true in other countries, where more wheat is grown than any other cereal grain. Wheat starch manufacture is economical today because of the recovery of wheat gluten, a valuable protein by-product. Wheat gluten, as a result of its unique property of increasing protein content without disturbing the properties of the other ingredients, its bland flavor and odor, and its ready compatibility with carbohydrates, fats, and other proteins, is very desirable as an additive to a variety of baked goods and other foods and as an improver for low-protein flours.

Historically, the manufacture of starch from wheat constitutes one of the oldest processes for preparing starch. Wheat starch was produced in ancient Egypt and Greece, probably by fermentation of enough of the other components to liberate much of the starch. The starch was used to stiffen linens; mummies wrapped in such linens have been found in the pyramids. It was also used in making papyrus, an early Egyptian paper. Separation of flour into starch and protein has been reported by Pliny the Elder, who states in his writings that the natives of a Greek Island, Chios, were the pioneers in the manufacture of starch (about 130 B.C.). Leonardo da Vinci proposed the use of starch to stiffen fabrics used for wings of kites and

[1] This is a laboratory of the Northern Utilization Research and Development Division, Agricultural Research Service, U.S. Department of Agriculture.

gliders. In the 15th and 16th centuries, wheat starch was also used to give stiffening and finishing effects to linens. Starch seems to have been introduced into England during the reign of Elizabeth in the 1500's, when a Flemish woman was brought into England to give instructions on making wheat starch. It is claimed that starch was manufactured on a commercial scale shortly thereafter (1).

II. Early Manufacturing Methods

There were many early industrial processes for manufacturing wheat starch, but only a few ever became well known. Most were concerned with the recovery of starch without much regard for the yield or quality of gluten. One such method of preparing wheat starch was the Halle fermentation process. The essential purpose of the process was to destroy as much of the gluten as possible so as to liberate the more resistant starch from the wheat. Steps in this process were steeping, or softening the whole grain; crushing the softened grain; and fermenting to destroy the gluten by chemical and biochemical reactions, thus obtaining soluble waste products. These steps were followed by separating the starch from the fermentation liquor, refining to remove impurities, and drying. By the Halle process the gluten was totally destroyed and was not available for recovery. The starch product was relatively impure and somewhat colored; also the yield of starch was low.

The Halle process, and others like it were subsequently displaced by the Alsatian process, in which it was possible to recover gluten. By this method the grain was subjected to prolonged nonfermentative steeping in water. The softened grain was then placed in bags of mesh to permit easy passage of starch while holding back the gluten. The bags of grain were passed between a series of rolls in which the setting between the pairs of rolls became progressively smaller. The starch was squeezed out and collected, leaving the hulls and gluten in the bags. Further purification of the starch was made on starch tables. If gluten was desired, a rather tedious washing procedure was required to separate it from the hulls. The yield of gluten was usually low.

The Martin or dough-ball process was proposed in Paris about 1835. This procedure offers a relatively simple means for obtaining gluten and starch from wheat flour. More refined material can be obtained from flour than from whole wheat. The Martin process (2, 3) involves making a stiff dough containing about 40% water. After being allowed to hydrate for an hour, the dough is rolled between fluted rolls or kneaded in a trough with reciprocating rolls under a spray of water to wash away the starch and leave the gluten in a single, coherent mass. This procedure is advantageous in providing a high recovery of good quality gluten in easily handled form. The starch is refined on tables and dried.

During World War II, workers at the Northern Regional Research Laboratory proposed two methods for recovering starch from wheat flour. The first, called the alkali process (4), was chemical in nature and involved dispersing and dissolving the wheat protein in 0.03N sodium hydroxide solution. It produced a denatured protein and a good grade of wheat starch. The second process, called the "batter process," involved making a so-called slack dough or batter, mechanically breaking up the batter in the presence of additional water, and washing the starch away from the gluten (5, 6). In contrast with the Martin process, the gluten is recovered as fine curds. About the same time, Canadian workers announced the development of a similar procedure (7). The procedure was used in several plants during the war.

Wet milling the whole wheat kernel to procure starch was also used in several plants during World War II. The procedure followed was analogous to that used in the wet milling of corn and yielded starch of excellent quality (8). The starch was converted to sirups and sugars by the same methods used in the conversion of corn starch.

III. Current Manufacturing Methods

Wheat starch is being manufactured in the United States in five plants. Wheat starch is also recovered commercially in Canada, South America, Australia, and many European countries. As far as is known, low-grade wheat flours are used as raw material for manufacturing the starch. Variations of the two basic processes, the Martin and the batter, are used in separating starch and gluten from wheat flour. The Martin process is used in most of the foreign plants and in several of the wheat starch factories in the United States. The batter process is used in the United States and in a few of the foreign plants. One Canadian firm reports the use of the alkali process (9).

Except for the one plant using the alkali process, the others employ procedures that have remained essentially the same for many years. However, considerable improvement has been made in equipment and in conversion of batch procedures to either semicontinuous or continuous operations. There are five essential steps in either the Martin or the batter process: (a) mixing the flour and water, (b) washing the starch from the dough or batter, (c) recovering the starch and gluten, (d) refining each fraction, and (e) drying them (Fig. 1).

For the mixing step, it is believed that continuous mixers have replaced most batch dough mixers in American factories. In one plant, conversion to a continuous mixing and kneading machine has almost doubled capacity (*10*). Other mixing devices are also recommended (*11, 12*).

Many devices have been described for the extraction of the starch by washing (*13–18a*), and it is in this step that the Martin and batter processes differ sharply. In the former, the equipment might be a pair of reciprocating rolls that knead the dough in a trough under a water spray, or perhaps very elaborate countercurrent washers that upgrade the starch from the gluten

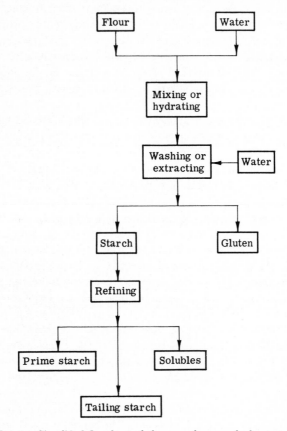

FIG. 1.—Simplified flowsheet of the manufacture of wheat starch.

mass. In the batter process, the feed is passed to a cutting pump together with additional water, and the gluten curds are separated from the starch slurry on shaker screens.

The crude starch milk is passed over fine screens to remove fine fibers and small pieces of gluten. This starch slurry is then further refined by passage through a continuous centrifuge system, which has replaced the old tabling or settling techniques. In the United States, the Merco centrifuge, a specially designed nozzle-discharge centrifuge, is generally used (*19, 20*). Use of this centrifuge and others like it (DeLaval, Sharples, Westphalia, Starcosa) has greatly increased the yield and quality of prime wheat starch in addition to saving time and conserving valuable floor space.

The starch is dried by conventional means, generally in continuous driers, such as tunnel, roll, spray, or flash driers. During the course of starch refining, a tailing starch is usually obtained. This starch has a higher protein content than prime material. It is dried in the same fashion as prime starch.

The gluten is also dried, but its method of drying depends on the type of final product desired. When undenatured or vital gluten is required, special techniques are needed to prevent overheating and denaturation of the protein. Commercially, gluten is dried in vacuum ovens at relatively low temperatures after it has been cut into pieces or otherwise subdivided; wet gluten is mixed or beaten with dried gluten from the process, and the mixture is air-dried in a flash drier employing a stream of warm air (*21*) or a dispersion of wet gluten containing about 10% solids is spray-dried (*22, 23*). These procedures all yield dried gluten that retains many properties of the original wet gluten.

The processing and wash waters accumulated during the separation of starch and gluten from wheat flour are for the most part discarded, even though they contain as much as 10% of the total flour weight.

IV. Recent Innovations in Manufacturing Methods

1. Continuous Batter Process

Chemical engineers at the Northern Regional Research Laboratory (NRRL) have described a continuous version of the batter process. A number of improvements make possible the recovery of starch from low-grade wheat flour on a pilot plant scale (*24, 25*). Variations of this process are probably in use in at least one plant in the United States.

This process involves mixing flour and water in the proper proportions to obtain an elastic, but free-flowing smooth batter. After the mixing operation, the batter is broken up mechanically in the presence of additional water. The starch is quickly and almost completely washed out, leaving the gluten suspended in the slurry in the form of lumps or curds. Gluten is separated from the starch by screening the slurry. The starch and the gluten may be further refined and dried by conventional means.

A continuous pilot plant for processing up to 400 pounds of flour per hour was assembled from conventional, readily available equipment. It is quite versatile and amenable to simple scale-up. Flours milled from different types of wheat have been processed successfully in the pilot plant.

Figure 2 is a flow diagram depicting the separation of gluten and starch

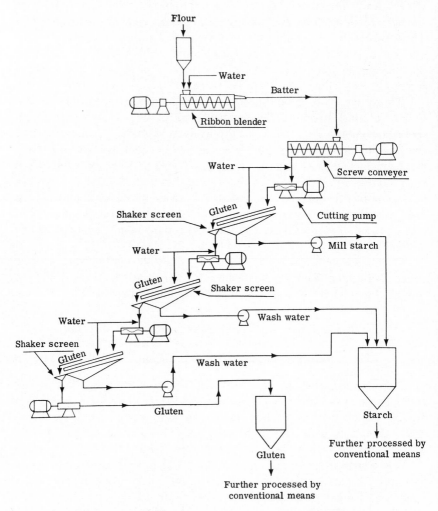

Fig. 2.—Flowsheet of the improved batter process (25).

from wheat flour by the NRRL continuous batter process. In this process, flour and water are fed continuously at controlled rates to a ribbon blender. The weight ratio of water to flour ranges between 0.7 to 1 and 18 to 1, depending upon the type of flour used. A soft wheat flour requires a lesser amount of water; a hard wheat flour might need a water to flour ratio as high as 1.8 to 1. The mixing water is heated to 48°–57° to facilitate hydration of the gluten and to reduce the usual mixing time necessary to procure a batter of proper consistency. Generally, a longer mixing time is needed when soft wheat flours or other low-protein flours are processed.

The smooth, elastic batter is conveyed to the washing or "cutting" pump where sufficient cold water is added to give a total water to flour ratio of 3 to 1. Here the batter is intimately contacted with the wash water by agitation of the pump impeller. Thus, the starch is washed from the gluten, which remains in the form of small curds. The gluten curds are

Table I

Results of Typical Batter Process Experiments (25)

Type of wheat flour:	Patent, soft white winter	Patent, soft red winter	Patent, hard red winter	Patent, hard red spring	First clear, hard red winter	Second clear, hard red winter
Flour composition						
Protein, %[a,b]	9.2	11.2	14.3	14.6	16.6	17.3
Ash, %[a]	0.39	0.34	0.41	0.41	0.79	1.47
Gluten recovery from 100 lb. of flour (about 12% moisture), lb.[a]	7.0	9.8	13.0	13.7	14.6	16.6
Gluten purity % Protein[a]	81.0	81.0	80.7	79.6	84.8	74.9
Crude starch[c] recovery from 100 lb. of flour (about 12% moisture and 3% protein), lb.[a]	76.5	72.1	73.0	71.0	69.6	67.7

[a] Moisture-free basis.
[b] Protein = N × 5.7.
[c] Includes wash-water solids.

removed from the crude starch slurry by a gyrating screen through which the starch passes. More starch is removed from the gluten by further washing.

Table I shows typical separations obtained from a number of flours milled from different types of wheat and includes two lower grade flours milled from hard red winter wheat. While the products recovered varied in quantity and composition, they were quite similar in view of the wide range of flours processed. The protein content of the crude starch (including wash-water solids) varied slightly from flour to flour, but, in general, averaged about 3%. The recovery of total protein in the gluten fraction was 80% or higher in most flours processed, except those milled from the soft white winter wheat. Protein content of the gluten recovered from each of the flours was from 75 to 85%.

These results adequately illustrate the versatility of the improved batter process. This process offers a method of providing a good supply of wheat starch and a valuable by-product, the gluten. Operation of the process has shown it to be simple, easily controlled, and amenable to instrumentation; and the process can be effected with a minimum requirement of labor, power, and water. Its continuous nature affords a minimum delay of material, which reduces the chance of enzymic or microbiological degradation of the fractions.

This process has been experimentally applied to long-extraction wheat flours ranging from 72 to 96%; results indicate that flours up to 85% extraction can be processed satisfactorily to give products essentially equal in quality and yield to those recovered from commercial second clear flours (25a).

2. Use of Air-Classified Flour

The introduction of fine grinding and air classification of wheat flours by the milling industry offers the possibility of a new source of raw material for wheat starch manufacture. By control of particle size, flour fractions ranging in protein content from 3 to 25% can be obtained (26–29).

Studies in which the high-protein fraction was used as the raw material in the production of wheat starch have been carried out by European and Australian workers. It is necessary that high-protein fractions be used so that the gluten can be removed from the starch more readily. Good yields of starch and gluten were obtained when the standard wet-processing techniques were applied to these fractions (30, 31). A German company is now using a high-protein fraction from an air-classified flour as raw material for starch in part of its plant operation (32).

3. Ammonia Process

The National Research Council of Canada recently developed a laboratory process to make starch and vital gluten from low-grade, high-ash wheat flour (33). The process is similar to the alkali method mentioned previously, but utilizes ammonium hydroxide in place of sodium or potassium hydroxide. As a result, the gluten can be recovered in undenatured form.

Scientists from the Council say that the process has promise of being perfected on a commercial scale. A flow sheet including material balance for a proposed plant capable of handling 50 tons of flour per day is shown in Figure 3.

V. PRODUCTION AND USES OF WHEAT STARCH

1. Production

The exact annual production of wheat starch in the United States is unavailable (34). However, a very rough estimate of annual wheat starch production would be of the order of 125–150 million pounds.

2. Uses[2]

Wheat starch is sold by the manufacturers in powdered, modified, and pregelatinized forms. It has many of the same uses as starches from corn,

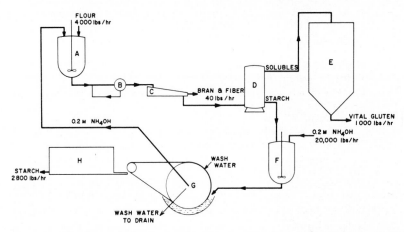

FIG. 3.—Flowsheet of the ammonia process. (A—slurry tank; B—recirculating mill; C—vibrating screen; D—continuous centrifuge; E—spray drier; F—wash tank; G—vacuum filter; H—tunnel drier.)

potato, tapioca, or rice; however, its equal or slightly higher cost usually limits the commercial outlets to those which need its superior properties. Wheat starch is considered superior for laundry work, probably because of the large range in granule sizes in the starch. The smaller granules penetrate the fibers of the fabric, whereas the larger ones coat the exterior surface. The pure-white color of wheat starch makes it useful as a component in some pharmaceutical tablets and in cosmetic preparations. The cold gel of a wheat starch paste is a desirable characteristic for some food uses. Wheat starch is a natural additive for many food products which already contain wheat flour, such as cakes. The tailing starch is used in the manufacture of wallpaper paste; in addition to having very good adhesive properties, the

[2] See also Chapter XII.

wheat paste has good water retention and possesses a slip-and-slide property that is important to the paperhanger (*35, 36*). One wheat starch manufacturer has produced monosodium glutamate from wheat starch by a fermentation process (*37*).

There are many possibilities for converting wheat starch to other useful products. Such products as dialdehyde starch, starch xanthides, and organic acids from the fermentation of starch offer potential outlets for large quantities of starch from wheat.

VI. REFERENCES

(*1*) J. A. Radley, "Starch and Its Derivatives," Chapman and Hall Ltd., London, 1953.
(*2*) C. A. Brautlecht, "Starch—Its Sources, Production, and Uses," Reinhold Publishing Co., New York, N.Y., 1953.
(*3*) J. W. Knight, "The Chemistry of Wheat Starch and Gluten and Their Conversion Products," Leonard Hill, London, 1965.
(*4*) R. J. Dimler, H. A. Davis, C. E. Rist, and G. E. Hilbert, *Cereal Chem.*, **21,** 430 (1944).
(*5*) G. E. Hilbert, R. J. Dimler, and C. E. Rist, *Am. Miller*, **72,** No. 4, 32 (1944).
(*6*) C. E. Rist, *Sugar J.*, **11,** No. 9, 26 (1949).
(*7*) A. L. Shewfelt and G. A. Adams, *Can. Chem. Process Inds.*, **27,** 502 (1944); *Can. J. Research, F.*, **23,** 373 (1945).
(*8*) R. L. Slotter and C. T. Langford, *Ind. Eng. Chem.*, **36,** 404 (1944).
(*9*) J. R. Crozier, *Can. Food Ind.*, **30,** No. 1, 26 (1959).
(*10*) T. F. Meinhold and H. W. Logsdon, *Chem. Process. (Chicago)*, **19,** No. 7, 15 (1956).
(*11*) J. F. Walsh, D. M. Levitt, and A. H. Goodman, U. S. Patent 2,517,149 (1950); *Chem. Abstr.*, **44,** 9587 (1950).
(*12*) A. K. Kilander and L. B. Edsall, U. S. Patent 2,530,823 (1950); *Chem. Abstr.*, **45,** 785 (1951).
(*13*) R. W. Callaghan and G. W. Elverum, U. S. Patent 2,388,902 (1945); *Chem. Abstr.*, **40,** 758 (1946).
(*14*) L. B. Edsall and A. K. Kilander, U. S. Patent 2,453,310 (1948); *Chem. Abstr.*, **43,** 1204 (1949).
(*15*) J. J. Von Edeskuty and J. F. Zalar, U. S. Patent 2,555,908 (1951).
(*16*) W. Honsch, *Staerke*, **7,** 107 (1955).
(*17*) R. A. Anderson, C. Vojnovich, V. F. Pfeifer, and E. L. Griffin, Jr., *Am. Miller*, **87,** No. 12, 18 (1959).
(*18*) L. Schmiedel and E. Heder, *Staerke*, **14,** 324 (1962).
(*18a*) F. Morton, *Food Eng.*, **37,** No. 12, 83 (1965).
(*19*) Flow diagram No. 26-22, "Wheat Starch Separation and Purification," Merco Centrifugal Co., succrs., Dorr-Oliver, Inc., Stamford, Conn. (1955).
(*20*) C. E. Schmalz and T. F. Meinhold, *Chem. Process. (Chicago)*, **18,** No. 7, 14 (1955).
(*21*) J. B. Regan and H. Flather, Australian Patent 107,603 (1939).
(*22*) W. B. McConnell, *Can. J. Technol.*, **33,** 256 (1955).
(*23*) Anon, *Food Eng.*, **31,** No. 12, 73 (1959).
(*24*) R. A. Anderson, V. F. Pfeifer, and E. B. Lancaster, *Cereal Chem.*, **35,** 449 (1958).
(*25*) R. A. Anderson, V. F. Pfeifer, E. B. Lancaster, C. Vojnovich, and E. L. Griffin, Jr., *Cereal Chem.*, **37,** 180 (1960).
(*25a*) R. A. Anderson, A. J. Peplinski, and V. F. Pfeifer, *Cereal Sci. Today*, **10,** No. 4, 106 (1965).

(26) D. G. Elias and R. A. Scott, *Milling*, **79,** 240 (1957).
(27) Anon., *Northwest. Miller*, **257,** No. 18, 10 (1957).
(28) D. G. Elias, *Am. Miller*, **86,** No. 8, 15 (1958).
(29) V. F. Pfeifer and E. L. Griffin, Jr., *Am. Miller*, **88,** No. 2, 5 (1960).
(30) W. M. Honsch, *Staerke*, **10,** 324 (1958).
(31) P. F. Pelshenke and W. Kempf, *Staerke*, **11,** 185 (1959).
(32) G. Jäckering, personal communication, 1960.
(33) K. L. Phillips and H. R. Sallans, *Cereal Sci. Today*, **11,** No. 2, 61 (1966).
(34) Anon., "Starch," United States Tariff Commission, Washington, D. C., 1960,
    p. 24.
(35) D. K. Dubois, *Baker's Dig.*, **33,** No. 12, 38 (1959).
(36) F. E. Horan, *Trans. Am. Assoc. Cereal Chem.*, **12,** 258 (1954).
(37) Anon., *Chem. Week*, **89,** No. 24, 123 (1961).

CHAPTER III

THE MANUFACTURE OF RICE STARCH

By J. T. Hogan

Southern Regional Research Laboratory,[1] New Orleans, Louisiana

I. Introduction

Rice, *Oryza sativa* L., has been one of the most commonly used grain products since ancient times. It is the staple food of the greatest number of people, and over half the world's population eats rice as the main article of diet. No historian can be accurate about the first appearance of rice because rice cultivation is older than recorded events. Wherever and whenever rice originated, its cultivation has spread around the world (*1*).

Rice is grown in all tropical countries in eastern and southeastern Asia including the larger nearby islands, especially Japan. The total annual world production is approximately 4.9 billion cwt. The principal rice producing countries are China, India, Pakistan, Japan, and Indonesia. Thailand, Indochina, Burma, and the Philippines also produce large quantities of rice. These nine countries account for more than 90% of the total world production. The important areas of production other than Asia are the United States, Spain, Italy, Egypt, and Brazil.

Rice was first produced commercially in this country in South Carolina in about 1685, and its cultivation gradually spread into North Carolina, Georgia, Alabama, Mississippi, and Florida (*2*). After the Civil War, this

---

[1] This is a laboratory of the Southern Utilization Research and Development Division, Agricultural Research Service, U.S. Department of Agriculture.

situation changed abruptly. By about 1887, the important rice-producing area had shifted from the Atlantic seaboard to the Southern States, with a rapid increase in rice acreage along the Mississippi River in Louisiana. Rice growing extended to the prairies of southeastern Texas in about 1900 and to the prairies of eastern Arkansas in 1905. In California, commercial production of rice was begun in 1912 in the vicinity of Biggs. In recent years, rice production has begun again in Mississippi. Although the United States produces only 60 million cwt., slightly more than 2% of the world total, approximately half the domestic production is exported.

II. RICE CULTURE IN THE UNITED STATES

The primitive, laborious rice cultivation methods of the Orient have been replaced in the United States with tractor farming, seed-planting by airplane, modern irrigation systems, power-combine harvesting, and modern drying and milling methods (3).

Rice does not have to be grown in water; but since it is a water-tolerant plant, flooding rice fields is the most efficient and desirable method of weed and insect control. Consequently, rice is grown in water in the United States and in most of the important rice-producing areas. The rice farmer prepares his soil in much the same way as for a wheat or barley crop by plowing, harrowing, and preparing the proper seed bed. Since rice fields must be kept evenly flooded, the grower must also level his land and prepare it for flooding. Rice is sown by broadcasting from airplanes or by using mechanical seeding machines. Fields are flooded with water about 4 inches deep. They are kept flooded for a period of about 75–100 days or until just before the rice is ready to harvest. When the rice is mature for harvesting, the fields are drained so that harvesting machinery can move into the fields. Large combines thresh the rice and unload it into spouted auger wagons that convey it to the dryer. Rice is harvested by combines when the moisture content of the grain is approximately 20%. As rice cannot be processed or stored at this moisture level, it is necessary to remove water from the grain until the moisture content is 12–13% or less. This operation is carried out in rice dryers that force heated air through a moving column of rice (4). Drying cannot be rapid because excessive temperature or too rapid removal of moisture from the grain will result in cracking or "checking." Rice with a moisture content of 20% usually requires three dryings at intervals to reduce the moisture content to a level at which it can be safely stored. After rice is dried, it is sold directly to a mill for processing, stored in commercial warehouses or elevators, or stored in warehouses or bins on the farm. The market condition at the time of harvest usually determines whether a farmer sells or stores his crop.

III. Rice Varieties

Many varieties of rice are produced throughout the world. It has been estimated that there are approximately 7000 known varieties of rice (5). The United States government, in cooperation with states in which rice is grown, maintains rice experiment stations. One important function of these stations is to work with farmers toward improving varieties of rice by combining the best domestic hybrids with the most promising foreign types. The objectives of the program are higher field yields, earlier maturation, better milling qualities, disease and insect resistance, and improved cooking qualities.

Rice varieties are classified as short, medium, and long, depending on the length and shape of the grain. Both medium- and long-grain varieties are grown in the southern states. Nato, Zenith, and Magnolia are popular medium-grain varieties. Sunbonnet, Bluebonnet 50, Texas Patna, and Rexoro are the commonly grown long-grain varieties. Short-grain rice production is confined to the California rice-producing areas. The medium-grain varieties tend to be slightly sticky or moist when cooked. The short-grain rices are even stickier. The long-grain varieties are easier to cook so that the grains are separated and flaky when ready for table consumption. Personal preference determines which type of rice is used. Rice varieties are also classified from the growers' standpoint as early, midseason, and late maturing. Zenith and Magnolia are early varieties; Bluebonnet is a midseason variety; and Rexoro is a late-maturing rice.

IV. Rice Milling

The rice grain is made up of the hull (husk), the seed coat (pericarp), the embryo (germ), and the starchy endosperm (6). The seed coat consists of six layers of differentiated types of cells, the last being the aleurone layer, which is rich in proteins, lipids, and B-complex vitamins (Fig. 1) (7). Proteins and mineral salts are present in the aleurone cells and also in the outer starch-containing cells.

Unhulled dried rice grain is called "paddy" or "rough" rice. It arrives at the mills in large sacks or in bulk. Different varieties and different grades of rice must be segregated and kept in separate lots. The first step in milling rice is to remove the hull or husk and yet preserve most of the kernels as whole grains. In the milling process, the rough rice is dumped into large bins from which it is conveyed through a series of machines in which it is clipped, screened, and fanned to remove stones, dirt, straw, and other foreign matter (Fig. 2) (8).

The cleaned rough rice is passed between the faces of large revolving "shelling" stones (9). Clearance between the stones is determined by the length of the rice grain. Centrifugal motion causes the grain to stand in a perpendicular position; the shelling stones are placed just close enough together to crack the ends of the hulls free from the grain without crushing the grain. Many mills use the hulls for fuel to generate power; in some mills they are dumped as waste. Other uses for rice hulls are given in Section VI.

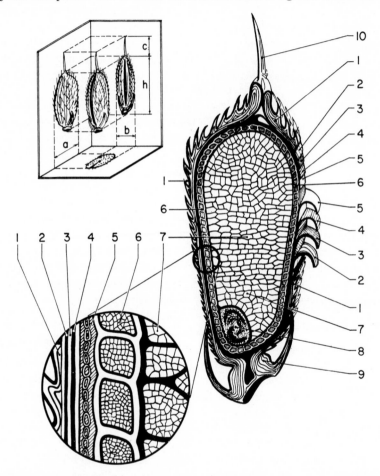

Fig. 1.—Structure of the rice grain (?): 1, hull (glume and palea); 2, epicarp; 3, mesocarp; 4, gross layer; 5, testa; 6, aleurone layer; 7, starchy endosperm; 8, embryo; 9, non-flowering glumes; 10, apex or beard; a, breadth; b, thickness; h, length; c, length of the beard.

Although each rice variety has a characteristic length and breadth of kernel, the individual variations that naturally occur within each variety cause some of the grains to be unhulled on the first shelling; these grains

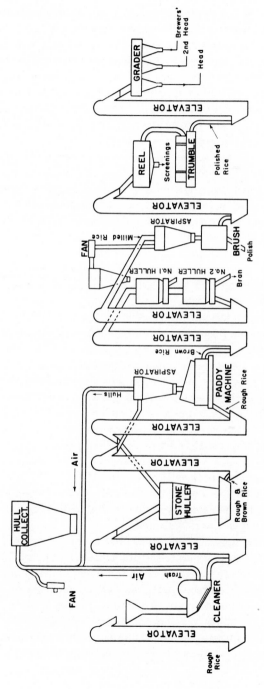

Fig. 2.—Flow plan of rice milling operations.

must be returned to a second, and sometimes a third pair of shelling stones set more closely together to shell all the grains completely.

From the shelling stones, the rice is conveyed to a device called the "paddy" machine or separator, which separates the hulled from the unhulled grains. This separator rocks back and forth continuously, shaking the grains over the surface of an inclined shaker box, the surface of which is covered with diagonally staggered metallic plates that form zigzags. The unhulled grains leave the box at the higher end, while the hulled grains leave the box at the lower end, because of the difference in the specific gravity and coefficient of surface friction of the hulled and unhulled grains.

The hulled rice at this stage of the milling process is known as "brown" rice; its color ranges from brown to green. In the next milling step, the brown rice is conveyed to the "hullers," which scour off the outer bran coats and germ from the rice kernels. The term "hullers" is a misnomer because these machines remove the bran, not hulls, from the rice kernel. The huller is a grooved, tapered drum revolving concentrically within a cylinder, spaced to rub off the bran with as little kernel breakage as possible. Loosened bran and smaller kernel pieces pass through the huller screen and are later separated by aspiration and screening.

The bran is a powdery, brown product of slightly sweet taste. Although it is palatable when fresh and rich in lipids, minerals, and B-complex vitamins, practically all rice bran is sold as a by-product for animal feed.

The milled rice kernel has a creamy tinge and is known as under-milled rice. This rice is passed onto the brush which removes most of the inner bran coat or polish. Polish is a powder of definite sweet flavor and contains a relatively larger proportion of carbohydrates and less fat and crude fiber than the bran. It, too, is sold as a by-product for animal feed. The rice resulting from this operation is termed polished rice.

At this stage the rice kernel consists of the white, starchy endosperm, together with fragments of the aleurone layer. Rice may be sold in this form as polished uncoated rice, or it may be conveyed to machines known as trumbles, in which it is coated with talc and glucose. This inert, harmless coating is used to give the rice a gloss.

Even with care, some of the kernels are broken during milling. A series of machines or classifiers separate the different size kernels. The whole and three-quarter kernels are screened into a fraction and designated as "head" rice; the one-third to three-quarter size grains are classed as "second-heads"; the one-quarter to one-third length of grains are known as "screenings"; and the still smaller fragments are termed "brewers" since they form a useful brewing adjunct. Table I shows the yields of products and by-products obtained from rough rice in the milling process (10).

Rice is further graded according to its degree of freedom from red rice, speck, foreign grains and seeds, chalky kernels, moisture, soil, weevils, and mustiness. Purity standards have been set by the United States Department of Agriculture (11).

Table I
Mill Yields[a] of Products and By-products from Rough Rice (10)

	(%)
Hulls	17.0–21.0
Bran	8.0–14.0
Polish	1.8–4.0
Head rice	37.0–65.0
Second heads	2.6–11.7
Screenings	3.1–11.0
Brewer's rice	2.0–4.9
Loss and trash	1.2–3.0

[a] As received basis.

V. USES OF MILLED RICE

Rice is used predominantly as whole milled rice, and the largest share of the world's rice is consumed in the boiled form. Methods of cooking differ widely depending upon heating facilities in a community and upon ethnic origins and national tradition. Milled rice is the major rice product of the continental United States with consumption averaging between 5 and 6 lbs. annually per capita over the past three decades. This currently represents an annual United States consumption of nearly 1.5 billion lbs. of rough rice, priced at $8–11 per cwt.

The brewing industry uses practically all the broken grades of rice, one-half billion lbs. (rough rice equivalent), amounting to nearly one-fifth of the total domestic consumption. This rice is used as a source of starch in brewing and is competitive with corn, although some brewers claim rice starch has some peculiar advantages not obtained from other starches in making premium beers. Current price of broken grades is approximately $5–6 per cwt.

Rice is also converted into a parboiled product (12). Briefly the process consists of the following steps: rough rice is subjected to a high vacuum to remove air from the hulls and from the microscopic pores deep within the rice kernel. Without releasing the vacuum, hot water is run into the tank until high pressure is developed. This pressure dissolves vitamins and other water-soluble components from bran, hull, and germ and forces them into the endosperm. Then the tank is drained, and the rough rice is subjected to live steam. A vacuum is applied again to dry the wet rice partially. Further drying is accomplished by use of conventional drying apparatus. After 8 hr. in tempering bins, all rice reaches approximately 12–13% moisture content. The effect of this treatment is to force the water-soluble minerals and vitamins from the outer layers to the starchy heart of the grain. Steaming gelatinizes the kernel starch to seal in the nutritive elements. Parboiled rice is milled in the conventional manner. However, the grain has been toughened so that kernel breakage during milling is greatly reduced. The polished milled rice is a rich cream color, but cooks to the same snowy whiteness as untreated rice.

White milled rice is also cooked and subsequently dehydrated and packaged for consumer use as a quick-cooking product. For reconstitution, the product in the proper amount of water is brought to a boil, and the mixture is allowed to stand several minutes. Proportions of water and rice, as given in the cooking directions, are such that the rice completely absorbs the water.

Milled rice is also industrially processed as a canned cooked product and as an ingredient in soups. Because parboiled rice has less of a tendency to disintegrate under the rigid processing conditions of canning, it is almost exclusively used as the raw material in these processes. A large outlet for white milled rice on the American market is as puffed rice, a breakfast cereal prepared by exploding moist kernels. Broken milled rice serves as the raw material for the manufacture of rice starch on a very limited scale.

VI. Rice By-products

Rice hulls are an excellent abrasive (13). Their high silica content makes them desirable in the polishing of castings. Rice hulls are one of the best conditioners for commercial fertilizers, and thousands of tons are used annually for that purpose. Rice hulls are used in the manufacture of hand soaps. The finely divided ground hulls may be used in the manufacture of furfural. A more recent development, which is attracting interest both here and abroad, is the ammoniation of rice hulls for cattle feed and soil fertilizer (14).

Until recently, when it was found to be rich in lipids (15), rice bran had been used exclusively as a livestock feed. By extracting fresh rice bran with commercial hexane, a crude oil of low free fatty acid content is obtained. This oil can be refined and bleached by standard methods to give a high-grade edible oil. Its smoke, flash, and fire points compare favorably with other edible oils. It is resistant to oxidative rancidity; it can be winterized, and the storing quality of the hydrogenated product is superior to that of cottonseed and peanut oils (16).

Rice polishings, consisting of the peripheral layers of the rice endosperm, are composed of approximately 94% of digestible nutrients and are high in vitamin content. As such, rice polishings have largely been used for livestock feeding.

Another by-product is rice flour, which is broken milled rice ground into flour. It is used in place of wheat flour in cakes and bread for people who are allergic to wheat and as a dusting powder for packaged refrigerated biscuits.

VII. RICE STARCH MANUFACTURE

1. Introduction

Rice starch has been manufactured for many years in Europe, principally in Germany, Belgium, and The Netherlands. From about 1932 until 1943, it was manufactured commercially in the United States (17). In recent years, no rice starch has been produced in the United States because raw material costs preclude competition with corn and wheat starches. Small amounts of rice starch are imported from Europe from time to time for specialty uses in making face powder or other preparations on which the margin of profit is great.

Rice starch granules are bound into a rigid structure by proteins in close association with the starch (18). Chemical treatment is necessary to separate this protein fraction from the starch in the manufacturing process. A summary of the composition of rice endosperm is given in Table II (19). The glutelin or alkali-soluble fraction forms the major component in the composition of rice protein (20).

Table II
Chemical Composition[a] of Broken Rice (19)

Constituent	Range (%)	Average (%)
Ash	0.36–0.61	0.48
Protein (%N × 6.25)	6.0–10.0	8.0
Lipids	0.26–0.95	0.54
Starch	87.2–93.5	90.2

[a] Moisture-free basis.

2. Alkali Steep Method

Because rice starch granules are very small and are surrounded by a water-insoluble protein matrix, it is necessary to soften the granules by chemical means first. Orlando Jones, who operated a starch factory in London in 1840, patented a process which embodies the general principles of the processes now in use (21). The rice is steeped for 24 hr. in five times its weight of a solution of caustic soda, consisting of 1 part of caustic soda

to 350 parts of water, to soften and partially disintegrate the kernels. The
caustic soda solution is drawn off, and the kernels are then washed at least
twice by vigorous stirring in an excess of water. The water is drawn off,
and the rice is dried in bags. The dried rice is then ground in an attrition
mill, and the finely ground flour is stirred into 10 times its quantity of
caustic soda solution. Stirring greatly assists in accelerating the solubilization of the protein in the caustic solution. After 24 hr., the starch is permitted to settle for 20 hr. The major portion of the protein is contained in
the supernatant caustic solution which is carefully siphoned off. The starch
is resuspended in 20 times its quantity of water and vigorously stirred. The
diluted starch milk is screened to separate whatever fiber is present. Washing, settling, and siphoning are repeated, and the refined starch milk is
allowed to settle. The starch is then recovered and dewatered either by
suction or pressure; the mass is then dried. The dried starch is crushed into
coarse lumps, packaged, and shipped.

Throughout the years, variations have been introduced into the Jones
alkali steep method. Steeping in alkali is often done in perforated bottom
tanks, and the alkali steep solution is recirculated through the rice mass.
Separation of starch from water and alkali is done by centrifugation. Frequently the alkali steep solution is heated prior to steeping, usually at
44°–54° (22).

Jaschke (23, 24) improved the alkaline steeping method of Jones by
introducing the use of more modern equipment in a continuous process.
Instead of initially steeping the broken kernels, the rice is subjected to a
dry crushing by means of a roller grinding mill which affords three passes
of the grain between the meshing ribbed rollers. Settings of the rollers are
adjusted to obtain complete rupture or breakdown of the plant cell walls
enclosing the starch granules.

The pulverized rice is introduced into a wooden tank and steeped with
a 0.25–0.33% solution of caustic soda. The tank is provided with a combination rotary stirrer and siphoning tube. One ton of pulverized rice
requires approximately 1000 gal. of caustic solution. Stirring of the pulverized rice is continued for 12 hr., and the separated starch is allowed to
settle. The supernatant liquor containing the protein and cellular constituents of the grain is siphoned into a reservoir for protein recovery. The
siphoning operation effects separation of the bulk of the protein content
from the starch.

Clear water is then introduced into the steeping tank in the ratio of
1000 gal. of water to 1 ton of pulverized rice and washing proceeds for a
relatively short time under vigorous agitation. After the rice settles, the
wash liquor is siphoned and delivered to the protein recovery reservoir.
The rice is then delivered to a wet mill, Buhr-stone-type, and ground with

alkaline solution of the same strength as used for steeping. Maceration in the mill reduces the grain structure and permits more efficient solubilization of the remaining protein.

The slurry of rice and alkaline solution is conveyed to a reel provided with silk bolting cloth, and the liberated starch is removed as a starch milk by passage through the cloth along with the alkaline solution. The fibrous material is reground in the wet mill to effect further separation and screened. The remaining fibrous material is passed into the protein recovery reservoir.

The starch milk at 5°–10° Bé is introduced into a series of continuous centrifuges, usually 3, for separating additional protein from the starch. Separation depends upon the difference in specific gravity of the starch and protein. Protein separated in the centrifuges is delivered to the protein recovery system. The starch enriched milk, 20°–30° Bé, is then dewatered to approximately 30–40% moisture content in a perforated basket centrifuge. Removal of excess water by drying is accomplished in a countercurrent dryer, thereby subjecting the incoming starch to a progressively increasing temperature as it nears the point of discharge.

Protein is recovered by neutralizing the combined effluents of alkaline solution, wash waters, and fibrous materials from the screenings with hydrochloric acid. This is carried out in the protein recovery tank which is provided with a stirrer. After neutralization, the precipitated protein is allowed to settle, and the supernatant liquor is siphoned off as waste. The precipitated, semi-liquid protein material is dewatered in a filter press, and the filter cake is subsequently dried in a steam-heated jacketed rotary dryer. Rice protein is utilized as a cattle feed supplement.

3. American Process

In brief, the process used in the United States prior to discontinuance in 1943, was essentially as follows (17, 25): The raw material for starch manufacture was broken rice obtained as a product from rice mills in the Arkansas area. The broken rice was charged as received into wooden steeping tanks in which it was steeped with water containing sulfur dioxide for a period of 72 hr. The steeping was a batch process; steep-water was simply circulated over the rice in the tank during the steeping period. As the water circulated, live steam was injected in sufficient quantity to maintain the temperature of the water at 49°.

The steeped rice was ground in a Buhr mill, and the product was passed through reels and over shaking screens to remove hulls and fibers, which were discarded. The slurry containing the rice and protein was adjusted to a sodium hydroxide concentration of 0.4%. The alkaline slurry was then passed to Westphalia centrifuges from which two streams emerged. One stream was rich in protein, while the other contained the greater portion of the starch along with some protein. Each stream was returned to the centrifuges for additional separation of starch and protein.

In this particular process, the final protein slurry was discarded. The starch was recovered in Sharples centrifuges. The starch cake was flushed from the centrifuges with water, and the resulting starch suspension was filtered. Continuous rotary filters were used for this operation. The filtered starch cake was dried in a continuous Proctor and Schwarz dryer capable of drying the starch in 30–40 min.

4. Village Method

Das Gupta and Subrahmanyan (26), in a study of the preparation of starch from indigenous Indian grains and tubers, describe a small-scale process of rice manufacture. Best yields are obtained by steeping ground broken rice (100-mesh) for about 48 hr. in 0.5% caustic soda solution, followed by centrifuging for 15 min. at 2000 rpm. Two grades of starch, one of about 97% purity and the other of 92%, are thus obtained. The process has been employed for local village production of rice starch in India.

Many manufacturers maintain that rice starch cannot be prepared by tabling the slurries. This is due to the small size and hence slow settling of the granules. In Burma, however, rice starch has been successfully prepared by use of level tables (27). Approximately 200 lb. of broken rice are soaked in 50–100 gal. of 0.3–0.5% sodium hydroxide solution for 1–2 days in a perforated false bottom steel tank. The alkali solution is drained off after 10 hr. The softened rice kernels are thoroughly washed with water, and the rice is ground in a wet stone mill with about equal volumes of a 0.25% sodium hydroxide solution to prepare a slurry of approximately 5°–10° Bé. The resulting slurry is diluted with 0.25% alkali solution to about 3°–4° Bé and passed over screens on shakers equipped with No. 14 silk bolting cloth. It has also been found that saturated lime water may be used for diluting the slurry prior to screening to assist in flocculating the fibrous material for retention on the screens. After screening, the starch milk underflow is tabled on level tables about 22 in. wide and 85 ft. long. The starch may be resuspended and retabled to improve purity or it may go directly to a dewatering centrifuge of the perforated basket type. In the absence of industrial drying equipment, the starch cake is broken into lumps and sun-dried. Recovery varies from 60% to 94% of the available starch, depending upon the care exercised in tabling.

5. European Process

Rice starch manufacture in Europe today efficiently utilizes the alkali steep method by application of modern industrial equipment on a continuous basis. Raw material consists of the broken rice supplied by rice mills.

Composition of broken rice is given in Table II (*19*). The rice is given a preliminary cleaning in a riddle to remove extraneous trash and is then passed over a vibrating screen to free the rice from dirt. Inasmuch as the rice has been classified, loss of rice from cleaning is negligible. The bulk rice, 25–30 cwt., is placed in a large steeping tank; dilute sodium hydroxide solution of 1.005 specific gravity is added until the rice is covered to a depth of several feet. After a soaking period of 10 hr., the steep liquor is drained off to the protein recovery unit. This steeping operation and run-off is repeated several times before the rice becomes soft.

The contents of the steeping vessels are then run through a hammer-mill or stone-mill disintegrator with a simultaneous flow of dilute sodium hydroxide solution to adjust the starch slurry output to a specific gravity of about 1.20. The slurry is fed to a slurry tank equipped with agitators, and the pH is adjusted to 10 with dilute sodium hydroxide solution; the liberated starch is removed by passage over high frequency vibrating screens or horizontally mounted silk covered reels. The screen or reel overflow is again slurried with dilute sodium hydroxide solution, reground in a second set of attrition mills to free additional starch, and rescreened with vibrating screens or reels to recover the remainder of the liberated starch. To reduce the volume of water required, a counter-current system is used in which the overflow from each set of screens is successively flushed upward with counter-current starch milk and rescreened. Underflows are concentrated in small cone receivers beneath the screens or reels to insure a rapid and almost continuous flow of starch milk through the system.

Overflow from the last stage of screening is dewatered to about 35–45% moisture, and the fiber cake is dried in a steam tube rotary dryer for use as animal feed.

The starch milk underflow from the screening is pumped to imperforated basket centrifuges of the suspended bottom-discharge type. Starch cake is built up in the basket, and the lighter proteinaceous material is carried in the overflow. After filling, the discolored surface of the centrifuge cake containing protein and other off-color materials are removed by means of plow-type scrapers. A separation based on color may be made in plowing out the starch cake. The outermost layers are of the higher purity and the innermost have a higher protein and extraneous material content. Each may be separately processed as different grades based on purity, or the innermost layers can be returned for further purification.

For specialty purposes, the refined starch may be bleached with sodium hypochlorite at a pH slightly above 8.3 for about 1 hr. Residual chlorine is eliminated with acid or sulfur dioxide, and the pH is adjusted to 7. The starch is dewatered and washed on a continuous rotary vacuum filter, again taken up in clean water, and dewatered to about 35% moisture in a perforated basket centrifuge.

The moisture is then reduced to approximately 12% in rotary, steam-heated, counter-current air dryers, after which the starch is pulverized and bagged for shipment. Yields vary from 75% to 80% of the available starch.

Effluent waters from the steeping, dewatering, and centrifugation operations are neutralized with acid or sulfur dioxide to the isoelectric point of the protein (pH 6.4); the precipitate is allowed to settle, and is recovered in filter presses or centrifuges. This dried protein concentrate is utilized as an animal feed constituent.

VIII. References

(1) D. H. Grist, "Rice," Longmans, Green and Co., London, 3rd Ed., 1959, p. 3.
(2) R. K. Walker, "Rice," Louisiana State Dept. of Agriculture and Immigration, Baton Rouge, La., 18th Ed., 1960, p. 3.
(3) M. R. Kopmeyer, "Rice—The Most Important Food in the World," Rice Consumer Service, Louisville, Kentucky, 1951, p. 4.
(4) W. C. Dachtler, "Research on Conditioning and Storage of Rough and Milled Rice," U.S. Dept. Agr., ARS 20-7 (Nov. 1959), p. 22.
(5) J. N. Efferson, Rice J., Ann. Issue, 59, No. 7, 1 (1956).
(6) J. K. Santos, Philippine J. Sci., 52, 475, plates 1–7 (1933).
(7) L. Borasio and F. Gariboldi, "Illustrated Glossary of Rice Processing Machines," Food Agr. Organ. U. N., Rome, 1957, p. viii.
(8) H. S. Autrey, W. W. Grigorieff, A. M. Altschul, and J. T. Hogan, J. Agr. Food Chem., 3, 593 (1955).
(9) A. Aten and A. D. Faunce, "Equipment for the Processing of Rice," Food Agr. Organ. U. N., FAO Agr. Develop. Paper, No. 27, 1953.
(10) E. R. McCall, C. L. Hoffpauir, and D. B. Skau, "The Chemical Composition of Rice—A Literature Review," U.S. Dept. Agr., ARS, AIC-312, 1951, p. 8.
(11) "United States Standards for Rough Rice, Brown Rice, and Milled Rice," U.S. Dept. Agr., AMS, Washington, D.C., 1961.
(12) S. A. Matz, "The Chemistry and Technology of Cereals as Food and Feed," Avi Publishing Co., Westport, Conn., 1959, p. 444.
(13) E. C. Lathrop, Rice Ann., 13–16, 69 (1952).
(14) A. Sonnier, Rice J., 66, No. 13, 7 (1963).
(15) J. F. Jurgens and C. L. Hoffpauir, J. Am. Oil Chemists' Soc., 28, 23 (1951).
(16) R. O. Feuge and P. B. V. Reddi, J. Am. Oil Chemists' Soc., 26, 349 (1949).
(17) Starches, Dextrines and Related Products, U.S. Tariff Comm. Rept., 2nd Ser., 138 (1940), p. 42.
(18) B. S. Rao, Proc. Indian Sci. Congr., 35th, Part II, presidential address, 1 (1948).
(19) E. R. McCall, J. J. Jurgens, C. L. Hoffpauir, W. A. Pons, Jr., S. M. Stark, Jr., A. F. Cucullu, D. C. Heinzelman, V. O. Cirino, and M. D. Murray, J. Agr. Food Chem., 1, 988 (1953).
(20) D. B. Jones and F. A. Csonka, J. Biol. Chem., 74, 415 (1927).
(21) O. Jones, British Patent 8,488 (1840).
(22) F. B. Wise, Bull's Eye Assoc. Rice Millers, 1, No. 11, 18 (1921).
(23) O. Jaschke, U.S. Patent 1,681,118 (1928); Chem. Abstr., 22, 3799 (1928).
(24) O. Jaschke, Rice J., 32, No. 9, 14 (1929).
(25) R. G. Hyldon, personal communication (1963).
(26) H. P. Das Gupta and V. Subrahmanyan, Agr. Livestock India, 4, 645 (1934).
(27) U T. Nyun, U T. Nyun, and D. T. Tin, J. Burma Res. Soc. (Rangoon), 39, 33 (1956).

PROPERTIES AND USES OF RICE STARCH

BY T. J. SCHOCH

Moffett Technical Center, Corn Products Co., Argo, Illinois

I. PHYSICAL PROPERTIES[1]

Rice starch consists of very small polygonal granules with diameters ranging from 4 to 8 microns. This granule size is the smallest of any of the common starches; only certain, rare, non-commercial starches have smaller granules, for example, *Amaranthus cruentus* and *Caladium colocasia*. Two practical applications of rice starch, cosmetic dusting and cold-water sizing of fabrics, depend on this small granule size. These uses will be discussed later. Certain industrial methods for drying rice starch may cause aggregation of the granules into "micro-lumps," perhaps because of a slight surface gelatinization of the granules which causes them to adhere to one another. For example, rice starch is commonly dried in flash dryers; if proper conditions of temperature, humidity and air flow are not maintained in the dryer, gritty aggregates of 50–100 granules may be obtained (1). Commercial rice starch is processed under alkaline conditions, which may be a contributing cause of aggregation by inducing surface gelatinization of the granules. Obviously, the presence of any such gritty particles will impair the use of rice starch as a dry-dusting powder. Usually these aggregates disintegrate into individual granules when the dry starch is suspended in water. However, in extreme cases of maltreatment during drying, the aggregated granules will persist even in water suspension, and will thereafter paste as micro-lumps when cooked. Hence a primary quality control test on rice starch is microscopic examination: (*a*) in mineral oil or glycerol medium or (*b*) in water medium. The first test provides evidence of micro-lumps in the dry state, the second test indicates the persistence of such aggregates in the wet state. While most commercial rice starches show some evidence of aggregates, the proportion of these should be minimal.

All commercial rice starch is manufactured by some variation of an alkaline steeping process. In general, excess alkali is removed by washing

[1] The author gratefully acknowledges the inclusion of unpublished data obtained by Eileen C. Maywald, F. E. Kite, and Jonas Montvila.

with water, and no attempt is made to neutralize the final starch slurry before filtering and drying. Hence the pH of the starch is generally around 8. This slight alkalinity is not objectionable for most uses of rice starch. High pH favors ready dispersibility and slow settling of the starch granules in water, and these qualities are desirable in the starching of fabrics. In the case of cosmetic powders, a slightly alkaline starch may help to counteract skin acidity. However, the starch should, of course, be appropriately neutralized for enzymic conversion or for any fundamental studies.

The gelatinization temperature of a starch is the point at which the individual granules first commence to swell and simultaneously lose their interference crosses as viewed under the polarizing microscope. Not all granules of a particular sample gelatinize at the same temperature, but rather over a range of some 8°–12°. As determined microscopically with the Kofler hot stage, the gelatinization range of a commercial rice starch available in the United States was 68°–78°. However, the gelatinization temperature undoubtedly depends on the variety of rice. Thus the "birefringence endpoint," or temperature at which all the granules of a particular rice starch sample have lost their polarization crosses, ranges from 62° to 76° (2, 3).

Since the gelatinization temperature of rice starch is usually somewhat higher than other common starches, it requires higher cooking temperatures to effect a viscous paste. Other than this, its viscosity behavior is not significantly different from that of corn starch. Thus the Brabender viscosity of rice starch (Fig. 1) is typical of most normal non-waxy cereal starches, showing the following characteristic features: (a) a moderate pasting peak, corresponding to maximum volume occupied by the swollen granules; (b) a moderate decrease in viscosity during prolonged cooking due to limited fragmentation and solubilization of the relatively stable swollen granules; (c) a high "setback" or increase in viscosity on cooling due to retrogradation and congelation of the linear fraction.

The viscosity of a cooked starch paste depends primarily on the extent of swelling and solubilization of the starch granules. Rice starch shows moderately restricted swelling when heated in water to progressively higher temperatures (Fig. 2), as determined by the method of Leach and co-workers (4). This swelling pattern is similar to that of corn starch, which rice starch resembles in viscosity behavior. In sharp contrast, potato starch swells enormously to give very viscous but fragile pastes that thin excessively on cooking or agitation. The small size of the rice starch granules does not appear to affect its pasting or congelation in any way.

While numerous studies have been made on rice starch and rice flour, much of this work is published in Japanese-language journals or in difficultly obtainable Indian publications. A primary objective has been to

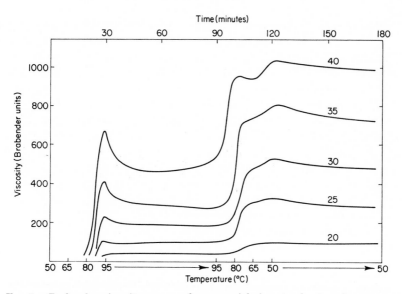

FIG. 1.—Brabender viscosity curves of commercial rice starch at various concentrations. Numerals on curves represent concentration, in grams of starch per 500 ml. Pastes were heated to 95°, held 1 hr., cooled to 50°, and held 1 hr.

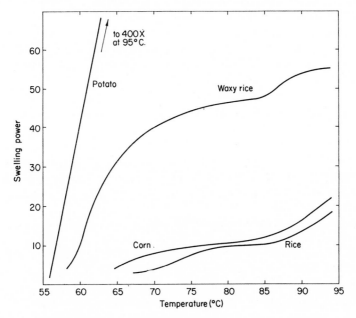

FIG. 2.—Swelling patterns (corrected for soluble starch) of potato, waxy rice, corn, and normal rice starches.

relate the cooking qualities of whole-grain rice with such character-istics as gelatinization temperature, content of linear fraction, and retro-gradation. In many instances, these tests have been run on milled rice flour and not on the refined starch. Consequently, results are somewhat obscured by the presence of protein and fatty acid. Nevertheless, certain broad generalizations may be made which are valid on a relative basis.

Normal non-waxy rice varieties can be roughly classified into two groups: *indica* in which the starch has a comparatively high content of linear fraction (usually in the range of 21–33%), and *japonica* with a relatively lower content (17–19%) of linear fraction (*3, 5*). In general, the *indica* varieties of whole-grain rice cook to a semi-dry flaky product, which shows considerable congelation and retrogradation on cooling. In contrast, the *japonica* varieties cook to a moist sticky product that retains this consistency on cooling or on standing in accordance with the lower content of linear fraction. Both in Southeast Asia and in the United States, there are definite regional preferences for each of these two rice types. It seems to be generally agreed that there is no correlation between gelatinization temperature of the various rice starches and their content of linear fraction (*2, 3, 5, 6*); this is perhaps not surprising since corn and sorghum starches have the same Kofler gelatinization temperatures as their waxy counter-parts (*1*). Attempts have been made to correlate the ease of cooking of whole-grain rice with the gelatinization temperature of the starch. The author suggests that the cooking qualities of the rice may be more closely related to the swelling pattern of the starch or milled flour when cooked in water to progressively higher temperatures. This provides a better index of water absorption on cooking.

The chemical structures of the linear and branched fractions from various rice starches have not received extensive study. Earlier work (*7*) on an unspecified variety of rice starch gave a linear fraction content of 18.5%; the average branch length of the branched fraction was 22.4 D-glucose units by periodate oxidation. More recent work (*8, 9*) suggests wide variation in both the iodine affinity and the viscometric molecular weight of the linear fractions from various rice starches as shown in the following tabulation:

Source of linear fraction, rice variety	Iodine affinity of linear fraction (%)	Mol. wt. of linear fraction
Century Patna	18.1	100,000
Caloro	15.0	140,000
Rexoro	16.3	325,000
Zenith	17.2	310,000

It appears that the starches from different rice varieties show a much wider range in composition and in chemical characteristics than do the starches from other cereal sources. Considerable research on known varieties of rice starch is required to clarify present obscurities.

Like other cereal starches, rice starch contains 0.60–0.85% fatty acid, probably bound in adsorbed state by the linear fraction. This can be readily removed by extraction with hot 85% methanol (10).

II. Uses of Rice Starch

The primary applications of rice starch are: (a) as a cosmetic dusting powder, (b) as a laundry stiffening agent in the cold-starching of fabrics, and (c) as a "custard" or pudding starch. The first two applications utilize its small granule size; the third use depends on the bland flavor of its pastes. As a cosmetic or dusting powder, rice starch is favored because of its covering power; hence the absence of gritty aggregates is essential. Its use has been particularly recommended for infants because of its non-toxicity and the absence of irritant effects if inhaled. However, the high price of rice starch precludes its use as an industrial dusting agent for such applications as bread-dusting or as a releasing agent for automobile tire molds.

Use of rice starch as a laundry stiffening agent is probably of Chinese origin, although the practice is now common in England and to some extent in the southern United States. A small amount of the uncooked starch is suspended in cold water, and the garment to be starched is immersed in this suspension and then wrung out. The small-granule rice starch penetrates deeply into the interstices of the fabric. The damp garment is then ironed, which causes gelatinization of the starch granules *in situ*, thus bonding the fibers together and imparting a stiff "boardy" finish. This is primarily an internal stiffening or bonding action, quite different from the soft flexible sizings obtained with soluble cooked laundry starches, as more commonly employed in northern climates. As a small boy in Brooklyn of pre-World War I, the writer recalls the practice of Chinese "hand laundries" at a time when stiff-bosomed men's shirts and hard-finished detachable collars and cuffs were in vogue. The hand ironer invariably had a glass of rice starch suspension available. Periodically, he would stir this suspension with a forefinger, take a sip and expertly spray it by mouth on that portion of the garment requiring additional stiffening, and then immediately cook and polish the starch sizing with a hot sadiron. This gave a hard smooth stucco of pasted starch on the surface of the fabric.

III. Waxy Rice Starch

Waxy or "glutinous" rice has been grown in the Orient for many centuries and has found extensive use in certain traditional pastries, confections, and other foods in India, Thailand, China, Java, and Japan. A superlative survey of the waxy starches, including rice, is given by Hixon and

Brimhall (*11*). Waxy rice was the first of the common starches to be identified by its red-staining reaction with iodine (Arthur Gris, 1860) (*11a*). Waxy rice has been grown for some years in California by American-born Japanese farmers, and the grain has been milled into flour for local use as a thickener in various food preparations. In particular, the pasted flour imparts certain desirable qualities of viscosity and transparency to thickened sauces.

The Brabender viscosity of refined waxy rice starch (Fig. 3) is very similar to that of waxy maize and waxy sorghum starches with a high pasting peak, extensive breakdown of viscosity during cooking, and very little setback on cooling. The viscosity pattern of the milled flour is very

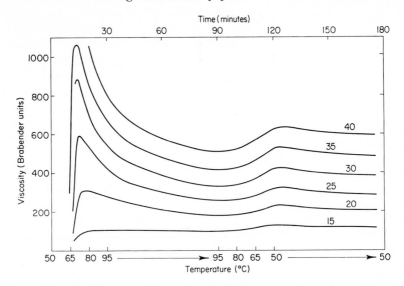

Fig. 3.—Brabender viscosity curves of laboratory-prepared waxy rice starch at various concentrations.

similar to the refined starch, though twice as much flour must be used to produce a given viscosity. The flour contains approximately 7% protein, and this may have an inhibitory effect on the swelling of the starch granules and the viscosity of the resultant paste.

Helen Hanson and co-workers (*12–14*) discovered that gravies and cream sauces thickened with waxy rice flour showed great stability toward prolonged cold storage and toward freezing. Even after the most rigorous conditions of storage, frozen foods thickened with this flour can be thawed and reconstituted, with no evidence of viscosity change, curdling, or the syneresis of water. This discovery should have particular application to such frozen "convenience foods" as fruit or meat pies, egg custards, and starch-thickened soups. While only the milled waxy rice flour has been commercially available in the United States, small amounts of the refined waxy starch have been marketed in Western Europe as a thickener for frozen fruit-pie fillings.

As shown in Figure 4, aqueous 5% pastes of waxy rice starch show no syneresis until after 20 freeze-thaw cycles. In comparison, waxy maize or waxy sorghum starch is stable for only three freeze-thaw cycles, and corn starch shows very extensive syneresis after a single freeze-thaw (15). While waxy rice starch shows markedly increased syneresis at pH 3.5, this

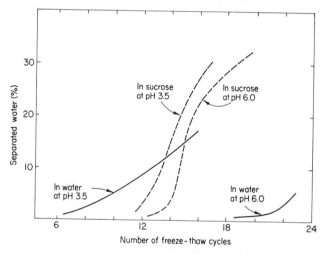

Fig. 4.—Freeze-thaw stability of waxy rice starch pastes in water and in 37° Brix sucrose solution, as determined at pH 6.0 and 3.5.

degree of stability is still beyond any normal requirement in practical use. The presence of sucrose modifies the behavior somewhat, but without any major alteration in the general pattern. Aqueous pastes of waxy rice starch have been stored at 4° for well over a year without any separation of water. The stability of cooked pastes of the unrefined flour is almost as good as that of the starch.

No explanation can be offered for this unique resistance of waxy rice starch toward insolubilization by freezing. In general, if a solution of the branched starch fraction is frozen and thawed, the molecules contract and associate to an insoluble condition which gives a B-type x-ray spectrum. Hence branched starch molecules are actually subject to retrogradation under extreme conditions, though this intermolecular bonding is not nearly as strong as with linear molecules. For example, if the branched starch fraction is insolubilized by freezing from solution, it can be readily redissolved merely by heating to 50° (*16*). In contrast, highly branched glycogen from animal tissue or from sweet corn is not insolubilized by freezing from solution, presumably because its branch length is too short to associate. K. H. Meyer and M. Fuld (*17*) methylated waxy rice starch, then hydrolyzed and obtained 6% of tetra-O-methyl-D-glucose. This corresponds to an average branch length of 16–17 D-glucose units, midway between glycogen and the normal branched fractions of various starches. Consequently, it might be presumed that waxy rice starch has a branched structure which is too highly ramified to permit association. However, Hassid (*18*) has determined the average branched length of waxy rice starch to be 20 D-glucose units by periodate oxidation, and this value is indistinguishable from the branched fractions of normal starches. Further study is required to ascertain whether the unusual stability of waxy rice starch is due to some anomalous difference in chemical structure, or perhaps related to its small granule size.

IV. REFERENCES

(*1*) T. J. Schoch and E. C. Maywald, *Anal. Chem.*, **28**, 382 (1956).
(*2*) J. V. Halick, H. M. Beachell, J. W. Stansel, and H. H. Kramer, *Cereal Chem.*, **37**, 670 (1960).
(*3*) B. O. Juliano, G. M. Bautista, J. C. Lugay, and A. C. Reyes, *Agr. Food Chem.*, **12**, 131 (1964).
(*4*) H. W. Leach, L. D. McCowen, and T. J. Schoch, *Cereal Chem.*, **36**, 534 (1959).
(*5*) B. O. Juliano, G. B. Cagampang, L. J. Cruz, and R. G. Santiago, *Cereal Chem.*, **41**, 275 (1964).
(*6*) J. V. Halick and V. J. Kelly, *Cereal Chem.*, **36**, 91 (1959).
(*7*) D. M. W. Anderson, C. T. Greenwood, and E. L. Hirst, *J. Chem. Soc.*, 225 (1955).
(*8*) H. Y. Tsai, A. T. Phillips, and V. R. Williams, *Agr. Food Chem.*, **8**, 364 (1960).
(*9*) A. T. Phillips and V. R. Williams, *J. Food Sci.*, **26**, 573 (1961).
(*10*) T. J. Schoch, *J. Am. Chem. Soc.*, **64**, 2954 (1942).
(*11*) R. M. Hixon and B. Brimhall, in "Starch and Its Derivatives," J. A. Radley, ed., Chapman and Hall, Ltd., London, 1953, Vol. 1, p. 252.
(*11a*) A. Gris, *Bull. Soc. Botan. (France)*, **7**, 876 (1860).
(*12*) H. L. Hanson, A. Campbell, and H. Lineweaver, *Food Technol.*, **5**, 432 (1951).
(*13*) H. L. Hanson, K. D. Nishita, and H. Lineweaver, *Food Technol.*, **7**, 462 (1953).
(*14*) J. G. Davis, J. H. Anderson, and H. L. Hanson, *Food Technol.*, **9**, 13 (1955).
(*15*) F. E. Kite, E. C. Maywald, and T. J. Schoch, *Staerke*, **15**, 131 (1963).
(*16*) T. J. Schoch and D. French, *Cereal Chem.*, **24**, 231 (1947).
(*17*) K. H. Meyer and M. Fuld, *Helv. Chim. Acta*, **24**, 1404 (1941).
(*18*) W. Z. Hassid, personal communication, June 26, 1957.

CHAPTER IV

MANUFACTURE OF POTATO STARCH

By R. H. Treadway

Eastern Regional Research Laboratory,[1] Philadelphia, Pennsylvania

I. Introduction

The American potato starch industry is not nearly as old as the European; potato starch was first produced in the United States in 1811 in New Hampshire. Potato starch was our leading starch in the nineteenth century. The United States Tariff Commission reported that by about 1880 there were more than 150 potato starch factories operating in Maine, New Hampshire, Vermont, Michigan, Wisconsin, Ohio, and Minnesota (1). The industry, from the beginning up to recent times, has been largely made up of numerous small plants instead of several large factories.

In the early years, special varieties of potatoes were grown for starch manufacture much as is now done in Europe. These varieties were not of good cooking quality but contained a relatively large amount of starch. In the past several decades, however, the American economy has been such that it is apparently impossible to grow special types of potatoes profitably

---

[1] This is a laboratory of the Eastern Utilization Research and Development Division, Agricultural Research Service, U.S. Department of Agriculture.

for industrial use. Thus, all American potato production is in varieties used for food. About 10% of the total potato crop (average annual crop for 1958–1962, 266 million hundredweights) is normally made up of substandard potatoes unsuitable for the food market because they are too small, too large, misshapen, or damaged. Nearly all the cull and surplus potatoes that are not fed to livestock are used in starch manufacture.

In spite of the fact that potatoes used for starch production must be sold by the grower at a low price, starch manufacture is to be regarded as an integral part of a healthy potato industry. Diversion of cull and surplus potatoes to starch factories has done much to improve the quality of food stock and establish more orderly marketing in the potato industry. Some manufacturers are engaged in food processing and starch manufacture in the same plant. Lower grade potatoes, separated from "field run" stock, together with peelings and trimmings from the food processing line, are ground for recovery of starch.

Late in the nineteenth century potato starch lost its strong position to corn starch, which could be manufactured at a lower price. Potato starch then entered the category of specialty starches. By 1900, the number of potato starch factories had decreased to around sixty. In 1920, there were about twenty factories concentrated in Maine with a combined daily capacity of somewhat less than 75 tons of starch. The number of plants in Maine has remained at about this figure, but the total productive capacity has increased markedly because of construction of new plants and modernization of existing facilities. In the last 20 years, an extensive potato starch industry has been established in several western states, principally in Idaho.

Potato starch production is confined to the northern states where late crop potatoes are stored throughout the winter. It is difficult to operate a plant economically unless the raw material is available over a period of several months each year. The operating season or "campaign" is from about October to about June of the following year, which comprises around 200 operating days. Rarely, though, is the supply of cull potatoes sufficient and distributed so that plants can operate at capacity throughout the season.

Cull potatoes sold at 25–35 cents per 100 pounds offer a salvage outlet for growers, who transport the potatoes usually no farther than about 25 miles and are frequently stockholders in the starch factory. The annual production of potato starch is subject to considerable variation, in general paralleling the size of the potato crop. During periods of potato surpluses in recent years, the United States Government has paid a subsidy of 30–60 cents per 100 pounds of potatoes diverted from the food market to starch processing. In the past few years, the raw material cost paid by Maine starch processors has been somewhat under 3 cents per pound of starch recovered. Maine potatoes ordinarily yield about 10% starch based on the weight of raw material ground. Potatoes grown in the northwest yield about 12.5% starch at the plant.

II. Statistics of Production

At present there are less than twenty potato starch plants in Maine, with a total estimated productive capacity of about 314 tons of starch per day. These plants are all located in Aroostook County in the northern part of the State where potato production is most concentrated. The largest plant can produce 35 tons of starch per day. Two of the plants have daily capacities of 30 tons of starch; three have capacities of about 20 tons each; eight have 15-ton capacities, and the rest produce less than 15 tons a day each. The newest plant in Maine began full-scale operation in 1961 and is most modern in every respect. It has facilities that will permit converting much of its starch output into modifications and derivatives. Maine's factories approached the 100 million pounds annual level of production for the first time in the 1950–1951 campaign and reached 112 million pounds in 1956–1957. Maine starch production for each of the 4 years following 1957 was well below the record figure. However, total production for 1961–1962 rose to the relatively high figure of 83 million pounds.

Potato starch production was started in Idaho in 1941 with establishment of two plants (2). Additional plants were built in 1942 and 1944, which, along with the increased production in Maine, took care of the essential needs for potato starch during World War II when imports of foreign starches were quite low. During the War, potato glucose sirup was produced in Idaho and other locations in the northwest. This was an emergency proposition during the time when beet, cane, and corn sugars and sirups were scarce; production of potato glucose sirup was stopped at the end of the War because of poor economics.

Since World War II, eight starch plants have been established in Idaho: two have estimated productive capacities in the range of 45 to 50 tons of starch a day; five have capacities in the range of 25 to 35 tons per day; the remaining plant can produce nearly 20 tons of starch daily.

Modern potato starch plants have been built in the last 10 years in the following other locations; Moses Lake, Washington (45 tons of starch estimated daily capacity); Monte Vista, Colorado (one having a 20-ton capacity and another nearly 35-ton capacity); Grafton, North Dakota (25-ton capacity).

Because of the 1961 surplus potato crop, Idaho produced an estimated 95 million pounds of starch during the 1961–1962 campaign. This is one of the largest, if not the record, seasonal figure for that state.

Total annual capacity for producing potato starch in the United States is estimated at about 290 million pounds, based on a 200-day campaign. Up to the present, however, the largest amount ever produced in one season was apparently in the neighborhood of 200 million pounds (1961–1962). Productive capacity is roughly divided as follows: 46% in Maine, 38% in Idaho, and 16% in Colorado, Washington, and North Dakota.

III. Processing

1. Raw Material

It is difficult to define a typical composition for potatoes. Based on examination and analysis of potatoes grown in Maine and other northern states over a number of years, eastern potatoes often contain 18–20% of total solids and western Russet potatoes typically about 22% solids. The following may be considered illustrative of potato composition expressed in percentages on the dry basis: starch, 75; nitrogenous compounds, 10; inorganic compounds, 4.5; sugars (freshly harvested potatoes), 2.5; organic acids (mainly citric) 2.5; crude fiber, 2; pectic substances, 1.0; fatty and waxy substances, 0.3; minor constituents, 2.0.

The starch content of potatoes may decrease during winter storage to a level much below that of freshly harvested stock. While storage houses are normally kept at 5° or above, temperatures between 0° and 5° will result in conversion of up to one-fourth of the starch to sugars (principally reducing) in about 3 months time (3).

Usually a starch factory has adequate potato storage capacity for several days of operations. Potatoes are removed from the storage bin by way of a flume in the floor, which carries them to a conveyor and at the same time removes stones and much of the dirt. The conveyor lifts the potatoes to the washer where the remaining dirt is removed. The common washer consists of a trough equipped with paddles for tumbling the potatoes in water to free them of dirt. The washed potatoes are elevated to a hopper from which they fall to a screw conveyor that regulates the raw material flow to the disintegrator.

2. Procedures

Potatoes are milled in water directly after leaving the washer. In brief, the basic steps in potato starch processing are as follows. The cells are thoroughly disintegrated to liberate the starch. Skin and fiber are then separated from the starch by screening the watery slurry or by passing it through a rotary sieve. Removal of the water solubles is effected by washing, and the remaining insoluble impurities are removed from the starch by means of specific gravity separation. The starch is then dewatered and dried. Elapsed time from grinding of the potatoes to bagging the starch is 1 hour or less in a modern factory.

Sulfur dioxide is added at two or three points in the processing to inhibit the action of the oxidative enzymes that discolor the starch. Sulfur dioxide is added to the slurry at the time the potatoes are disintegrated and at least once more, just before dewatering the purified starch.

There is great variation in the processing details and in the equipment used to produce potato starch (4,5). Maine plant operators have improved technology in all phases of starch manufacture. Better equipment and processing methods have been adopted as they became available through developments of American and European machinery manufacturers. Rasps of more efficient design were developed; more recently, hammer mills have come into common use for disintegrating potatoes. Vats have long been obsolete as the principal equipment for washing starch; tabling has given way almost entirely to use of centrifugals for purifying the starch. Maine processors were leaders in the adoption of rotary "turbo" ("ring story") and continuous-belt driers.

Idaho starch processors were the first in the United States to grind potatoes by employing a disintegrator that combines features of a centrifuge with those of a vertical hammer mill. In this disintegrator, a vertically suspended rotor with hammers in horizontal plane rotates at high speed within a 360°-screen enclosure. The potato macerate is swirled against the perforated cylinder, and the finely comminuted pulp is forced through the holes. Following disintegration of the potatoes, the pulp is screened or passed through a rotary sieve to separate the free starch. For plants that employ screening, screens ranging from 80 to 120 mesh are used to separate the coarse fiber and 120 to 150 mesh for removing much of the fine fiber. Continuous centrifugals are used to remove the "protein water" ("fruit water") from the starch and give a product substantially free of soluble impurities. Settling vats are employed in some of the Idaho plants to remove the small quantity of remaining fine fiber and insoluble impurities that settle at the top in the so-called "brown starch" layer. Several starch plants use "purifiers" (batch centrifuges) to wash the starch before final dewatering. The purified starch is usually dewatered by rotary vacuum filters.

Idaho plant operators were also the first in the United States to use cyclone "flash" driers. Although there is some variation in the number of stages and in the air temperature used, conditions employed in one of the leading plants will be used as an illustration. Pre-drying of the moist starch from the vacuum filter is effected in a screw conveyor through which 143° air passes countercurrently. The partially dried starch then drops into a high speed blower where it is mixed with 143° air. The moisture laden air and starch are separated in a cyclone dust collector. This is repeated by passing the starch through three additional blowers and cyclone separators. A fifth blower cyclone cools the starch before bagging.

Figures 1 and 2 present flow charts of the operations as practiced in the more modern American potato starch plants (6). The equipment and scheme of processing are similar in many respects to those employed in European starch plants; some of the equipment used by the American plants in washing and purifying potato starch is made in Sweden and

Factory production of potato starch

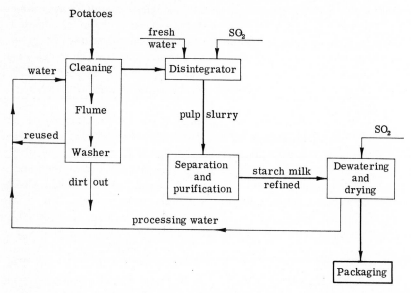

Fig. 1.—Outline of principal operations in potato starch processing. From Talburt and Smith (6).

Western Germany. Figure 1 depicts all the principal operations in brief form and Figure 2 charts details in the separation, purification, and final operations. The disintegrator used is of the previously described vertical hammer mill type. The centrifugal (rotary) sieves, first used in Europe, have been installed in several of the newest United States factories. The operating principles of a rotary sieve are illustrated in Figure 3. In construction, the rotary sieve bears some resemblance to a centrifugal pump, but with slotted sieve plates in place of the impeller vanes. The pulp slurry enters the rotary sieve through a central feed pipe and then flows radially outward along sieve plates. Centrifugal force drives the starch milk through the slots in the sieve plates, from which it is discharged through an outlet.

The fiber that cannot pass through the slots is discharged through a separate outlet. Several centrifugal sieves are usually employed in series. An advantage over ordinary screen separation is that the solids' content of the waste pulp from the centrifugal sieve is about three times that of pulp from the conventional screen. In the operations shown in Figure 2, the extracted pulp having 13% solids' content is pressed to 23% solids and then dried to provide a component for livestock feed.

Purification and separation

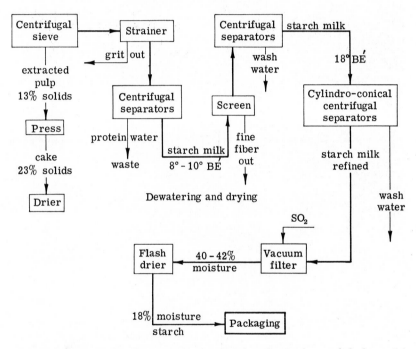

Fig. 2.—Detail of steps in separation, purification, dewatering, and drying potato starch. From Talburt and Smith (6).

Centrifugal separators operating at high speed are used to wash the starch milk received from the rotary sieves. Figure 4 presents a cut-away diagram of a centrifugal separator. In centrifugal refining, the starch milk passes through the separator bowl in which starch grains are removed from the remaining suspension by continuous ejection through nozzles in the bowl wall. The protein water effluent is replaced to a considerable extent by clean water. Centrifugal separators can also act as concentrators. Thus, in the Figure 2 example, the starch milk leaving the first centrifugal separator at 8°–10° Bé is increased to 18° Bé by passage through the second separator.

In the flow chart used as an example, the final purification of starch milk is carried out by passage through a battery of cylindroconical centrifugals. These compact vertical units provide efficient removal of soluble impurities and separation of the starch from the wash water by centrifugal force. The dewatering and drying steps as shown in Figure 2 are effected by the use of a continuous vacuum filter and a flash drier. Some modern plants dewater with a batch centrifugal and dry in a rotary drier.

Fig. 3.—Diagrammatic sketch of a rotary sieve used to separate fibrous material from potato starch. (Photograph of "Rotosieve" through the courtesy of The DeLaval Separator Company, Poughkeepsie, New York.)

3. Final Product

As indicated in Figure 2, potato starch manufacturers strive to turn out a product containing about 18% moisture. This more or less represents an equilibrium moisture content at normal temperature and relative humidity.

Examination of a number of commercial potato starch samples has disclosed that a good quality starch has approximately the following specifications and properties: ash, 0.35%; cold water solubles, 0.1%; nitrogen, trace; total sugars, trace; fat, practically nil. Potato starch is unusual in that it contains phosphorus in the range of 0.06–0.1% (7). Phosphorus is present as dihydrogen orthophosphate groups esterified with the amylopectin fraction.

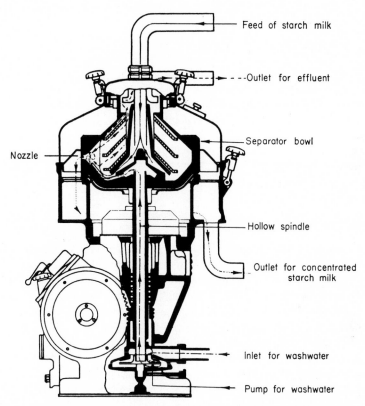

FIG. 4.—Continuous centrifugal separator or concentrator used in washing and concentrating potato starch suspension. (Photograph through the courtesy of The DeLaval Separator Company, Poughkeepsie, New York.)

Potato starch develops the heaviest consistency of the commercial starches on pasting, but its viscosity breaks down on continued heating and agitation to give a paste of considerably lower viscosity. Because its pastes are electroviscous, they are sensitive to small concentrations of added electrolyte (7). Thus, potato starch exhibits a higher viscosity in distilled water than in hard water containing appreciable amounts of calcium salts.

High-grade potato starch has a reflectance value of at least 90 (relative to magnesium oxide = 100), as measured by light having a wavelength of 450 mμ (8).

Total acidity of good quality potato starch, expressed as milliliters of 0.1N sodium hydroxide required for neutralization of 100 g. of dry starch to a phenolphthalein end-point, is of the order of 10 units (9).

IV. By-products of Starch Manufacture

1. Extracted Pulp

The extracted pulp (pomace) is no longer discharged to streams and rivers. When it is at all practicable, the pomace is used as livestock feed either in dewatered or dried form. Analysis of a sample of dried waste pulp showed the following percentage composition: moisture, 4.5; starch, 54.6; uronic acid anhydride, 16; pectin, 12; "pentosans" (pentoglycans), 9.5; crude fiber, 15.6; ash, 1.0; fat, 0.4; protein (6.25 × % nitrogen), 5.9; sugars, trace (10). (The total is more than 100%, probably because of overlapping in the uronic acid anhydride, pectin, and pentosan determinations.) About 400–450 lb. of pulp solids are obtained per ton of starch produced (9).

2. Protein Water Constituents

The soluble constituents of potato occurring in the protein water present a much more difficult problem of recovery than that posed by the extracted pulp. About 450–650 lb. of protein water solids are obtained per ton of starch produced (9). While several methods of utilizing or disposing of the protein water constituents have been seriously considered, none has as yet been commercially adopted in the United States.

The protein water typically contains 1–3% solids. Nitrogenous compounds constitute about 60% of the total solids. Up to two-thirds of the nitrogenous constituents are free amino compounds, and one-third is protein. The non-nitrogenous constituents of the protein water are sugars, acids, inorganic salts, and a number of minor constituents.

For recovery of the nitrogenous constituents from the protein water, one can consider the alternatives of preparing a powdered concentrate containing several of the principal amino compounds or of isolating purified individual compounds. Laboratory studies have shown that ion-exchange is an effective method of separating amino compounds from the other constituents (11, 12). Certain of these free amino compounds, the amino acids asparagine and glutamine for example, give some promise of finding medicinal applications. A concentrated mixture of the principal amino compounds in addition to potential pharmaceutical uses might also be of value as a nutritional supplement, food flavoring agent, or nutrient in industrial fermentations.

Another approach to the problem of utilizing protein water constituents is to evaporate most of the water under reduced pressure to provide a liquid concentrate. It has been found possible to make a fluid, stable concentrate containing as high as 60% solids. From the standpoints of stability and fluidity of the product, it is apparently better to remove the protein by heat coagulation before preparing the concentrate. There are indications that such a concentrate containing all the noncoagulable soluble constituents of the protein water should be useful as a nutrient in fermentations.

In some situations, starch factory operators may want to consider aerobic microbiological treatment of protein water to reduce the pollutional effect of the organic constituents (13). Although such a solution may not lead to a salable by-product, it can accomplish a great reduction in the B.O.D. (biochemical oxygen demand) of the waste. A similar fermentation is carried out commercially in the United States on milk waste (14).

V. Starch Fractions, Modifications, and Derivatives

Potato starch fractions imported from The Netherlands are available in the United States. Following extensive research in America and elsewhere, Dutch chemical engineers developed a successful process and built a plant that can produce sizable quantities of amylopectin and amylose daily (see this Volume, Chapt. XX). Uses for potato amylopectin and amylose are still largely in the experimental stage. Amylose derivatives are finding some use in industry.

Most of the potato starch is sold in the native, unmodified form. Sizable tonnages, however, are also converted annually into dextrins, pregelatinized starch, "thin-boiling" starches (by acid treatments), and oxidized or "chlorinated" starches (usually by treatment with sodium hypochlorite). The use of oxidized potato starch is increasing in adhesive and sizing applications in which increased paste clarity and diminished tendency to thicken on cooling are desired.

Much research has been conducted on the production of starch esters such as starch acetate, and on ethers such as allylstarch and hydroxyethylstarch. A considerable tonnage of hydroxyethyl ether of potato starch is produced by two manufacturers in the United States, and the carboxymethyl derivative is imported from The Netherlands. Some derivatives in which relatively few of the hydroxyl groups of the starch molecule are substituted are available. These disperse in water to give pastes of unusually high consistency.

VI. Utilization of Potato Starch

American potato starch is used in its various outlets in approximately the following proportions, expressed in percentages: paper, 60; textiles, 30; food, adhesives, and miscellaneous, 10. Since corn starch is by far the leading domestic starch in the United States, potato starch generally has to offer some advantage for it to find use in a particular application.

In reviewing the previous and current demand for potato starch, one must also consider corn and tapioca starches with respect to price and supply. During the period prior to World War II, domestic potato starch nearly always sold at a higher price than corn starch. Imported potato starch at times sold at about twice the price of domestic corn starch. For many years this price relationship restricted the use of potato starch to special applications in which its unique properties made it preferable. The availability of imported tapioca starch at a price generally competitive with corn starch was another factor limiting the demand for potato starch during the decade preceding World War II. Tapioca imports reached the high level of 433 million pounds in 1937 compared with 685 million pounds of corn starch sold that year in the United States (1). The demand for domestic potato starch in 1937, however, was only sufficient to result in the sale of only 17 million pounds of starch. Starch produced from corn in the United States in the 1961 calendar year amounted to 2177 million pounds (15).

Most of the tapioca starch used in the United States during the 1930's was imported from The Netherlands Indies (now the Republic of Indonesia). The outbreak of the war in the Pacific late in 1941 cut off imports from this source. As a result of the expansion and modernization of the American potato starch industry started in 1938, the factories were able to furnish a sufficient supply of this starch for the most essential uses and to replace in part the unavailable imported root and tuber starches.

Following World War II, importation of tapioca starch resumed. Thailand and Brazil are now the principal suppliers to the United States. Although the annual amounts of tapioca starch imported into the United States are subject to considerable variation, the quantity has been below 200 million pounds in most of the recent years on which reports are available (16). This tonnage is approximately equal to the American production of potato starch in 1960–1961 and is enough to furnish strong competition for both corn and potato starch, particularly in paper sizing.

In recent years, potato starch and corn starch have been sold in the same general price range; frequently potato starch has been cheaper. Much of the time in the past few years potato starch has sold at 5 to 7 cents per pound at the plant.

1. Paper

Potato starch is used for four purposes in paper manufacture: (a) beater sizing, in which bonding of cellulose fibers is promoted during sheet formation; (b) tub sizing, in which the preformed sheet is passed through a dilute size solution; (c) calender sizing, in which a smooth finish is imparted; and (d) surface coating, which is an optional step in finishing high-grade papers. Potato starches and dextrins are also used as adhesives for paperboard in the fabrication of folding, corrugated, and laminated "solid-fiber" boxes.

Cold-water-soluble potato starch is considered outstanding in its performance in beater sizing. This type of potato starch, produced for many years in The Netherlands, is made by drum drying cooked starch.

Because of its unusually strong binding power for pigments, potato starch has assumed an important place in paper coating, a place formerly held almost exclusively by casein.

2. Textiles

Most of the potato starch used in the textile industry is employed in the sizing of cotton, worsted, and spun rayon warps. In this application the starch tightly binds the loose fibers to the surface of the thread and strengthens the warp to resist abrasion and breakage during weaving. Potato starch pastes penetrate the fibers deeper before congealing than cereal starch pastes do and consequently impart added strength. The toughness and flexibility of films of potato starch relative to other starches permits warps to be woven at lower humidity than would otherwise be possible.

The smooth clear pastes obtained with potato starch also have other advantages in warp sizing. The smooth finish on the warp is easy to remove in the desizing step. The low tendency of potato starch pastes to "set back" or retrograde to a gel is of advantage following shutdowns. Potato starch is used to a considerable extent in the finishing of cotton sewing thread and in cloth finishing. The smooth surface obtained on cloth provides a superior "feel."

3. Food

Much of the potato starch utilized in the food industry is used in bakers' specialty items, such as Swedish and German style breads, in crackers, and in matzoth. It is also used as a thickener in soups and gravies. Potato starch has been pelleted successfully to make puddings similar to those ordinarily made from tapioca starch. Pregelatinized potato starch is used in considerable quantity in "instant" puddings. The dry formulation of instant puddings is principally soluble starch, sugar, and flavoring. Upon addition of cold milk, the starch quickly dissolves and then sets to a gelled pudding. Potato starch is a good thickening agent for pie fillings in which a particular gel type is desired. Native potato starch is not used in fruit pie fillings because of its susceptibility to acid hydrolysis, but a cross-linked potato starch is well adapted for the purpose. The properties of potato starch gels of different concentrations, pH, and sugar contents are described in the literature (17).

Potato starch is used in the confectionery industry for the following purposes: (a) as a medium for molding cast candies such as jelly beans, "orange slices," and gum drops; (b) as a bodying agent for imparting smoothness and stability to caramels and marshmallow; (c) as a thickening agent in synthetic jellies; and (d) as a dusting agent, perhaps mixed with powdered sugar, for candy gums, chewing gum, and so on. Thin-boiling starch rather than thick-boiling starch (unmodified) is ordinarily used as an ingredient in candy manufacture.

4. Adhesives

Although some potato starch used in adhesives is of the thin-boiling and oxidized modifications, most of it used for this purpose is in the dextrinized form. It is well known that films of dextrins made from root and tuber starches, such as tapioca, sweetpotato, and potato, have greater flexibility and resistance to checking than dextrins from cereal starches. Potato dextrins are used in many applications that require a dextrin of high paste tackiness and of flexible residual film, for example, as binders in sandpaper and abrasive cloth, in bookbinding, and in rug sizing. Potato dextrin films are also outstanding for their ease of remoistening; this property is desired in mucilages used for gumming stamps, labels, envelopes, and paper tape.

5. Miscellaneous Uses

There are a number of miscellaneous uses of starch that cannot be classified under the general categories discussed above. Examples of these uses include (a) as an additive in baking powder, (b) as a fermentation raw material, (c) as a binder for tablets, (d) as a builder for soap, (e) as a raw material for nitrostarch manufacture, (f) as a consistency stabilizer for oil well drilling muds, (g) as an attractant in insecticidal mixtures, (h) as a boiler feed water treating agent, and (i) as a clarifying agent for waters used in mining operations. Undoubtedly, potato starch is used in many of these applications. Manufacturers and distributors of potato starch seldom disclose information concerning the lesser uses of their product.

VII. Outlook for Potato Starch

The American potato starch industry has made great strides during the past 20 years in providing consumers with more and higher quality starch than heretofore available. The established uses of potato starch provide a constant demand for the product. It is impossible to predict exactly how fluctuations in the size of future potato crops may affect the volume of starch production. However, many leaders in the potato industry believe that there will be closer grading of tablestock potatoes in the future along with marketing agreements that will permit shipment of only the better grade potatoes to the food market. This should provide an adequate supply of culls even in years of only moderate volume of potato production. Continued growth of the potato starch industry depends primarily on whether the manufacturers can continue to match the competition of other starches in quality, supply, and price.

VIII. References

(1) U.S. Tariff Comm. Rept., Ser. 2, No. 138, (1940).

(2) H. Beresford and M. J. Aslett, "Potato Starch Production in Idaho," Univ. Idaho, Agr. Expt. Sta., Bull. 259 (1945).

(3) R. H. Treadway, M. D. Walsh, and M. F. Osborne, Am. Potato J., 26, No. 2, 33 (1949).

(4) C. A. Brautlecht, Ind. Eng. Chem., 32, 893 (1940).

(5) G. J. Muller, Chem. Met. Eng., 48, No. 3, 78 (1941).

(6) W. F. Talburt and O. Smith, ed., "Potato Processing," Avi Publishing Co., Inc., Westport, Conn., 1959, p. 381.

(7) G. C. Nutting, J. Colloid Sci., 7, No. 2, 128 (1952).

(8) P. E. Meiss, R. H. Treadway, and L. T. Smith, Ind. Eng. Chem., 36, 159 (1944).

(9) W. W. Howerton and R. H. Treadway, Ind. Eng. Chem., 40, 1402 (1948).

(10) R. H. Treadway and W. W. Howerton, in "Crops in Peace and War: 1950–51 Yearbook of Agriculture," A. Stefferud, ed., U.S. Dept. Agr., U.S. Govt. Printing Office, Washington, D. C., 1951, p. 171.

(11) E. G. Heisler, J. Siciliano, R. H. Treadway, and C. F. Woodward, Am. Potato J., 36, 1 (1959).

(12) E. G. Heisler, J. Siciliano, R. H. Treadway, and C. F. Woodward, Am. Potato J., 39, 78 (1962).

(13) E. A. Weaver, E. G. Heisler, N. Porges, M. S. McClennan, R. H. Treadway, W. W. Howerton, and T. C. Cordon, U.S. Dept. Agr., AIC-350 (1953), 8 pp.

(14) N. Porges, T. S. Michener, Jr., L. Jasewicz, and S. R. Hoover, U.S. Dept. Agr. Handbook, No. 176, U.S. Govt. Printing Office, Washington, D. C., 1960, 25 pp.

(15) U.S. Dept. Agr., Agr. Stat., (1963), p. 43.

(16) "Starch," U.S. Tariff Comm. Rept., (1960), p. 72.

(17) R. T. Whittenberger and G. C. Nutting, Ind. Eng. Chem., 40, 1407 (1948).

CHAPTER V

MANUFACTURE OF TAPIOCA, ARROW-ROOT, AND SAGO STARCHES

By Lee Shipman

General Foods Corporation, Dover, Delaware

I. Manufacture of Tapioca Starch

The manioc plant, valuable for its large tuberous roots that are rich in starch, thrives in most equatorial regions between the Tropic of Cancer and the Tropic of Capricorn. It is known by various names such as yucca (Central America), mandioca (South America), and cassava (Africa and Southeast Asia). Manioc belongs to the family of Euphorbiaceae and the greater number of species cultivated belong to *Manihot utilissima*, Pohl.

There are many varieties having different local names, but these cannot be relied upon to distinguish one type from another because the same variety may have a different name in another locality within the same country. The manioc plant was discovered in central Brazil; consequently, many varieties are identified by Portuguese names. But the crop is an important food source in many countries, and the varieties have become so mixed that there is a wide variation in the raw material used for native tapioca starch production. Most modern tapioca starch manufacturing plants use fresh cassava roots grown by proven agricultural methods. However, a good quality starch has been made in some of the potato starch plants in Europe using peeled, dried cassava roots imported from Africa. This process is much more difficult to control and is very costly when compared with the use of fresh roots; the viscosity characteristics of tapioca starch from dried roots are also different from those of fresh roots.

Two varieties of manioc are generally cultivated; bitter and sweet. The milky sap of the plant contains a β-D-glucoside, phaseolunatin (linamarin), the decomposition of which gives rise to hydrocyanic acid. Those varieties containing little or no hydrocyanic acid are called "sweet" (or mandioca aipim) and are grown for table use, as are potatoes in the more temperate zones. The hydrocyanic acid content is dependent upon the age of the plants, the method of cultivation, the richness of the soil in nitrates, the climate and altitudes of the region, and the characteristics of the species or variety. It has been observed that the raw roots of a sweet variety grown in one region can become bitter under diverse conditions of climate and altitude (1). Although sweet varieties contain little or no hydrocyanic acid, the bitter may contain as much as 250 mg. per kg. of the fresh root (2).

The bitter varieties are cultivated for industrial purposes because the roots have a higher starch content. During the process of starch manufacture, all the hydrocyanic acid disappears during washing and drying. The manioc plant is fairly demanding upon the soil; therefore, fertile sandy-clay or sandy-loam soils are preferable. If poor land is used, or that which is heavy and improperly drained, the root production will suffer and the starch content will be low. Soils rich in phosphates produce high field yields both of roots and starch. The land upon which manioc is to be grown must be completely cleared of trees, stumps, and grasses. The land should be cultivated once or twice before planting and to work in the first application of fertilizer. Fibrous wastes from the starch manufacturing plant may be sparingly employed as an organic manure; liquid wastes may be sprayed on the fields. Green manures in the form of *Crotalaria anagyroides*, *C. usaramoensis*, or *C. juncea* are also advisable (2).

The manioc plant is propagated from 8–10-in. cuttings taken from the lower part of the stalk. These are placed 6–8 in. deep in furrows 3 ft. apart and are completely covered with earth. In another method one end of the cutting is sharpened and inserted at a 45° angle into the freshly tilled soil leaving a few inches of stalk exposed to the air. In either method there are usually about 4000 plants per acre (10,000 per hectare). Manioc should be planted at the beginning of, or just before, the rainy season. A second planting can be made near the end of the rainy season provided the dry season is not severe and prolonged. Dry soil conditions produce roots lower in starch, whereas more moist soil conditions yield roots with higher starch content. Manioc will not tolerate wet marshy soil or standing water caused by prolonged heavy rains. Under too moist conditions the roots develop a brown rotten core that may not be perceptible in the whole unbroken root. Core rotting is avoided by planting the cuttings in mounded earth or ridges. For mechanical cultivation, planting is done in ridges which are plowed three to four feet apart.

The young plants must be kept clear of weeds during the first three months of growth. Thereafter, weeding should be done 2–3 times during the growing period. The length of time for the manioc to reach maturity varies with climate. In subtropical countries, Southern Brazil for example, the growing period is 16–18 months; in Java the roots are fully mature and are dug after 10–12 months. Manioc is a shrubby plant with palmate leaves of 3–7 lobes; when fully grown it is from 3 to 9 ft. in height. The roots resemble large sweet potatoes and occur in a whorl about the central stem. At harvest time the best stalks are cut with a machete, stacked in the shade, and later cut into pieces just before planting. The roots are usually pulled by hand; sometimes an adze or pick is used in digging the larger ones and those more deeply buried. Potato diggers and plows have been tried in some locations as a means of harvesting, but these experiments have shown that many roots are left in the ground and a great many roots are damaged. A satisfactory digger for manioc roots has not yet been found.

The normal yield of roots is from 5 to 15 tons per properly cultivated acre (12 to 37 tons per hectare); but soil, climate, cultivation, variety, use of fertilizers, disease, and insect pests all affect the yield. Epidemics of bacteriosis result in poor yields or crop failures. Withering leaves, gray spots on the leaves, and exuding of latex on the stems and branches are symptoms of the disease. Stalk cuttings from these plants should not be used for planting. The stems of plants which have been attacked by bacteriosis show definite dark parallel lines under the bark. The progress of the disease results in rotting of the stems and roots (1). Preventive measures involve the use of resistant varieties, careful selection of cuttings, crop rotation, and destruction by burning of infected plant materials. Other diseases are mosaic and root rot, both of which occasionally attack other tropical plants. The use of resistant varieties and crop rotation are about the only means of combating these defects.

Some insects attack manioc, the most common being a small diptera which deposits eggs on the under sides of the leaves. A secretion from the eggs causes a multiplication of the leaf cells resulting in the formation of a sac around each egg. The larvae develop in these sacs. This pest defoliates the plant and diverts the plant energy from growth. As a consequence, the starch content of the roots suffer. Insecticide sprays and burning and burying of infected leaves are common means of controlling the pest.

In addition to the use of proven agricultural methods such as care in planting, fertilizing, weeding, and control of disease and insect pests, good harvesting practices are also essential to assure prime raw material for the manufacture of top-grade tapioca starch. Roots are cut from the stem ends and the tip ends trimmed to avoid introduction of woody waste and dirt into the manufacturing process.

The composition of the roots varies according to such factors as age, variety, soil, and climate. Starch content has been found to be as low as 12% and as high as 33%. The normal range at harvest time is from 22 to 31%. Moisture content varies directly with starch content on a weight basis; the normal content is between 60 and 75%. The rest of the root is cellulose (about 2%) proteins (3%), fats, minerals, and soluble and insoluble carbohydrates. Young roots, that is those less than 9 months old, are apt to be high in moisture (close to 70%) and low in starch (18–20%). Conversely, very large old roots (over 24 months) are woody and difficult to disintegrate in the manufacturing plant. Starch content of old roots is also low. In the manufacture of prime quality tapioca starch, the roots must be fresh. Roots should not be dug more than 24 hours before processing since spoilage takes place very rapidly.

1. Determination of Starch in Roots

The starch content of roots is frequently the basis used by the larger starch makers for determining the root purchase price. Each truck or cart load of roots arriving at the plant from the fields is evaluated on the basis of a 3–4-kg. sample. The root sample, washed free of dirt and dried with a towel, is weighed in air and then in water using a specific gravity balance. The specific gravity thus obtained is used as the basis for determining the starch content by reference to an appropriate table. Actual starch determinations by chemical analysis are used to establish the relationship between specific gravity and percentage of starch in roots. For example, roots with a specific gravity of 1.064 have a starch content of about 15%, and those with a specific gravity of 1.145 contain 33% starch. A less accurate and less convenient method is to determine the moisture content of a sample of ground roots then $92.7 - \%$ moisture $= \%$ starch in the whole root (1). In the modern starch plant, trucks or wagons bringing in roots are weighed to provide data on raw material input and the operating efficiency of the factory.

2. Water Requirements

Another prerequisite for the production of high quality tapioca starch is an adequate supply of pure, soft water. A factory which grinds 100 tons of roots per day will require 125 gal. per min. of water. If the water is hard and contains iron, a lime–alum treatment followed by filtration is advisable. Water drawn from rivers or streams will probably need chlorination as well.

Care should be exercised in the use of river waters as they are usually difficult to free from fine silt, especially in the rainy season. These waters are often microbiologically impure as well.

3. Hand Methods of Starch Extraction

The starch granules, embedded in the root cells, are released by rupturing the cell walls by mechanical or biochemical means. The extraction of starch can be accomplished by hand peeling and grinding on a stationery grater using only crude equipment such as pails, tubs, and screens made of woven fibers. This simple process is used by many natives in rural areas of the tropical regions to obtain starch from the "sweet" variety of manioc for baking cakes and bread.

4. Tapioca Flour, Tapioca Meal, Gaplek, and Gari

The purified starch extracted from the manioc root is commonly referred to in the trade as "tapioca flour"; but tapioca starch and tapioca flour are the same. Occasionally, some producers overseas refer to ground dried whole root as "tapioca flour," but it is more properly tapioca meal as it contains a considerable amount of fiber and root peel. Manioc root chips, which are peeled and dried, are called gaplek or raspa de mandioca; a fine meal is prepared from this product by grinding and sifting. It is used as a native food or is mixed with wheat flour as an extender in bread making. When the peeled roots are rasped to a pulp and then toasted and dried in a copper pan, a product known as *farinha da mandioca* (in Brazil) results. If the pulp is fermented in a closed vessel, pressed to remove the liquid, toasted, and dried, the resulting meal is called gari, a staple food in the diet of many Africans. A small amount of starch may be obtained as a by-product of making these manioc root foods. But increased demand for high grade tapioca flour has resulted in improved manufacturing facilities for producing large quantities of tapioca starch. The requirements of quality, quantity, and end use of the tapioca starch determine the processing equipment to be employed for the manufacture.

5. Industrial Grade Tapioca Starch Manufacture

Industrial grade tapioca starch is produced in Thailand by hand labor using wooden tubs for settling the starch. Water is usually drawn from a nearby stream and is often used without treatment. Power for turning the root washer and rasp and for actuating the shaking screens is supplied by a gasoline motor or by a water wheel in the nearby stream. The roots are fed by hand into a rotary washer-peeler. This machine is simply a slatted rotating drum through which the roots travel while being sprayed with water. The roots are washed and partially peeled as they pass through.

From the washer, the roots fall into a grinder. This is often a crude machine consisting of a short rotating wooden log about a foot in diameter with nails projecting a few millimeters from the surface. A stationary wooden plate, also studded with sharp nails, is located to provide a small clearance with the rotating log. Roots are torn apart to form a coarse pulp which is mixed with a little water and allowed to ferment in a cement tank or wooden tub for a day or two in order to break up the root cells and release more starch. The fermented pulp is then poured by hand onto a shaking screen fitted with fabric that resembles mosquito netting. A spray of water over the screen washes through the starch and some fiber. The starch milk is then channeled to a large cement or wooden tank and allowed to settle. The waste coarse pulp, deposited outside the factory, is carted away or sometimes is spread on large patios to sun dry. In some cases the pulp is toasted and dried in pans over a wood fire. Wet pulp is often fed to cattle and hogs.

When the starch milk has settled, the supernatant water is drawn off and the starch cake dug up with wooden paddles. This starch is mixed with fresh water, usually in wooden tubs, and stirred by hand with wooden paddles. It is again allowed to settle, and the supernatant liquid is drawn off. The free water remaining on the surface of the starch cake is blotted up with rags. Starch cake dug from the settling tubs is crumbled and spread on bamboo mats to sun dry. Sometimes the starch is dried on a large cement surface heated by a wood fire underneath. A heavy wooden roller may be drawn over the lumps of starch to pulverize them and facilitate drying. Wooden rakes are then used to turn the starch over and expose new surfaces for drying. The product is off white, high in fiber and ash, and may have many dark specks and other contaminants. It is characterized by a high bacteria count, a sour odor, low pH, and low viscosity, all of which are a result of the processing method and the fermentation of the root pulp. The product is bought from many small producers by dealers who may grind, screen, and blend it with better starch in order to up-grade the quality. The product is not suitable for food purposes in the United States, but is satisfactory for certain textile sizings and for manufacture of corrugated paper board.

6. Semimechanized Tapioca Starch Manufacture

Another method of tapioca starch manufacture, used in Southern Brazil, is more mechanized but again involves some crude wooden equipment. The roots are washed by tumbling in a water-filled U-shaped trough fitted with paddle arms which move the roots along to the peeler. Peeling is accomplished in a slotted rotating drum with an internal water spray, or in a U-shaped slotted trough with paddle arms which toss the roots and carry them through the peeler. The roots with 75–80% of the thin outer peel rubbed off are fed into a Jahn rasp for grinding. The rasp has a stationary plate and a rotating drum both fitted with sawtooth blades about 0.5 in. apart on the long axis. A retaining screen in the bottom has slotted holes 5 × 14 mm. The rasp disintegrates the roots into a relatively fine pulp, which collects in a tank. A piston pump is used to deliver the pulp, which has been mixed with a small amount of fresh water, to a series of vibrating screens fitted with 50- or 60-mesh phosphor bronze gauze. Usually a small spray of fresh water is applied to assist in the separation of starch and coarse fiber and to keep the screen meshes clean. Some plants have six-sided rotating screens 8 ft. long for separating starch and coarse fiber. The panels are covered with a similar fine screening, and a water spray above helps to keep the meshes clear as the machine rotates. A further screening on 100–150-mesh gauze may also be carried out as a second refining step.

The starch milk having a density of 2–3° Baumé flows into a cement settling basin which is 100 ft. long, 25 ft. wide, and 6–8 in. deep. The settling of the starch creates a very gradual inclined slope to the exit channel. When the basin is full, the surface of the starch cake is cleared of free water using a squeegee and cloths. The starch cake is transferred to wooden boxes and then to tanks filled with fresh water. These tanks are of wood or cement, about 8 ft. square and 5 ft. deep, and are fitted with a motor-driven stirring paddle. The resuspended starch, brought to 4–5° Baumé, is subjected to a second settling process called tabling. The tables are long narrow channels of wood or treated cement. They may be arranged in multiple sets where the starch liquor flows from the top floor of the table house through two or more sets of tables to the exit or waste channel. In still another arrangement, the tabling is all on one floor, but the flow of starch milk is directed down and back through a series of parallel channels 80–90 ft. long and 12–15 in number. When these tables are full, the surface water is blotted up with cloths. Then the cake is removed, crumbled, and spread on canvass covered trays that are placed in racks on wheels. The racks are rolled into a dryer house. This building is usually a barn-like structure with brick wood-burning furnaces the full length of the basement. The open work floor consists of narrow walkways and tracks in which the racks are rolled. Louvres and vents in the eaves of the building allow the natural convection from the heat of the furnaces to carry away the moisture-laden air. In some instances a draft will be induced by the use of large fans. This drying process requires 24–36 hours depending upon atmospheric conditions. The starch becomes yellow if 2 to 3 days are required for drying. Tapioca starch dried in this way carries a strong smoky odor from the wood fires used to supply the heat. As racks with freshly loaded trays are pushed into the dryer house, the ones bearing the dried tapioca starch are rolled out.

The dried starch is often sold in the pearl form (un-milled), but some manufacturers have installed attrition mills and centrifugal sifting reels fitted with 14 X silk screens in order to produce a powdered tapioca starch. Bagging is frequently done in 60-kg. cotton bags, but most of the tapioca starch now exported from Brazil is shipped in multiwall kraft bags. The quality of the starch produced by this semi-mechanized system varies among the numerous small mills in southern Brazil. A few producers make consistently clean white starch, while others make starch that is unsatisfactory for food purposes but is very good for certain industrial purposes, especially in paper and adhesive manufacture.

7. Modern Methods of Tapioca Starch Manufacture

The most modern mills in Brazil are mechanized with electrical equipment. Diesel-electric generators are used to furnish the power either as a complete source of energy or as stand-by power in case of failure in the municipal supply.

Approximately 200 H.P. are needed for the processing of 50 tons of roots per 24 hours (*3*).

Water is supplied from wells or cisterns and is usually treated with lime and alum, and filtered before use.

The processing system currently employed in the modern tapioca plants in Sao Paulo, Brazil, was established in order to produce starch that would meet the high quality standards required by the users of food-grade tapioca starch in the United States. Proper sanitation, a high degree of extraction efficiency, elimination of iron piping and equipment, and effective quality control are among the prerequisites for food-grade tapioca starch.

Freshly dug roots, which have been weighed and sampled, are washed and peeled in the same kind of rotating washers and peelers previously described, but they are continuously inspected as they come from the peeler. Roots with too much peel as well as those with woody ends or other defects are removed, trimmed, and returned to the head end of the peeler. Grinding in the primary stage is done in Jahn Rasps or hammer mills having retaining screens with circular holes of 3.5-mm. diameter. The ground pulp is pumped to brush washers which extract the freed starch. These brush washers are troughs 20 ft. long with finely perforated U-shaped copper plates fitted to the bottom. Inside is a rotating shaft with cross arms fitted with curved brushes. The angular set of the brushes resembles an interrupted spiral conveyor; the movement of these brushes carries the pulp along and works it against the perforated copper plate to extract the strach from the pulp. A gentle spray of water from a pipe mounted above the machine assists in leaching out the starch. The resulting starch milk, having a density of 2–3° Baumé, is passed over vibrating screens fitted with 120-mesh gauze which removes fine fiber. The pulp discharged from the first brush washer undergoes a second grinding in a second rasp or hammer mill in which the retaining screens have 1-mm. holes. The reground pulp is pumped to a second brush washer from which the starch milk passes to the first vibrating screen, while the spent pulp is discharged from the factory as waste or to a pulp drying section in another part of the factory. The first vibrating screen produces starch milk which is pumped to a second set of vibrating screens fitted with a 200-mesh phosphor bronze gauze. Just before this final screening, a 0.2% sulfur dioxide solution is added at the rate of approximately 0.137 gal. per 2.2 lbs. of dry starch. The sulfur dioxide solution is supplied from a special generator in which the gas from burning sulfur is taken up by a counter current spray of water in an absorption column. The addition of sulfur dioxide improves starch color, aids in the subsequent settling steps, and prevents deterioration of the starch from the action of bacteria and mold. Also, sulfur dioxide prevents a sticky latex of insoluble carbohydrates from plugging screens and centrifuge cloths.

Pulp from the second vibrating screen is sent to the waste effluent or to the pulp drying section. The starch may be washed and concentrated in a Uhland-type horizontal centrifuge in some factories or sent directly to the settling tables.

The table house has successive sets of channels 130 ft. long and 1.5 ft. wide on three or four floors. They are constructed of wood, painted concrete, or glazed tile. The starch, fed in a slurry at a concentration of 3–4° Baumé, settles as the liquor flows from one set of tables to the next. The final settling basin, outside the factory, accumulates last traces of starch in the final liquor after several days of processing.

Every 12 hours the tables are cleared by a stream of high-pressure water. Starch from the tables is washed several times in tile-lined tanks, then dewatered in basket-type batch centrifuges to a moisture content of 35–38%. The thin inner core of the centrifuge cake, containing impurities and grey colored starch, is scraped out. The cake is then crumbled and sent to vacuum batch dryers. These dryers are generally heated with steam, and, unless care is exercised, lumps of cooked starch or charred starch develop during the drying. It is almost impossible to avoid some incipient gelatiniza-tion in the vacuum dryers; therefore, screening on vibrating and centrifugal sifters is essential to remove lumps and coarse particles. Some factories employ an attrition mill to grind this coarse material and then add it back to the screened starch. The best quality starch cannot be obtained by this practice, however. The screened starch is packed into 50-kg. or 100-lb., multiwall, valve-type bags for export. The valve bags represent a sanitary way of packaging and can be filled automatically.

Another process for the manufacture of high-grade tapioca starch em-employs centrifugal separators especially designed for the purpose. It is a complete tapioca starch processing plant supplied by Alfa Laval of Sweden. Some modern plants in Thailand have obtained consistently good results with this process since the entire operation from root to finished starch requires only forty minutes, whereas the tabling-settling process described above requires about 18 hr. In hot, humid climates, the faster process is preferred because it avoids the development of microorganisms which lower the viscosity and pH and increase the color and odor of the finished product.

In the centrifugal separator process, the washed and peeled roots are comminuted in a chopping machine which facilitates the feeding of roots at a regulated rate to the rasping step. The finely ground pulp is introduced into the small end of a vertically revolving, conical refining screen. The centrifugal action forces the starch through the screen, while the pulp migrates into the larger diameter from which it is discharged. These refiners are arranged in two batteries of two or three screens in series with a second rasping of the pulp in between. The starch milk comes out with a density of 2–3° Baumé.

It has been recognized in recent years that the finest quality tapioca starch results when the enzyme-bearing "fruit waters," that is root juices, are removed early in the process. Nozzle centrifuges perform this function effectively while giving the starch a preliminary washing and removing some fine fiber. The starch milk is introduced into the top of the centrifuge and enters the base of the rapidly revolving bowl (3500–5100 rpm) near the central shaft. A series of nozzles of carefully selected diameter are arranged around the periphery of the bowl. Fresh wash water, introduced at the bottom of the machine, is pumped up through the central spindle and into the separator bowl. The washed and concentrated starch leaves through the nozzles and passes out of the machine at 11–12° Baumé to the next processing step, while the fruit water and fiber discharges near the top of the separator. The liquid waste can be sent to the sewer or pumped to the root washing and peeling section in order to reduce consumption of fresh water.

The starch milk is next treated with sulfur dioxide solution and diluted to 8° Baumé. It is then passed over vibrating screens of 120 to 150 mesh and subsequently over 200-mesh phosphor bronze gauze to remove fine fiber.

From the screening section, the starch milk passes to a second centrifugal washing and concentrating station similar in function to the first. The concentrated starch milk at 19° Baumé is then subjected to a final refining in a so-called purifying centrifuge. This is a batch-automatic machine which passes through the following cycle: filling, grey starch removal, reslurrying, washing, reslurrying, and discharge of heavy slurry (18–20° Baumé). The cycle is hydraulically operated, and the grey starch is returned to the first refining stage while the heavy slurry is discharged to an intermediate tank fitted with an agitator (4). An automatic density controller is usually employed in this process to regulate the density of the starch milk supplied to the separators.

The purified starch slurry in the intermediate tank is the supply for the dewatering and drying steps. Either a batch-continuous centrifuge or a continuous vacuum filter may be used to dewater the starch. The dehydrating centrifuges are lined with a canvas cloth and may be operated manually or may be equipped with a hydraulic system to control the machine automatically through a cycle consisting of filling, spinning, cutting out, and discharge of the dewatered starch. A cycle requires 14–16 minutes. The ejected starch has a moisture content of 35–37%. The vacuum filters consist of a large revolving cloth-covered drum with the lower portion passing through a starch slurry kept under constant agitation. A suction behind the filter pad draws a layer of starch onto the drum as it rotates and removes free water. Dewatered starch with a moisture content of 37–38% is removed by means of a scraper as the drum completes a revolution.

Final drying of tapioca starch, to 12% moisture, is accomplished in most installations by a flash dryer. Air at high velocity is passed through a heat exchanger to raise the temperature to 150°–160°. Starch is drawn into the riser duct through an air lock, and, in a matter of seconds, the excess moisture is "flashed" off. The turbulent hot air carries the starch to a series of cyclones from which it falls into a collector while the moist air discharges out through the exhaust stack. From the collector, the starch, now at 10–12% moisture, is cooled in a stream of cool filtered air and delivered into the final cyclone. Centrifugal sifters or planetary sifters with silk or nylon screens of $14 \times \times$ mesh are usually employed to remove coarse particles, which are returned to the wet process.

As with the other mechanical processes described, the screened starch is delivered to a bagging and weighing machine.

A complete quality control system is necessary to assure the highest extraction efficiency, a 90% recovery of the starch in the roots with the foregoing process. A uniform grade "A" quality is achieved only with a continuing quality control program for testing raw material, starch milk streams at various points, and the finished starch coming from the dryer. Regular periodic cleaning of all equipment is also essential to the operation, because quality and efficiency of the production can be seriously affected if the machinery and piping are allowed to collect coatings of latex, mold, and the like.

An examination of twelve starch characteristics and their relationship to the manufacturing process will emphasize the need for good quality control and sanitation. Analytical methods vary among tapioca starch users, and special test methods have been devised to suit particular purposes. However, AOAC methods are used for such tests as moisture, ash, pH, and residual sulfur dioxide.

8. Characteristics

a. *Appearance*

A sample of tapioca starch produced in a mechanical system with reasonable care will present a very white appearance in the dry state. If one examines small portions of starch placed side by side from separate bags of a given production, considerable variation in color and small specks might be noticed from bag to bag. This is particularly true where there is little or no in-process control and where variation occurs in through-put, holding times, or cleaning. In an effective sampling and testing program during production, off-standard starch will be discovered and separated from the best product.

b. *Mesh*

For most industrial and food purposes, it is desirable to have the tapioca as fine as possible. Such starch will pass a United States number 140-mesh screen with not over 1% retained. The presence of coarser starch can usually be attributed to torn dry starch sifter screens or loose screen panels. Periodic tests of production will reveal these problems before tons of production are spoiled.

c. *Odor*

When tapioca starch is retained in a tightly closed jar for a few hours, a subjective evaluation of odor can be made. In cases where the presence or absence of off-odors is in question, a portion of the starch can be wetted in an open beaker and sniffed as it is stirred. Sour odors are most common in tapiocas where a slow processing system permits microorganisms to produce organic acids (lactic and butyric). Contamination begins at the first extraction step and continues to develop in intensity throughout the successive stages of the process. Sour odors are usually present in starches having a low pH. Starch intended for food use should contain few microorganisms and be free from off-odors. For industrial use, standards may be lower. The adoption of a regular cleaning schedule and the use of sulfur dioxide will minimize the problem of spoilage and sour odors. If unsanitary conditions have been allowed to persist for a long time, a disinfection of the whole plant may be required. This involves complete cleaning to remove scale, deposits, and discolored films from the piping and every piece of processing equipment. Then a dilute solution of one of the approved sanitizing agents is circulated for a few hours followed by a complete and thorough washing with fresh water.

Odors other than sour can be picked up by tapioca starch during shipment by stowage in freighters with other commodities. Coffee, rubber, hides, bones, and pepper should not be shipped in the same hold with tapioca starch.

d. pH

The normal pH of the fresh manioc root is 6.3–6.5. The process water should be approximately pH 5–6. Therefore, any pH value of tapioca starch outside this range is the result of old or spoiled raw material and/or factors in the processing. As mentioned before, low pH is often accompanied by a sour odor in the tapioca starch. Spoilage of roots caused by their being out of the ground several days before processing, and spoilage of starch slurries caused by prolonged holding in the tanks or by addition of chemicals are among the common causes of high or low pH. Certain chemicals may be added to improve texture and palatability and to impart stability, but they must follow conditions set forth by the U.S. Food and Drug Administration. Such products must be labeled as "modified," the name of the additive given, and information provided to show how the starch has been modified (5).

e. Moisture

Moisture in tapioca starch is influenced by drying techniques and/or storage conditions. Equilibrium moisture is 12.5% at 60% relative humidity and 21°. Under humid conditions, tapioca starch picks up moisture, while in dry atmospheres it loses moisture. Under ordinary circumstances, the rate of moisture change is gradual in the commonly used multiwall kraft bags. Experience teaches that shipping and receival moistures between the tropical producing areas do not differ by more than 0.5% on the average. However, when the flour is stored in the producing areas, a moisture gain of 1–2% is possible and arrival moistures can be as high as 15%.

Molds will develop and cause the starch to become lumpy and discolored when the moisture content exceeds 18%. It is important therefore to evaluate the starch coming from the dryer and to avoid storage of the finished product in areas with very high humidity for prolonged periods.

f. Ash

Tapioca starch that has been carefully refined and processed and stored under sanitary conditions will have an ash content below 0.2%. High ash is usually indicative of sand, dirt, or other foreign material in the finished starch. Careful washing of roots and protecting the processing and bagging areas against insects and blowing dust are precautions required for the manufacture of the highest quality tapioca starch.

g. *Color*

Since tapioca starch is frequently used as a thickening agent in foods or as a sizing or bonding agent in industrial applications, color of the cooked product is important. Tapioca forms a translucent gel that will have a blue or grey coloration if iron is present. Process water should be essentially free of iron; iron piping and equipment should be avoided as well. Complexes of iron and tannins from the roots as well as combinations of irons and traces of hydrocyanic acid from the root juices will impart grey and blue tones of color to the gelatinized starch.

h. *Contamination*

Minute pieces of root peel, fiber, dirt, insect fragments, and the like constitute contaminants in tapioca starch. Effective refining and screening as well as maintenance of sanitary processes are important ways of minimizing contamination. It is therefore important to make frequent checks on the process and final product in order to detect and eliminate sources of contamination.

i. *Pulp*

It is important in some applications for the tapioca starch to be low in pulp, or root fibers. One means of measuring pulp content is to wash a sample of the starch on a 200-mesh screen. The tapioca starch granules will pass through the screen while the fiber will be retained. The retained fiber is then washed into a graduated cylinder and allowed to settle, and the volume of fiber accumulated on the bottom of the cylinder is read from the graduated scale. Centrifuging and screening operations, when improperly carried out, allow fine fibers to escape with the starch.

j. *Acid Factor*

The titration of a slurry of 25 g. of starch to pH 3.0 with $0.1N$ hydrochloric acid solution gives the so-called acid factor, expressed as the number of milliliters of acid required (6). This is a special characteristic of starch that is important to some of the dextrin manufacturers; it has not been found important in food use. Apparently, buffering substances in the process water, additives, and incomplete washing all influence the final acid factor of tapioca starch.

k. *Cold Viscosity*

Where high concentrations of starch in water are to be pumped or stirred as in some food manufacturing processes, cold viscosity becomes important. This characteristic reflects the degree of incipient gelatinization that occurred during drying. Since tapioca starch entering the dryer is at a critical moisture, a temperature above the start of the gelatinization range (59°) before moisture loss results in granule swelling. A partially gelatinized starch readily imbibes water so that starch–water slurries are thick and difficult to stir or pump if there has been appreciable cooking in the dryer. Flash dryers minimize incipient gelatinization, whereas vacuum dryers, unless carefully controlled, induce a great deal of cooking in the starch. Cold viscosity is measured in a 60° funnel with a pre-cut stem and 5-mm. orifice. A slurry of 100 g. of starch mixed with 100 ml. of water at 30° is stirred for 5 min. The number of seconds to collect 100 ml. of the slurry is taken as the cold viscosity of the starch. Slurries which exceed 100 sec. are difficult to handle.

l. *Hot Viscosity*

Viscosity and clarity of cooked tapioca starch are its most important characteristics. The intended use of the starch determines the importance of viscosity factors and the means of measuring them. Viscosity development in a dilute slurry as recorded in the Brabender Amylograph-Viscograph is a means of determining the gelatinization temperature, the rate of viscosity development, the maximum viscosity, and the viscosity loss after the peak. In unmodified tapioca starch, these factors are influenced by variety and age of the roots at harvest time as well as the climate, soil, fertility, and rainfall during the growing period. The process of extracting the starch from the roots has some influence on the final viscosity of the tapioca starch, especially if the starch is subjected to degradation through the action of microorganisms. Here again, a sanitary process and rapid through-put will produce starch with essentially the same viscosity as in the fresh roots.

II. Arrowroot Starch

Arrowroot starch is obtained from the root of the tropical plant *Maranta arundinacea*. It is a perennial that grows 2–5 ft. high with oval lanceolate leaves and white oval flowers arranged in clusters. The root-stock has cylindrical elongated roots about 1 in. thick and 8–18 in. long with pale brown scales at each joint. The plant is propagated from root cuttings or seeds (7).

The roots are harvested after 10–12 months when they should contain 22–28% starch and 65–75% water. The scales covering the roots must be carefully removed or the starch will have a bitter flavor and yellow color. Tapioca and arrowroot starch are similar and are extracted by the same process. For this reason, tapioca was once called Brazilian Arrowroot. The roots are washed and ground in rasps or hammer mills to a fine pulp. After the starch is separated from the starch and pulp by screening, it is twice washed and allowed to settle in tanks and then dried.

Arrowroot starch granules are somewhat larger (15–70 microns) than tapioca (5–15 microns), and settle to a very hard cake in the tanks.

Most of the arrowroot produced on a commercial basis comes from the island of St. Vincent in the West Indies. In St. Vincent there are some 20–30 privately owned mills, mostly on estates, and one central factory recently constructed by the government. Production was estimated at 8.0 million lbs. in 1958–59 and practically the entire output is exported (8).

III. Sago Starch

Sago starch comes from the pith of certain palm trees, principally *Metroxylon sagu*, and *M. rumphii*. The trees are propagated from suckers and are planted 30 trees per acre. It takes from 10–15 years of growth for the trees to reach maturity, at which time they are from 30 to 50 ft. high. The harvest time is critical; it must be after the flowering of the tree but before the fruit forms.

The mature trees are felled and the trunks, containing about 40% starch, are cut into logs 3–4 ft. long. The soft woody bark is removed and the starchy pith dug out with a hoe and grated into material resembling sawdust (9). The grated pith is kneaded with water and filtered through sieves to extract the relatively large (20–60 microns) starch granules (10). The starch is settled in troughs and is sun- or kiln-dried. One trunk will have from 600 to 800 lb. of pith yielding 200 to 400 lb. of sago starch.

Moist sago starch is used to make a popular native food, pearl sago. The moist starch cake is pressed through a perforated sheet of iron or tossed in a hammock-shaped cloth to produce round pellets. These are sized by screening and then roasted in shallow pans to partly gelatinize and dry the sago pearls.

The production of sago starch is confined mainly to Indonesia with a small amount also produced in Sarawak, Malaya, and North Borneo. It is a native industry where manufacture is carried out mostly by hand labor. The principal uses of sago starch are as textile sizings and adhesives.

IV. REFERENCES

(1) J. M. de Godoy, "Fecularia e Amidonaria," Tecnologia Agricola, 2nd Ed., Sao Paulo, Brazil, 1940.

(2) L. W. J. Holleman and A. Aten, "Processing of Cassava and Cassava Products in Rural Industries," Food and Agriculture Organization of the United Nations, Rome, Italy, 1956.

(3) G. Van Biema and L. Shipman, *Food Eng.*, **24**, No. 3, 56, 132, 182, 184 (1952).

(4) "De Laval Separators in the Manioc (Cassava) Starch Industry," Technical Bulletin No. 6001 E-2, AB Separator, Stockholm, Sweden.

(5) *Federal Register*, **27**, 8759 (1962).

(6) C. A. Brautlecht, "Starch," Reinhold Publishing Corp., New York, N.Y., 1953, pp. 134–135.

(7) Reference *6*, p. 278.

(8) U.S. Tariff Commission, "Starch," Report on Investigation No. 332–37, Washington, March, 1960, pp. 48–49.

(9) R. M. Johnson and W. D. Raymond, *Colonial Plant Animal Prod. (Gt. Brit.)*, **6**, No. 1, 20 (1957); *Econ. Bot.*, **11**, 326 (1957).

(10) O. B. Wurzburg, *Econ. Bot.*, **6**, 211 (1952).

CHAPTER VI

STARCH IN THE PAPER INDUSTRY

By Edward K. Nissen
Technical Service, Union Starch & Refining Co., Inc., Granite City, Illinois

I. Introduction

Paper production in the United States was 37.6 million tons in 1962 and 38.6 million tons in 1963. These volumes, and their continued increase, keep the paper industry in its present position as the fifth largest industry in the United States. Although cellulose fiber is the basic component of paper, large quantities of other materials are used by the industry to provide specific properties to meet end use requirements and to facilitate efficient production. In 1962, the paper industry consumed 1.2 million tons of clay, 46 thousand tons of titanium dioxide, 48 thousand tons of synthetic binders, and 150 thousand tons of starch (1). This latter figure makes the paper industry the largest single industrial consumer of starch products.

121

II. The Industry

This chapter is devoted primarily to the functions of starch in the paper industry. However, for purposes of orientation, a brief description of paper processing is presented.

The paper making process consists basically of preparing a fibrous form of cellulose and converting the fibers into a continuous web of paper. The major domestic source of such fibers is wood, although cotton linters, cotton rags, and waste paper are important secondary sources. Any cellulose-containing plant is a potential source of fiber and, in some parts of the world, wheat and rice straw, bagasse, flax, and esparto grass are important raw material sources.

1. Pulping

For the preparation of wood pulp, whole logs may be ground or cut into chips for chemical treatment prior to reduction to fiber. The resultant wood pulp is classified by its treatment as follows:

a. *Mechanical or Groundwood*

Whole logs are reduced to fiber form by grinding. This groundwood pulp is the chief fiber component for newsprint and moulded products such as egg cartons. It is also used in some publication grades of paper.

b. *Semimechanical*

Whole logs, generally hardwood, are subjected to chemical treatment prior to grinding. The pulp is employed in making newsprint and publication grades.

c. *Semichemical*

Logs, primarily hardwood, are reduced to chips and given a relatively mild chemical treatment. The softened chips are reduced mechanically to fiber. This pulp is used principally for corrugating medium but, after bleaching, is now finding increasing use in book and printing papers.

d. *Chemical*

Logs are reduced to chips and subjected to sufficient chemical treatment to dissolve or substantially soften the lignin binder. The chips are generally reduced to pulp without additional mechanical treatment. Any type of wood may be "cooked" using one of three chemical processes: sulfite, soda, or sulfate. The sulfite process involves an acid treatment in which calcium, sodium or magnesium bisulfite is the primary cooking chemical. In the soda process, caustic soda (sodium hydroxide) is the pulping agent. The sulfate, or kraft, process also involves an alkaline treatment to which sodium sulfide is added.

The chemical pulps are used singly or in combination to some degree in almost all paper products made in the United States.

2. Paper Making

Wood pulp is further refined mechanically to develop its inherent strength, and various additives, such as dye, rosin size and alum, may be incorporated in the pulp slurry. The finished pulp, or stock, is then ready for the paper machine.

The function of the paper machine is to form a continuous web from the fiber slurry and to dry it to a moisture content of about 5–6%. Two basic machine types, the Fourdrinier and the cylinder, are used for this purpose.

a. *Fourdrinier Machine*

The Fourdrinier machine (Fig. 1) consists of integral sections known as the Fourdrinier or wire (A), press (B), first dryer (C), size press

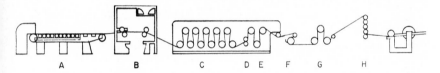

Fig. 1.—Fourdrinier Machine: A, Fourdrinier or wire section, B, presses; C, first dryer section; D, size press; E, second dryer section; F, coating station; G, third dryer section; H, calender stack.

(D), second dryer (E), coater (F), last dryer (G), and calender stack (H). The size press and coater are found on many, but not all, machines.

A dilute pulp suspension, about 0.1% fiber, is fed into the head box and forced through a narrow opening (slice) onto the full width of an endless wire belt. The pulp stream and wire velocities must be approximately the same to effect gravity drainage of water from the pulp suspension through the wire. Near the end of the wire, suction boxes are used for removing additional water. As the sheet leaves the wire it is about 85% water, but is sufficiently strong to support its own weight. The wet sheet then passes through a series of presses where the sheet is smoothed and the moisture is reduced to about 75%.

In the first dryer section, the sheet is passed over steam heated dryer drums with felt and wire side alternating against the drums. Unless exceptionally heavy grades are being made, the wet sheet is held against the dryer rolls by asbestos dryer felts.

The sheet emerges from the first dryer section at about 6% moisture and is rewetted at the size press, generally with a dilute starch paste. Following the size press, the sheet is again dried as in the first section. For machines containing coating sections, the web is coated as described later, and once again dried to the desired moisture level.

The dry sheet may then be passed through a vertical series of steel rolls known as a calender stack to obtain certain desirable properties such as smoothness, finish, and gloss. A starch size may also be applied at the calender stack. At this point, the final web is wound on reels for ultimate shipment.

b. *Cylinder Machine*

The cylinder machine consists of a series of vats containing dilute pulp suspensions. A wire-covered cylinder rotates in each vat. The cylinders pick up a thin mat of fibers which are in turn transferred to a felt riding in contact with the cylinders. In this way, a sheet of desired thickness is built up by a layering process. From this section the sheet passes through the pressing, drying, coating and calendering steps much as has been described for the Fourdrinier.

With both the Fourdrinier and the cylinder machine, there are four major points of starch addition: wet end, size press, calender stack, and coating. Each of these areas of application will now be discussed in detail.

III. WET END APPLICATION OF STARCH

The cellulose fiber that is the basic raw material in the paper making operation would make a relatively low strength, poorly formed sheet if used unaltered on the paper machine. The fiber is, therefore, mechanically refined to promote fiber-to-fiber bonding. A fiber slurry is refined by passing it through disc or plug type refiners or by circulating it in a beater. Refining is accomplished by subjecting the individual fiber to high mechanical stress as it passes between two hard metal or stone surfaces. The fibers are cut or brushed to effect fibrillation; that is, the primary cell walls of the fibers are ruptured and the exposed inner layers subsequently frayed into minute fibrils. This increases the surface area available for fiber contact and, thus, makes possible an increase in bonding between fibers.

For a long time, the strength development of the sheet was attributed to physical interlocking of fibrils. It is now recognized that strength results from covalent bonding, polar bond attractions, or hydrogen bonding (2). Investigative work by Jayme and Hunger (3) revealed, through electron photomicrographs, that separate portions of the wood fiber cell may become hydrogen bonded on being formed into a sheet after refining. Swanson (4) supports the hydrogen bonding theory while acknowledging the need for much more investigative work. Cushing (5) points out that the cellulose molecule itself has a multiude of hydroxyl groups potentially capable of interacting through hydrogen bonding. In a molecular state, these hydroxyl units are also strongly polar, but, since attractive forces decrease with the inverse seventh power of the distance, close association is necessary for maximum bonding. There is, of course, a practical limit to refining for strength development beyond which the sheet loses desirable characteristics such as porosity, flexibility, brightness, and opacity. The paper maker must adjust his mechanical equipment to obtain the optimum combination of properties.

It is not always possible by refining alone to develop a furnish that will produce an acceptable sheet. Often it is necessary to add binders to enhance the properties of the finished paper; starch is the major binder used for this purpose.

The addition of starch to the wet end of the paper machine is generally referred to as beater sizing. This term is a misnomer in that sizing properly refers to a process to increase the ability of a sheet to resist being wetted by water. Such sizing is obtained normally by precipitating rosin size on the fiber with alum. While rosin sizing does increase water resistance, beater sizing with starch does not significantly change the water resistance of the sheet. In some instances, the use of oxidized starch improves sizing (2). This is attributed to the beneficial effect the starch has on precipitating the rosin size and not to the sizing properties of the starch itself.

Although starch may be used at the wet end to compensate for poor refining or inadequate base fiber, its primary function is to increase the paper strength, to lay surface fuzz, and to increase stiffness and rattle or both. Use of starch also permits the inclusion of inorganic fillers without sacrificing the critical strength of the finished sheet.

The ability of starch to improve the strength of paper has long been known; however, knowledge of the mechanisms of interfiber bonding and the relationship of starch retained in the sheet to final paper strengths are of recent origin. Houtz (6) showed the differences obtained in bursting strength when using 4% of corn, sweet potato, tapioca, or white potato starches. Waters (7) reported retention figures for pearl corn and potato starch in the head box, white water tray, and finished paper.

These and similar early work on wet end adhesives ably demonstrated what effects can be obtained under given conditions without too much reference as to why they were obtained. However, Leech (8) assumed that paper strength depended upon four factors: fiber strength, fiber-to-fiber bonding strength, number of bonds (or bonding area), and distribution of the bonds. To be effective, therefore, a beater adhesive must add to one or more of the above factors.

Swanson (4), recognizing the importance of hydrogen bonding in fiber-to-fiber contact, reasoned that cellulose fibrils were still very large relative to molecular dimensions and that the actual areas of contact were necessarily small when the rigid, rough solid surfaces were brought in contact. He suggested that beater adhesives bridge the distances between fibrils and establish bonds that would not otherwise be formed, resulting in ultimate better paper appearance and strength.

Many factors determine which particular starch product is most effective in a given mill. These factors include the grades of paper being made, refining conditions and capacity, fiber type (or types) used, individual mill preference, and, of course, economics. Perhaps the ideal wet end adhesive could be defined as that product which gives maximum product strength and appearance improvement with maximum starch retention and minimum cost coupled with the absence of deleterious side-effects such as pigment fallout. No starch in use today meets all these requirements exactly, but many fit the needs of individual mills closely.

Starches used as wet end adhesives are primarily potato, tapioca, sorghum and corn, generally in unmodified form. Modified starches, such as cationic corn and potato, oxidized corn, and dialdehyde corn starches, are showing increasing usage. Pregelatinized corn and potato starches are also used to a limited extent.

Pregelatinized starches are used in mills where a dry additive is needed because of a lack of adequate cooking facilities. Precooked starches are added as late in the beating cycle as possible, consistent with good dispersion and mixing with the beaten fiber. The cooked starch is sensitive to breakdown under shear. Prolonged beating with the fiber will cause excessively low starch retention. Objections to the use of pregelatinized starch sometimes arise from the presence of bits of un-gelatinized starch that cause translucent spots, known as "fish eyes" or "shiners," in the finished sheet. Pregelatinized potato starch has been preferred to corn in this respect because of its lower retrogradation tendencies.

In some mills, raw starch is added dry to the pulp furnish. Since the ungelatinized granule is very resistant to mechanical shear, the problem of shear breakdown is eliminated. However, the efficacy of starch added without cooking is contingent upon the starch being gelatinized in the wet sheet on the dryers since ungelatinized starch makes no contribution to sheet strength. Hence, the sheet temperature must reach 74°–90° while there is still adequate water to swell the granule. This procedure is not very effective with native pearl starch, but chemically modified starches are used with success in the fine paper field due primarily to their reduced gelatinization temperature. A moderately oxidized corn starch, for example, has a gelatinization temperature of about 60° and is satisfactory in this type of application. Mill experience has shown that oxidized corn starch, added dry, is as effective in some systems as pregelatinized corn starch added to the beaters and has the added advantage of not affecting the drainage rate on the wire. Addition rates are in the range of 20 to 40 pounds per ton of fiber.

No single starch is equally effective in all grades of paper. The configuration of the fibers in the sheet largely determines which starch types are the most effective. For loosely constructed sheets containing relatively large, slightly refined fibers (described as "free" sheets by the paper maker), poorly dispersed starch pastes containing large, swollen, unruptured granules are most effective. These papers are exemplified by the coarse grades, such as kraft wrapping and bag papers, linerboard, and roofing felt, where tapioca, potato or cationic corn are the preferred starches. Conversely, fine grades, such as bond and ledger papers, benefit most from starch added in colloidal form. These relatively highly refined sheets show much greater strength improvement when lightly cooked native pearl starches are used.

This correlation between paper types and starches has been explained in terms of a "spot-welding" theory. The starch, as mentioned before, is effective only when bridging a gap and creating a fiber–starch–fiber bond. In the free or low density sheet, the fiber interstices are relatively large, colloidal starch particles are poorly retained, and relatively weak bonds are developed. However, large swollen granules (about 20μ) successfully bridge the large gaps and produce a strong bond. In the slow or high density sheets, the fibers are smaller, form a much more compact mat, and effectively retain the smaller colloidal starch particles. The use of a highly dispersed starch adhesive in these sheets results in a great many more fiber–starch–fiber bonds.

The "spot-welding" theory accounts for the efficacy of the large granule root starches, such as potato and tapioca, as wet end adhesives for low density sheets. Native pearl corn is also effective when careful control is used to insure maximum granule swelling without rupture prior to adding to the furnish. For high density sheets, oxidized starches are particularly effective. They have an added value in their unique ability to improve rosin sizing by causing the alum to precipitate the rosin size in a more effective form (2). Sizing efficiency may be increased by as much as 25–50% with the addition of 2–5% of a hypochlorite-oxidized starch.

The large size of the starch molecule contributes significantly to its value in paper making. Houtz (6) has shown that thoroughly cooked and dispersed starches of increasing molecular weight give corresponding strength increases.

Just as it is a practical impossibility to recommend a given starch for a given grade, it is equally difficult to prescribe a specific quantity to use. Depending upon starch type and mill conditions, effective additions may range from the extremes of 0.5 to 7.0% based on the dry weight of fiber. Too much starch impairs drainage on the wire and may adversely affect the properties of the finished sheet. According to Cobb and co-workers (9), the maximum strength advantage is gained with undegraded starch at an addition level of 0.5% of starch, based on fiber. The initial rapid sorption of starch on fiber has been placed at about 0.35 to 0.40% by Cushing and Schuman (10). These are theoretical considerations, however, and practical experience has shown the normal mill addition rate to be in the range of 2 to 5%.

There is a significant difference between the quantity of starch added to the sheet and that effectively retained by the sheet. Measurement of starch retention is difficult because of the problems involved in laboratory simulation of such paper machine conditions as continuous refining, wire suction, and white water recirculation. Waters (7) evaluated starch as a wet end adhesive by measuring starch concentrations in the machine head box, first white water tray, and the finished 20 pound bond sheet. His data showed retention figures of 26.7% for potato starch and 9.45% for corn starch under the conditions specified.

Such low retention values may be attributed to the anionic character of both starch and cellulose. Hence, there is no electrostatic attraction between the two. It is necessary to bring the starch and cellulose into close contact if hydrogen bonding is to occur. In order to improve starch retention and thereby gain greater efficiency, retention aids are often used in the wet end. Colloidal alumina floc formed by alum improves starch retention (11). The complex formed by alumina, starch, and fiber is subject to disruption by mechanical shear. To take full advantage of the retentive action of alumina, the cooked starch must again be added as close as possible to the end of the beating cycle. The relationship between improved starch retention and increased paper strength presupposes that the starch present is in its most usable form. Obviously, an improperly prepared starch will do little to enhance paper properties regardless of its degree of retention.

The continuous preparation of starch for wet end addition is widely used. Advantages of continuous cooking are that cooking conditions may be changed easily and promptly and that storage of cooked paste is minimal. This latter factor is important since overcooking and shear breakdown can occur on storage. Dry starch is slurried at about 0.25 pound per gallon and passed through a jet where the slurry is instantaneously gelatinized with steam. The exit paste temperature (about 96° for corn starch) is automatically controlled by a temperature sensing element connected to a steam control valve. Flow of starch through the system may be controlled by a rotameter or metering pump. This system enables the selection of a temperature that will give the desired degree of swelling or dispersion.

Conventional batch cooking consists of slurrying starch in the cook tank, heating, for example, to 96°, and holding at that temperature for 10 minutes. It is important to use minimum batch sizes to prevent overcooking and mechanical breakdown on holding.

Regardless of the method of preparation, the cooked starch may be added to the beater or, as is preferred in many mills, at the fan pump which delivers stock to the head box.

The use of specialty starches in the beater has been somewhat restricted, in many cases for economic reasons. Those of greatest interest in recent years have been the cationic and dialdehyde starches.

From the anionic nature of cellulose and starch, it would seem that a cationic material would be a natural bridge between fibers. One might predict that such a material would have a high degree of retention and exhibit relatively large strength increases for low application rates as compared, for example, with native corn starch. Work on unbleached sulfite pulp by Nissen (12) has shown comparable strength increases in finished sheets with 1% cationic starch as compared with 3% corn starch. Mill experience has shown cationic starches to be particularly effective in low density, long fibered sheets. The production and use of cationic starch is discussed in more detail in Chapter XVI.

Much interest has been shown recently in the use of dialdehyde starches for wet end adhesives. These highly specialized products, discussed in Chapter XVIII, have the unique property (for starch) of improving the wet strength of paper (13, 14). In the paper industry, wet strength is generally obtained by the addition of urea–formaldehyde or melamine–formaldehyde resins. Urea–formaldehyde treated sheets require a substantial curing time, and melamine–formaldehyde treated paper is extremely difficult to salvage. By using dialdehyde starch with cationic starch as a retention aid, and later by using cationic dialdehyde starches, wet strength properties of the finished papers approaching those of resin treated papers have been obtained. The advantages of short curing time and ease of broke recovery have been demonstrated (*13, 14*).

IV. Size Press Application of Starch

The size press application of starch in the paper industry is often referred to as tub sizing or surface sizing. As in the wet end application, this sizing does not impart any degree of water resistance to the sheet. Originally the starch was applied by immersing the sheet in a tub of starch solution, passing the saturated sheet through press rolls, and air drying the web. This method is still practiced in some older mills making such high grade sheets as specialty rag bonds. The original name "tub sizing" still persists, even in reference to modern size press applications.

1. Type of Size Presses

In most instances today, surface sizing of paper is accomplished in size presses which may be of the vertical or horizontal design. In the vertical size press, the rolls are mounted in a vertical plane and the sheet passes through horizontally. The starch is applied through a shower to the top side; at the bottom, the roll may revolve in a starch solution, or the starch may be applied through a shower similar to that on the top side. The horizontal press has the rolls mounted horizontally and the sheet passes down through the rolls in a vertical plane. The starch is generally applied to both sides by control shower heads and the excessive starch paste overflows the ends and returns to a supply tank.

2. Purpose of Size Press Operation

A starch paste is applied at the size press to improve appearance and erasability, to inhibit ink penetration, and to form a hard firm surface for writing or printing. Additional functions of a surface size are to improve strength, to reduce surface fiber picking, to provide resistance to colloidal solutions such as blood, and to prepare the sheet for subsequent coating.

The major use of the size press is to improve the writing and printing characteristics of sheets such as bond, ledger, tablet, envelope, chart, and business grades. Foote (*15*) has pointed out that the improvement in writing qualities is related to the increased contact angle of ink on paper sized with starch. Casey (*2*) also mentions the increased contact angle with oil obtained by surface sizing with starch.

3. Application

Regardless of the end use requirements, the method of surface sizing is basically the same—a starch paste is applied to the sheet and then squeezed from the sheet, and the sheet is subsequently dried. The mechanical operation of the size press equipment and the type of starch used control the degree and type of sizing obtained. Lee (*16*) has pointed out that the surface sizing varies from complete penetration to surface filming only.

For any given starch type, the degree of penetration and pick-up may be varied to some extent by changing roll nip pressure, starch temperature, and puddle depth at the nip. Higher temperatures, greater puddle depth and higher nip pressures contribute to greater penetration. Necessary changes beyond the physical limitations of the equipment require a change in the starch paste itself.

For surface sizing applications, corn starch is the major product used. Tapioca, potato, and wheat starches are also used, particularly in areas in which these starches are readily available and procurement is economically favorable. Native starches are enzyme-converted to a low viscosity for use. Preconverted starches, such as oxidized or hydroxyethyl, are also widely used.

The type of starch used in the size press is ordinarily dictated by the mill equipment available and the properties desired. Size press conditions vary over a large range, most of which would fall within the broad limits of 2–12% solids, 50°–70°, and a viscosity of 35–60 Dudley seconds corresponding to a Brookfield viscosity of 10–50 cps. (No. 1 spindle, 20 rpm.).

Several viscosity grades of preconverted starches are needed to meet the full range of requirements. A lightly oxidized product would meet the low solids, high viscosity requirements, while a relatively highly oxidized product would be required for high solids, low viscosity work. The same considerations would apply to hydroxyethylstarches.

Recently, utilization of enzyme-converted starches has become quite popular in the paper industry. Besides the obvious economic advantages, new starch and enzyme technology and equipment have prompted this move in many areas. There are undoubtedly very few grades of paper which are not, in at least a few mills, now being surface sized with enzyme-converted starch.

It would be beyond the scope of this chapter to survey all the enzyme converting procedures used. The following tabulation is a representative conversion cycle for producing a paste for surface sizing application:

Starch solids	18% (buffered with $CaCO_3$)
Time to temperature (80°)	5 min.
Time at temperature	18 min.
Time to inactivation temperature (100°)	5 min.
Time at inactivation temperature	15 min.

Continuous agitation with direct steam injection and an automatic cam controlled temperature cycle are generally used. The increased demand for automation is reflected in recent trends toward automatic viscosity control such as is provided by the Norcross system (Norcross Corp., Newton, Massachusetts). Following completion of the converting cycle, the converted paste is diluted to 12–15% with cold water, to reduce the storage temperature, and then further diluted as needed to meet the machine requirements.

Variations of the cycle described include the use of a dual temperature plateau for high solids (30–35%) conversion, using, for example, an additional hold period at 70° for 5 minutes, and a continuous temperature increase cycle of about 1°–2° per minute from the start of the conversion to the inactivation temperature for relatively low (10%) concentration slurries.

A medium viscosity hydroxyethylstarch or an oxidized starch, 50 Dudley seconds at 12% solids measured at 60°, is often used for printing grades where ink feathering, erasability, and surface pick are important factors. Native starches converted to the same viscosity levels are also used. In some instances animal glue, usually a bone colloid type, is used with the enzyme-converted starch to improve its inherently low erasability factor. Addition of 5–10% of glue based on starch weight is typical.

When some degree of water resistance is also desired, as in pigmented offset grades, wet strength resins are used in conjunction with starch. In a typical instance, 10% of melamine resin based on starch weight may be added just prior to use on the machine. The slight additional wet-rub resistance imparted by the resin is generally enough to inhibit coating rub off when the sheet is printed.

Numerous other additives are used with starch at the size press for meeting special sheet requirements.

V. CALENDER APPLICATION OF STARCH

The second important area for the surface sizing of paper products is the calender stack. In this application, the paper passes around a series of steel rolls, one or more of which may transfer a starch film to the paper surface.

The calender operation is the final stage prior to winding the sheet on the reel and is not followed by any further dryers. Therefore, the drying of the wetted sheet must be accomplished by a combination of absorption of some water into the sheet and evaporation of moisture by the latent heat of the sheet. Because of these factors, the calender sizing operation is restricted to heavy papers such as liner board, food board, and box boards.

The purpose of calender sizing, as described by Stephenson (*17*), is to enhance surface characteristics needed for a particular type of board or to correct certain inherent defects in the board surface. The type of starch used and its formulation are dependent on fiber furnish, machine conditions, and the end use requirements for the sheet. The following examples are given to illustrate the use of certain starch types for meeting specified end use requirements.

1. Heavyweight Papers and Liner Board

A large volume of heavyweight kraft papers and liner boards manufactured today are surface sized on the calender stacks to improve their scuff resistance and printability. This application requires a starch that will set up rapidly, and thus remain on the paper surface. Improvement in printability is a matter of promoting uniform ink absorption with the elimination of feathering, rather than changing the sheet profile as would be done by coating. Native or thin boiling starches are generally used at concentrations ranging from 2 to 5%. In this range, a lubricant is seldom needed to prevent picking of fibers by the roll or sticking of the web to the roll.

2. Cylinder Boards

For cylinder boards, a surface application of starch provides better gloss ink holdout and, in some cases, improves ply bonding. This application requires a low-viscosity starch with good film forming ability. Generally, a hydroxyethylstarch or an oxidized starch is used at 10–20% solids. At these concentrations, an emulsifiable wax is included in the formula to reduce the tack of the paste and eliminate fiber pulling on the stacks. Some absorption of the starch into the sheet is necessary to improve the ply bonding strength.

3. Base Coat Surface Preparation

Many food board mills use starch on the calender stacks to prepare the sheet for subsequent functional coatings. The starch size partially satisfies the absorption demand of the board and provides a more uniformly absorptive base sheet for coating. In this application, medium-

or low-viscosity oxidized or hydroxyethylstarches are used at 6–12% solids. Occasionally, some pigment is included in the size. Waxes may or may not be used in accordance with individual machine conditions.

4. Curl Control

Many packaging grades of boxboard, such as cereal, suit, and gift boxes, are coated on the top side only in preparation for printing. This one side preparation results in an uneven water absorption between top and bottom sides and causes curl in the finished sheet. Low-viscosity oxidized starches at 18–24% solids are often used at the calender to film the bottom side. Moisture absorption at both sides is then more nearly the same, and curling is reduced.

As can be seen from the aforementioned examples, the starches used in calender application range from the native starches to the most highly modified oxidized and hydroxyethylstarches. Careful selection of the starches does not always insure good sizing performance; care must also be exercised in making certain that the starch is thoroughly cooked and that concentration and temperature are closely controlled at the calender boxes. Efficient circulation in the calender box is also very important to prevent wide temperature gradients across the box. Excessive cooling in quiescent areas can cause localized areas of thickening or set back and uneven absorption of starch on the sheet.

VI. Starch for Paper Coating

The use of starch as an adhesive in pigmented coatings for paper and paperboard is a subject covered by many excellent reference works (18–23). An attempt will be made here to describe briefly the history of coating development, purposes for coating, adhesive requirements, system rheologies, and their application to specific coating processes.

1. History of Coating

Untreated paper does not provide a good printing surface. In the nineteenth century attempts were made to correct this deficiency by coating the sheet with crude clays using animal glue as a binder. Casein adhesives, introduced in the 1890's (24), soon supplanted glue as a binder, but coating methods remained highly secret and relatively crude and slow. It was not until the early 1900's, when the larger paper companies entered the coating field, that coating technology began to advance from art to science; and improvements in equipment and formulations were made that permitted starch to be accepted as a coating binder. In the mid-1940's, as the paper industry kept pace with advanced printing technology and increased packaging demands, the production of coated paper and paperboard and consumption of starch began to soar. Castagne (25) has presented a comprehensive analysis of this trend that shows a growth in coated paperboard capacity from 1,170,510 tons in 1950 to 4,275,000 tons in 1960 with no apparent leveling off. Coated printing papers have shown a similar surge from 1,020,000 tons in 1950 to 1,960,-000 tons in 1961. Competition for the adhesive market has spurred starch suppliers to improve the quality and performance of their product in order to maintain their present dominant role in this field.

2. Purpose of Coating

In the paper industry, coating refers to the application of one or more layers of noncellulosic material to the paper surface. This chapter is confined to aqueous coating systems that contain pigment as the primary coating material and a starch adhesive to bond the pigment particles to each other and to the paper. The most commonly used pigments are clay, calcium carbonate, titanium dioxide, or combinations of these. Satin white (calcium sulfoaluminate), zinc sulfide, barium sulfate, calcium sulfite, calcium sulfate, and diatomaceous silica pigments are also used, but to a much lesser extent. Coating may be accomplished either on the paper machine as an integral part of the paper making operation or off machine as a separate process. In either case, the basic process differs only in the auxiliary equipment needed to perform the coating operation.

The primary purpose of coating is to enhance the printability and appearance of the paper. Some specialized functions such as vapor- or water-resistance may be required, but these are almost always required in addition to good printability. In such specialized areas, protein adhesives or acrylic, styrene–butadiene, or polyvinylidine chloride latices are used. Since they are not generally used with starch, they will not be discussed in this chapter. However, an excellent discussion of the synthetic latices has been provided in a Tappi Monograph (26).

3. Adhesive Requirements

The primary purpose of the adhesive in the pigment–adhesive mix, commonly referred to as a coating color, is to act as a carrier for the pigment, to bind the pigment matrix to the fibers as well as to itself, and to provide desirable flow characteristics.

The adhesive should (a) be easy to prepare, (b) have a high adhesive strength, (c) be inexpensive and readily available, (d) have a reproducible viscosity which is stable on prolonged storage, (e) have no detrimental effect on paper properties, and (f) be unaffected by external conditions such as wetting after being applied to the sheet. No single adhesive meets all these requirements with complete satisfaction. Starch, however, adequately meets enough of them to make it the largest volume adhesive used in paper coating.

4. System Rheology

Measurement of the mechanical characteristics of starch pastes has been covered in Volume I, Chapter XVI, but, as the authors pointed out, reference to clay–starch systems was purposely deleted from the discussion. The rheology of pigment–starch coating colors, a very complex subject, has been studied in detail in recent years because it is a most important determinant in the selection of a starch product for any given application.

Prior to the development of the concept of plastic flow by Bingham (27), coating colors were generally accepted as exhibiting straight line flow patterns regardless of the rate of shear applied to the color. Single point viscosity determinations on two different colors would be identical, and yet the colors would perform differently on the coaters. Following the work of Bingham, the concept of thixotropy was developed and applied to coating colors to explain their behavior better when used on various coaters. Many detailed papers on thixotropy have been published such as those by Cobb and co-workers (9, 28) and Pryce-Jones (29, 30) (see also reference 19).

Thixotropic flow may be defined as a flow associated with an internal structure that is destroyed *temporarily* by the application of some force, but reforms on standing. A significant time interval is required for the structure to reform. A force-flow curve of a thixotropic color shows a hysteresis loop (31). As the rate of shear increases, the up curve bends away from the stress axis, but the down curve is essentially straight. The area of the loop is a measure of thixotropic breakdown.

Thixotropic behavior can be superimposed on the basic flow systems— Newtonian, plastic, pseudoplastic or dilatant. Thixotropy should not, however, be considered as the opposite of dilatancy. Thixotropy and dilatancy can coexist in the same system—thixotropy at low rates of shear, dilatancy at high rates of shear (19).

Except for the very low solids colors used in size press coating, the colors used for coating in the paper industry are thixotropic in nature. It is apparent that no single point viscosity determination will adequately characterize such colors. Consequently, rotational-type viscometers are used to measure the viscosities of the colors produced. The instruments used may be generally divided in two types: (a) the low-shear viscometers, such as the Stormer, MacMichael, and Brookfield, and (b) the high-shear viscometers, such as the Hercules Hi-Shear and Hagan. Low-shear viscometers are generally used for routine control purposes with established formulations, while the high-shear instruments are useful for obtaining fundamental rheology data (*32*).

There are many factors in a coating system which affect the flow properties of the color. Among these are the pigment species, particle size of pigment, base exchange properties of pigment, absorptive qualities of raw stock, solids content of coating mixture, amount and type of adhesive, amount and type of mineral dispersing agent, pressure of coating rolls, and speed of machine. From this it can be seen that an understanding of pigment rheology as well as starch rheology is also necessary in the evaluation of coatings. Much work has been done in this area by Albert (*33*) and Asdell (*34, 35*), particularly with respect to clay, the prime coating pigment. For our consideration, pigment theory will not be discussed except to say that the first step in the preparation of a coating color is to provide a well dispersed pigment. Pigment particles may be strongly bonded initially and must be disassociated to provide an acceptable coating color. Particle dispersion or disaggregation is generally accomplished by mechanical force, and the dispersion is stabilized by the use of chemical dispersing agents to prevent flocculation. A method of measuring the degree of dispersion based on relative sediment volume has been devised by Robinson (*36*). The method is useful in determining the effectiveness of dispersing equipment.

Assuming a properly dispersed pigment is available for color makedown, it is evident that any characteristic of the starch which upsets the dispersion balance of the pigment slurry will have a strong effect on the color rheology. The effect of starch on the flow characteristics of clay slurry has been described by Rowland (*37*). He shows that starch may produce a thickening effect on clay by complexing the dispersing agent and thereby limit its effectiveness. In other cases, in which an excess dispersing agent is present, the starch may reduce the concentration of the dispersant to a point of optimum effectiveness. Obviously, rheological measurements will be most significant and useful on the completely formulated color. Even in this instance, some dwell time should be allowed for the redistribution of water and ions to take place before measuring the viscosity of a color.

The most important properties of a starch-based coating color are its water holding capacity and its viscosity. Both of these factors may be altered significantly by changing the type of starch used, or its concentration. In general, if the water holding power is too low, water will leave the color too rapidly, resulting in a high viscosity on the sheet surface. This high viscosity prevents the natural leveling of the coating surface with concomitant patterning on the finished sheet. If the water holding power is too high, the color will remain "wet" on the paper surface. This will result in a puddle of color that will tend to pick off the sheet on the dryer drum surface producing dryer marks. Longer drying times are also required, resulting in slower machine speeds and thus lower production.

Some flexibility in the use of a coating color having a given water retention value may be obtained by varying the internal sizing of the base sheet. Colors having relatively low water retention values may be used on grades having high internal sizing where the penetration of the water is controlled by the base sheet itself.

Frost (38) has shown the relationship between water retention and wax pick values when using starch as an adhesive in the coating color. In general, the higher the water retention, the greater the adhesive retention, and the stronger the finished coating.

The degree of water holding power needed in a coating will depend to a great extent on the type of coater used. For air brush or air knife coaters, it is desirable to have a color with a relatively low water retention value. The basic principle for this type coater requires the removal of the coating overlay by an air stream. For satisfactory operation, rapid water release to the base sheet is needed to set the coating and thus permit the overlay removal.

For high speed roll and blade coaters, a high water holding power is needed. In operation, the color is thinned as it passes between the rolls or under the blade. High water holding power is needed to prevent excessive migration of water and adhesive into the sheet, and lowered coating strength. Also, on roll coaters, low water retention allows water to soak into the sheet leaving a pigment film on the roll, a condition known as "drying on the roll." This condition is undesirable since the coating buildup results in marks on the coated sheet.

Hemstock and Swanson (39) used a roll-inclined plane test, previously described by Arnold (40), for examining the water holding power of coating colors. Using this technique, which is adaptable for general comparisons, one cubic centimeter of coating color is placed on an inclined plane of plate glass, and a highly polished roll allowed to roll by gravity over the drop of color. The resultant smear area is measured. The roll is then wrapped with a standard base sheet and the test is repeated. The greater the water holding power of the color, the closer will be the smear area to that with the uncovered roll. With practice, this method enables the coating chemist to predict the performance of a new adhesive.

At comparable formulations and viscosities, the water holding ability of hydroxyethylstarch is generally better than that of oxidized starch, which in turn is superior to that of enzyme converted pearl starch. The choice of starch will depend on the degree of water retention needed as well as gloss, print, and strength requirements.

As has been pointed out previously, the type of coating machinery and the experience of the individual mill are as important as any other factors in determining adhesive requirements. Since specific coating uses could not possibly be covered in their entirety, a description will be given of the coating methods in use today along with the coating color requirements of each.

5. Coating Methods

a. *Brush Coating*

This is one of the oldest paper coating methods. Color is applied to the sheet by an applicator roll after which the coating is smoothed out and leveled by the reciprocating action of a series of badger hair brushes. Following the brushing, the paper is generally air dried and calendered for smoothness. This method requires a very low solids color of 25–30% and, consequently, considerable drying capacity following the coater. When starch is used as the adhesive, hydroxyethylated or oxidized products are preferred. Because of the low speed of this method and the high coating costs, practically no brush coating is now practiced in the United States.

b. *Roll Coating*

Since the early 1930's, roll coating has played a very important part in the manufacture of pigment coated paper. This type of coating, in its most general form, consists of applying the color with a metering roll to a distribution roll (or rolls) which in turn apply a film of color to an applicator roll. The applicator roll applies the coating to the sheet. Although there are many types and variations of roll coaters in use today, two basic processes are in common use—the Kimberly-Clark–Mead process and the Consolidated process.

The Kimberly-Clark–Mead (KCM) process is the simpler of the two processes. It consists of three rolls—metering, distribution, and application. The rolls may be used to coat both sides of a sheet simultaneously or one side only. When one side is coated, a back up roll is used on the uncoated side. In actual operation, primary coat weight is controlled by regulating the nip dimension and pressure between the metering roll and the application roll. The distribution roll further reduces the film thickness as it is transferred to the application roll, but its primary function is to insure a uniform distribution of color. Coat weight is also controlled to a lesser extent by varying the total solids and viscosity of the coating color. Total solids are generally in the range of 50–65%, and viscosity ranges from 5,000 to 25,000 cps.

The KCM coater is generally used in an on-machine location on almost any grade of paper for which roll coating is suitable. Examples are label, publication grades, offset and letterpress, and book grades as well as paperboard. One limitation of the equipment is the splattering and film-splitting pattern developed at machine speeds above 1200–1400 feet per minute.

The Consolidated coater is a more complicated roll coating system originally developed by Massey (41) and first put into operation by the Consolidated Water Power and Paper Company (now Consolidated Papers, Inc.) in Wisconsin Rapids, Wisconsin.

In this system, the metering is accomplished by the use of two rubber covered counter-rotating rolls. The initial color film thickness is controlled by adjusting the gap between the metering rolls and regulating the relative speeds of the metering and distribution rolls. Both meter rolls run at the same speed which may or may not be equivalent to that of the distribution rolls. The coating color is drawn down into the nip, and the film splits as the roll surfaces separate. The film from one roll is then partially transferred to the adjacent distributing roll. The distribution rolls successively transfer lighter color films, which finally reach the applicator roll where the full film is transferred to the sheet.

Coating patterns are controlled by adjusting the color viscosity, using oscillating distribution rolls and regulating the machine speed. Too high a color viscosity will result in "snap back" or "orange peeling" at the transfer nip leaving a strong pattern on the sheet. Too low a viscosity will result in color being thrown by the rolls, again leaving a definite pattern on the sheet from the color splashes.

The adhesive commonly used in the Consolidated process is enzyme-converted pearl corn starch. Regardless of the type of starch used, the primary criterion for the color is its performance on the machine. Machine speed, coat weight desired, and base stock used, will determine the total coating solids used; this will generally range from 60 to 65%, with Brookfield viscosities in the range of 1,500 to 15,000 cps., measured at 100 rpm.

The use of high solids coatings necessitates the use of high solids enzyme conversion procedures in order to preserve the water balance. It is imperative that powerful, positive action blending equipment, such as sigma blade mixers or ribbon blenders, be used to insure proper heat distribution and uniform conversion. A typical procedure for high solids enzyme conversion is shown in the following tabulation:

Starch solids	35%
Time to temperature (80°)	15 min.
Time at temperature	45 min.
Time to inactivation temperature (105°)	15 min.
Time at inactivation temperature	30 min.

The time cycle will vary according to the steam supply and equipment available. Once an optimum time cycle is established, viscosity adjustments are made by changing the amount of enzyme used. The high final temperature is necessary to inactivate the enzyme completely at the high solids in a reasonably short time.

Occasionally, the starch may be converted in the presence of pigment. This procedure is not generally used because pigments absorb enzyme to various degrees, and the final excessively hot coating color must be cooled before use.

The preceding discussion of two roll coating systems is not meant to imply that they are the predominant machines used in the paper industry. Rather, they are representative of the simple and more complex roll coaters used by the industry. Other coaters in common use are the St. Regis modification of the Faeber gravure roll (42), reverse roll (43), Levelon (44), and variations of these (see also reference 23).

c. Air Knife Coating

The air knife coater might well be called a profile coater because of its unique ability to apply a uniform coat weight across the entire paper web. The process consists of an applicator roll which applies an excess of coating to the web (45) (Fig. 2). As the web passes over the breast roll, a sheet of air impinging on the coating doctors off the excess.

For this application, it is desirable to use a starch having a relatively low water holding capacity. This enables the coating to dry out to some extent on the surface of the web as the water is absorbed by the sheet, thus enhancing the subsequent doctoring or wiping off of the excess color.

By its nature, the process requires a low solids color, most commonly in the range of 40–45%. The color viscosity is generally in the 200–300 cps. range (Brookfield at 100 rpm.), although some operations have been reported as high as 850 cps. An oxidized or enzyme-converted corn starch is preferred for air knife coating.

d. Blade Coating

The most recent and perhaps most important innovation in the field of paper coating has been that of the trailing blade. The basic concept of blade coating was patented in 1945 by Trist (*46*) for the application of oil phase emulsions. The paper industry was quick to apply the basic concept to paper coating, and several blade coaters were soon in operation on lightweight grades, particularly bread wrap. The greatest inroads, however, were made a few years later when the method was pioneered by Blandin Paper Company (*47*) for lightweight publication grade papers. Trailing blade use expanded rapidly after the original blade coater at Blandin was put into operation in October 1955.

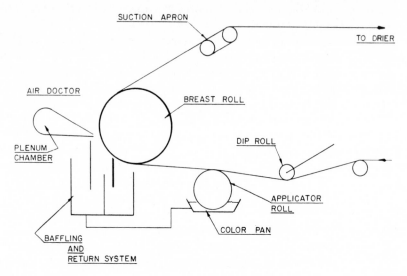

FIG. 2.—Air knife coater.

In its initial concept, the blade coater consists of a rubber covered roll and spring steel doctor-type blade. As the paper travels around the roll, it is wetted by a puddle of color retained by the blade; the surface is doctored smooth as it passes under the blade. The effect is to produce a plane coated surface giving excellent printing reproduction. Blade coating cannot, of course, remedy major profile defects in the web going to the coater, but it will produce a very uniform coated surface on a good base stock. While the air knife produces a uniform coat weight across the sheet conforming to the profile, the trailing blade levels out the profile and produces a nonuniform coat weight but a uniform surface.

As an initial step toward using computer control in blade coating, Escarfail and Benkala (*48*) suggest the application of the hydrodynamic pressure theory to flow under the blade, referring to the pressure generated when a film of liquid is squeezed between two surfaces. They also point out that, under comparable conditions, blade coating will unquestionably produce a smoother surface than will roll coating. Considering the forces involved in film splitting, they attributed this to the absence, in the trailing blade method, of a negative pressure between film and web as the web leaves the coating nip. This negative pressure is felt to be the major cause of roll coating patterns.

In all these considerations, it is obvious that the adhesive plays a major role in determining the suitability of the blade coating color. Effective blade coating colors must be highly thixotropic because of the high shear forces encountered at the blade surface. In high speed trailing blade operations, the color viscosity may be in the 15,000–30,000 cps. range (Brookfield at 100 rpm.) for satisfactory operation. Despite the apparent high viscosity, the extremely high shear forces between the blade and back roll cause the pseudoplastic colors to thin out substantially at the nip. This need for highly pseudoplastic flow characteristics in the coating color is an important consideration in the choice of an adhesive for trailing blade coating.

In some instances, flow modifiers (49) are used to modify the rheological properties of the colors. Specialized end use requirements such as water resistance occasionally dictate the use of a protein or synthetic latex, but their volume usage is small relative to starch usage (50).

For trailing blade colors, hydroxyethylated, oxidized, and enzyme-converted corn starches are used. Enzyme-converted starches have some advantage in that they may be adjusted to any desired viscosity range, and, generally, the conversion yields a starch paste which is stable and relatively resistant to shear breakdown. The hydroxyethylated and oxidized starches have their advantages in allowing the cooking of clay and starch together with resultant better dispersion. They also are more adaptable to continuous cooking methods now finding favor in the paper industry, have greater water holding power during application, and show better viscosity stability (absence of set back) in storage. Regardless of the type of starch used or the viscosity requirements, the adhesive ratio is generally maintained in the range of 15 to 18% starch based on the weight of clay.

For a thorough description of a modern blade coating operation, the reader is referred to Van Derveer (51).

It seems quite certain that the rising demand for coated papers will retain the paper industry in its present position as the major starch consuming industry. The importance of this position will continue, in conjunction with technological advancement within the paper industry itself, to provide the incentive for continuing advancement in starch technology for paper applications.

ACKNOWLEDGMENT

Schematic drawings in this chapter were prepared by Mr. D. Pendegrass, Union Starch & Refining Co., Inc.

VII. REFERENCES

(1) Anon., "Coatings for Paper," *Chem. Eng. News*, 86 (Sept. 9, 1963).

(2) J. P. Casey, "Pulp and Paper," Interscience Publishers Inc., New York. N.Y Vol. 1, 1952, p. 552.

(3) G. Jayme and J. Hunger, *Zellstoff Papier*, **6**, 341 (1957).

(4) J. W. Swanson, *Tappi*, **43**, No. 3, 176A (1960).

(5) M. L. Cushing, *Tappi*, **44**, No. 3, 191A (1961).

(6) H. Ĥ. Houtz, *Tech. Assoc. Papers*, **24**, 131 (1941).

(7) J. R. Waters, *Tappi*, **44**, No. 7, 185A (1961).

(8) H. J. Leech, *Tappi*, **37**, No. 8, 343 (1954).

(9) R. M. Cobb, D. V. Lowe, E. Pohl, and W. Weiss, *Paper Trade J.*, **105**, No. 7, 33 (1937); *Tech. Assoc. Papers*, **20**, 299 (1937).

(10) M. L. Cushing and K. R. Schuman, *Tappi*, **42**, 1006 (1959).

(11) B. W. Rowland, *Paper Trade J.*, **97**, No. 21, 249 (1933).

(12) E. K. Nissen, unpublished data (1962).

(13) C. L. Mehltretter, T. E. Yeates, G. E. Hamerstrand, B. T. Hofreiter, and C. E. Rist, *Tappi*, **45**, 750 (1962).

(14) B. T. Hofreiter, G. E. Hamerstrand, D. J. Kay, and C. E. Rist, *Tappi*, **45**, 177 (1962).

(15) J. E. Foote, *Paper Trade J.*, **109**, No. 14, 182 (1939).

(16) H. N. Lee, *Paper Trade J.*, **107**, No. 6, 53 (1938).

(17) E. E. Stephenson, *Paper Trade J.*, **143**, No. 14, 33 (1959).

(18) Anon., "Machinery for Paper Coating," *Tappi Monograph* **No. 8** (1950).

(19) J. P. Casey, "Pulp and Paper," Interscience Publishers Inc., New York, N.Y., Vol. 3, 1961, pp. 1007–1130.

(20) Anon., "Preparation of Paper Coating Colors," *Tappi Monograph* **No. 11** (1954).

(21) Anon., "Starch and Starch Products in Paper Coating," *Tappi Monograph* **No. 17** (1957).

(22) Anon., "Paper Coating Pigments," *Tappi Monograph* **No. 29** (1958).

(23) Anon., "Pigmented Coating Processes for Paper and Board," *Tappi Monograph* **No. 28** (1964).

(24) R. H. Mosher, "The Technology of Coated and Processed Papers," Chemical Publishing Co., Inc., New York, N.Y., 1952, p. 84.

(25) M. R. Castagne, *Pulp Paper*, **35**, No. 14, 39 (1961).

(26) Anon., "Synthetic and Protein Adhesives for Paper Coating," *Tappi Monograph* **No. 22** (1961).

(27) E. C. Bingham, *Natl. Bur. Stds. Sci. Paper* **No. 278** (1961).

(28) R. M. Cobb and D. V. Lowe, *J. Rheology*, **1**, 158 (1930).

(29) J. Pryce-Jones, *J. Oil Colour Chemists' Assoc.*, **19**, 295 (1936).

(30) J. Pryce-Jones, *J. Sci. Inst.*, **18**, 39 (1941).

(31) See, for example, J. B. Batdorf, in "Industrial Gums," R. L. Whistler, ed., Academic Press Inc., New York, N.Y., 1959, p. 659.

(32) Anon., "Testing of Adhesives," *Tappi Monograph* **No. 26** (1965).

(33) C. G. Albert, *Tappi*, **34**, No. 10, 453 (1951).

(34) B. K. Asdell, *Paper Mill News* (May 31, 1947).

(35) B. K. Asdell, *Paper Mill News* (June 26, 1948).
(36) J. V. Robinson, *Tappi*, **42**, No. 6, 432 (1959).
(37) B. W. Rowland, *Paper Trade J.*, **112**, No. 26, 311 (1941).
(38) F. H. Frost, *Tappi*, **35**, No. 7, 16A (1952).
(39) G. A. Hemstock and J. W. Swanson, *Tappi*, **40**, No. 10, 833 (1957).
(40) K. A. Arnold, *Paper Trade J.*, **117**, No. 9, 28 (1943).
(41) P. J. Massey, U.S. Patent 1,921,369 (1933); *Chem. Abstr.*, **27**, 5188 (1933).
(42) G. L. Booth, *Tappi*, **39**, No. 12, 849 (1956).
(43) R. E. Vokes, *Tappi*, **36**, No. 6, 64A (1953).
(44) K. Halladin, *Paper Trade J.*, **145**, No. 5, 34 (1961).
(45) K. E. Terry, U.S. Patent 2,139,628 (1938).
(46) A. R. Trist, U.S. Patent 2,368,176 (1945); *Chem. Abstr.*, **39**, 3708 (1945).
(47) C. A. Richardson, *Tappi*, **40**, No. 8, 155A (1957).
(48) J. P. Escarfail and J. E. Benkala, *Pulp Paper*, **38**, No. 43, 53 (1964).
(49) J. H. Hern, *Tappi Coating Conference* (1961).
(50) Anon., "Paper Coating Additives," *Tappi Monograph* **No. 25** (1963).
(51) P. D. Van Derveer, *Paper Trade J.*, **147**, No. 13, 33 (1963).

CHAPTER VII

STARCH IN THE TEXTILE INDUSTRY

BY JACK COMPTON AND W. H. MARTIN

Institute of Textile Technology, Charlottesville, Virginia

I. INTRODUCTION

Starch and starch derivatives are used by the textile industry in four general areas: (*a*) as a size to strengthen warp yarns and improve their resistance to abrasion during weaving, (*b*) in finishing, to change the hand and appearance of fabric after it is bleached, dyed, or printed (starch in this application is sometimes used as a binder for other materials, such as clay, or in conjunction with thermosetting resins), (*c*) in printing, to increase the consistency of printing pastes, and (*d*) as a component in finishes to glaze and polish sewing thread.

147

Of the starches available in commercial quantities, corn starch is used most commonly by the textile industry in the United States, probably for economic reasons. The amount of starch used in sizing to prepare yarns for weaving is much larger than that used in other textile operations. Consequently, this discussion on the use of starch in the textile industry will emphasize the sizing operation. Textile uses of starch derivatives will not be described, since the manufacture and uses of these materials are described elsewhere.

II. Sizing of Warp Yarns

Sizing operations are confined to the warp yarns to improve their ability to withstand the mechanical operations of the weaving process, as well as to add weight to the yarn in some instances. The process of sizing is often called slashing, and the terms will be used interchangeably in this discussion.

Yarns spun from staple fibers such as cotton are slashed with starch solutions to improve the strength and abrasion resistance of the yarn and to

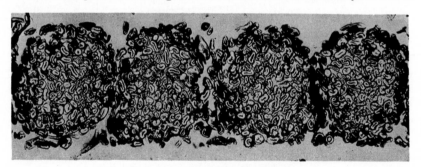

Fig. 1.—Photomicrograph of cotton yarn slashed with starch sizing. The starch is stained with iodine to increase the visibility of the sizing.

reduce the fuzz of the yarn by cementing the protruding surface fibers to the body of the yarn. The strength of the yarn is increased 10–30% by this action, and the increased stiffness facilitates handling in starting the warp through the loom. To accomplish these actions, size films are applied as a thin coating on the surface of the spun yarn and should penetrate the yarn only far enough to provide satisfactory adhesion. If the size permeates the spun yarn, the yarn will be too stiff. The amount of size added to spun yarns is usually 10–15% of the weight of the yarn, although smaller amounts can be used. A photomicrograph of sized cotton yarns is shown in Figure 1; the starch is stained with iodine to emphasize its location.

Yarns composed of continuous filaments are slashed with starch, chemically modified starches, water-soluble synthetic polymers, or mixtures of these materials. The filament yarns are sized to provide abrasion resistance and also to cement the individual filaments together. The filaments are cemented to prevent the formation of "fuzz balls" which occur when a single filament breaks and is pushed back along the body of the yarn. If the filaments are not cemented together, the broken filaments accumulate until they cause sufficient entangling to stop the loom. Cementing the filaments provides a stopping place for a "fuzz ball" because the filament will break at the bonding site. Materials used to size filament yarns thus must penetrate the yarn completely. The amount of size added to filament yarns is 3-5% of the weight of the yarn, and this small amount does not cause excessive yarn stiffness.

III. Properties of Size Solutions

To provide useful protection to warp yarns during weaving, size solutions must have specific properties. The desirable characteristics of size solutions and films have been discussed by several authors (1–4). The important properties of size solutions can be divided into the following subjects.

1. Low Cost

An average cotton textile mill will produce 34 million yards of fabric weighing 8.5 million pounds and containing 200,000 pounds of sizing each year (5). In most instances, the size is added to improve the efficiency of the weaving operation and is removed in the first wet-processing operation. Since a large amount of material is used to achieve a temporary change in yarn properties, the cost of the material used must be low. Starch is admirably suited for sizing because it is inexpensive and has many of the other desirable characteristics of sizing materials. Unmodified corn starch is often used in sizing because it is less expensive than acid-modified or oxidized starches. Some textile mills have installed bulk handling equipment so that starch can be purchased in large quantities to take advantage of prices that are slightly lower than for starch sold in bags (6, 7). In sizing synthetic fibers, starch does not provide films with suitable adhesive properties, and mixtures of starch with synthetic polymers are often used. When such mixtures are necessary, the maximum amount of starch consistent with satisfactory weaving performance is used (8, 9).

2. Easy Preparation

In most textile mills, relatively unskilled workers prepare the size solutions. Large amounts of size are used, and the properties of the sizing solutions must be consistent. For these reasons, the size solutions must be easily prepared with a minimum of attention from the operator. When unmodified starches are selected, they must be modified in the mill because the viscosity of solutions made from these starches is too high. Automatic equipment for modification during size preparation is available to those mills using unmodified starch as a starting material (10–12).

3. Uniform Viscosity and Solids Content

The amount of size on the slashed warp yarn must be uniform, not only to insure uniform weaving performance but to minimize fluctuation in the weight of the greige fabric. In addition, the penetration of the size into the yarn and, consequently, the adhesion of the size are properties affected by the viscosity, size box roll pressure, and solids' content of the size solution.

Size viscosity can be measured with a Norcross viscometer or a Zahn cup (1, 13, 14). The solids content of sizes can be measured with a refractometer or by determining the weight loss after drying a size sample. Recently, an instrument has been developed to measure the amount of size on the yarn during the slashing operation (15).

The temperature of application of the sizing solution must be kept constant since the viscosity of starch solutions is increased as the temperature decreases. Starch solutions made with modified starches undergo less change in viscosity with temperature than those made with unmodified starches and are often used in slashing for this reason.

4. Low Foaming

The slashing operation, like most other industrial processes, is run at maximum speed to minimize labor and overhead costs. The mechanical action of the yarn as it enters the sizing solution agitates the surface of the solution and can create foam which will cause nonuniform size deposition. The additives used to modify the properties of the starch film can be the source of the foaming problem if the pH of the size solution is alkaline since these compounds are often soaps or surfactants. It is important, therefore, to keep the pH of the size slightly acidic. Most starch manufacturers buffer the starch sold to the textile industry to a pH of 5.5 to 6.5. In addition, some mills add acetic acid or zinc chloride to the size during cooking (3). Anti-foam compounds usually are not needed.

5. Other Properties

Sized yarns are dried with hot air or in contact with rotating steam-heated cylinders. If the size solution remains tacky during drying, the yarn will tend to stick to the cylinders or adjacent yarns will adhere to one another. The first two or three cylinders on which the yarn is dried may be Teflon-covered to reduce sticking problems, and metal rods are inserted transverse to the sheet of warp yarns to free or split out those yarns that stick together.

Size solutions are often held overnight, and occasionally are stored during weekend shut-downs. Resistance to microbiological action is desirable during these storage periods. Starches are used in preference to flours in sizing partially because of their improved resistance to microbial action. Resistance to microbiological attack is improved by mildewcides and fungicides, which are added during the preparation of the size solution.

In recent years, pollution of streams by starch waste from sizing and desizing has become a problem for many textile mills. The waste from sizing operations is particularly troublesome during clean-up periods because relatively small amounts of concentrated waste are discharged. The high starch content of these wastes causes a large biochemical oxygen demand (B.O.D.) in the effluent, which results in stream pollution unless a high dilution factor is present. Although starch also causes a large portion of the B.O.D. of the effluent during desizing, the solution discharged is of more constant composition and easier to treat by conventional waste disposal procedures.

The waste disposal problem has become so acute for some mills that they have changed from sizing with starch to using mixtures of starch and materials with low B.O.D., such as carboxymethylcellulose (16). Starch ethers with reduced B.O.D. have also been introduced to help alleviate the pollution problem.

IV. PROPERTIES OF SIZE FILMS

Numerous attempts have been made to relate the properties of size films with weaving performance. These screening investigations have been helpful in eliminating unsuitable sizes. However, it has not been possible to select from satisfactory sizes the optimum material for weaving a particular style of fabric by testing size films, sized yarns, or by small-scale weaving tests (17–20).

Weaving performance is calculated as a percentage of the amount of fabric that could be produced when looms run continuously. In weaving many fabric styles, weaving efficiencies of 90 to 95% are common and a difference of 1% in weaving efficiency can result in a loss or gain by the mill of thousands of dollars over a year of production. For this reason, it is important to be able to measure small differences in weaving efficiency. Laboratory-scale tests are not sufficiently precise to detect the differences in film and yarn performance associated with these small differences in weaving performance. Nevertheless, the general properties of size films needed for satisfactory weaving performance are described in the following paragraphs.

1. Adhesion to Fibers

Probably the most important characteristic of a size film is its ability to adhere to the fiber during the weaving operation. If good adhesion between film and fiber is not attained, the size film is quickly shed and does not protect the warp as it is abraded during weaving. Starch films adhere well to cellulosic fibers because the two materials are similar chemically, and hydrogen bonding probably occurs between film and substrate. In addition, the stress-strain properties of starch films are similar enough to those of cellulosic fibers that the film and fiber stretch and flex in a similar manner. The extent to which the size solution is cooked affects its film-forming properties and adhesive properties. The viscosity of the solution influences the extent to which the size film penetrates the yarn so that poor penetration of the fiber is associated with excessive shedding during weaving.

2. Abrasion Resistance

As previously mentioned, the primary reason for sizing is to provide a smooth, abrasion-resistant surface to protect the yarn during weaving. The size film must be hard enough to resist abrasion, but soft enough to flex and stretch as the yarn is processed. The type of starch used and the materials added during cooking are selected to achieve the proper balance of properties to insure abrasion resistance of the sized yarn.

3. Ease of Removal

Another important property of the size film is its ease of removal during wet processing (21). Starch films are moderately easy to remove with enzymes or acids and usually cause little difficulty in wet processing. Hard size deposits created when starch is coagulated during sizing can create areas that resist removal as can overdrying on the steam cylinders after the size solution is applied. Modified starches are more readily removed than unmodified starch and are sometimes specified for this reason.

4. Other Properties

The size films should not cause static generation, although this is not a major problem for starches. In general, the yarns sized with starch are woven at sufficiently high humidities that static generation is not encountered.

The size films should be resistant to damage by heat and overdrying since it is common practice to dry sized yarns to a moisture content below that at which the yarn is woven. It is sometimes necessary to overdry the main portion of the warp yarns to insure drying of the selvedge yarns;

furthermore, most mills prefer overdrying to underdrying to prevent mildew damage, which may occur if the yarn is not sufficiently dried during slashing.

V. PREPARATION OF WARP SIZES

Warp sizes usually contain three ingredients: (a) film-forming materials, usually starch, or a mixture of starch and starch derivatives, or synthetic polymers; (b) film modifiers, such as fats used as softeners, or glycerine used as a humectant; and (c) lubricants, such as paraffin wax.

A typical formula for slashing cotton warp yarn is: corn starch, 80 lb.; softener, 5 lb.; and water, 100 gal.

Corn starch is used most commonly in slashing in the United States; in European countries, potato starch is preferred. The preference for the type of starch is probably based upon economic considerations and habitual practices, although root starches such as potato starch generally produce films that are tougher and more flexible than those of corn starch and are preferred in slashing fine-count yarns. Wheat starch is more difficult to isolate in reasonably pure form, and, therefore, is not commonly used in slashing.

Other ingredients in size solutions are added to increase the flexibility or lubricity of the starch films deposited on the yarn. Utilization of these materials is important in size preparation, but a comprehensive discussion of their characteristics is outside the scope of this work. The reader is referred to texts on the subject for additional information (1, 3, 4, 22).

In preparing size solutions, the starch must be cooked with vigorous mechanical action above its gelatinization temperature. The starch molecules must be freed from the granular form so that films will form as the size solution is dried. Incomplete cooking causes variations in the consistency of the sizing solutions and produces films with poor physical properties. Obviously, the use of these solutions will yield sized warps with poor weaving performance.

1. Kettle Cooking

If open steam coils are used for cooking starch in an open kettle, the kettle should be filled with cold water to a level somewhat below that required for the finished size. The steam line should be well insulated to minimize condensate formation, and a filter should be inserted in the line close to the kettle to remove rust particles and other solids. The required amount of starch should be added gradually to the cold water with constant stirring to form a smooth, lump-free suspension of uncooked starch. The same weight of starch must be added in each batch prepared.

If the starch is to be modified in the cooking kettle, the enzyme or oxidizing agent should be added and the temperature raised according to the recommendations of the supplier of this ingredient. Temperature control during the modification step is vital to the preparation of size formulations with uniform characteristics and is best accomplished by automatic equipment.

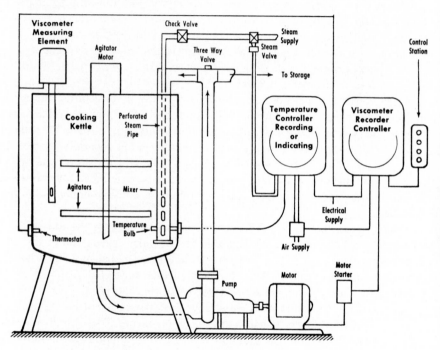

Fig. 2.—Drawing of Sizeometer for the preparation of starch size solutions (courtesy of Norcross Corporation).

At the end of the modification cycle, or if modified starch is used, the temperature is brought to a full boil in a definite time period and maintained as specified by the starch manufacturer. Rigid control of the time and temperature of cooking is also important to obtain size solutions with a reproducible viscosity. When the cooking is completed, the softeners and lubricants are added, and the batch of size is stirred until uniform. Sometimes the softeners and lubricants are added with the starch; this can be done if the supplier so specifies but may reduce the cooking efficiency.

After the starch is cooked, it should be brought to the finished volume by the addition of hot water if necessary. Cold water should not be used because it can create lumps of precipitated starch that cannot be readily dispersed.

In Europe, pressure cookers are used to prepare size solutions. It is stated that such equipment requires shorter cooking cycles than open kettles; however, pressure cookers are not common in the United States.

2. Sizeometer Cooking

Although cooking time and temperature can be controlled manually, automatic controls relieve the operator of responsibility and generally lead to more uniform size preparation. One automated process uses the viscosity of the solution as a means of controlling the extent of cooking. In this equipment, called a Sizeometer (Fig. 2), the starch solution is withdrawn

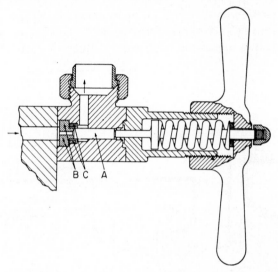

Fig. 3.—Drawing of size homogenizer valve: A, plug valve; B, homogenizer seat; C, impact ring (courtesy of Manton Gaulin Company).

from the bottom of the cooking kettle by a pump and returned to the kettle through a vertical pipe that extends nearly to the bottom of the kettle. The end of the pipe is closed and slots are cut in the sides. The cooking is achieved by steam injected from a perforated pipe arranged concentrically within the slotted vertical return pipe. The temperature of the size solution is automatically maintained, and the cooking is continued until the solution reaches the desired viscosity as measured by a viscometer. The finished size is then transferred to a storage kettle (11).

3. Homogenizer Cooking

Since mechanical action is an important part of the cooking operation, the size solution after gelatinization may be pumped under pressure of about 2000 psi. through a specially designed orifice, where the solution is exposed to vigorous shearing forces (23). One type of homogenizer valve is shown in Figure 3. The size solution is pumped under high pressure into the port of valve seat B. The solution is sheared between the valve seat and the bottom of the valve A. The ring C helps confine the solution and increases the shearing action. Because of the efficiency of the mechanical action, it is possible to use homogenizers in cooking unmodified starch and obtain size solutions with the characteristics of modified starches cooked in kettles

4. Jet Cookers

With the more recently developed jet cookers (10, 12), size solutions can be cooked in seconds according to the needs of the slashing operation. A typical jet-cooking apparatus is shown in Figure 4. Starch slurry and

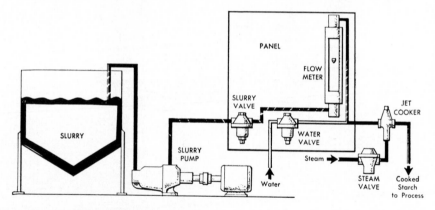

Fig. 4.—Drawing of equipment used to prepare starch size solutions by jet cooking (courtesy of A. E. Staley Mfg. Company).

steam under high pressure are supplied to the cooking valve. In some installations, water is provided to dilute the cold slurry prior to cooking. The starch slurry is metered into the cooking valve, in which the steam is allowed to impinge upon a thin film of the slurry. The heat gelatinizes the starch, and the mechanical shearing action of the expanding steam disrupts the swollen granules. The cooked starch is then ready for the sizing operation. Figure 5 shows the design of two valves used in jet-cooking operations.

VI. APPLICATION OF WARP SIZES

A typical slasher used in the application of warp sizes is shown in Figure 6. Several section beams, each containing several hundred warp yarns, are

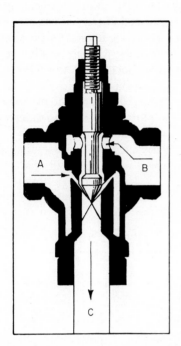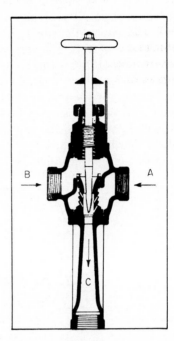

FIG. 5.—Drawings of two types of injector valves used in cooking starch with steam: A, steam; B, starch slurry; C, cooked starch (courtesy of A. E. Staley Mfg. Company and Corn Products Sales Company).

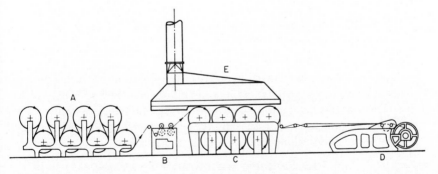

FIG. 6.—Drawing of equipment used in slashing warp yarns; A, warp yarn on section beams; B, size box; C, steam drying cans; D, loom beam take-up assembly; E, hood for removing steam.

placed in a creel at one end of the slasher. The yarns are combined into sheet form and passed under the immersion roll of the size box as shown in Figure 7. The amount of size in the size box is regulated at a constant level by automatic controls. The yarn passes through the size solution and the excess is removed by the squeeze rolls (Fig. 7). The wet yarn is then dried as it passes over cylinders heated by steam (Fig. 6).

An amount of size solution equivalent to the weight of the yarn sized is usually applied in slashing. After the yarn is dried, the remaining size adds from 7 to 15% to the weight of the spun yarn and 3 to 5% to the weight of the filament yarn. Since the consistency of the size solution affects the amount of size deposited on the yarn, it is important that the size

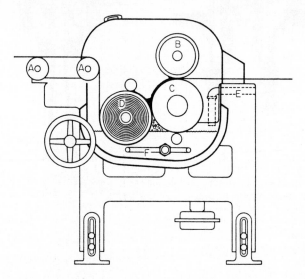

Fig. 7.—Detailed drawing of size box used to apply size solutions: A, lead in rolls; B, top squeeze roll; C, bottom squeeze roll; D, immersion roll (courtesy of Ira L. Griffin & Sons).

cooking procedures and the temperature of the size solution during application be accurately controlled. The amount of foam and the level of the size in the size box must also be controlled to maintain uniform sizing. Other variables in sizing are important, and the reader is referred to more detailed discussions of the slashing operation (1–4, 9, 22, 24).

VII. Finishing with Starch Solutions

Starch and starch derivatives are used in textile finishing operations to change the stiffness or hand of the fabric, to modify the appearance by filling the interstices of the weave, and to add weight (25). Since the finish provided by starch is temporary, its use is confined to inexpensive fabrics or to materials such as shade cloth or book bindings that are not washed. Fabrics finished with starch alone are quite stiff and brittle, and the finishing solutions usually contain relatively large amounts of film-modifying materials. Starch is also used in conjunction with thermoplastic or thermosetting resins to obtain a stiffened finish; when used in this manner, it provides a permanent change in the fabric properties.

1. Changes in Fabric Hand

To obtain changes in hand, fabric in the last stage of finishing is immersed in a dilute solution of cooked starch, squeezed to remove the excess solution, and dried on steam-heated cylinders or on a tenter frame set at the desired width. The fabric may also be passed through a calender consisting of a heated roll and a roll with a resilient surface. In some calenders, the rolls are run with a surface speed faster than the movement of the fabric. This operation, called friction calendering, polishes the surface of the fabric.

The composition of solutions used to modify fabric hand varies considerably with fabric construction and the fabric properties desired. A typical formula for light-weight goods is: 10 lb. of corn starch, 20 lb. of softener, and 50 gal. of water. For heavier fabrics or stiffer finishes, the amount of starch is increased.

2. Back Filling

Back filling is a process of applying a mixture of starches, or of starch and a filler, such as talc or clay, to the back of the fabric without obscuring the weave on the face of the fabric. This type of finish increases the stiffness and the opacity of the fabric by filling the interstices of the weave with the starch mixture. Fabrics thus prepared are used in window shades and in bindings for books.

The finish is applied by one of several pieces of equipment. In the back-fill padder or "Tommy Dodd" shown in Figure 8, the fabric is held face up tightly against the surface of a roll partially immersed in the back-fill mixture. A portion of the mixture adheres to the fabric, and the excess is scraped off by a knife or doctor blade. A second doctor blade is used to keep the surface of the immersion roll free of the mixture.

The back-filling operation may also be accomplished by use of a "skimming" pad or "Betty Dodd." In this equipment (Fig. 9), the starch solution is transferred by a furnisher roll to the applicator roll, where the excess is scraped off with a doctor blade. The solution is transferred to the back of the fabric, and the excess is removed by a second doctor blade. Fabrics processed on either the "Tommy Dodd" or the "Betty Dodd" must be dried without contact with the back of the fabric, and are usually calendered to obtain a smooth finish.

A typical formula for back-filling fabric is (*25*): starch acetate, 30 lb.; corn starch, 85 lb.; sulfonated tallow, 45 lb.; talc, 100 lb.; and water, 100 gal.

VIII. Use of Starch in Printing and Thread Glazing

Thickeners are used in printing to give the printing paste the consistency necessary to produce a clean, sharply-defined pattern of color.

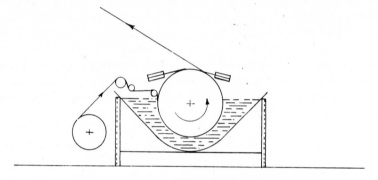

Fig. 8.—Schematic diagram of "Tommy Dodd" back-fill padder.

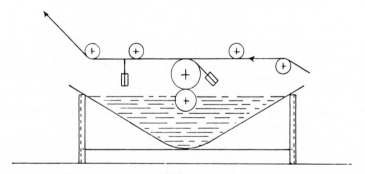

Fig. 9.—Schematic diagram of "Betty Dodd" back-fill padder.

Vegetable gums and derivatives of cellulose and starch are more suitable for use in printing pastes than unmodified starch. Because of their low cost, however, corn and wheat starches are mixed with other thickeners or are sometimes used alone as the thickening ingredient in printing pastes. To be useful, a thickener should not be affected by the other chemicals in the printing paste, should not affect the color or cause pigment agglomeration, and should be readily removed after the color is fixed (*26*). Starch pastes sometimes react with the dyes used in printing, are affected by acids and alkalies, and yield solutions with unstable viscosities. For these reasons, unmodified starches are usually mixed with gum tragacanth in making the pastes (27).

Starch solutions are prepared in much the same way as for sizing, but the final printing paste is used at room temperature and hence has a much higher viscosity than a warp size. A typical formula for a printing paste is: corn starch, 230 lb.; stearic acid, 1 lb.; boiling water to make 120 gal.; after the cooked solution is cooled to room temperature, the dye and other chemicals are added.

Starch is also used as an ingredient in the solutions applied to sewing thread in the final finishing operation. The exact compositions of the solutions used in this operation are not readily available, but they usually contain starch, glue, and wax. The solution is applied by passing the thread over a roll partially immersed in a trough containing the hot solution. The thread then passes over rotating brushes as it is dried by a stream of hot air. The resulting finish improves the luster of the thread and reduces friction during the sewing operation.

IX. REFERENCES

(1) Auburn University, Department of Engineering Extension, "The 1963 Textile Slashing Manual," Auburn, Alabama, 1963.
(2) C. R. Blumenstein, *Textile Ind.*, **127**, No. 8, 58 (1963).
(3) P. V. Seydel, "Warp Sizing," W. R. C. Smith Pub. Co., Atlanta, Georgia, 1958.
(4) K. Ward, Jr., ed., "Chemistry and Chemical Technology of Cotton," Textile Book Publishers, New York, N.Y., 1955.
(5) R. C. Pillsbury, *Whitin Rev.*, **28**, No. 2, 5 (1961).
(6) M. W. Hancock, *Textile Bull.*, **89**, No. 5, 58 (1963).
(7) Anon., *Textile World*, **112**, No. 9, 50 (1962).
(8) G. F. Gosling and J. H. MacGregor, *J. Textile Inst., Proc.*, **54**, 24 (1963).
(9) National Starch and Chemical Corp., "Kofilm Manual," New York, N.Y., 1960.
(10) Corn Products Sales Co., Industrial Div., "Nemo Jet Cooker Modified by Corn Products," New York, N.Y.
(11) Norcross Corp., "Norcross Sizeometer," Bull. No. V1220, Newton, Massachusetts.
(12) A. E. Staley Mfg. Co., "Staley's Automatic Jet Cooking System," Tech. Bull. No. B32, Decatur, Illinois, 1961.
(13) H. C. Olsen, *Textile Ind.*, **126**, No. 10, 135 (1962).
(14) Anon., *Textile World*, **112**, No. 6, 38 (1962); No. 8, 33 (1962); No. 9, 52 (1962).
(15) Strandberg Engineering Labs. Inc., "The M620 Size/Wet Pickup Recorder," Greensboro, North Carolina.
(16) B. W. Dickerson, *Ind. Wastes*, **1**, 10 (1955).
(17) D. N. E. Cooper, *J. Textile Inst., Trans.*, **53**, 94 (1962).
(18) T. Radhakrishnan, P. C. Mehta, and B. R. Shelat, *Textile Res. J.*, **27**, 439 (1957).
(19) R. P. Ramirez and J. P. Vidosic, *Textile Res. J.*, **26**, 531 (1956).
(20) H. W. Saffer, H. A. Rutherford, and D. M. Cates, *Textile Res. J.*, **29**, 849 (1959).
(21) Anon., *Dyer*, **129**, No. 5, 695 (1963).
(22) "Cotton Warp Sizing Handbook," 2nd Ed., E. F. Houghton & Co., Philadelphia, Pennsylvania, 1949.

(*23*) Manton-Gaulin Mfg. Co., Inc., "How to Improve Slashing and Reduce Sizing Costs with a Gaulin Homogenizer," Everett, Massachusetts,

(*24*) G. R. Merril, A. R. Macormac, and H. R. Mauersberger, "American Cotton Handbook," 2nd Ed., Textile Book Publishers, New York, N.Y., 1949.

(*25*) J. T. Marsh, "Introduction to Textile Finishing," Chapman & Hall, Ltd., London, England, 1948.

(*26*) R. W. Jacoby, *Textile Ind.*, **122**, 110 (1958).

(*27*) American Association of Textile Chemists and Colorists, "The Application of Vat Dyes," AATCC Monograph No. 2, Lowell, Massachusetts, 1953.

CHAPTER VIII

STARCH IN THE FOOD INDUSTRY

By Elizabeth M. Osman

State University of Iowa, Iowa City, Iowa

I. Introduction

Starch plays a leading role in determining the texture of many foods, and texture is of vital concern to both the consumer and the food manufacturer for it is a major factor governing the acceptability and palatability of most food products.

The exact meaning of the term "texture" differs rather widely from one segment of the food industry to another. The problem has been discussed in some detail by Matz (*1*) who defined his usage of the word as "those perceptions which constitute the evaluation of a food's physical characteristics by the skin or muscle senses of the buccal cavity, excepting the sensations of temperature or pain. This definition is intended to exclude the chemically initiated sensations of taste and, of course, does not regard texture as having a visual component." In completely ruling out appearance, he differed from the definition of the Taste Testing and Consumer Preference Committee (1958) of the Institute of Food Technologists (2), as well as from that commonly used by the baking industry, whose concept was expressed by Dalby and Hill (3) as follows: "Appearance, feel to the touch, softness and, finally, mouth feel all contribute to the concept of texture in the broad sense." Whichever of these definitions one accepts, the influence of starch in many food products remains unquestioned.

II. PROPERTIES OF STARCH IMPORTANT IN FOOD PROCESSING AND STORAGE

The desired textural qualities are obtained from starch as a result of changes which occur during and after cooking. Gelatinization of starch has been described in detail in Chapter XII of Volume I, but a brief resume here of the process, as it applies to food, will help in the subsequent discussion. Although the general sequence of changes is common to all starches, the temperature at which each change occurs and its magnitude depend on the species of starch, damage it may have incurred during isolation, subsequent physical or chemical modification or derivatization, and the presence of other substances in the aqueous medium in which the gelatinization takes place. Such factors as rate of heating and amount of shear caused by agitation also affect the changes which occur.

1. Gelatinization Temperature

Starch granules in their natural condition undergo no noticeable change in microscopic appearance when they are suspended in cold water. Even mild warming of the suspension produces little apparent change; birefringence is retained, the very limited uptake of water is reversible, and the amount of swelling is scarcely noticeable. This behavior is the result of the strong intermolecular bonds in the crystalline areas of the granules which resist dissolution. However, if these bonds have been destroyed by mechanical or chemical treatment, or by previous gelatinization and drying of the starch, swelling in cold water occurs. Many starch derivatives are also soluble in cold water if the degree of substitution is sufficiently high. Introduction of strongly ionizable groups, such as dibasic phosphate groups, causes repulsion between the charged polymeric chains and is particularly effective for obtaining solubility in cold water.

Except when types of treatment such as those mentioned have been used no obvious changes occur in the suspended starch granules until the temperature of the water reaches about 60°–70°, when the granules suddenly swell to many times their original size. This rapid swelling occurs almost instantaneously for each granule; but, just as the individual granules within any given sample vary slightly in their appearance, they also vary slightly in the temperature at which they gelatinize, with the large granules gelatinizing first (4). The temperature range over which gelatinization occurs is characteristic of the particular species (Table I). Since investigators differ somewhat in their technique for

Table I

Gelatinization Ranges of Various Food Starches (5)

	Temperature at Loss of Birefringence (°C)		
	Initiation	*Midpoint*	*Termination*
Corn	62	66	70
Waxy corn	63	68	72
High-amylose corn (55% amylose)	67	80	[a]
Grain sorghum	68	73.5	78
Waxy sorghum	67.5	70.5	74
Barley	51.5	57	59.5
Rice	68	74.5	78
Rye	57	61	70
Wheat	59.5	62.5	64
Pea (green garden peas of normal amylose content)	57	65	70
Potato	58	62	66
Potato (heat–moisture treated)	65	71	77
Tapioca	52	59	64

[a] Some granules still birefringent at 100°.

measuring gelatinization, values reported by different workers are not entirely comparable.

The presence of dissolved substances in the aqueous medium surrounding the starch may exert a strong influence on the range of the gelatinization temperature. This effect is considered in detail later in the chapter.

2. Paste Clarity

As the starch granules swell in water, the opaque suspension gradually becomes translucent. Samec (6) observed that a sudden change in light transmission occurs at a definite temperature. Methods based on this property have been used for identifying and characterizing starches

(*7*, *8*). Of greater importance to the food industry, however, is the clarity of the final cooked paste. This clarity is much greater for pastes of waxy grain, root, and tuber starches than for ordinary cereal starches. Clarity is also affected by the presence of other substances in the mixture. For example, sugars greatly increase the clarity of pastes of ordinary cereal starches such as corn starch. On the other hand, food emulsifiers such as glyceryl monostearate make the pastes much more opaque. Certain other surface active agents, such as sodium lauryl sulfate, which appear to form complexes with amylose equally well (*9*), greatly enhance the clarity of the pastes (*10*).

In many starch-containing foods, suspended particles of proteins or other substances mask the clarity of the starch paste. In others, clarity contributes greatly to the eye-appeal of the food. Cherry and berry pie fillings are more tempting when the fruit is clearly seen through transparent thickened juice than when it is largely concealed by a cloudy paste. Gravies of certain oriental foods characteristically have greater clarity than the usual occidental gravies.

3. Viscosity and Visco-Elasticity

The textural quality usually desired most when starch is incorporated in a food product is viscosity. Among the numerous examples of products in which this property is desired are cream soups, gravies, and many sauces, puddings, and pie fillings. Some starch pastes are stringy and mucilagenous, customarily undesirable properties in food products, and these starches ordinarily receive special treatment to eliminate this property before they are used in foods. However, in some foods, such as certain oriental dishes, a small amount of visco-elasticity is considered characteristic of the type of food.

The changes in viscosity with heating that are shown by amylographs or similar instruments are of value in studying the behavior of starches during cooking, but the exact conditions of the test should be considered in predicting performance in a particular food product. The rate at which viscosity increases after the starch granules undergo their initial swelling depends on the particular species of starch and its previous treatment and on the presence of other substances in the surrounding aqueous medium. Katz (*11*) interpreted such hot-paste viscosity curves in terms of a progressive swelling and hydrating of the starch granules, together with their breakdown.

The temperatures reached in the instruments used to record viscosity changes during pasting are frequently different from those used during food preparation. In the amylograph, in which a thermoregulator controls the increase of temperature within the cooking vessel, pastes are usually heated to 95°. With the Corn Industries Viscometer, which employs a constant temperature bath surrounding the cooking beaker, most studies have been made with the bath held at 92°, producing a temperature in the starch paste of about 90°; a few (12, 13) have used the bath at 100°, giving a final paste temperature of about 96°–98°, on the assumption that this temperature more closely approximates conditions usually used in food preparation. However, the heating of starch-containing foods during cooking is far from uniform. In the home, products are often thickened with starch in a saucepan over direct heat. Here, the mixture is usually brought to a boil and held there for varying lengths of time. But sometimes a double-boiler is used, with the result that the temperature of the food never reaches boiling temperature. The temperature reached in the steam-jacketed kettles frequently used to cook starch-thickened products in institutions often falls far below the boiling point. Processing in commercial plants, especially in canning, is usually done in autoclaves which reach temperatures appreciably above 100°. Agitation under these various cooking conditions also varies and differs from that provided in laboratory instruments. Allowance for these differences must be made in the application of research data to practical usage.

4. Increased Susceptibility toward Amylase Action

Although amylases can digest raw starch granules to an extent dependent on both the source of the enzyme and the type of starch (14), digestion following gelatinization of the starch is much more rapid at temperatures below those which would inactivate the enzyme. The extent of this activity depends on the rate of temperature increase, the ratios of water and of enzyme to starch, the gelatinization temperature of the starch, the thermostability of the enzyme, and the presence of other ingredients which would affect the swelling of the starch granules or the activity of the enzyme. Apparently the only food products in which such amylase hydrolysis has been the subject of investigation are those leavened by yeast, in which the diastatic action provides substrate for fermentation. Presumably amylase action may occur to an extent sufficient to affect the properties of certain other products such as quick loaf breads, in which temperature rise within the product is slow enough to allow amylolysis to occur.

5. Destruction of "Raw Cereal" Flavor

The flavor characteristic of starch is important to many foods. A "starchy" flavor, caused by materials other than carbohydrate in the starch granule, seems to be associated with most untreated starches.

However, the common cereal starches, such as corn, grain sorghum, and wheat, have a more pronounced and persistent flavor, commonly known as "raw cereal." This flavor becomes less apparent during cooking, and may be masked entirely by other marked flavors. The point at which the starchy flavor is no longer noticeable to an objectionable degree commonly serves the homemaker as a criterion of "doneness" for cooked cereals and starch-thickened foods.

Because they receive no further cooking, the pregelatinized starches used in "instant" puddings, icings, and the like must be relatively free from this starch or raw cereal flavor. Potato, tapioca, and waxy cereal starches have been preferred for such uses, partially on the basis of flavor. However, a process has been described for the production of pregelatinized cereal starches that is claimed to eliminate the starchy flavor (15). In the process a sequestering agent, such as tetrasodium pyrophosphate, is added prior to the drying step. This agent appears to function by forming complexes with the traces of metallic ions, such as iron and copper, that occur in commercially prepared starch and which act as catalysts for oxidation of the lipid materials present. The less pronounced starchy flavor in tuber and waxy cereal starches may result from their lower lipid content (16). Treatment of ungelatinized starch with an alkali metal phosphate, citrate, or tartrate is also claimed to be effective (17). Another method consists of treatment with alcohol and ammonium hydroxide (18).

6. Gel Formation and Retrogradation

When a starch paste cools, the molecules become less soluble and tend to aggregate and partially crystallize. If the paste is extremely dilute, precipitation results, but at the higher concentrations found in foods, three dimensional gel networks are formed from the polysaccharide molecules. Portions of both amylose and amylopectin molecules become involved in crystalline micelles which are matted together, united by molecular filaments (19, 20). Such alignment and crystallization of amylopectin molecules is partially inhibited by their ramified structure and is limited chiefly to the outer branches (21). These crystalline areas, both within the swollen granules and, more importantly, in the aqueous solution between the granules, determine to a large degree the strength and rigidity of the gel which is formed. Parts of the macromolecules that are involved in the crystalline micelles lie in amorphous regions between the micelles, and the ability of the gel to be stressed to a degree without breaking has been attributed to the capacity of the portions of the molecules in these regions to be extended (22).

Other factors that affect the formation and characteristics of starch gels are the size and morphological structure of the granules and their age and previous treatment (21), the paste concentration, cooking time and temperature, agitation during cooking, time and temperature of storage after cooking, and added ingredients (23, 24).

Several investigators (25–27) have reported that starch gels held and dried at elevated temperature produced x-ray patterns indicative of crystalline structure; the A-type appeared to be produced at temperatures above 50°, as contrasted to the B-type common for pastes at 20° (see Volume I, Chapter XI). Sterling (27) reported that the diffraction patterns of gels dried at 70° appeared to be relatively weaker than those from gels dried at room temperature and suggested that the weaker gel strength at the higher temperature results from lower crystallinity.

Teegarden (24) found that when the temperature of constarch gels which had been held at 5° was raised to 25°, the gel strength approximated that of gels held at the higher temperature alone.

Starches containing both amylose and amylopectin ordinarily form gels readily at relatively low concentrations. Potato starch has much less tendency toward gel formation than might be anticipated from its amylose content; perhaps the unusually great length of the linear molecules in potato starch or a slight degree of branching interferes with their alignment to form micellar structures (28). Although the ramified structure of waxy starches prevents gel formation at lower concentrations, gels will form from pastes of high concentration, about 30% in the case of waxy corn starch (28).

When starch gels are held for prolonged periods of time, they shrink and some of the liquid phase separates from the gel. This effect is highly magnified when the gel is frozen and thawed, although the difference appears to be one of degree rather than of kind. The change in the gel structure brought about by increased crystallization (retrogradation) of the starch molecules may be considered as merely a continuation of those changes which convert the viscous paste into a gel. Although gel formation may sometimes be considered desirable in a food product, the changes associated with retrogradation, which include the separation or "curdling" of frozen, starch-thickened sauces upon thawing and the staling of baked goods, are seldom wanted. Skin that forms on the surface of starch pastes is apparently another example of retrogradation, and one which is often troublesome in food processing.

Retrograded amylopectin is reported to return to its original dispersed state merely by heating to 50° to 60°, but the retrogradation of amylose cannot be reversed even by autoclaving (*28*). The difference has been assumed to be the result of the much larger crystalline areas which can be formed by the linear amylose molecules. There are indications, however, that changes associated with retrogradation of amylopectin in food systems may not be as reversible as they are in simple starch–water systems. Osman and Cummisford (*29*) found that liquid separation from frozen white sauces prepared with waxy corn or waxy sorghum starch was much less after they were heated to approximately 90° than when they were heated to 35°, but it was not entirely eliminated.

III. Starches Used in Foods

1. Natural Starches

Different food products make different demands on the starches used in their production, depending upon the particular combination of viscosity, gel formation, clarity, and length of paste desired, and upon the effects of the other ingredients present. Formerly the choice of a starch was confined to the various natural starches available or to combinations of them. Today the food processor has available not only these starches but also the products of their chemical modification and derivatization. With this variety of materials, an economic choice requires that the processor be well acquainted both with the properties of all these starches and with the behavior he can expect from each in his product.

a. *Corn and Grain Sorghum Starches*

Corn starch and grain sorghum starch, because of their abundance and low cost, are used whenever their properties allow. They represent by far the greater part of the starch used in food products in the United States. The properties of grain sorghum starch resemble those of corn starch so closely, except for its somewhat higher gelatinization temperature, that the two starches may be used interchangeably for many purposes. These starches form viscous, relatively short and opaque pastes with typical cereal flavor, and, unless they have received special treatment, their pastes set to stiff gels. They are widely used for thickening sauces, gravies, puddings, and pie fillings, except when greater clarity is desired or when gel formation on cooling is not wanted. They are not suitable for products which are to be frozen because of the pronounced tendency of their pastes to retrograde under this treatment. For use in canned products, special treatments, usually with mild oxidizing agents, rid the starches of thermophilic microorganisms which otherwise might prove resistant to the heat of the canning process (30–33).

Corn starch finds numerous uses in the baking industry. Addition of starch makes hard wheat flour more nearly like the soft wheat flour preferred for cakes and many types of cookies, yielding a more tender product without an increased need for sugar or fat. In cracker manufacture, pregelatinized starch is sometimes used to make the flour more manageable when it is very strong. Flour alone seldom produces the proper strength in ice cream cones and sugar wafer shells; corn starch, as well as tapioca starch, have been used in combination with flour for this purpose. Use of a specially treated, neutralized cornstarch is claimed to have advantages (34).

In addition, these starches find numerous uses in "dusting" to facilitate certain baking operations. Often they are given some special treatment to prevent lumping. Milling with a hydrophilic fatty acid ester of polyethylene glycol is one method that has been used (35).

Starch is also used as an inert ingredient in baking powder where it functions to prevent release of carbon dioxide in the closed can by absorbing moisture and by mechanically separating the particles of the acidic ingredient and the sodium bicarbonate, and to regulate the concentration of the sodium bicarbonate so that the carbon dioxide evolved will be the expected amount—at least 12%, by Federal regulation (36). The inert ingredient usually used is a redried corn starch with its moisture content reduced to about 5%. To lessen the tendency for redried starch to develop an undesirable flavor during storage, it frequently is given a mild treatment with an oxidizing agent prior to drying. Redried starch is also used in powdered sugar in a concentration of about 3% to prevent caking.

Another use of redried corn starch is in molding gumdrops and similar candies. Molds are made by impressing the desired shapes in a layer of the starch. The hot cooked jelly is then poured into the molds and held until it has gelled and adjusted to the correct moisture content. To make the dried starch retain the shape of the impressions, a small amount of edible oil is thoroughly blended with it.

Salad dressing, as distinct from mayonnaise, contains starch paste in addition to egg to emulsify the oil. The minimum oil content is set by Federal regulation at 30% for salad dressing and 65% for mayonnaise (37). Since the viscosity of the starch paste is chiefly responsible for the emulsifying action, the starch used must be resistant to the action of the acetic acid in the vinegar, not only to maintain the desired thickness of the dressing but also to keep the emulsion from breaking. Frequently a mixture of starches, such as corn and tapioca starch, is used to produce the desired texture and stability, although modified starches have also found use in this product.

b. Waxy Corn and Sorghum Starches

The waxy starches have several characteristics that recommend them for certain food uses. Most notable are paste clarity, high water-binding capacity, and resistance to gel formation and retrogradation. However, the stringy, cohesive character of pastes of the unmodified waxy starches makes them unsatisfactory except in a very few products such as salad dressing, in which they are mixed with other starches. A method (38) for making pellets from waxy corn starch for use as a substitute for pearl tapioca was developed when supplies of the latter were cut off during World War II. The return of tapioca to the market eliminated need for the substitute, but the modified and derivatized waxy starches now have an important place in the food industry.

c. Rice Starch

Much of the characterization of different varieties of rice starch has been made on rice flour, sometimes following extraction of lipids. Although there are varietal differences in rice starches, especially in amylose content (39), it is unlikely that they are responsible for all the reported differences between rice of different varieties. All rice starches have characteristic small granules which probably exert considerable influence on the properties of the rice starch pastes, but properties reported for single samples of rice starch may not be typical of all varieties. The tender, opaque gels formed from rice starch seem to offer no particular advantage in food use, and most of the rice starch consumed is in the form of the whole grain. Some rice starch is also used in the brewing industry. For a detailed study of rice starch, see Chapter IIIa.

d. Waxy Rice and Waxy Rice Flour

Waxy rice flour was found to contribute freeze-thaw stability to white sauces and puddings far in excess of that produced by any other thickening agent (29, 40–42) until the advent of some of the newer modified and derivatized starches. Improved freeze-thaw stability has been attributed to the starch component of the waxy rice flour (40). However, the freeze-thaw stability of sauces prepared with purified waxy rice starch was far less than that of sauces prepared with waxy rice flour, although better than those prepared with the other starches tested (29, 40). It must be concluded that ingredients in the flour other than starch are partially responsible for improved freeze-thaw stability.

Jordan (43) found that waxy corn flour also produced a sauce that gave no appearance of separation after 12 months of frozen storage. She based her judgment entirely upon scores by a panel rather than on any objective measurements. She also reported that a white sauce thickened with wheat flour, although showing syneresis upon thawing, was reconstituted by heating to give a product similar to a freshly made sauce. This latter observation is in marked contrast with those of the other investigators (29, 40), who used slightly different methods in preparing and evaluating the sauces.

The flavor of waxy rice flour in white sauces has been found objectionable by some individuals (29, 44) although this flavor is said to develop only at higher temperatures (44). Waxy rice flour has also been found to have an adverse affect on flavor when used in guacamole, an avocado spread, in sufficient concentration to reduce the watery separation that forms when that product is thawed after freezing (45); but, when used in conjunction with sodium alginate, the amount needed was not enough to be objectionable.

e. *Wheat Starch*

At a given concentration, pastes prepared from wheat starch have lower viscosity and yield more tender gels than those from corn or sorghum starch. They find use in the baking industry not only in making possible the use of hard wheat flour for cake production and the like but in improving the quality of cakes over that obtained with cake flour alone. Dubois (46) has reported that replacement of 30% of the cake flour by wheat starch in angel food and other foam type cakes results in significant improvement in volume, grain, texture, and eating properties. He also reported improved freshness retention. His results indicated that wheat and corn starches gave quite comparable results up to 20% replacement of wheat flour, but that only the former showed further improvement at the 30% level, a fact probably related to the weaker gel formation of the wheat starch. Substitution of wheat starch for 30% of the flour in pastry is claimed to give increased tenderness such that a 17–20% reduction in shortening is possible (47). Ungelatinized wheat starch is said to increase cookie spread when used to replace 30% of the flour, whereas spread is decreased with pregelatinized wheat starch (48). Thus, by substitution of ungelatinized or pregelatinized wheat starch in a cookie formula, changes in the proportion of sugar, shortening, or other ingredients that affect spread can be made without altering the final size and shape of the cookie. Such considerations are of great importance to the cookie manufacturer who must produce cookies of uniform diameter and thickness in order to get a fixed number in a standard package.

A modified, thick-boiling wheat starch is reported to be useful in salad dressings, soups, and baby custards (*49*).

See also Chapter II.

f. *Potato Starch*

Much potato starch is used in foods in those countries in which it is the principal starch of commerce. As a result, the somewhat long body and clarity that potato starch contributes have come to be recognized as characteristic of many of the native foods. An example is the type of pudding known as Danish dessert. Potato starch is also reported to find use in bakers' specialty items, soups and gravies, and in instant puddings (*50*). A cold-water-soluble, oxidized potato starch suitable for instant pudding has been described (*51*). An interesting use of potato starch reported by Japanese investigators is to enhance the gel strength of the fishmeat jelly, kamaboko (*52, 53*). A Dutch patent (*54*) describes production from potato starch of a product resembling pearl tapioca for use in foods.

See also Chapter IV.

g. *Tapioca Starch*

Tapioca starch has the bland flavor and paste clarity typical of root starches. These properties are desirable for many food uses. But its long, cohesive paste, also typical of root starches, is far from desirable. For food use, therefore, tapioca is found primarily in the form of chemically modified products or in the form of partially gelatinized small pellets or "pearls". These pearls are produced by spreading the damp starch on iron plates, where it is stirred constantly while being heated enough to cause partial gelatinization of the granules which agglomerate into irregular pellets, becoming hard and translucent when cooled.

In the use of the pearl form or its precooked variation, "instant" tapioca, care is taken to keep agitation at a minimum to prevent breakdown of the pellets, with the resulting development of a stringy paste. These forms of tapioca, which have been treated to produce less stringy products than the powdered starch, are useful for pie fillings, particularly fruit fillings. Pearl tapioca has long been used to thicken cream type and fruit puddings. The chemically modified tapioca starches now find similar use and are also suitable for baby foods. Tapioca starch is used extensively in starch blends for salad dressings. It has also been used to modify the characteristics of the flour used in making ice cream cones (*55*).

h. *Arrowroot Starch*

The limited amount of arrowroot starch produced is used mostly in a few specialty foods especially designed for children and invalids. For many years, it has been regarded as being particularly easy to digest, although there seems to be a paucity of data to support this theory. The most common product containing arrowroot starch is the so-called arrowroot biscuit, in which the amount of wheat flour used is about eight times as great as that of arrowroot (*55*). Although these are unquestionably wholesome, easily digested biscuits, the contribution of the arrowroot flour to these properties appears to be minor.

i. *Sago Starch*

The high strength of the gels made from high-fluidity sago starch has led to its use in confections (*56*), although the gels, like those of corn starch, lose their clarity on standing (*55*).

2. Modified and Derivatized Starches

a. *Acid-Modified Starches*

Thin-boiling starches, prepared by heating a suspension of granular starch below its gelatinization temperature with a very low concentration of acid, are among the oldest modified starches. Corn starch of the 60-fluidity type is the standard starch used for gum confections (*56*). The viscosity of the hot jelly prepared from this type of starch is much lower than would result from unmodified corn starch of the same concentration; consequently, the hot jelly can easily be poured into molds. On the other hand, strength of the resulting gel is improved. Improved gel strength may result from acid hydrolysis of the amylopectin in preference to the gel-forming amylose. The acid treatment also increases the clarity of the paste. The molds used for shaping are prepared, as previously described, from molding starches. See also Chapter IX.

Acid-modified wheat starch has been proposed for partial replacement of flour in angel cakes (*57*). It is reported to have a greater tenderizing effect than an equal amount of unmodified wheat starch.

b. *Oxidized Starches*

Although the starches commonly referred to as "thin-boiling" are those produced by mild treatment with acid, mild oxidation yields other starches with weakened granules that give hot pastes of reduced viscosity. Production of these starches is commonly carried out by a method similar to that used for the acid-modified starches except that alkaline hypochlorite is used instead of acid. This treatment, like the acid treatment, increases the clarity of the paste, but it reduces the strength of the resulting gel to a much greater extent. These starches are, therefore, only of interest to the candy manufacturer who wants a very tender gum confection of high clarity. Kerr (*58*), however, has claimed that calcium peroxide can be used to produce an oxidized starch that will give a strong gel as well as a high degree of clarity.

c. *Cross-Linked Starches*

The swelling and ultimate breakdown of starch granules during cooking can be controlled by the introduction of a suitable amount of cross-bonding between the starch molecules. In root starches, and especially in the waxy cereal starches, this type of derivatization is widely used. When aqueous suspensions of unmodified root or waxy cereal starches reach the gelatinization temperature, the granules swell rapidly to form viscous pastes, long in character, which thin upon continued cooking because of breakdown of the fragile, highly swollen granules. The excessively stringy, cohesive character of these pastes is unsuitable for most food products, although the accompanying high clarity and water binding capacity and the tendency to resist retrogradation are very desirable characteristics. Controlled swelling of the granules through cross-bonding reduces stringiness without interfering with the desirable aspects of these starches. Resistance toward acid hydrolysis is increased, but stability toward freezing and thawing is not significantly altered.

Cross-linked starches for food use are prepared by reaction of the ungelatinized starch with epichlorohydrin (*59*), phosphorus oxychloride (*60, 61*), water-soluble metaphosphates (*62*), or acrolein (*62a*). Cyanuric chloride (*63*) and mixtures of adipic or citric acid with acetic anhydride (*64*) have also been patented for cross-linking starch.

Cross-linked waxy cereal or root starches have proved excellent for use in such products as fruit pie fillings in which clarity of paste is a particular asset. They are widely used in canned pie fillings because of the stability and clarity of the thickened product. Their resistance to acid hydrolysis has made them useful in salad dressings. They form the base of a batter mix which has been patented for coating foods for deep-fat frying (*65*).

Although cross-linked waxy corn starches appear to improve freeze-thaw stability of white sauces over those made with underivatized waxy corn starch, the improvement is too small to make them suitable for use in most frozen starch-thickened products (*29*). Large portions of the starch molecules are unchanged by the small degree of derivatization which inhibits granular swelling to a degree suitable for food starches, and the tendency toward retrogradation is only slightly reduced. Introduction of acetyl or propionyl groups, in combination with cross-linking, has been claimed to prevent retrogradation and to produce a starch of greatly improved stability toward freezing and thawing (66).

d. *Starch Phosphates*

The intermolecular association that causes retrogradation may be reduced by replacing some of the hydroxyl groups with acetyl or propionyl groups, or by introducing ionizing groups which cause the molecules to repel one another. An indication of the latter effect was given by the improved stability of frozen white sauce thickened with carboxymethylstarch (40). Introduction of more strongly acidic groups might be expected to increase stability even more, and the recently developed starch phosphates in which at least part of the phosphate groups are monoesters and therefore not involved in cross-bonding are highly resistant to retrogradation during freezing and thawing. Their polyelectrolyte character also gives them clarity and high water-binding capacity and prevents gel formation. The viscosity and length of the paste and whether or not the starch is cold-water-dispersible depend upon the degree of substitution, amount of cross-bonding, and extent of degradation which have occurred during manufacture.

Various alkali metal phosphates are used to produce starch phosphates. One method employs an alkali metal orthophosphate to yield a cold-water-dispersible product containing usually about 1% phosphorus, presumably in the form of monoesterified orthophosphate groups (67, 68). Solutions of this product can be treated with aqueous alcohols to decrease the color, inorganic phosphates, and content of lower viscosity starch fractions, thereby increasing the viscosity (69, 70). This starch phosphate is reported to have excellent stability toward freezing and thawing both in a water paste (71) and in a white sauce formula (72). It has been suggested as a replacement for vegetable gums as well as other types of starch.

Another method of preparing starch phosphates uses a meta-, polymeta-, pyro-, or tripolyphosphate, or a mixture of these (73). By choice of the reagent and the pH of the reaction mixture, both mono-starch phosphate and cross-bonded distarch phosphate esters can be formed simultaneously or in sequence in almost any ratio desired. Starches manufactured for food use by this method are usually prepared from waxy cereal starches so that the natural clarity and water-binding capacity of the starch itself will augment that produced by the phosphate groups introduced. Slight cross-bonding counteracts the long body and cohesiveness which would otherwise result from use of this type of starch and also improves stability toward high temperature, shearing action, and acid. Thus the product has all the desirable characteristics of a cross-bonded waxy starch combined with those of the monophosphates, including excellent stability toward freezing and thawing. It is therefore suitable for use in many types of food products, particularly starch-thickened frozen foods, which have presented so many problems to the food industry.

See also Chapter XIV.

e. *Pregelatinized Starches*

Use of pregelatinized starches has grown so rapidly that their comparatively recent development tends to be forgotten. The process of precooking followed by drying, usually on hot rolls, has been applied to a wide variety of natural, modified, and derivatized starches. The products have the common property of being cold water-dispersible, but the dispersions formed reflect the characteristics of the raw starches. The dispersions are not entirely like the freshly cooked pastes prior to drying because the drying process has usually been accompanied by some breakdown of the swollen granules as well as by some retrogradation. For this reason, a greater weight of pregelatinized than of raw starch is needed to produce a given viscosity, and the texture is somewhat different.

One of the largest food uses of pregelatinized starch is in the popular "instant" puddings—packaged powders which need only to be mixed thoroughly with milk and allowed to stand about 5 minutes to yield a simple pudding. These powders consist of mixtures of pregelatinized starch with sugar and flavorings, together with salts which produce enough viscosity in the milk to keep the starch suspended until it hydrates.

A second large use is in pie fillings. Cream pie fillings can be produced in the same way as instant puddings. For fruit pies, the pregelatinized starch is often prepared from a cross-bonded waxy cereal starch. Because the starch is pregelatinized, the filling is subjected to only the heating it receives during baking, and even this can be eliminated if desired. The juice, thickened without heating, keeps the fruit suspended, and loss of the fresh flavor of the fruit is avoided. In the preparation of frozen fruit pies, all cooking prior to freezing can be eliminated.

Pregelatinized starch has been suggested for a variety of other uses. As an example, substitution for about 4% of the flour in cakes has been reported to improve the eating quality (74). It has been used as a component of a cream puff mix (75) and of a soufflé mix (76). Its use as a gravy-forming agent in a hydratable animal food has been patented (77).

See also Chapter XXII.

f. *Heat–Moisture Treated Starches*

Heating in the presence of moisture insufficient to cause gelatinization results in marked changes in the properties of starches, particularly those obtained from tubers or roots. Because these changes are not such that the economic value of the starch is improved, their application to refined starches has not been exploited commercially. But the conditions which bring such changes about occur not infrequently in food processing, and wider recognition of the modifications that can result would be useful in understanding and controlling those operations in which they may occur.

A heat–moisture treated potato starch that resembled corn starch more nearly than ordinary potato starch in many of its properties was prepared by Sair and Fetzer (78). Study of this phenomenon was continued by Sair, but his data have never been published. A few of his findings are presented here, with his permission (79), to indicate more clearly the nature and scope of this alteration of the properties of starch and some of the conditions which bring it about.

Microscopic appearance of the ungelatinized starch granules under either natural or polarized light was unchanged by this treatment. But pastes prepared from the treated starches differed from those of the corresponding untreated starches to degrees which appeared to be inversely related to the extent of crystallinity in the original starch granules. Viscosities of the pastes (Table II) serve as examples of the changes observed. Those starches, chiefly cereal, which gave an x-ray diffraction pattern of the A-type, indicative of a high degree of crystallinity, underwent comparatively little change during heat–moisture treatment. In contrast were those starches, chiefly tuber or root, which gave before treatment a B-type x-ray pattern, indicating a low degree of crystallinity, and after treatment a C-type pattern, indicating a moderate degree of crystallinity.

Changes in viscosity were only one type of indication of the alterations which had occurred. Gelatinization temperature, measured by loss of birefringence under polarized light, was raised as much as 5° to 10° by treatment of potato starch (Table I). Other characteristics of the paste were profoundly altered. Pastes of potato starch are characteristically highly transparent and visco-elastic, with little or no tendency to set into a gel. Those prepared from a typical potato starch following heat–moisture treatment were short and opaque and formed opaque, rigid gels similar to those from cornstarch.

The extent of the change which occurred in the starch was related to the moisture present although the exact function of the water was not entirely clear. It was postulated that the combination of heat and moisture allowed the starch molecules, or parts of them, to shift position to yield a more compact, crystalline structure. This change toughened the granules and made them more resistent to swelling when they were heated in water. In general, the result was an increase in the gelatinization temperature and a lowering of the paste viscosity. That the change was largely associated with the amylose fraction of the starch seemed

Table II

*Viscosities of 4% Pastes Prepared from Starches Heated at 105°
for 3 Hr. at 100% Relative Humidity (29)*

Starch	Hot viscosity[a] (cp.)		Cold viscosity[b] (cp.)		X-ray pattern	
	Untreated	Treated	Untreated	Treated	Untreated	Treated
Canna	2810	368	—	2500	B	C
Potato	2300	1010	4600	1786	B	C
Arrowroot	955	515	3125	780	C	A
Sago	57	181	1855	1175	C	A
Tapioca	770	938	2250	1827	A with trace of C	A
Sweet potato	638	513	1120	773	A	A
Corn	429	418	2240	1980	A	A
Rice	241	224	1045	691	A	A
Wheat	101	96	1710	1107	A	A

[a] Taken with MacMichael viscometer at 95° immediately after paste was prepared.
[b] Taken with MacMichael viscometer after holding period of 16 hr. at 25°.

to be indicated by the fact that waxy cereal starches were little affected, although their pastes were somewhat stabilized.

Contrary to its effect on most starches, heat–moisture treatment actually raised the hot viscosity of tapioca starch paste somewhat; but it decreased the translucency and visco-elastic character of the paste, and the increased viscosity was thought to result from the toughened granule being more resistent to breakdown. The same might be true for sago starch. Amylograph curves for starches treated in this way would be interesting. However, the behavior of these starches indicated that the affect of heat–moisture treatment is not always predictable.

The importance of time and temperature in determining the extent to which the characteristics of a starch are altered by heat–moisture treatment are indicated by the gels formed from potato starch (Figure 1).

IV. Effects of Other Food Ingredients on Starch

Gelatinization of a food starch in water and characterization of the resulting paste provides important information for the food processor, but it is not enough. Other ingredients are present in starch-thickened foods, and few of these are devoid of some influence on the behavior of the starch. Most complete foods, however, contain so many interacting ingredients, and present knowledge of the interactions is so meager, that conclusions drawn from these complicated systems concerning the exact role of the starch are often misleading. Study of simpler systems, preferably with only a single ingredient in addition to starch and water, appears to offer greater opportunity at present for basic understanding of the behavior of the starch.

1. Sugars

The effects of sugars on the properties of starch pastes are of considerable practical importance in the preparation of such pie fillings as lemon, fruit with starch-thickened juice, and the various cream types, as well as in puddings and sweet sauces. Attention has centered chiefly on the effects of sucrose, although information on other sugars is of value when dextrose, invert sirup, or corn sirup is used as all or part of the sweetening in these products.

Sucrose impedes swelling of starch granules in hot water (*12, 80–83*). Through its water binding capacity, the sucrose apparently withholds the water from the granules. Microscopic examination has shown that increasing concentrations of sugar cause correspondingly greater inhibitions in the normal swelling of the starch granules, and that high concentrations markedly increase the temperature at which birefringence disappears.

Small additions of sucrose to a 5% cornstarch paste slightly increased the maximum viscosity reached (*12*), the effect being greatest when the weight of the sugar was about 20% that of the starch–water paste (Fig. 2). At higher concentration (50%), the sugar reduced the maximum viscosity and, more markedly, the rate at which it was attained. Reduction in the rate of swelling of waxy corn starch has also been reported, but no reduction in the maximum viscosity was observed, and the maximum viscosity obtained with a hard wheat flour was greatly increased, apparently indicating effects of constituents of the flour other than the starch (*82*).

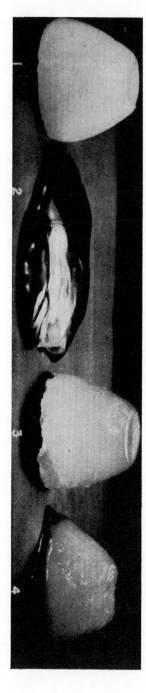

Fig. 1.—Effect of heat–moisture treatment on gel-formation by potato starch (79): 1, untreated corn starch; 2, untreated potato starch; 3, potato starch heated at 93° for 8 hr. at 100% relative humidity; 4, potato starch heated at 100° for 16 hr. at 100% relative humidity.

The effects of other sugars on corn starch pastes have been found (*10*) to be qualitatively similar to those of sucrose, but quantitatively the differences (Fig. 3) are sufficient to be of importance in food

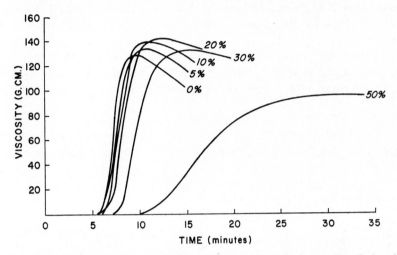

FIG. 2.—Effect of sucrose on gelatinization of 5% corn starch in a Corn Industries Viscometer with water bath at 100° (*12*).

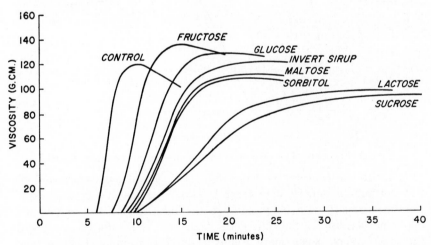

FIG. 3.—Effect of different sugars on gelatinization of 5% cornstarch in a Corn Industries Viscometer with water bath at 100° (*12*).

processing (*12*). The disaccharides exhibited a greater effect than the monosaccharides when used at the same concentration by weight, and, therefore, at lower molar concentration, but the reason is not readily apparent. Täufel and Berschneider (*84*) studied the swelling of potato

starch granules in the presence of sucrose, D-glucose, and other mono-
and polyhydroxy compounds. They developed a method of calculating
the number of molecules of water bound per hydroxyl group and concluded that it is greater for sucrose than for glucose, although considerably less than for 2-propanol. Further studies of this type would be of
interest.

The strength of gels formed from starch pastes has been found to
decrease as the amount of sucrose added is increased (12, 80). Quantitative effects of other sugars differ somewhat (12).

2. Acids

The pH of most foods lies within the range of 4 to 7, within which
slight variations in acidity produce only minor effects on viscosity during

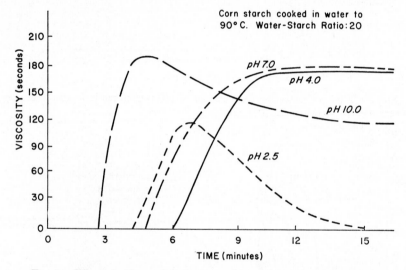

FIG. 4.—Effect of pH on gelatinization and breakdown of cornstarch (85).

cooking of starch–water systems (85) (Fig. 4). When citrate and bi-
maleate buffers were used to control pH (86), somewhat greater variation in viscosity was observed, but the influence of the anions was
apparent because of the differences between the results obtained with
the two buffers. Some more complex starch-containing systems react
very differently, presumably because of the effect of pH on another
component of the system. Such a system is corn starch in milk, which
will be discussed in a later section on effects of proteins.

Certain foods, such as salad dressing and lemon and fruit pie fillings,
have much lower pH values. The use of special starches, particularly
cross-bonded starches, to counteract the hydrolytic effects of the acid

in salad dressing has already been discussed. The same types of starches are also useful in fruit pie fillings, but in these the effect of the acid is counteracted to some degree by the high sugar concentration that inhibits swelling of the starch granules.

Addition of citric acid to a wheat starch paste to give solutions 0.05 to 0.20N caused the maximum viscosity obtained in the amylograph to be greater and to occur at a lower temperature, but also caused the paste to break down rapidly (87). Addition of a high concentration of sucrose to the acidic paste, through its action in reducing granular swelling, retarded the hydrolysis. As a result, the maximum viscosity

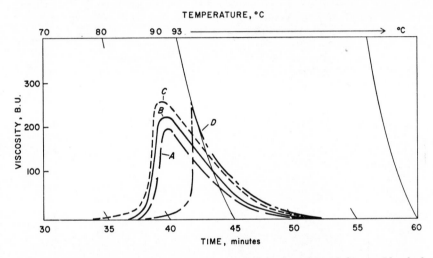

FIG. 5.—Effect of citric acid and sucrose on gelatinization of starch from unbleached soft wheat flour heated in an amylograph to 93° (87): A, 0.200N citric acid solution; B, 10 g. sucrose/100 ml. 0.200N citric acid solution; C, 20 g. sucrose/100 ml. 0.200N citric acid solution; D, 40 g. sucrose/100 ml. 0.200N citric acid solution.

was still higher than without the sugar, but occurred at a higher temperature (Fig. 5). Breakdown of the paste was somewhat slower at all but the highest level of acid used (0.200N). Under the conditions used, a high concentration of either the sugar or the acid interfered with gel formation. A study of the effects of these same variables under conditions of more rapid heating than that provided by the amylograph, with correspondingly shorter time for hydrolysis, would be interesting.

3. Salts

Effects of salts on the swelling of starch granules and on the viscosity of starch pastes have been investigated for more than a century (88). Such investigations are of importance to the food industry because of the frequent presence of electrolytes in food systems. Their effects on other food components, especially proteins, complicate studies of many food products. Examination of simpler systems, consisting only of starch, water, and a single salt, can be of value in interpreting results obtained in more complex systems.

Several factors have led to confusion in the literature on this subject. First, most of the studies were done before present instruments for controlling the conditions of cooking and continuously recording the appar-

Table III

Influence of Anions and Cations on Pasting of Corn Starch[a] (90)

| | Temperature (°C) | | Viscosity (B.U.) | |
Salt	Viscosity increase	Maximum viscosity	Maximum (first)	After 15 min. at 95°
Control	72	91	525	340
Sodium salts				
Iodide	64	79	770	330
Bromide	74	90	640	390
Phosphate	78	94	610	750
Acetate	80	95	590	650
Chloride	80	95+[b]	580	550
Citrate	84	—	—	770
Tartrate	84	—	—	760
Sulfate	85	—	—	430
Chloride salts				
Calcium	79	85	690	390
Magnesium	82	94	610	480
Potassium	78	95+[c]	600	550
Sodium	80	95+[b]	580	550

[a] Electrolyte concentration, 0.1N; starch 7%.
[b] Held 2 min. at 95°.
[c] Held 1 min. at 95°.

ent viscosity changes of the system were available. Recent studies giving continuous records of changes throughout the cooking process show that sampling after a different heating period might reverse the relative values from a certain salt at two concentrations or from two different salts at the same concentration since the amylograph curves for these systems may cross. Thus, comparisons of the complete records of changes in viscosity or other paste characteristics during the entire cooking period are more valuable.

A second cause of confusion lies in the use of potato starch which, because of its polyelectrolyte character due to the ester-bonded phosphate groups, is much more sensitive to the presence of other ions in solution than are the cereal starches. Furthermore, because of the cation-exchanging properties of the phosphate groups, the behavior of potato starch may depend on the mineral content of the water used in its manufacture.

Sodium chloride in concentrations as low as $0.00001N$ has been reported to exert a small but distinct depressing effect on the viscosity of potato starch paste during heating (89). With $0.001N$ sodium chloride,

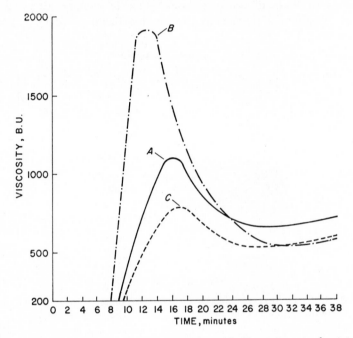

FIG. 6.—Effects of sodium chloride and calcium chloride treatments of potato starch on gelatinization (92): A, potato starch washed with distilled water; B, potato starch treated with sodium chloride; C, potato starch treated with calcium chloride.

the viscosity was so low that very little granule swelling could have occurred. In marked contrast, the viscosity of corn starch paste was affected very little during heating with sodium chloride in concentrations up to $0.1N$, although both the viscosity and the temperature at which increased viscosity was observed were raised by $1.0N$ sodium chloride (90) (Table III). A study of wheat starch gelatinization employing changes in light transmission of the paste showed that $2N$ sodium chloride increased the gelatinization temperature by $13°$ while $5N$ sodium chloride lowered it (91).

Although small concentrations of sodium chloride lowered the viscosity of potato starch, the sodium form of the starch, obtained by ion-exchange treatment with sodium chloride produced a much higher maximum viscosity than the untreated starch (92) (Fig. 6). The calcium form of the starch, however, showed a lower maximum viscosity. Because of the absence of significant bound phosphate groups in cereal starch, no effect was produced in the viscosity curves of corn starch which had been subjected to similar treatment.

Low concentrations of calcium chloride are even more effective than sodium chloride in reducing the viscosity of potato starch, but, at concentrations of $0.5N$ or $1.0N$, calcium chloride slightly increases the maximum viscosity of corn starch, providing further evidence that the

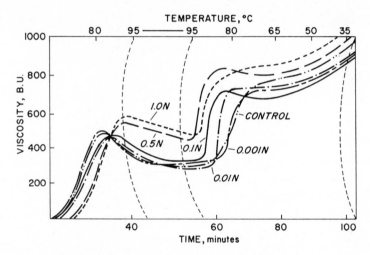

FIG. 7.—Effect of potassium chloride on gelatinization of 7% corn starch heated in the amylograph to 95° (90).

response of potato and cereal starches to electrolytes may be qualitatively as well as quantitatively different.

Changes in concentration of a particular salt, such as potassium chloride, frequently result in a displacement of the amylograph curves obtained with corn starch (Fig. 7). However, with some salts, such as sodium sulfate, a complete change in the character of the curve occurs with evidence of the introduction of a two-step gelatinization (Fig. 8). From this last set of curves, it is obvious that at one concentration or at one temperature a salt may be found to increase the viscosity of a corn starch paste, whereas it may cause a decrease in viscosity at a different concentration or temperature.

In spite of the wide variations in the shapes of the amylograph curves, certain values for temperature and viscosity during gelatinization (90) fall in an order which is in good agreement with the Hofmeister-Pauli lyotropic series discussed by Samec (*88*). When the sodium salts were arranged in order of increasing temperature at maximum viscosity, the order (Table III) agreed essentially with the lyotropic series for anions. The temperature at the point at which the first recorded increase in viscosity was observed was in the same order. Maximum viscosity values were in the reverse order. However, viscosity values after a longer cooking period showed no such correlation with the lyotropic series. A similar comparison of the chloride salts of calcium,

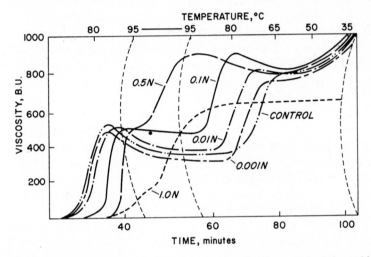

FIG. 8.—Effect of sodium sulfate on gelatinization of 7% corn starch heated in the amylograph to 95° (*90*).

magnesium, potassium, and sodium showed less agreement with the order given by Samec (*88*) for cations. Values obtained with sodium and potassium were so nearly the same that their failure to lie in the given order represented no important deviation, but values for calcium were far out of line and suggested that factors other than those involved in the lyotropic series must be considered in explaining its action.

Although the effects of electrolytes on cereal starches are far less than on potato starch or on proteins, they are sufficient to require consideration in the interpretation of changes occurring in starch-containing foods.

4. Fat and Surfactants

The frequent statement that fat retards gelatinization of starch is not completely supported by the literature. Although most surfactants raise the temperature at which maximum viscosity of a starch paste occurs, triglycerides lower it (*93*). The temperature at which maximum viscosity of a 6% corn starch paste was reached in the amylograph was progressively lower as the amount of fat was increased until the weight of fat was 8 to 12% that of the starch–water mixture. Degree of saturation of the fat from iodine number 38 to 132 or source of fat had no effect on the viscosity curve.

Lord (*94*) reported little effect from the addition of 1% fully esterified fat on the temperature of gelatinization of defatted wheat starch, determined by increased light transmission. Strandine and co-workers (*95*) reported that determination of sedimentation volumes of a 4% wheat flour paste showed that 20% lard based on the weight of flour had little effect on granular swelling at 60° and above, and that the sedimented granules appeared to be very similar when observed under the microscope.

Effects of fatty acids on starch pastes appear to differ from one system to another. Mitchell and Zillmann (*96*) suggested that the factors responsible are (*a*) the type and concentration of amylose, (*b*) the amylose–fatty acid ratio, and (*c*) the location of the fatty acid in the homologous series. They reported that, in general, fatty acids caused increases in the viscosities shown by the amylograph, but that these increases were not as great with potato and tapioca starches as with corn, wheat, and rye starches. They furthermore found that pelargonic acid produced a greater effect than either higher or lower members of the fatty acid series, with myristic acid and above showing very little effect.

The apparent discrepancy between the above results and those reported by Gray and Schoch (*97*) probably stem partially from differences in the system used and in the method of addition of the fatty acid. The latter investigators reported that fatty acids from caprylic to arachidic depressed the swelling power and solubles of potato starch, with myristic showing the greatest effect. Results were much more pronounced on potato starch than on corn starch and much greater if the fatty acid in the form of its salt was heated with the starch slurry below gelatinization temperatures, presumably to allow greater opportunity for the fatty acid to penetrate the granules and complex the amylose. Although all fatty acids reduced the maximum viscosity obtained in the amylograph, they inhibited the breakdown of the resulting paste, with stearic acid providing the greatest stabilizing effect.

Nonionic surfactants serve a variety of needs in the food industry as emulsifying and foaming agents and in functions directly dependent upon their interaction with starch. Brokaw (*98*) has recently discussed the food uses of monoglycerides. These are used to improve the texture of dehydrated potatoes, either granules or flakes. They also prevent gel formation in other starch-containing foods, such as hot cooked farina breakfast cereal, lemon pie filling, and a variety of sauces, gravies, and soups. Spaghetti and rice are reported to be less sticky after addition of monoglycerides. Many other nonionic surfactants would presumably have the same effects to varying degrees, just as they do in retarding the hardening or "staling" of bread, which is discussed in a later section of this chapter.

A wide variety of nonionic surfactants of the general type suggested for use in foods form complexes with amylose (9). Diglycerides prepared from hydrogenated soybean oil, however, have little tendency to complex with amylose, and the triglycerides have none. Most of these surfactants, when added to a mixture of starch, water, and purified soybean oil, cause a marked increase in the temperature at which viscosity increases (93). Two, however, decrease this temperature and thereby fail to support the theory which has been proposed by Gray and Schoch (97) to explain the repressing effects of certain surfactants on the swelling and solubilization of starch granules. Gray and Schoch attributed these effects to the formation below 85° of a complex with the linear fraction which might, in some cases, break down at higher temperatures, with consequent loss of the repressing effect on the swelling. But Osman and Dix (93) found that when methyl α-D-glucoside 6-laurate and lecithin were added to a mixture of starch, water, and soybean oil, they reduced the temperature of maximum viscosity in the amylograph, without changing the viscosity attained. Some explanation other than the forming and breaking of a complex between the surfactant and the amylose appears necessary.

There are some indications that complexing of the surfactants may be related to the characteristic humps that appear in the amylograph cooling curves of systems containing these substances (93). This type of hump is not found with defatted starch alone, but it does appear with corn starch from which the native lipids have not been removed and may be obtained with defatted starch by addition of glyceryl monostearate. The hump is also removed from the curve of native corn starch by addition of fat or of calcium chloride, either of which might extract the natural fatty acids from the swollen granules.

Although the effects of some nonionic surfactants on amylograph curves of corn starch and on the iodine affinity of amylose can be related to certain aspects of their chemical structure, no adequate explanation of their effects on starch systems is yet available.

5. Proteins

In starch-containing foods, proteins are often present. The proteins are either natural accompaniments of the starch in its native environment or have been added in the form of milk or eggs. Explanations offered for the behavior during processing and storage of foods containing starch and protein together have almost invariably treated the changes which occur in the two substances separately, disregarding the possibility of any interactions between them. Yet some information has been reported which suggests that the effects of these types of materials are not always independent.

White sauces prepared with waxy rice flour have been found (29, 40) to be markedly more stable to freezing and thawing than those prepared with waxy rice starch isolated from the flour. Further evidence

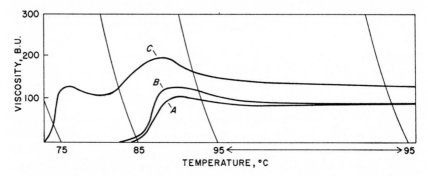

Fig. 9.—Gelatinization of 5% corn starch in (A) water, (B) 5% lactose solution, and (C) a natural protein-free milk system (99).

of the importance of other ingredients than starch in a white sauce formula was furnished (29) by differences in the stability of white sauces and starch-water pastes prepared from the same samples of various starches. In general, the white sauces were more stable than the corresponding pastes.

The importance of milk proteins in determining the viscosity of a starch–milk paste was shown by comparison (99) of the shapes and final viscosities of amylograph curves of cornstarch and water, 5% lactose solution, and the natural protein-free milk system (Fig. 9) with those of corn starch and skim milk (Fig. 10). Different milk samples produced the two types of curves shown in Figure 10. Those giving curve A with 5% corn starch could be altered to give curve B either by heating at temperatures above 80° (100) or by the addition of only a small amount of sodium hydroxide, about 0.004 mg./ml., which raised the pH value less than 0.1 unit. Addition of a similar amount of hydrochloric acid either to a milk which had received previous treatment with heat or sodium hydroxide or to a sample which in its original condition produced curve B, altered the milk so that it produced curve A. A comparable change of pH through natural souring processes, however, failed to alter the curve.

Although treatment at somewhat higher temperature than required for high temperature–short time pasteurization may partially account for the large number of commercial pasteurized skim milk samples which produced curve B, some other explanation is needed for the occasional untreated raw milk samples which also yielded this curve. The phenomenon appears to be related to the milk proteins and to the effect of environmental conditions on them, but the nature of these effects is not yet understood.

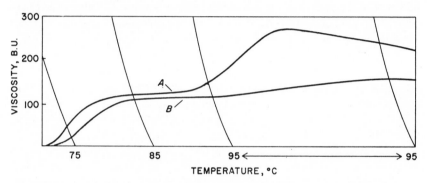

FIG. 10.—Gelatinization of 5% corn starch in two samples of skim milk (99).

A better understanding of the interrelationships between starch and proteins and other food constituents would be of great value in controlling the properties of starch-containing foods.

V. Some Starch-Containing Foods

Starches which occur naturally in many foods greatly influence the textures of the food. An exhaustive survey of such foods is beyond the scope of this chapter. Examples of the role of starch in shaping the characteristics of a few foods of high starch content are given, however, to indicate the breadth of application of starch chemistry to food science and to suggest that greater study of starch-containing foods might aid the starch chemist's understanding of this complex polysaccharide.

1. Bread

a. *Bread Making*

The long-accepted idea that gluten is the main factor in determining the rheological and gas-holding properties of bread dough and the structure of the baked loaf is gradually giving way to a recognition of the importance of starch in these functions. Rotsch (*101*) showed that completely protein-free bread could be made from wheat, corn, rye, or potato starch in combination with certain carbohydrate adhesives, including gelatinized potato starch. This bread had good grain, texture, and volume, although Rotsch stated that gluten is undoubtedly a more ideal binding agent. Jongh (*102*) went a step further and prepared bread from wheat starch and water in about the same proportion as in normal dough and added only sodium chloride, yeast, and sugar. The dough behaved like a concentrated starch suspension rather than like a normal flour dough and yielded a baked loaf with a very coarse, irregular structure and thick cell walls which hardened during cooling. But with addition of a small amount of glyceryl monostearate, the dough acquired plastic properties and produced a loaf with a loose crumb and fine, regular structure.

Sandstedt (*103*), using a different approach to the problem, showed the essentiality of starch by baking loaves from reconstituted wheat gluten with different starches and with nonstarch fillers. With wheat starch, he obtained an essentially normal loaf. When he replaced the starch with glass beads approximating ungelatinized wheat starch granules in size, he obtained a loaf with a fairly normal, though small, exterior, but with an interior characterized by badly ruptured and collapsed cells (Fig. 11). He further showed that different starches cause marked differences in gas retention (Figs. 11 and 12), a characteristic usually considered to be dependent on the quality of the gluten rather than on that of the starch.

During the production of a loaf of bread, starch performs a series of functions which begin as soon as the dough is mixed. Normal starch swells very little in cold water and hence is resistant to enzyme attack. However, milling causes varying proportions (usually about 2–4%) of the granules to be damaged (*104*), either extensively or in a limited segment (*105, 106*). The fully damaged granules and the damaged portions of those which are only partly sound swell extensively in cold water (*103, 105, 106*). The swollen portions are readily digested by amylases, although at a somewhat slower rate than boiled starch.

Flour milled from sound wheat has a relatively high content of beta-amylase and very little alpha-amylase (*107*). Theoretically, up to about 60% of the damaged starch may be converted by beta-amylase into maltose for yeast fermentation. The other product of beta-amylase action is beta-limit dextrin, which has high water-holding capacity. Sandstedt and co-workers (*108*) studied "synthetic" doughs prepared by recombining wet gluten and starch from flours, with and without

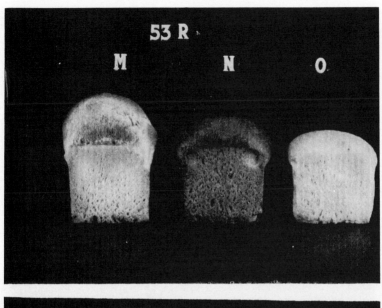

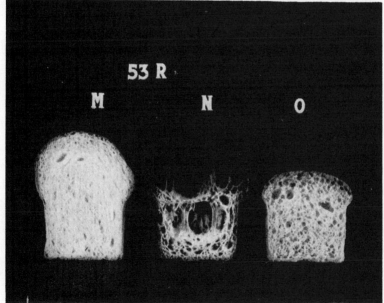

FIG. 11.—Loaves baked from doughs reconstituted from gluten and: M, wheat starch; N, glass beads; O, rice starch (*103*).

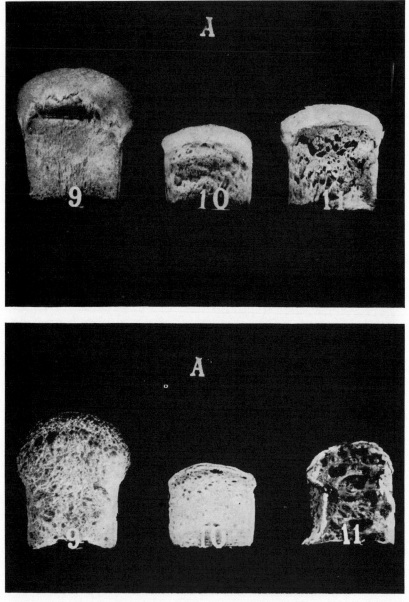

FIG. 12.—Loaves baked from doughs reconstituted from gluten and: 9, potato starch; 10, corn starch; 11, waxy corn starch (*103*).

the supernate obtained by centrifugation of the starchy material. They found that the material in the supernate, which they referred to as amylodextrin and which Sandstedt (103) later equated with limit dextrin, had a major effect on the absorption capacity of the flour, increasing it by about 10%. The handling properties of the dough were influenced by this fraction. Without it, the dough was not sticky even when very slack, and small differences in added water made abnormally large differences in the slackness. The baked product also was affected by this fraction. Loaves baked from reconstituted doughs without this fraction had greater oven spring and greater volume, but the crumb was decidedly tough and rubbery.

Flours used in bread making are usually supplemented by alpha-amylase to provide better gas production. Alpha-amylase may attack ungelatinized starch granules slowly, but its chief action in the dough, like that of beta-amylase, is on the damaged granules. Its liquifying and dextrinizing action, combined with the saccharifying action of the beta-amylase, brings about rapid and practically complete saccharification of the damaged granules, mainly during the early stages of fermentation (109). The importance of this increased maltose for yeast fermentation depends on the level of sugar added to the dough.

The historical enzyme supplement for bread has been malted wheat or barley flour, but today fungal enzyme supplementation is used extensively in the United States. The use of bacterial amylase preparations has also been investigated (110), but their high thermostability gives rise to a sticky, gummy crumb.

Sandstedt (103) has shown that in the unbaked dough, before the sound starch granules have been made flexible by gelatinization, the granules are oriented parallel to the surface of the gluten film with no evident segregation of granules or protein. He suggested that there must be a strong adherence of protein to starch for the films to have sufficient strength so that leaks will not occur between the gluten and the surface of the starch granules and so that the granules will not be forced out of the film by the increasing pressure during its expansion.

During baking, most of the remaining starch is gelatinized and undergoes swelling, which is restricted by the limited amount of water present (only about 75% based on the dry weight of the ingredients). This starch is now available for hydrolysis, which is therefore limited during baking only by the concentration of amylases present, their thermostability, and the length of the time which elapses between the beginning of gelatinization of the starch and the heat-inactivation of the amylases.

Walden (111, 112) found that the temperature at any particular point of the interior of a loaf of bread during baking rises very slowly at first. Once the heat has penetrated to that point, however, the temperature rises very rapidly until it levels off slightly below 100°, within 5–8 min. He concluded that the entire action of wheat alpha-amylase during baking occurred within 4 min., while that of the more thermolabile beta-amylase must occur in less than 2.5 minutes. The reactions which occur during baking are essentially completed by the time the temperature nears 100°, and the additional baking time merely drives off steam.

As the gas cells expand during baking, the starch granules, already oriented parallel to the film surface, are gelatinized and thus become softer and more flexible. They become greatly stretched and even more completely oriented (103). Although deformed, they retain their identity and do not disintegrate, probably because of the deficiency of water. The protein forms the continuous phase of the film, throughout which the granules are distributed.

Sandstedt (103) suggested that, if gluten functions as an adhesive for binding the starch granules, the nature of the surfaces of the starch granules must be as important to firm adhesion as the nature of the gluten. At the fermentation stage, only the surfaces of the granules would seem to be responsible for the differences in gas retention observed in doughs reconstituted from a single gluten with various starches. Examples of such differences in gas retention were found by comparison of doughs reconstituted with wheat starch and with rice and corn starches. The first had excellent baking properties, whereas the last two had poor gas retention; the doughs proofed slowly and produced no oven spring (Fig. 11). A sample of "commercial" wheat starch also produced a reconstituted dough with poor gas retention, but preliminary treatment of the starch with malt alpha-amylase greatly improved the resulting dough (108). Sandstedt (103) suggested that the improving effects of malt, generally attributed to its action on gluten, may come from its action on the surface of the starch granules.

Bread made with glass beads and with waxy corn starch substituted for the wheat starch indicated that starch also has a function to perform during baking (103). As previously noted, the exterior appearance of the loaf made with glass beads (Fig. 11) indicated that the gas retention was reasonably good, but the collapsed cells in the interior suggested that cell films did not develop the necessary degree of rigidity during baking, possibly because water was not removed from the gluten by adjacent gelatinizing starch. Collapse of cell walls during the baking of bread made with waxy corn starch (Fig. 12) could possibly be attributed to the fragile nature of the swollen granules of this type of starch which could not withstand the pull caused by the gas expansion.

The foregoing discussion shows that progress has been made concerning the physical and chemical changes which occur during the production of a loaf of bread and the role of starch in these changes. It also indicates that much further study is needed before the whole sequence of reactions will be clarified.

b. *Bread Staling*

A problem of major importance to the food industry is the staling of products prepared from batters and doughs. Because of its greater economic importance, the staling of bread has received much more attention than that of other products of this type. The changes which occur are common to all baked batters and doughs although in products of very low moisture content the rate at which staling takes place is almost imperceptibly slow (*113*). Unless crackers or crisp cookies have been exposed to a moist atmosphere, actual staling reactions occur at such a slow rate that the type of deterioration which limits shelf-life is usually not due to staling but to development of oxidative rancidity in the fat. Cakes, with their higher content of sugar and shortening, also are reported to firm at slower rates than breads (*114*), but the changes which are first apparent in cakes, as well as in breads, rolls, doughnuts, and similar products, are those which are collectively known as staling. The consumer identifies staling as the development of a firmer, more crumbly structure in the interior of the product, a softer, somewhat leathery crust in bread, and an undesirable flavor.

The properties of stale bread crumb suggest drying as a causative factor, but Boussingault (*115*) demonstrated more than a century ago that staling could occur without loss of moisture, a fact which has been verified by more recent investigators (*116, 117*). He further showed that bread which had become stale without loss of moisture would become fresh again when heated at 60° or higher.

Boutroux (*118*) was possibly the first to suggest that changes in starch were an important factor in staling. Without presenting any experimental evidence, he suggested that amylodextrin separated as a solid when bread cooled. Lindet (*119*) later reported experiments which showed that starch was indeed involved in staling. He observed a progressive decrease in the soluble starch, as well as in amylodextrin of the crumb, during aging, a process for which he introduced the term "retrogradation."

Although all the changes which occur during staling cannot be explained by retrogradation of the starch, a host of later workers have shown that it is undoubtedly the most important single factor. Numerous reviews of this work have been published (*104, 120–122*). Therefore, the present discussion is limited to a brief summary of observations related to the starch itself.

Increased firmness, crumbliness, and opacity of bread crumb on aging are consistent with the changes which would be expected from starch retrogradation, as is the decrease in the capacity of the crumb for imbibing water. More direct evidence of involvement of starch is the decrease in the amount of polysaccharide which can be leached from the crumb after aging, the increased crystallinity of the starch shown by a change in the x-ray diffraction pattern of the alcohol-precipitated crumb from the V-pattern characteristic of fresh bread to a V-pattern with superimposed B-pattern, and a decrease in the susceptibility of the crumb to attack by amylases.

The changes characteristic of retrogradation in pastes of whole starch are magnified in solutions of amylose and led to the assumption that amylose is responsible for both the retrogradation of starch pastes and the staling of bread. The decrease in "soluble" starch which can be leached from bread crumb after staling appears to agree with this hypothesis. Prior to the introduction of Schoch's butanol precipitation method for fractionating starch (123), the classic fractionation method was leaching swollen granules. The soluble material that diffuses out of the granules has been shown to be preponderantly the linear fraction (124). The assumption was made that the carbohydrate material leached from bread crumb was also amylose.

Schoch and French (125) showed that the iodine affinity, and hence the amylose content, of the soluble material leached from fresh bread not only was not preponderantly amylose, but that the amylose content was far below that of whole defatted wheat starch. They concluded that the amylose must therefore be made unavailable during the baking and cooling of the loaf. That other constituents of the bread were not involved in this change was evident from the fact that the solubles from freshly prepared 50% pastes of defatted wheat starch likewise had lower iodine affinity than the parent starch. They concluded that, in both the 50% paste and the freshly baked and cooled bread, most of the amylose was already retrograded and not involved in the subsequent staling.

When alcohols were added to a solution of wheat amylopectin to a concentration of 10–30% and the mixture refrigerated, a crystalline precipitate, insoluble in water at room temperature, was formed. However, when heated, it began to gelatinize at 52° in a manner analogous to natural starch granules. Schoch and French (125) suggested that the staling of bread and of 50% wheat starch pastes, in which the decrease in swelling power and insolubles is likewise reversed at temperatures of about 50° and above, is caused by an oriented association of the amylopectin molecules. Association of amylopectin molecules would also explain why Noznick, Merritt, and Geddes (126) did not prevent the staling reaction when they substituted waxy maize starch for the wheat starch in bread.

The concept that changes indicative of retrogradation and staling are caused by intermolecular association of the starch was supported by observations that bread prepared from flour in which part of the starch had been replaced by cross-linked starch gave increased firmness (127, 128), crystallinity (129), and organoleptically determined changes ordinarily attributed to staling (128).

Numerous methods for retarding development of characteristics associated with staling, especially the firmness, have been tried with varying degrees of success. Modification of the starch with cereal, fungal, or bacterial alpha-amylase retarded the firming (110) and loss of susceptibility to beta-amylase (130) of bread crumb. Zobel and Senti (129) showed that the enzyme did not prevent the development of increased crystallinity during aging. They suggested that hydrolytic cleavage of the starch chains in the amorphous regions between the micelles resulted in greater freedom of the micelles to move independently of one another, causing the decrease in rigidity.

A more widely used method consists of addition of a surface active agent (131–135). These compounds are present in many baked products, commercial or homemade, since they are not only frequently added to commercial baking formulas for their softening effect, but are present as emulsifiers in many shortenings.

The ability of many surface active agents to form complexes with amylose has been reported (9, 94, 95, 136, 137); but, if staling involves only the amylopectin fraction of the starch, the complexing of amylose is not significant, although the resulting inhibition of granular swelling during the initial stages might be involved (120, 133, 136–138).

Gray and Schoch (97) have recently reported that polyoxyethylene monostearates and glyceryl monostearate repress the swelling and solubilization of waxy sorghum starch as well as ordinary corn starch and potato starch. They have advanced the theory that these surface active compounds form helical complexes with the outer linear branches of the amylopectin molecules which restrict their dilation and hence their swelling. This might also explain the pronounced effects of these same compounds in retarding the staling of bread, since such complexing of the outer branches of the amylopectin would prevent aggregation.

Preservation of bread by freezing has met with considerable success and has been the subject of a number of studies, although the equipment involved somewhat limits its application. Cathcart and Luber (139) reviewed early work on this method and also reported experiments indicating that development of an "off" aroma was the chief factor limiting the time that bread remained acceptable during frozen storage. However, even at −35° a gradual firming of the crumb was apparent.

Because staling occurs most rapidly in the first few hours after baking, best retention of freshness is obtained if the bread is frozen as soon after baking as possible, a fact which has been demonstrated by both objective tests for firmness and taste-panel evaluation (140, 141). Like the retrogradation of a starch paste, bread staling occurs most rapidly at temperatures near 0°. Therefore, the length of time required to lower the temperature of the bread below its freezing point affects its firming (140). The length of time required for thawing is less important. A temperature of −18° or below prevented a significant increase in firmness from occurring within as short a period as one week. Moisture distribution in frozen and defrosted bread after 7 weeks of storage at −7° and −18° was essentially the same as that of freshly baked, unfrozen bread (142).

Pence and Standridge (143) observed that yellow layer, chocolate layer, angel food, and pound cakes all showed a linear increase in firmness with time during storage even at temperatures as low as −12°. The rates of increase in firmness of all but pound cake were small. Both flavor and texture appeared to be unaffected by differences in rate of freezing between 1 to 2 hours and 10 to 12 hours (144).

2. Potatoes

Causes of the variation in cooking quality of potatoes from "waxy" at one extreme to "mealy" at the other has been the subject of investigation for many years. Starch has long been associated with these textural differences, but its role is not clear. As early as 1897, Couden and Bussard (145) stated that mealy potatoes were those in which the cells separated from one another, and nonmealy potatoes were those in which such separation did not occur. Later, however, Gilmore (146) claimed that mealiness resulted from the presence of sufficient starch within the cells to bring about their rupture when boiled in water. The resulting breakdown in cellular structure was assumed to constitute the condition known as mealiness. Appleman (148) on the other hand, discarded the idea that the cells burst and suggested that a large volume of swollen starch in the cell caused it to tend to assume a spherical form which resulted in its drawing away from adjacent cells. Thus, the amount of starch would be directly related to the mealiness of the product by causing separation of the cells.

A general relationship between specific gravity and mealiness of potatoes has been recognized for many years and has been so widely used as a means of separating mealy and waxy potatoes that mechanical means for continuous separation of tubers into different specific-gravity groups have been devised (149, 150). Because starch is the major component of potatoes, the general conclusion has been reached that it is largely responsible for the texture. However, many observations have been reported which did not show a direct relationship between starch content and mealiness, and other factors contributing to potato texture have been sought. Sweetman (147) has discussed early investigations on this subject. More recently, Bettelheim and Sterling (151) reported a significant correlation between the starch content and organoleptic scores for potato texture. They found no direct relationship between characteristics of the pectic substances and texture (152). However, they found that the combined variations in starch content, calcium content, and the intrinsic viscosity of the Calgon-soluble fraction of the pectic materials accounted for 94% of the variation of texture scores (153). They suggested that starch content is the chief cause of cell separation in the cooked product but that it is counteracted to some degree by the calcium content and the molecular size of the pectic substances in the middle lamella and cell wall. These observations agree with reports that addition of calcium (154–156) had a firming effect on potato tissue, while removal of calcium decreased cell adhesion (157). Personius and Sharp (158) simulated the changes produced in cooking potatoes by treating potato tissue with a cold gelatinizing agent followed by ammonium oxalate.

In recent years, microscopic studies have yielded useful information about the effects of cooking on potato tissue.

Sterling (159) found no cell wall rupture in Russet Burbank or White Rose potatoes after boiling 1 hour, although he reported that the cell separation in the former was much more evident than in the latter. The former is usually classed as a mealy variety and the latter as nonmealy. Reeve (160) also observed cell separation, which he attributed to weakening of the adhesive properties of the middle lamellae, aided by swelling of the gelatinized starch within the cells, causing their walls to distend and push apart. However, he also observed cell rupturing brought about by the swelling of the starch. Gelatinized starch which escaped from the ruptured cells was believed to cause the gummy or sticky texture of White Rose. Later, Reeve and Notter (161) found a close agreement between cell rupturing and stickiness, with pronounced stickiness in samples with 10% or more of the cells ruptured.

Reeve (160, 162) observed that no sloughing occurred when potatoes were preheated in water at 75° for 30 min. or more before they were cooked. Potter and co-workers (163) reported that microscopic examination of riced cooked potatoes showed that those which had received such a preheating had more broken granules but no more soluble starch than those which had had no preheating. The amount of soluble starch was reduced by the preheating because of retrogradation. "Precooking" provides a method of producing potato flakes that give a mealier product, not only from potatoes with high solids content, but also from those with low solids content (164, 165). Similar preheating has also found use in the production of potato granules (166) and has been suggested for potato chips to reduce blistering (167).

Further improvement of potato flakes has been obtained by supplementing the effect of preheat treatment with addition of emulsifiers after the final cooking to precipitate that portion of the free amylose which has not already been retrograded (168). "Blue Value" tests showed that the free amylose was greatly reduced after such treatment.

Freezing of par-fried potatoes before finish-frying improved the product by yielding a less cohesive interior texture and a more tender crust (169). Microscopic examination of the tissue after frozen storage indicated growth of ice crystals and apparent shrinkage of the gelled starch within the cells. Finish-frying failed to restore the gelatinized starch granules to the size required to completely fill the plant cells, although the reticulation remaining in the cell walls was only slight.

Longrée (170) had previously observed a "cottony" texture in frozen and thawed potato tissue which appeared to indicate some loss of moisture-reabsorbing capacity. Harrington and co-workers (171) had exploited the fibrous structure of potato tissue which had been slowly frozen and thawed to produce very porous dehydrated potatoes in the forms of slices and cubes. As the result of a microscopic study of these dehydrated potatoes, Reeve (172) concluded that the lack of severe swelling and cell rupturing upon reconstitution in hot water indicated an alteration of the water-reabsorbing capacity of the gelled starch contents of the cells. Further indication of a change in the starch was the reduction in the blue color produced by iodine staining of the extracellular solutions of the rehydrated cubes.

Conversion of starch to sugar when uncooked potatoes are stored under refrigeration has long been recognized (173). Reversal of this reaction in some varieties by holding them at room temperature is also well known (148). It is common practice to return potatoes from cold storage to a temperature of approximately 21° for 2 to 4 weeks before use. Such reconditioning is particularly important in the production of potato chips or French-fries since too great an accumulation of sugar causes undesirable dark color.

3. Rice

Starch comprises approximately 90% of the total dry substance of polished rice. Since gelatinization of starch is the most obvious change that occurs during the cooking of rice, attempts have been made to correlate the quality of the cooked product with characteristics of the starch. In general, short- and medium-grain varieties of rice become somewhat sticky upon cooking. Although this type is preferred in some oriental countries and is in some demand in the southern part of the United States, there is a distinct preference for the drier, flaky quality usually found in the long-grain product, both for home use and for processing into canned foods such as soups. The short-grain varieties, however, are used exclusively for making puffed rice and are also reported to be used successfully for precooked canned rice and in dry quick-cooking rice products (174). They are preferred in the brewing industry because of their easier dispersibility. Both types are used in the manufacture of dry breakfast cereals other than puffed rice, and both are used in the preparation of parboiled rice.

Length of grain, however, is not completely reliable as an indication of the cooking quality of rice, for a number of varieties give cooked products which are exceptions to the type expected on the basis of this classification. Rice of the "best quality" or that with long grains absorbs more water at near-boiling temperature, thus giving a higher "swelling number," than does rice of inferior quality or of medium- or short-grain (175–178). Batcher and co-workers (179) found a positive correlation between water uptake during a standard cooking procedure and taste-panel scores for cohesiveness, as well as a negative correlation between total solids in the residual cooking water and cohesiveness. However, Halick and Keneaster (180) observed no difference between the swelling numbers of long-grain varieties known to differ greatly in cooking and processing characteristics.

Hogan and Planck (181) reported that, when the hydration was carried out at 70° for 20 or 30 min. rather than at near boiling temperature, differences between short-, medium-, and long-grain types were readily observed. Furthermore, it was possible to detect long-grain varieties that were not true to type. The water absorption values of the hydrated kernels agreed with the cohesive properties and cooking characteristics of the grain. High water-absorption values obtained under these conditions indicated poor cooking quality and stickiness; long-grained rices with superior quality, yielding dry, fluffy products were characterized by low water absorption at 70°.

Halick and Keneaster (180) used an empirical starch–iodine blue test to differentiate between long-grain rice samples. Hogan and Planck (181) pointed out that, under the particular conditions used in which the amylose responsible for development of the blue color was leached from the ground rice at 77°, the test may actually have been a measure of the rupture of the starch granules.

Rao and co-workers (175) reported that amylose content, determined by a potentiometric iodine titration, was closely related to the swelling number of the 22 samples of Indian rice they examined. Williams and co-workers (39) examined a number of varieties of rice grown in the southern United States and found a trend toward higher amylose content in the longer-grain varieties. But Halick and Kelly (182) pointed out that two atypical long-grain varieties, Century Patna 231 and Toro, have approximately the same amylose content, yet differ widely in their gelatinization characteristics. On the other hand, "gelatinization temperatures," determined as the temperature at which an increase in viscosity of a 20% slurry of ground rice was first recorded by the amylograph, differed greatly and reflected their known cooking qualities. Toro, with the cooked appearance of a medium-grain rice, gelatinized at a temperature comparable to most medium-grain varieties, whereas Century Patna 231, known to require an unusually long cooking time, showed an unusually high "gelatinization temperature." The method used by Halick and Kelly for determining "gelatinization temperature" with the amylograph employed such a high concentration of ground rice that the viscosity rose abruptly with the first swelling of the starch granules, in contrast to the situation which exists with concentrations normally used for study of viscosity changes throughout the cooking period in which the viscosity rises slowly only after the starch granules have undergone considerable further swelling. The temperatures determined by this method agreed well with gelatinization values obtained by the orthodox method of determining loss of birefringence or granule swelling microscopically (Table IV). This later study gave further evidence of the lack of any direct relationship between amylose content and gelatinization temperature.

.A method closely related to determination of gelatinization temperature was used by Little and Hilder (185) who showed a high correlation between the microscopically determined extent of alteration of the starch granules in powdered rice heated in water at 62° for 30 min. and taste-panel scores for cohesiveness for cooked samples of the same lots of rice.

Halick and Kelly (182) reported that amylograph curves of 10% ground rice slurries (half the concentration used by them for deter mination of the "gelatinization temperature") yielded useful information about the cooking properties of rice samples. Webb and co-workers (186) after using the amylograph test for several years in the evaluation of several hundred breeding selections and new varieties of rice, concluded that transition temperature, peak viscosity, and resistance to thinning during 10 min. holding at 95° in the amylograph furnished useful information which was of even greater value if considered collectively with the amylose content and gelatinization temperature of the rice sample. The possible significance of the differences in the molecular weight of the amylose fraction from different varieties is not yet apparent and requires further study (187, 188).

Yasumatsu and Fujita (189) have recently employed the plastograph to estimate the "free" and "bound" water in cooked rice. Although a

Table IV

Gelatinization Characteristics and Amylose Contents of Rice Varieties (183)

| | | | | Gelatinization temperatures | |
Variety	Grain type	Amylose (%)	Amylograph (°C)	Granule swelling (°C)	BEPT[a] (°C)
Mochi Gomi	Short	0.0	60	—	63
Caloro	Short	13.9	66	66	65
Asahi	Short	18.1	66	68	67
Arkrose	Medium	16.7	66	67	68
Improved Blue Rose	Medium	18.3	66	65	62
Toro	Long	13.3	66	68	64
Cody	Short	13.6	67.5	69	68
Magnolia	Medium	11.4	67.5	67	65
Zenith	Medium	16.4	67.5	68	68
Calrose	Medium	14.5	67.5	67	65
Rexark	Long	15.9	67.5	67	66
Nato	Medium	14.9	69	68	68
TP 49	Long	27.9	69	69	69
Rexoro	Long	28.0	69	70	69
Texas Patna	Long	26.2	70.5	72	70
Bluebonnet 50	Long	—	72	75	72
Improved Bluebonnet	Long	25.7	72	73	72
Fortuna	Long	22.3	72	74	73
Sunbonnet	Long	24.9	73.5	74	72
Early Prolific	Medium	12.3	76.5	75	75
Century Patna 231	Long	14.7	76.5	77	76

[a] Birefringence end-point temperature by method described by Pfahler, Kramer, and Whistler (184).

linear relationship between moisture and mobility (the reciprocal of "consistency") was obtained for raw rice flour, similar to that reported by Hlynka (190) for wheat flour, the relationship for cooked rice was expressed by two intersecting lines (Fig. 13). The intersection appeared to be characteristic of the type of rice, occurring at a higher moisture content with the long-grain Thai rice than with the short-grain Japanese rice. They interpreted these results to indicate that the greater part of the water content up to the point of intersection enters the network of gelatinized starch as a sort of bound water, whereas the water added beyond that point is free water and has a great effect on mobility. Cooked rice retrograded by standing at 4° for 24 hr. appeared to lose bound water through the formation of micelles, causing syneresis; and the intersection occurred at a lower moisture content (Fig. 14).

Although there seems to be little doubt that the properties of the rice starch and the changes it undergoes during cooking are of major importance in determining the characteristics of the cooked product,

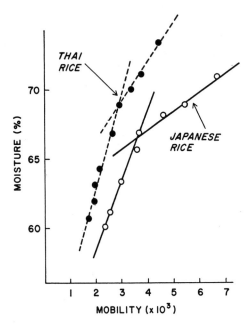

Fig. 13.—Relation between moisture and mobility of cooked rice (189).

the possible influence of other factors should not be overlooked. Dawson and co-workers (178) suggested that proteins, fats, cell wall carbohydrates, and minerals may influence cooking quality. They further suggested that the "alkali test," which has been used to indicate cohesiveness, may involve protein, fat, and mineral components of the rice, as well as the starch (191). It has also been suggested that the differences in behavior of sediment formed by addition of a Millon reagent (trichloroacetic acid and mercuric acetate) to several varieties of white rice, which seemed to bear some relationship to grain length and palatability characteristics, might indicate involvement of proteins or amino acids (192). Environmental effects, as well as variety, have been reported to have a significant effect on the composition of rice (*193*).

An example of the way in which nonstarch ingredients may affect the properties of cooked rice may be found in the report that monoglycerides, either used to coat the rice grains prior to cooking or dispersed in the cooking water, show promise of reducing stickiness (*98*). It was suggested that the action occurred through complexing of the amylose leached from the swollen granules during cooking. However, a possible additional explanation may lie in the known effect of monoglycerides in delaying the swelling of starch granules (*93*).

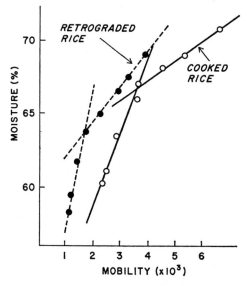

Fig. 14.—Relation between moisture and mobility of cooked rice and retrograded rice (*189*).

A study of the histology and histochemistry of raw and cooked rice kernels by Little and Dawson (*194*) led them to suggest that suppression of the swelling of the starch in rice kernels to a small fraction of its capacity, and the different patterns of disruption of the structure of the kernel during cooking, may be attributed largely to delaying or limiting effects of the cell walls or such nonstarch components as proteins. The effectiveness of the cell walls in this respect might be related to thickness, composition, and distance apart, and that of protein to its composition and concentration. Differences in microscopic appearance between varieties were noted, but observations were not sufficient to establish a relationship between structure or nonstarch components and cooking characteristics. Further studies along this line might be useful.

The time required for rice to cook is related to the rate of penetration of water into the kernel. Desikachar and Subrahmanyan (195) reported that cracks which developed in rice kernels soaked in water appeared to be responsible for their greatly reduced cooking time.

Roseman (196) obtained porous precooked rice with exceptionally rapid rehydration properties by freezing and thawing. Further investigation revealed that these freeze-processed rice samples gave the expected B-type x-ray pattern and the reduced susceptibility to beta-amylase hydrolysis characteristic of retrograded starch (197). When ground, the freeze-processed rice had a lower water-holding capacity at 80° and above than raw rice, in accord with its retrograded nature. However, the whole-grain freeze-processed rice, because of its porous structure, had a much greater water-holding capacity than the whole-grain raw or cooked unfrozen product.

Adequate penetration and distribution of water throughout the rice kernel are critical to the quality of the product in the parboiling of rice (198). Failure to bring about complete gelatinization of the starch throughout the endosperm during parboiling results in grains containing opaque spots indicating the presence of ungelatinized starch granules. These grains are susceptible to breakage during milling (198). In addition to visual examination for such grains, measurement of the volume of hot-air (250°) expanded rice and determination of soluble starch by an empirical iodine blue value have been suggested for objective evaluation of the degree of parboiling (199).

Ferrel and Pence (200) considered these methods unsatisfactory for application to certain precooked instant or quick cooking rice products and found that the amylograph gave more useful results with these materials. They heated a slurry of the ground sample to 95° and held it at this temperature for 20 min. Untreated rice gave the expected high viscosity peak followed by a pronounced reduction in viscosity during the holding period. The curve flattened out in proportion to the degree of precooking of the rice, providing an empirical but useful method for evaluating the extent of precooking.

VI. References

(1) S. A. Matz, "Food Texture," Avi Publishing Co., Westport, Connecticut, 1962.

(2) A. Kramer, Food Technol., **13**, 733 (1959).

(3) G. Dalby and G. Hill, in "Bakery Technology and Engineering," S. A. Matz, ed., Avi Publishing Co., Westport, Connecticut, 1960, Chapt. 23.

(4) J. A. Radley, "Starch and Its Derivatives," John Wiley and Sons, Inc., New York, N. Y., Vol. 1, 1954, p. 89.

(5) T. J. Schoch, personal communication.

(6) M. Samec, Kolloid-Beih., **3**, 123 (1912).

(7) D. H. Cook and A. J. Axtmayer, *Ind. Eng. Chem., Anal. Ed.*, **9**, 226 (1937).

(8) W. L. Morgan, *Ind. Eng. Chem., Anal. Ed.*, **12**, 313 (1940).

(9) E. M. Osman, S. J. Leith, and M. Fleš, *Cereal Chem.*, **38**, 449 (1961).

(10) A. L. Elder and T. J. Schoch, *Cereal Sci. Today*, **4**, 202 (1959).

(11) J. R. Katz, *Textile Res.*, **9**, 69 (1938); *Chem. Abstr.*, **33**, 5220 (1939).

(12) M. L. Bean and E. M. Osman, *Food Res.*, **24**, 665 (1959).

(13) E. M. Osman and G. Mootse, *Food Res.*, **23**, 554 (1958).

(14) R. L. Gates and R. M. Sandstedt, *Cereal Chem.*, **30**, 413 (1953).

(15) J. A. Korth, U.S. Patent 2,884,346 (1959); *Chem. Abstr.*, **53**, 12719 (1959).

(16) K. A. Clendenning and D. E. Wright, *Can. J. Res.*, **23B**, 131 (1945).

(17) J. W. Evans, U.S. Patent 2,806,026 (1957); *Chem. Abstr.*, **52**, 612 (1958).

(18) G. Harris, U.S. Patent 3,102,054 (1963); *Chem. Abstr.*, **59**, 12094 (1963).

(19) K. H. Meyer, "Natural and Synthetic High Polymers," Interscience Publishers, Inc., New York, N. Y., 2nd Ed., 1950, p. 477.

(20) K. H. Meyer, in "Advances in Colloid Science," E. O. Kraemer, ed., Interscience Publishers, Inc., New York, N. Y., Vol. 1, 1942, pp. 143–182.

(21) K. H. Meyer, P. Bernfeld, R. A. Boissonnas, P. Gürtler, and G. Noelting, *J. Phys. Colloid Chem.*, **53**, 319 (1949).

(22) C. Sterling, *Food Res.*, **21**, 491 (1956).

(23) C. C. Kesler and W. G. Bechtel, in "Starch and Its Derivatives," J. A. Radley, ed., John Wiley and Sons, Inc., New York, N. Y., Vol. 2, 1954, pp. 402–438.

(24) S. M. Teegarden, unpublished M.S. Thesis, University of Illinois, Urbana, Ill., 1961.

(25) J. R. Katz and J. C. Derksen, *Z. Physik. Chem.*, A, **165**, 228 (1933).

(26) R. S. Bear and D. French, *J. Am. Chem. Soc.*, **63**, 2298 (1941).

(27) C. Sterling, *Staerke*, **12**, 78 (1960).

(28) T. J. Schoch and A. L. Elder, in "Use of Sugars and Other Carbohydrates in the Food Industry," *Advan. Chem. Ser.*, **12**, 21 (1955).

(29) E. M. Osman and P. D. Cummisford, *Food Res.*, **24**, 595 (1959).

(30) H. H. Schopmeyer and G. E. Felton, U.S. Patent 2,218,221 (1941); *Chem. Abstr.*, **35**, 1260 (1941).

(31) J. W. Evans and E. M. VanPatten, U.S. Patent 2,916,405 (1959); *Chem. Abstr.*, **54**, 7193 (1960).

(32) Corn Products Refining Co., Brit. Patent 533,023 (1941); *Chem. Abstr.*, **36**, 678 (1942).

(33) O. B. Wurzburg and L. H. Kruger, U.S. Patent 3,058,853 (1962); *Chem. Abstr.*, **57**, 17156 (1962).

(34) R. L. Lloyd and B. F. Buchanan, U.S. Patent 2,394,791 (1946); *Chem. Abstr.*, **40**, 2557 (1946).

(35) B. M. Wimmer, U.S. Patent 2,749,244 (1956); *Chem. Abstr.*, **50**, 14144 (1956).

(36) L. H. Bailey, "Development of Use of Baking Powder and Baking Chemicals," *U.S. Dept. Agr., Circ.* No. **138** (revised 1940).

(37) Code of Federal Regulations, Title 21, Part 25.

(38) H. H. Schopmeyer, U.S. Patent 2,431,512 (1947); *Chem. Abstr.*, **42**, 1442 (1948).

(39) V. R. Williams, W.-T. Wu, H. Y. Tsai, and H. G. Bates, *J. Agr. Food Chem.*, **6**, 47 (1958).

(40) H. L. Hanson, A. A. Campbell, and H. Lineweaver, *Food Technol.*, **5**, 432 (1951).

(41) H. L. Hanson, L. R. Fletcher, and A. A. Campbell, *Food Technol.*, **11**, 339 (1957).

(42) H. L. Hanson, K. D. Nishita, and H. Lineweaver, *Food Technol.*, **7**, 462 (1953).

(43) R. Jordan, *J. Am. Dietet. Assoc.*, **39**, 590 (1961).

(44) A. M. Macfarlane, *Institutions*, **39**, No. 3, 140 (1956).
(45) T. S. Stephens, B. J. Lime, and F. P. Griffiths, *J. Rio Grande Valley Hort. Soc.*, **12**, 81 (1958); *Chem. Abstr.*, **52**, 17555 (1958).
(46) D. K. Dubois, *Baker's Dig.*, **33**, No. 6, 38 (1959).
(47) Huron Bakery Series, No. 100, Hercules Powder Co., Wilmington, Del.
(48) Huron Bakery Series, No. 104, Hercules Powder Co., Wilmington, Del.
(49) Anon., *Food Field Rept.*, **23**, No. 26, 21 (1955).
(50) R. H. Treadway, *Potato Handbook*, **5**, 45 (1960).
(51) F. Sichel, Ger. Patent 641,752 (1937); *Chem. Abstr.*, **31**, 6046 (1937).
(52) M. Okada and A. Yamazaki, *Nippon Suisan Gakkaishi*, **22**, 583 (1956–57); *Chem. Abstr.*, **52**, 7563 (1958).
(53) Y. Shimizu and W. Shimizu, *Nippon Suisan Gakkaishi*, **20**, 895 (1955); *Chem. Abstr.*, **50**, 8092 (1956).
(54) N. V. W. A. Scholten's Aardappelmeelfabrieken and Société des laboratoires de recherches pour applications industrielles "Solar," Dutch Patent 73,802 (1953); *Chem. Abstr.*, **48**, 8444 (1954).
(55) R. W. Kerr, in "Chemistry and Industry of Starch," R. W. Kerr, ed., Academic Press Inc., New York, N. Y., 1950, Chapt. 20.
(56) "The Story of Starches," National Starch Products Co., New York, N. Y., 1953.
(57) "Acid-Modified Food-Grade Raw Wheat Starches HMD981, HMD982, HMD973," Development Data VC-SD-3A, Hercules Powder Co., Wilmington, Del., 1963.
(58) R. W. Kerr, U.S. Patent 2,268,215 (1941); *Chem. Abstr.*, **36**, 2752 (1942).
(59) M. Konigsberg, U.S. Patent 2,500,950 (1950); *Chem. Abstr.*, **44**, 6666 (1950).
(60) G. E. Felton and H. H. Schopmeyer, U.S. Patent 2,328,537 (1943); *Chem. Abstr.*, **38**, 889 (1944).
(61) H. L. Wetzstein and P. Lyon, U.S. Patent 2,754,232 (1956); *Chem. Abstr.*, **50**, 13489 (1956).
(62) R. W. Kerr and F. C. Cleveland, Jr., U.S. Patent 2,801,242 (1957); *Chem. Abstr.* **51**, 18666 (1957).
(62a) C. D. Smith and J. V. Tuschoff, U.S. Patent 3,069,410 (1962); *Chem. Abstr.*, **58**, 5874 (1963).
(63) T. S. W. Gerwitz, U.S. Patent 2,805,220 (1957); *Chem. Abstr.*, **52**, 767 (1958).
(64) C. G. Caldwell, U.S. Patent 2,461,139 (1949); *Chem. Abstr.*, **43**, 3222 (1949).
(65) J. J. Ducharme, H. S. Black, Jr., and S. J. Leith, U.S. Patent 3,052,545 (1962).
(66) O. Wurzburg, U.S. Patent 2,935,510 (1960); *Chem. Abstr.*, **54**, 16886 (1960).
(67) H. Neukom, U.S. Patent 2,865,762 (1958); *Chem. Abstr.*, **53**, 5538 (1959).
(68) H. Neukom, U.S. Patent 2,884,412 (1959); *Chem. Abstr.*, **53**, 15612 (1959).
(69) R. Kodras, U.S. Patent 2,971,954 (1961); *Chem. Abstr.*, **56**, 6227 (1962).
(70) J. W. Sietsema and W. C. Trotter, U.S. Patent 2,993,041 (1961); Brit. Patent 857,868 (1961); *Chem. Abstr.*, **55**, 13887 (1961).
(71) J. J. Albrecht, A. I. Nelson, and M. P. Steinberg, *Food Technol.*, **14**, 57 (1960).
(72) J. J. Albrecht, A. I. Nelson, and M. P. Steinberg, *Food Technol.*, **14**, 64 (1960).
(73) R. W. Kerr and F. C. Cleveland, Jr., U.S. Patent 2,884,413 (1959); *Chem. Abstr.*, **53**, 16569 (1959).
(74) C. A. Glabau, *Baker's Weekly*, 12 (Sept. 14, 1959); 12 (Oct. 5, 1959).
(75) E. W. Johnson, U.S. Patent 2,919,986 (1960).
(76) A. S. Szczesniak, U.S. Patent 3,043,700 (1962).
(77) General Foods Corp., Brit. Patent 915,039 (1963); abstracted in *Food Technol.*, **17**, 904 (1963).
(78) L. Sair and W. R. Fetzer, *Ind. Eng. Chem.*, **36**, 205 (1944).

(79) L. Sair, unpublished research while a Corn Industries Research Foundation Fellow at the Northern Regional Research Laboratory, Agricultural Research Service, U.S. Department of Agriculture, Peoria, Illinois.

(80) S. Woodruff and L. Nicoli, *Cereal Chem.*, **8**, 243 (1931).

(81) G. M. Nevenzal, unpublished M.A. Thesis, University of California, Berkeley, California, 1931.

(82) E. E. Hester, A. M. Briant, and C. J. Personius, *Cereal Chem.*, **33**, 91 (1956).

(83) K. Täufel, J. Holló, J. Szejtli, E. Lászlo, and M. Tóth, *Nahrung*, **3**, 1051 (1959); *Chem. Abstr.*, **54**, 18996 (1960).

(84) K. Täufel and F. Berschneider, *Nahrung*, **2**, 683 (1958); *Chem. Abstr.*, **53**, 13635 (1959).

(85) "Corn Starch," Corn Industries Research Foundation, Washington, D.C., 1958.

(86) C. A. Anker and W. F. Geddes, *Cereal Chem.*, **21**, 335 (1944).

(87) A. M. Campbell and A. M. Briant, *Food Res.*, **22**, 358 (1957).

(88) M. Samec, "Kolloidchemie der Stärke," Verlag der Theodor Steinkopff, Dresden und Leipzig, 1927, p. 173.

(89) E. Wiegel, *Kolloid-Z.*, **67**, 47 (1934).

(90) E. M. Osman and T. B. Tipton, unpublished data.

(91) R. M. Sandstedt, W. Kempf, and R. C. Abbott, *Staerke*, **12**, 333 (1960).

(92) H. Rüggeberg, *Staerke*, **5**, 109 (1953).

(93) E. M. Osman and M. R. Dix, *Cereal Chem.*, **37**, 464 (1960).

(94) D. D. Lord, *J. Colloid Sci.*, **5**, 360 (1950).

(95) E. J. Strandine, G. T. Carlin, G. A. Werner, and R. P. Hopper, *Cereal Chem.*, **28**, 449 (1951).

(96) W. A. Mitchell and E. Zillmann, *Trans. Am. Assoc. Cereal Chem.*, **9**, 64 (1951).

(97) V. M. Gray and T. J. Schoch, *Staerke*, **14**, 239 (1962).

(98) G. Y. Brokaw, *Can. Food Ind.*, **33**, No. 4, 36 (1962).

(99) Q.-S. Hwang, unpublished M.S. Thesis, University of Illinois, Urbana, Ill., 1960.

(100) M. J. Stalder, unpublished M.S. Thesis, University of Illinois, Urbana, Ill., 1961.

(101) A. Rotsch, *Getreide Mehl Brot*, **3**, 153 (1949); *Brot Gebaeck*, **7**, 121 (1953).

(102) G. Jongh, *Cereal Chem.*, **38**, 140 (1961).

(103) R. M. Sandstedt, *Baker's Dig.*, **35**, No. 3, 36 (1961).

(104) M. M. MacMasters, *Baker's Dig.*, **35**, No. 5, 42 (1961).

(105) C. L. Alsberg, *Plant Physiol.*, **13**, 295 (1938).

(106) R. M. Sandstedt and H. Schroeder, *Food Technol.*, **14**, 257 (1960).

(107) E. Kneen and R. M. Sandstedt, in "Enzymes and Their Role in Wheat Technology," J. A. Anderson, ed., American Association of Cereal Chemists Monograph Series, Interscience Publishers, Inc., New York, N. Y., 1946, p. 275.

(108) R. M. Sandstedt, C. E. Jolitz, and M. J. Blish, *Cereal Chem.*, **16**, 780 (1939).

(109) L. A. Underkofler, *Baker's Dig.*, **35**, No. 5, 74 (1961).

(110) B. S. Miller, J. A. Johnson, and D. L. Palmer, *Food Technol.*, **7**, 38 (1953).

(111) C. C. Walden, *Cereal Chem.*, **32**, 421 (1955).

(112) C. C. Walden, *Baker's Dig.*, **33**, No. 1, 24 (1959).

(113) E. J. Pyler, "Baking Science and Technology," Siebel Publishing Company, Chicago, Ill., Vol. 2, 1952, p. 487.

(114) P. P. Noznick and W. F. Geddes, *Cereal Chem.*, **20**, 463 (1943).

(115) J. B. Boussingault, *Ann. Chim. Phys.*, [3] **36**, 490 (1852).

(116) W. G. Bechtel, D. F. Neisner, and W. B. Bradley, *Cereal Chem.*, **30**, 160 (1953).

(117) W. B. Bradley and J. B. Thompson, *Cereal Chem.*, **27**, 331 (1950).

(118) L. Boutroux, "Le Pain et la Panification," Librairie J.-B. Baillière et Fils, Paris, 1897, p. 259.

(119) L. Lindet, *Bull. Soc. Chim. France*, [3] **27**, 634 (1902).

(120) C. W. Bice and W. F. Geddes, in "Starch and Its Derivatives," J. A. Radley, ed., John Wiley and Sons Inc., New York, N. Y., Vol. 2, 1954, p. 202.

(121) F. R. Senti and R. J. Dimler, *Baker's Dig.*, **34**, No. 1, 28 (1960).

(122) P. F. Pelshenke and G. Hampel, *Baker's Dig.*, **36**, No. 3, 48 (1962).

(123) T. J. Schoch, *J. Am. Chem. Soc.*, **64**, 2957 (1942).

(124) T. J. Schoch, *Advan. Carbohydrate Chem.*, **1**, 247 (1945).

(125) T. J. Schoch and D. French, *Cereal Chem.*, **24**, 231 (1947).

(126) P. P. Noznick, P. P. Merritt, and W. F. Geddes, *Cereal Chem.*, **23**, 297 (1946).

(127) N. Prentice, L. S. Cuendet, and W. F. Geddes, *Cereal Chem.*, **31**, 188 (1954).

(128) W. G. Bechtel, *Cereal Chem.*, **36**, 368 (1959).

(129) H. F. Zobel and F. R. Senti, *Cereal Chem.*, **36**, 441 (1959).

(130) A. S. Schultz, F. D. Schoonover, R. A. Fisher, and S. S. Jackel, *Cereal Chem.*, **29**, 200 (1952).

(131) B. G. Carson, L. F. Marnett, and R. W. Selman, *Cereal Chem.*, **27**, 438 (1950).

(132) E. C. Edelmann and W. H. Cathcart, *Cereal Chem.*, **26**, 345 (1949).

(133) H. H. Favor and N. F. Johnston, *Cereal Chem.*, **24**, 346 (1947).

(134) O. Skovholt and R. L. Dowdle, *Cereal Chem.*, **27**, 26 (1950).

(135) C. W. Ofelt, C. L. Mehltretter, M. M. MacMasters, F. H. Otey, and F. R. Senti, *Cereal Chem.*, **35**, 142 (1958).

(136) E. J. Bourne, A. I. Tiffin, and H. Weigel, *J. Sci. Food Agr.*, **11**, 101 (1960).

(137) T. J. Schoch, in "Starch and Its Derivatives," J. A. Radley, ed., John Wiley and Sons, Inc., New York, N. Y., Vol. I, 1954, p. 167.

(138) L. F. Marnett and R. W. Selman, *Cereal Chem.*, **27**, 349 (1950).

(139) W. H. Cathcart and S. V. Luber, *Ind. Eng. Chem.*, **31**, 362 (1939).

(140) J. W. Pence, N. N. Standridge, T. M. Lubisich, D. K. Mecham, and H. S. Olcott, *Food Technol.*, **9**, 495 (1955).

(141) D. J. Kirk, *Baker's Dig.*, **37**, No. 1, 58 (1963).

(142) J. W. Pence, N. N. Standridge, D. K. Mecham, T. M. Lubisich, and H. S. Olcott, *Food Technol.*, **10**, 76 (1956).

(143) J. W. Pence and N. N. Standridge, *Cereal Chem.*, **35**, 57 (1958).

(144) J. W. Pence and M. Hanamoto, *Food Technol.*, **13**, 99 (1959).

(145) H. Couden and L. Bussard, *Ann. Sci. Agron.*, Ser. 2, Année 3, **1**, 250 (1897).

(146) J. W. Gilmore, *Cornell Agr. Expt. Sta. Rept.*, **230**, 503 (1905); cited by Sweetman *(147)*.

(147) M. D. Sweetman, *Maine Agr. Expt. Sta. Bull.*, **383** (1936).

(148) C. O. Appleman, *Md. Agr. Expt. Sta. Bull.* **167** (1912).

(149) R. Kunkel, *Am. Potato J.*, **27**, 59 (1950).

(150) I. J. Pflug, M. W. Brandt, and D. R. Isleib, *Mich. State Univ. Expt. Sta. Quart. Bull.*, **38**, No. 1, 29 (1955).

(151) F. A. Bettelheim and C. Sterling, *Food Res.*, **20**, 71 (1955).

(152) F. A. Bettelheim and C. Sterling, *Food Res.*, **20**, 118 (1955).

(153) C. Sterling and F. A. Bettelheim, *Food Res.*, **20**, 130 (1955).

(154) W. E. Pyke and G. Johnson, *Am. Potato J.*, **17**, 1 (1940).

(155) R. T. Whittenberger and G. C. Nutting, *Food Res.*, **15**, 331 (1950).

(156) K. G. Weckel, R. K. Sharschmidt, and G. H. Rieman, *Food Technol.*, **13**, 456 (1959).

(157) C. J. Personius and P. F. Sharp, *Food Res.*, **4**, 299 (1939).

(158) C. J. Personius and P. F. Sharp, *Food Res.*, **4**, 469 (1939).

(159) C. Sterling, *Food Res.*, **20**, 474 (1955).

(160) R. M. Reeve, *Food Res.*, **19**, 323 (1954).

(161) R. M. Reeve and G. K. Notter, *Food Technol.*, **13**, 574 (1959).

(162) R. M. Reeve, *Food Res.*, **19**, 333 (1954).

(163) A. L. Potter, E. M. Neel, R. M. Reeve, and C. E. Hendel, *Am. Potato J.*, **36**, 444 (1959).

(164) J. Cording, Jr., and M. J. Willard, Jr., U.S. Patent 2,787,553 (1957).

(165) J. Cording, Jr., M. J. Willard, Jr., R. K. Eskew, and J. F. Sullivan, *Food Technol.*, **11**, 236 (1957).

(166) W. O. Harrington, R. L. Olson, W. J. Weston, and M. L. Belote, *Am. Potato J.*, **36**, 241 (1959).

(167) E. M. Neel, A. L. Potter, and C. E. Hendel, *Potato Chipper*, **18**, No. 9, 46 (1959).

(168) Eastern Utilization Research and Development Division, Agricultural Research Service, U.S.D.A., Report CA-E-17, April, 1959.

(169) S. L. Spiruta and A. Mackey, *J. Food Sci.*, **26**, 656 (1961).

(170) K. Longrée, *Food Technol.*, **4**, 98 (1950).

(171) W. O. Harrington, R. L. Olson, and R. M. McCready, *Food Technol.*, **5**, 311 (1951).

(172) R. M. Reeve, *Food Res.*, **19**, 340 (1954).

(173) H. Muller-Thurgau, *Landwirtsch. Jahrb.*, **11**, 751 (1882).

(174) E. B. Kester, in "The Chemistry and Technology of Cereals," S. A. Matz, ed., Avi Publishing Co., Westport, Conn., 1959, p. 427.

(175) B. S. Rao, A. R. V. Murthy, and R. S. Subrahmanya, *Proc. Indian Acad. Sci.*, **36B**, 70 (1952).

(176) L. Borasio, *Giorn. Risicoltura*, **25**, 164 (1935); *Chem. Abstr.*, **29**, 7519 (1935).

(177) O. M. Batcher, K. F. Helmintoller, and E. H. Dawson, *Rice J.*, **59**, No. 13, 4 (1956).

(178) E. H. Dawson, O. M. Batcher, and R. R. Little, *Rice J.*, **65**, No. 5, 16 (1960).

(179) O. M. Batcher, P. A. Deary, and E. H. Dawson, *Cereal Chem.*, **34**, 277 (1957).

(180) J. V. Halick and K. K. Keneaster, *Cereal Chem.*, **33**, 315 (1956).

(181) J. T. Hogan and R. W. Planck, *Cereal Chem.*, **35**, 469 (1958).

(182) J. V. Halick and V. J. Kelly, *Cereal Chem.*, **36**, 91 (1959).

(183) J. V. Halick, H. M. Beachell, J. W. Stansel, and H. H. Kramer, *Cereal Chem.*, **37**, 670 (1960).

(184) P. L. Pfahler, H. H. Kramer, and R. L. Whistler, *Science*, **125**, 441 (1957).

(185) R. R. Little and G. B. Hilder, *Cereal Chem.*, **37**, 456 (1960).

(186) B. D. Webb, H. M. Beachell, and J. V. Halick, *Abstr. Am. Assoc. Cereal Chem.*, *48th Ann. Meeting, Minneapolis* (1963).

(187) H. Y. Tsai, A. T. Phillips, and V. R. Williams, *J. Agr. Food Chem.*, **8**, 364 (1960).

(188) A. T. Phillips and V. R. Williams, *J. Food Sci.*, **26**, 573 (1961).

(189) K. Yasumatsu and E. Fujita, *Cereal Chem.*, **39**, 364 (1962).

(190) I. Hlynka, *Cereal Chem.*, **36**, 378 (1959).

(191) R. R. Little, G. B. Hilder, and E. H. Dawson, *Cereal Chem.*, **35**, 111 (1958).

(192) R. R. Little and G. B. Hilder, *Cereal Chem.*, **37**, 475 (1960).

(193) E. R. McCall, J. F. Jurgens, C. L. Hoffpauir, W. A. Pons, Jr., S. M. Stark, Jr., A. F. Cucullu, D. C. Heinzelman, V. O. Cirino, and M. D. Murray, *J. Agr. Food Chem.*, **1**, 988 (1953).

(194) R. R. Little and E. H. Dawson, *Food Res.*, **25**, 611 (1960).

(195) H. S. R. Desikachar and V. Subrahmanyan, *Cereal Chem.*, **38**, 356 (1961).

(196) A. S. Roseman, *Food Technol.*, **12**, 464 (1958).

(197) A. S. Roseman and H. J. Deobald, *J. Agr. Food Chem.*, **7**, 774 (1959).

(198) D. K. Mecham, E. B. Kester, and J. W. Pence, *Food Technol.*, **15**, 475 (1961).

(199) R. L. Roberts, A. L. Potter, E. B. Kester, and K. K. Keneaster, *Cereal Chem.*, **31**, 121 (1954).

(200) R. E. Ferrel and J. W. Pence, *Cereal Chem.*, **41**, 1 (1964).

CHAPTER IX

PRODUCTION AND USES OF ACID-MODIFIED STARCH

By Paul Shildneck and C. E. Smith*

A. E. Staley Mfg. Co., Decatur, Illinois

I. Introduction

1. Definitions

a. *Acid-Modified Starch*

As considered in this chapter, acid-modified starch is a starch material in the form of superficially unchanged granules obtained by the action of acid on starch in water suspension at sub-gelatinizing temperature and characterized by the following differences from its parent starch: (a) less hot paste viscosity (1–8), (b) higher alkali number (9, 10), and (c) higher ratio of cold to hot paste viscosity (1, 3, 4).

* Deceased 1964.

217

The definition of acid-modified starch is arbitrarily limited in scope. It excludes acid-modified ungelatinized starch derivatives, acid-catalyst dextrins, and dehydrated acid-modified starch pastes. The latter two materials, from the standpoints of paste properties and end uses, are quite similar to the defined products.

b. *Starch*

The unqualified noun, starch, is used only to designate naturally occurring granules, that is, granules isolated from vegetable raw material with little or no attending modification.

2. Comparison of Acid-Modified Starch with Parent Starch

In addition to the three features noted in the foregoing definition, acid-modified starch differs from its parent starch in many other respects. Reported differences (for corn starch unless otherwise indicated) are: (*a*) lower iodine affinity (*9, 10*); (*b*) lower intrinsic viscosity (*9, 10*); (*c*) higher osmotic pressure, which signifies lower number average molecular weight (*11*) (potato); (*d*) less granule swelling during gelatinization in hot water (*5, 12*) (corn, tapioca, potato, sweet potato, wheat, rye, sago, canna); (*e*) increased solubility in warm water below the gelatinization temperature (*13*); (*f*) higher gelatinization temperature (*7, 14*); (*g*) higher critical absorption of sodium hydroxide (*14*); (*h*) slower rate of solution in cold anhydrous dimethyl sulfoxide (*14*); and (*i*) higher content of pentasol-precipitable fraction except for highly modified products (*15*).

On the other hand, acid-modified starch resembles its parent starch in a number of respects. The modified product has the same physical form (*16*), the same essential insolubility in cold water (*16*), and similar birefringence (*17, 18*).

3. History of Acid-Modified Starch

Lintner (*19*) was the first (1886) to describe the preparation and properties of a material meeting the foregoing definition of acid-modified starch. Potato starch was allowed to stand for several days at room temperature in contact with 7.5% aqueous hydrochloric acid or 15% aqueous sulfuric acid; then it was washed free of acid with water and dried. Naegeli (*20*), who previously had studied the action of cold aqueous acids on starch (1874), must have formed the defined product during the early stages of the acid treatment, but the final undissolved material (amylodextrin) consisted of highly fragmented granules. In 1897, Bellmas (*21*) obtained a German patent for a method differing from that of Lintner by the use of a more dilute acid at higher temperature for a shorter time. Duryea (22) independently discovered much the same variation of Lintner's method. Descriptions of early methods for preparing the so-called soluble starches, including the defined acid-modified starches, appear in later publications (23–26).

The modern method of manufacturing acid-modified starch on a large scale for industrial uses is essentially the same as that described by Bellmas and by Duryea. Also, "soluble" starch used as substrate in enzyme assays and as indicator for iodometric titrations is produced today on a relatively small scale by the Lintner method.

II. PRODUCTION

1. Industrial Products

Details of manufacturing procedures for industrial acid-modified starches have not been published. Among informative descriptions of methods which approximate those currently used for the large scale manufacture of acid-modified starches are those reported by Bellmas (21), Duryea (22), Katz (5), Gallay and Bell (6, 7), Meisel (27), Schopmeyer and Felton (8), Schoch and co-workers (10), and Kerr (28).

According to Bellmas (21), a fairly concentrated slurry of the starch in 1–3% aqueous mineral acid is stirred at 50°–55.5° until the desired viscosity modification is obtained. Reaction times of 12 to 14 hr. are mentioned. The slurry is then neutralized and the acid-modified starch is recovered by filtration, washing, and drying.

Duryea (22) used somewhat less concentrated acid (0.5–2%), somewhat higher temperature (55°–60°), an apparently thinner starch slurry (12°–15° Baumé), and a shorter reaction time (0.5–4.5 hr.). Duryea stressed that processing conditions required to yield a product of selected properties should remain constant from batch to batch if the parent starch is of uniform quality.

In industry, acid-modified starches are generally designated or classified according to fluidity number, an inverse measure of viscosity (29, 30). Fluidity number is the number of milliliters of a standard alkaline starch paste delivered by a funnel with a special tip in the time, generally 40–70 sec., required by the funnel to deliver 100 ml. of water. The standard starch paste is made by wetting 5 g. of starch, dry weight basis, with 10 ml. of distilled water, adding 90 ml. of 1% aqueous sodium hydroxide solution, stirring the mixture for 3 min., then allowing it to stand 27 min., all at 25°.

Katz (5) reports the relationship between acid concentration and product fluidity. In the modification of corn starch with sulfuric acid at

50° and 24-hr. reaction time (5), fluidity numbers range from 13 at 0.06% acid to 74 at 0.61% acid.

Gallay and Bell (6, 7) modified corn and potato starches with dilute hydrochloric acid at 50°. They studied the influence of acid concentration (0.77–2.92%) on speed of modification. Change in paste viscosity was measured by the MacMichael viscometer over wide ranges of starch concentration and viscometer rotation speed. Fluidity numbers ranged from 5 to 85 in the corn starch series and from 3 to 74 in the potato starch series.

Meisel (27) deviates from the conventional conditions for preparation of acid-modified corn starch by using a higher concentration of acid for a shorter time at a lower temperature. The object of the altered procedure is to obtain a thin-boiling starch whose ratio of Scott viscosity number (31) to fluidity number is higher than usual, thereby providing a fluid starch paste of increased body for the manufacture of a given type of gum drop confection. As an example, corn starch, water, and hydrochloric acid are mixed at 39° to form a 22° Baumé starch milk such that the filtered aqueous medium is 0.6N acid. About 3 hr. later, or whenever the starch tests 60 fluidity, the stirred mixture, still at 39°, is neutralized with soda ash solution to about pH 5.2. The starch is recovered from the neutralized slurry by filtration, washing, and drying.

Schopmeyer and Felton (8) describe the preparation of acid-modified waxy corn starch. As an example of their process, a 20° Baumé water slurry of the waxy starch is acidified to pH 1.8 with 62.5% sulfuric acid (1.1 parts of sulfuric acid per 100 parts by weight of slurry), agitated at 48°–55° for 5 hr., and then neutralized with sodium hydroxide solution. The modified starch, recovered by filtration, washing, and drying, has a fluidity of 62.

In a study of the properties of starch fractions, Schoch and coworkers (10) prepared two series of acid-modified corn starches by warming 40% starch slurries at 50° in 0.075N hydrochloric acid for 5 to 40 hr. and in 0.3N hydrochloric acid for 2 to 16 hr. Intrinsic viscosities of the products in the more dilute acid series ranged from 1.06 to 0.37; in the other series, the range was 0.89 to 0.24.

According to Kerr (28), acid-modified starch is made by stirring a slurry of starch in 0.1–0.2N sulfuric acid at 50°–55° until the desired viscosity change is obtained. The slurry is then neutralized with sodium carbonate and the acid-modified starch is recovered by filtration, washing, and drying.

Although Duryea indicates that acid-modified starch can be manufactured without in-process control, such control is widely used today in the production of starch materials designated by a specific fluidity or viscosity. One such method of control is to sample the reaction slurry periodically, measure the fluidity of the recovered starch, plot the fluidity number against reaction time, project the graph thus obtained to the desired fluidity, and stop the reaction at the corresponding time by neutralizing the slurry. In-process control is probably required for the following reasons: (a) susceptibility of the parent starch to acid modification and parent starch fluidity may vary slightly from batch to batch; (b) exact duplication of time–temperature–pH conditions from batch to batch is difficult; (c) blending of batches with different fluidities to obtain a mixture with the desired fluidity increases manufacturing cost and might lead to customer problems.

A variation of the Bellmas–Duryea method has been patented (32). Stated advantages of this patented method are faster reaction rate, decreased production of starch solubles, especially in the high fluidity products, and less fluidity increase when reaction time is extended beyond a specified minimum value. These advantages are achieved by adding a small proportion of soluble hexavalent chromium salt to the conventional acidified aqueous slurry of starch, maintaining the slurry at conventional reaction temperature until substantially all of the hexavalent chromium is reduced, then alkalizing the slurry to pH 8–9, immediately acidifying it to about pH 6, and recovering the starch by filtration, washing, and drying.

The Bellmas–Duryea method of preparing acid-modified starch is stated by Katz (5) to be applicable to corn, potato, waxy corn, tapioca, rice, and sweet potato starches. Sjostrom (12) has reported the light microscopy of thin-boiling wheat, rye, sago, and canna starches, all presumably made by the Bellmas–Duryea method.

2. Lintner Starch

The Lintner method has been referred to as the standard method of preparing soluble starch, a starch which forms a clear thin solution at 2% concentration in hot water (33). According to Lintner's original directions, potato starch is allowed to stand for 3–7 days at room temperature in contact with several weight proportions of 7.5% aqueous hydrochloric acid or 15% aqueous sulfuric acid. The modified granules are then washed free of acid with large proportions of water and dried. The author discloses the following specific combinations of acid concentration, time, and temperature: 7.5% hydrochloric acid for 7 days at room temperature; 7.5% hydrochloric acid for 3 days at 40°; 15% sulfuric acid for 7 days at 40°

Buttrose (34), in an examination of acid-degraded starch granules by electron and light microscopy, shows that tobacco and high-amylose corn starches respond to Lintner acid treatment (8% hydrochloric acid at 39°) in essentially the same manner as wheat, corn, waxy corn, and potato starches. Presumably all starches can be converted to the acid-modified form by appropriate treatment with aqueous acid.

3. Theory of Acid Modification

From measurements of osmotic pressures of the triacetates of amylose and amylopectin fractions prepared from a viscosity-graded series of acid-modified corn starches, Kerr (15; see also Vol. I, Chapter XX) concluded that acid preferentially cleaves amylopectin chains in the early stages of acid modification, up to about 20 fluidity. Kerr advanced the theory that the points of early attack lie in the amorphous intermicellar regions of the granule through which the gigantic branched amylopectin molecules pass as they extend from one crystalline micellar region to another (35). Reduction in paste viscosity of the acid-modified starch was attributed to disintegration of these amorphous regions and consequent weakening of the granule structure, permitting granule fragmentation with little swelling.

In a study (13) of the swelling and solubility patterns of various starches, Leach, McCowen, and Schoch found that 60-fluidity acid-modified corn starch is about four times as soluble as its parent starch in water at 85° (40% vs. 10%), but that the insoluble portion of the modified starch swells about 50% more in water at that temperature (and higher) than the insoluble portion of the parent starch. Soluble and insoluble starch substances were distinguished by heating the granules in water with gentle agitation followed by centrifugation at about 700 g to obtain a supernatant liquid phase of dissolved material and a sedimented phase of insoluble material. Like Kerr, these investigators propose that treatment of granular starch with warm dilute acid hydrolyzes the more accessible intermicellar areas, thereby weakening the network within the granule; consequently, when these so-called thin-boiling starches are cooked in water, the swollen granule falls apart to give pastes of reduced viscosity.

This seems to imply that fragmentation per se of the granule is chiefly responsible for reduced paste viscosity.

Another explanation is based on the generally accepted principle that the viscosity of diphasic colloid systems is governed mainly by phase volume relations (36, 37). It is well established that a conventional dilute paste of starch in hot water is a suspension of swollen granules and granule fragments (discontinuous gel phase) in a water solution of starch substance (continuous liquid phase) (5, 6, 13, 38–41). It has been observed that paste viscosity varies directly with the volume fraction of the discontinuous gel phase (5, 39, 40) and that 60-fluidity acid-modified corn starch is much more soluble in hot water than its parent starch (13). The authors of this chapter propose, therefore, that the principal reason for the lower paste viscosity of an acid-modified starch is its greater solubility in hot water and hence the lower volume fraction of discontinuous gel phase in its paste. In terms of this view, the observed greater fragmentation of the granule in hot water is due to solution of the hydrolyzed micellar regions; the fragmentation or disintegration is only incidentally associated with lower paste viscosity.

III. PROPERTIES

1. Behavior in Hot Water

As mentioned earlier, acid-modified starch differs characteristically from its parent starch as to behavior in hot water. The modified granules fragment more and appear to swell less during gelatinization (7, 12, 42). The gelatinized granules yield a lower volume proportion of discontinuous gel phase in the paste, a structural feature primarily responsible for reduced viscosity (6, 7). Also, the modified granule has a higher gelatinization temperature (7, 14) and more of it dissolves in hot water below and at the pasting temperature (13). These differences are magnified as the degree of acid treatment is increased.

One investigator observed microscopically (12) that acid-modified corn starch swells less in hot water than its parent starch and concluded that pastes of the former are the less viscous because they contain a smaller volume fraction of gel phase. Another investigator (5), observing the smaller volume fraction of gel phase settling in diluted pastes of acid-modified corn starch, advanced the view that the smaller sediment volume, and the reduced swelling of the granule in hot water, are due to depolymerization of starch chains by the acid. The analogy was drawn with Staudinger's observation that the swelling of polystyrene, in selected liquids, decreases with decreasing molecular weight of the polystyrene. Neither investigator determined the starch concentration in the gel phase or in the continuous liquid phase of the pastes. It was reported later (13) that starch concentration in the gel phase of 60-fluidity acid-modified corn starch at 85°–90° is considerably less than that in the gel phase of a control paste of parent starch. In other words, the swelling power of the hot-water-insoluble portion of the acid-modified starch exceeds that of the corresponding parent starch portion. About 40% of the 60-fluidity starch dissolved in the continuous liquid phase of the paste at 85°, compared with about 10% of the parent starch.

Still unanswered is the interesting question of whether the viscosity of a low solids starch paste depends mainly upon the phase volume ratio, or whether the average particle size or particle size distribution of the gel phase, at constant phase volume ratio, also has significant influence on paste viscosity. For example, is the pronounced thinning of a starch paste by homogenization caused by the change in particle size distribution of gel phase, at constant phase volume ratio, or is it caused by the change in that ratio by transferring starch material from the discontinuous phase to the continuous phase? The authors of this chapter have found no reports of studies bearing on this question.

The Kofler gelatinization temperature range of 80-fluidity acid-modified corn starch is 7° higher than that of its parent starch (13). This effect is attributed (13) to increased micellar organization in the acid-modified granule, a condition presumably brought about by acid hydrolysis of molecular chains that wander randomly through the amorphous unoriented regions of the granule, and by subsequent micellar association of the chain fragments thus produced.

2. Paste Viscosity and Gel Strength

Many comparisons between the paste viscosity of an acid-modified starch and its parent starch, all showing the pronounced paste thinning effect of acid treatment, appear in the literature (1–8). Three of the articles relate viscosity to the conditions of acid treatment as shown in Table I.

The Brabender Amylograph viscosity curves for a commercial 80-fluidity corn starch and parent corn starch have been published (4). The two starch products differ so much in paste viscosity that quantitative comparisons are difficult to make at the same starch concentration. Peak viscosity of the 7.5% parent starch paste, reached at about 90°, exceeds 1000 Brabender units. No viscosities of the 80-fluidity starch are reported at this concentration, presumably because they are too low to be measured accurately on the instrument, but extrapolation of values shown for starch concentrations in the range of 15–35% indicates that the 7.5% peak viscosity does not exceed 10–20 units.

Hot paste viscosity and gel properties of a series of commercial acid-modified corn starches have been reported (3). This study shows that increasing acid modification, indicated by decreasing hot paste viscosity, progressively lowers the rigidity and breaking strength of the cold aged gel. All pastes were cooked 30 min. at 91° and pH 6 in the CIRF viscometer at 9% starch concentration, and all gels were prepared by aging the paste under petroleum oil for 24 hr. at 25°. The range in fluidity numbers was from 10 to 70 by increments of 10, and the corresponding range of hot paste viscosities (including the parent starch) was from 3400 to 20 centipoises. The gel rigidities (dynes/sq. cm.) ranged from 1850 for the parent starch to 156 for the 70-fluidity product, and the corresponding gel breaking strengths (grams/sq. cm.) ranged from 194 to 13. That the acid treatment lowers hot paste viscosity more rapidly than it reduces gel strength is clearly revealed by the ratios of gel rigidity and breaking strength to hot paste viscosity as listed in Table II. Both ratios are greater for acid-modified starch than for the parent starch, and both ratios are markedly and progressively increased with increasing degree of acid treatment.

Table I

Influence of Process Conditions on Fluidity of Starches Acid Modified at 50°

Starch and acid	Acid conc. (% by wt.)	Time (hr.)	Fluidity
Corn starch sulfuric acid (5)	0.06	24	13
	0.13	24	32
	0.22	24	53
	0.29	24	64
	0.44	24	72
	0.61	24	74
Corn starch, hydrochloric acid (6)	2.05	0.25	10
		0.47	20
		0.67	30
		0.87	40
		1.13	50
		1.50	60
		2.25	70
Potato starch, hydrochloric acid (7)	2.05	0.67	3.0
		1.33	8.0
		2.0	15.5
		2.67	25.0
		3.33	37.0
		4.0	52.8

If the gelling power of a starch product is defined as the ratio of cold paste viscosity to hot paste viscosity under a standard set of conditions (3), acid-modified starches having different gelling powers at the same fluidity may be prepared (27). Gelling power is increased by increasing the concentration of acid and reducing the time of acid treatment; conversely, gelling power is decreased by reducing the acid concentration and increasing the reaction time.

The intrinsic viscosity (43) of acid-modified corn starch decreases with increasing degree of acid treatment. Table III shows this relation-

Table II
Hot Paste Viscosity and Gel Properties of Corn Starch and Acid-Modified Corn Starches (3)

Starch fluidity	Hot paste viscosity (poises)	Gel rigidity (dynes/ sq. cm.)	Gel breaking strength (g./sq. cm.)	GR^a/HPV^b	GBS^c/HPV
Unmodified	34.0	1850	194	54.4	5.71
10	15.1	1140	118	75.5	7.81
20	8.5	810	71.5	95	8.4
30	6.0	738	61.1	120	10
40	3.6	510	40.3	140	11.5
50	3.0	422	32.6	140	11
60	1.1	318	23.6	290	21
70	0.2	156	13.4	800	70

^{a} Gel rigidity.
^{b} Hot paste viscosity.
^{c} Gel breaking strength.

Table III
Intrinsic Viscosities, Alkali Numbers, and Fluidities of Acid-Modified Corn Starches

Acid and temperature	Acid conc. (% by wt.)	Time (hr.)	Starch fluidity	Alkali number	Intrinsic viscosity
Hydrochloric acid, 50° (10)	0.274	5	a	13.0	1.06
		16		18.0	0.66
		26		21.6	0.47
		40		27.2	0.37
	1.095	2		13.9	0.89
		7		22.6	0.44
		16		34.8	0.24
a (9)	a	a	20	11.5	1.05
			40	13.0	0.90
			60	16.5	0.60
			75	21.0	0.50
			90	26.5	0.35
a (44)	a		20	14.5	
			40	15.0	
			60	15.7	
			75	20.7	
			90	41.5	

^{a} Not reported.

ship, as well as the relationship between fluidity and intrinsic viscosity for different samples of acid-modified corn starch.

Paste viscosities of viscosity-graded acid-modified corn and potato starches have been measured using the MacMichael viscometer over wide ranges of starch concentration and viscometer rotational speed

(6, 7). From the graphs of M versus R, where M is deflection of the inner cylinder and R is the rotational speed of the outer cylinder, the investigators determined the critical starch concentration, that is, the concentration at which paste flow changes from laminar to structural (45). It was found that the critical concentration increases with increasing acid modification in both series of starches, beginning with 0.45% and 1.8% for unmodified potato and corn starch, respectively, and increasing to 2.7% for 74-fluidity potato starch and to about 8% for 80-fluidity corn starch.

3. Alkali Number and Reducing Value

The alkali number (44) of acid-modified starch, which rises progressively with increasing degree of acid treatment (9, 10, 44), is the milliequivalents of alkali consumed per 10 grams of dry substance starch material during a standard 1 hour digestion in $0.1N$ aqueous sodium hydroxide at the temperature of a boiling water bath. The alkali is consumed by acids produced from the reducing ends of the polymer chains (Vol. I, Chapter XXI) and is a measure of chain lengths (direct index of hydrolysis) rather than a quantitative determination of aldehyde content. Table III lists alkali numbers reported for several acid-modified starches and relates them to fluidity or to conditions of acid treatment.

The preferred measure of reducing value is the ferricyanide number (46); another measure is the copper number (47). The ferricyanide number is the milliequivalents of ferricyanide reduced per 10 grams of dry substance starch material in a standard procedure; the copper number is the milligrams of copper, as cuprous oxide, produced per gram of dry starch substance by reaction with alkaline copper sulfate in a standard procedure.

Below about 75 fluidity, the reducing value (47, 48) of an acid-modified starch is low and substantially the same as its parent starch (48). In the 75–90 fluidity range, however, apparently sufficient additional aldehyde groups have been formed by the acid hydrolysis to yield a measurably larger reducing value (48).

The copper numbers of commercial soluble starches, including Lintner starch, vary from 13 to 88; the range for different samples of unmodified corn starch is from 4 to 7, and for sago starch from 7 to 9 (47). Table IV shows the copper numbers of corn starch pastes modified with different low concentrations of sulfuric and sulfurous acids (49).

4. Molecular Weight, Iodine Affinity, Film Strength

By osmotic pressure measurements (11), a Lintnerized potato starch was found to have a number average molecular weight of 45,000–50,000.

Molecular weight of the parent starch determined in the same manner was about 110,000. Kerr (*15*) determined the number average molecular weights and other properties of amylose and amylopectin derived from a viscosity-graded series of industrial acid-modified corn starches. The modified starches, ranging in alkaline fluidity from 10 to 90 by increments of 10, and the parent starch, all defatted by extraction with boiling 85% aqueous methanol, were fractionated by the Schoch method (*10*). The fractions were completely acetylated and osmotic pressures of the triacetates were measured in chloroform solutions of

Table IV
Copper Reducing Numbers of Corn Starch Acid Modified for 20 hr. at 20–25° (49)

Acid	Acid normality	Copper number
Sulfuric	0.5	8.0
	0.4	5.95
	0.3	5.6
	0.2	4.8
	0.1	4.4
	0.05	—
Sulfurous	2.4	8.9
	0.5	6.1

increasing dilution. The number average degree of polymerization ($\overline{D.P.}_n$) values of the parent starch amylose and amylopectin acetates were 480 and 1450, respectively. As shown in Table V, the amylopectin acetate $\overline{D.P.}_n$ dropped rapidly to 625 at 20 fluidity (for the parent starch), slowly to 525 at 60 fluidity, and then more rapidly to 210 at 90 fluidity. The amylose acetate $\overline{D.P.}_n$ rose slightly to 525 at 20 fluidity, then gradually dropped to 190 at 90 fluidity.

The iodine affinity (*50*) of acid-modified starch changes little with increasing degree of acid treatment up to about 70 fluidity, in spite of a marked drop in paste viscosity (*9, 10*). This observation is consistent with the theory of acid modification that amylopectin chains are preferentially attacked by the acid. One report (*9*) shows iodine affinity ranging from 4.90 for 20 fluidity acid-modified corn starch to 3.30 at 90 fluidity another (*10*) shows a smaller range of 4.81 for corn starch reacted 5 hr. at 50° with 0.075N hydrochloric acid to 4.40 when the starch is heated 16 hr. at 50° with 0.3N acid. The corresponding ranges of alkali numbers in the two instances are 11.5–26.5 and 13.0–34.8.

Tensile strength and elongation of unsupported films cast from hot water pastes of a viscosity-graded series of acid-modified corn starches were found to be much the same as the corresponding values for a

Table V

Properties of Fractions from Acid-Modified Corn Starches (15)

Parent starch fluidity	Amylose Fraction					Amylopectin Fraction			
	$\overline{D.P.}_n$	Ferri-cyanide number	Alkali number	Iodine affinity	Yield (wt. percent of parent starch)	$\overline{D.P.}_n$	Ferri-cyanide number	Alkali number	Intrinsic viscosity
Unmodified	480	1.43	19.7	19.2	21.0	1450	0.46	4.8	1.25
10	—	—	—	11.9	34.9	920	0.59	7.05	1.07
20	525	1.59	20.4	16.6	37.0	625	0.85	9.7	0.70
40	470	1.80	22.8	17.1	28.8	565	0.91	10.8	0.65
60	425	2.01	27.9	18.0	25.2	525	1.00	11.1	0.58
80	245	3.72	43.0	18.1	23.1	260	3.31	25.9	0.26
90	190	6.90	—	16.3	12.0	210	4.27	27.6	0.29

control parent starch film (51). Pertinent experimental data are collected in Table VI.

Films from 80-fluidity acid-modified corn and white milo starches dried at either 30° or 80° are much more soluble in water at 30°–80° than control parent starch films dried in the same manner (52).

IV. Industrial Uses

1. In Manufacture of Textiles

Large tonnages of acid-modified corn starch are consumed annually by domestic textile manufacturers in warp sizing and fabric finishing. The bulk of this starch goes into production of cotton goods and cotton–synthetic blends; the remainder is distributed among spun rayon, viscose-acetate blends, and worsteds. Warp yarns, especially the finer grades, are sized to increase weaving efficiency by increasing yarn

Table VI

Effects of Acid Modification on Corn Starch Film Properties (51)

Starch fluidity	Intrinsic viscosity (dl./g.)	Film tensile strength (kg./sq. mm.)	Film elongation (%)
Unmodified	1.73	4.67	3.2
15	1.21	4.47	2.7
34	1.06	4.45	2.6
50	0.88	4.94	2.7
71	0.67	4.57	2.9
89	0.32	4.58	2.2

strength and abrasion resistance. The applied size may be left on the yarn to contribute to finish sizing; generally, however, the woven fabric is treated to remove the warp yarn size before it is finish sized to desired hand and weight.

Attention was drawn as early as 1917 to the utility of acid-modified starches in warp sizing and in the finishing of cloth (53).

In 1921 a report (54) on starch sizing of cotton warp yarn in three mills compared corn starch with two of its modifications: thick-boiling alkali- and thin-boiling acid-modified starch. The acid-modified starch was rated best, chiefly because it imparted superior strength and smoothness to the sized yarn. Although no comparisons of weaving efficiencies were reported, the greater strength and smoothness of the warp sized with acid-modified starch pointed to higher weaving efficiency.

The superiority of acid-modified corn starch over its parent starch in many textile applications depends upon more than paste viscosity reduction. In several instances, oxidized corn starches of the same paste viscosity do not perform as well as the acid-modified products, particularly in warp sizing. Possibly the explanation for this lies in the difference in film properties or in the more anionic character of the oxidized starch.

Today the textile manufacturer can obtain uniform acid-modified corn starches in a wide range of paste viscosities. Uniformity of paste properties, resulting in substantially constant textile performance, eliminates the problems associated with the use of unmodified starches having less easily controlled paste properties.

Coarse goods, such as heavy duck and two ply yarn fabrics, are woven from strong yarns that require little or no sizing for good weaving efficiency. When the warp yarn or woven fabric is sized with an acid-modified starch, the choice is generally a slightly modified product, one having a 20–30 fluidity.

Lighter yarns, for example those in cotton flannel, denim, drill, twill, coarse broadcloth, pillow tubing, sateen, and sheeting, generally require warp sizing for satisfactory weaving efficiency. For this purpose, and for weighting when desired, a thinner and more highly modified starch is selected, for example, one in the fluidity range from 40 to 60.

Still higher fluidity acid-modified starches are recommended for the sizing of warps in fine broadcloth, lawn, voile, and other fine fabrics. In these applications the starch fluidity will range from 60 to 90.

An average concentration of acid-modified starch in a size for cotton yarns is about one pound per gallon. Somewhat lower concentration (0.8–0.9 lb./gal.) is suitable for viscose–acetate yarns, still less (0.5 lb./gal.) is satisfactory for spun rayon, but worsted, cotton-polyester and worsted–polyester yarns require higher concentrations ranging from 1 to 2 pounds per gallon. The size bath generally contains other important ingredients, among which are softeners, lubricants, preservatives, and starch binders; such additives are used particularly in the sizing of blends of natural and synthetic fibers.

Mainly because of the premium prices of acid-modified starches, textile manufacturers are constantly on the alert for suitable methods of thinning the pastes of the cheaper parent starch in their plants prior to use. Among the methods that have been developed are (a) mechanical homogenization of a conventionally cooked paste (55), (b) continuous pasting of a starch–water slurry at super-boiling temperatures by indirect heating of the mechanically agitated slurry under pressure in a heat exchanger (55), and (c) continuous high temperature pasting by mixing a starch–water slurry with high pressure steam (56).

2. In Manufacture of Starch Gum Candy

In the manufacture of starch gum candy, a mixture of sugar, water, corn sirup, and starch is boiled at atmospheric pressure, and evaporated, to form a solution (jelly) of such character that when it is poured into molds, cooled, and aged, a gum confection of desired texture is obtained. Alternatively, a jelly of desired solids content may be prepared without evaporation of water by pressure cooking a mixture of jelly ingredients containing the necessary lower content of liquid water. Use of an un-modified thick boiling starch in either method of preparation necessitates a much lower starch solids content resulting in weak-bodied, short-textured products of high moisture content and excessive "tendency to sweat" (syneresis). At increased starch solids levels, even with prolonged cooking, incorporation of a food acid is required to reduce the starch viscosity.

Acid-modified starches, particularly the nonwaxy cereal types, were quickly adapted to the manufacture of gum candy because of their ability to form concentrated hot fluid pastes which set to firm gels on cooling and aging. Substitution of acid-modified starch for thick boiling native starch in the candy formula results in a soft tender gum without prolonged cooking or use of thinning acid. As in textile applications, the availability of a modified starch with uniform paste properties is advantageous to the candy manufacturer; it permits scheduling of production with increased confidence that interruptions due to viscosity variation in the base starch will not occur.

Two representative examples of the manufacture of starch gum candy follow.

Example 1

regular corn syrup	50 lb.	70-fluidity acid-modified corn starch	12 lb.
granulated sugar	40 lb.	water	100 lb.
refined dextrose	10 lb.	color and flavor as desired	

Procedure (open kettle cooking).—Slurry the starch with 5 gal. of water. Place the sugar, corn syrup, dextrose, and remaining water in the cooking kettle and heat the mixture to boiling. Add the starch slurry gradually to the boiling syrup and then concentrate the resulting fluid jelly by open kettle boiling to 76% solids (refractometer test). Add color and flavor. Pour the jelly into starch molds. Store the product first at room temperature for 16–24 hr. and then at 52° for 8–12 hr. Cool to room temperature. Separate molded gum from starch. Coat the gum with sugar and pack it when the surface is dry.

Example 2

regular corn syrup . . 50 lb.	70-fluidity acid-modified corn starch . . 12 lb.
granulated sugar . . 40 lb.	water . . . . 15 lb.
refined dextrose . . . 10 lb.	color and flavor as desired

Procedure (continuous pressure cooking).—Slurry the starch in the water. Place the sugar, corn syrup, and dextrose in a cooking kettle and add the starch slurry. Under good agitation, heat the mixture to 82°. Pump the hot fluid mixture through a jet cooker or other type of continuous pressure cooker providing a cooking temperature of 132° and a detention time of 10–60 sec. In this method, the combination of detention time, water content, and pressure cooking temperature determines the quality of the finished gum candy. Experience has shown that best results are obtained when slightly less than complete disintegration of the gelatinized starch granules occurs, that is, when microscopic examination of the candy reveals the presence of a few unfragmented granules. The hot jelly thus produced is molded, aged, and finished for packing as described in Example 1.

3. In Manufacture of Paper

Current annual domestic consumption of acid-modified starch in gum candy is large but it is only a fraction of that used in textiles.

The chief application for acid-modified starch in paper manufacture is calender sizing of special grades of paper to improve scuff resistance and printability. For example, Kraft board may be sized with a 12–24% paste of 60-fluidity corn starch to improve its printability, and unbleached liner board may be sized with a less concentrated paste of a 20–40-fluidity corn starch to increase scuff resistance. In the latter instance, a more viscous and rapid congealing starch is preferred because it is retained to a greater extent on the surface of the sheet where it will be more effective.

Acid-modified starch is also used in some paper mills for size press sizing of selected grades of paper. The paste is usually applied at 63°–68° to prevent congelation.

Consumption of acid-modified starch in paper manufacture is small compared with that in textiles. Papermakers have found it more economical to thin their starch with alpha-amylase at the time of application.

4. In Laundries

Acid-modified cereal starches compete with other starch products in commercial and home laundries. Acid modification improves the penetration and distribution qualities of the starch, thus providing a laundered fabric with better hand and appearance. Descriptions of laundry starch compositions based on acid-modified starches appear in a number of patents (57–59).

Acid-modified starch is also the basis for substantial manufacture of liquid laundry starch preparations for home use (60).

V. REFERENCES

(1) G. V. Caesar and E. E. Moore, *Ind. Eng. Chem.*, **27**, 1447 (1935).

(2) W. G. Bechtel, *Cereal Chem.*, **24**, 200 (1947).

(3) W. G. Bechtel, *J. Colloid Sci.*, **5**, 260 (1950).

(4) E. G. Mazurs, T. J. Schoch, and F. E. Kite, *Cereal Chem.*, **34**, 141 (1957).

(5) J. R. Katz, *Textile Res. J.*, **9**, 146 (1939).

(6) W. Gallay and A. C. Bell, *Can. J. Res.*, *B*, **14**, 360 (1936).

(7) W. Gallay and A. C. Bell, *Can. J. Res.*, *B*, **14**, 381 (1936).

(8) H. H. Schopmeyer and G. E. Felton, U.S. Patent 2,319,637 (1943); *Chem. Abstr.*, **37**, 6488 (1943).

(9) R. W. Kerr, in "Chemistry and Industry of Starch," R. W. Kerr, ed., Academic Press Inc., New York, N.Y., 2nd Ed., 1950, p. 682.

(10) S. Lansky, M. Kooi, and T. J. Schoch, *J. Am. Chem. Soc.*, **71**, 4066 (1949).

(11) M. Samec and S. Jencic, *Kolloidchem. Beih.*, **7**, 137 (1915).

(12) O. A. Sjostrom, *Ind. Eng. Chem.*, **28**, 63 (1936).

(13) H. W. Leach, L. D. McCowen, and T. J. Schoch, *Cereal Chem.*, **36**, 534 (1959).

(14) H. W. Leach and T. J. Schoch, *Cereal Chem.*, **39**, 318 (1962).

(15) R. W. Kerr, *Staerke*, **4**, 39 (1952).

(16) R. P. Walton, "Comprehensive Survey of Starch Chemistry," Chemical Catalog Co., New York, N.Y., Vol. 1, 1928, p. 170.

(17) H. T. Brown and G. H. Morris, *J. Chem. Soc.*, **55**, 449 (1889).

(18) D. French, in reference 9, p. 158.

(19) C. J. Lintner, *J. Prakt. Chem.*, **34**, 378 (1886).

(20) W. Naegeli, *Ann. Chem.*, **173**, 218 (1874).

(21) B. Bellmas, German Patent 110,957 (1897).

(22) C. B. Duryea, U.S. Patents 675,822 (1901) and 696,949 (1902).

(23) M. Witlich, *Kunststoffe*, **2**, 61 (1912).

(24) A. Oelker, *Kunststoffe*, **6**, 189 (1916).

(25) E. Parow, *Z. Spiritusind.*, **45**, 169 (1922).

(26) M. Samec, "Kolloidchemie der Stärke," Theodor Steinkopff, Dresden and Leipzig, 1927, pp. 221–226.

(27) H. Meisel, U.S. Patent 2,231,476 (1941).

(28) Reference 9, p. 76.

(29) W. G. Bechtel, *J. Colloid Sci.*, **4**, 265 (1949).

(30) H. Buell, *Intern. Congr. Appl. Chem.*, *8th, Washington and N.Y., 1912*, **13**, 63 (1912).

(31) Reference 9, p. 119.

(32) D. W. Hansen, U.S. Patent 2,432,195 (1947); *Chem. Abstr.*, **42**, 1442 (1948).

(33) J. C. Small, *J. Am. Chem. Soc.*, **41**, 113 (1919).

(34) M. S. Buttrose, *Staerke*, **15**, 85 (1963).

(35) K. H. Meyer and P. Bernfeld, *Helv. Chim. Acta*, **23**, 890 (1940).

(36) E. Hatschek, "Colloid Chemistry," The Chemical Catalog Co., New York, N.Y., Vol. I, 1926, p. 746.

(37) A. Einstein, *Ann. Phys.*, [4] **19**, 289 (1906).

(38) C. L. Alsberg, *Ind. Eng. Chem.*, **18**, 190 (1926).

(39) K. H. Meyer and M. Fuld, *Helv. Chim. Acta*, **25**, 391 (1942).
(40) W. Harrison, *J. Soc. Dyers Colourists*, **27**, 84 (1911).
(41) J. R. Katz, M. C. Desai, and J. Seiberlich, *Trans. Faraday Soc.*, **34**, 1258 (1938).
(42) E. A. Hansen and J. R. Katz, *Z. Physik. Chem.*, *A*, **168**, 339 (1934).
(43) Reference *9*, p. 675.
(44) W. Gallay, *Can. J. Res.*, *B*, **14**, 391 (1936).
(45) T. J. Schoch and C. C. Jensen, *Ind. Eng. Chem.*, **12**, 531 (1940).
(46) Reference *9*, p. 680.
(47) W. A. Richardson, R. S. Higginbotham, and F. D. Farrow, *J. Textile Inst.*, **27**, T131 (1936).
(48) R. W. Kerr, Ref. *9*, p. 77.
(49) G. B. Jambuserwala and K. R. Kanitkar, *J. Textile Inst.*, **31**, T1 (1940).
(50) Reference *9*, p. 676.
(51) N. E. Lloyd and L. C. Kirst, *Cereal Chem.*, **40**, 154 (1963).
(52) G. A. Hull and T. J. Schoch, *Tappi*, **42**, 438 (1959).
(53) Anon., *Posselt's Textile J.*, **21**, 5 (1917).
(54) W. R. Cathcart, *Textile World*, **59**, 2896 (1921).
(55) W. C. Carter, *Am. Dyestuff Reptr.*, **41**, P301 (1952).
(56) R. B. Pressley, *Textile World*, **112**, No. 8, 33 (1962).
(57) L. O. Gill, U.S. Patent 1,656,190 (1928); *Chem. Abstr.*, **22**, 1054 (1928).
(58) G. M. Bierly, U.S. Patent 2,014,794 (1935); *Chem. Abstr.*, **29**, 7692 (1935).
(59) J. F. Walsh and F. C. Miller, U.S. Patent 2,350,653 (1944); *Chem. Abstr.*, **38**, 5102 (1944).
(60) A. R. Fuller, U.S. Patent 2,796,354 (1957); *Chem. Abstr.*, **51**, 13433 (1957).

CHAPTER X

PRODUCTION AND USE OF
HYPOCHLORITE-OXIDIZED STARCHES

By Barrett L. Scallet and Ernest A. Sowell

Central Research Department, Anheuser-Busch, Inc., St. Louis, Missouri

I. Introduction

Hypochlorite oxidation of starch is one of the most useful reactions developed for the modification of starch. The earliest record of this reaction appears to be a patent issued to Samuel Hall in 1821 (1), describing "An Improvement in the Manufacture of Starch." Hall appeared before His Most Excellent Majesty King George the Fourth in the second year of his reign, to receive a letters patent under the Great Seal of England. Hall's purpose was primarily to bleach the starch, but his specification indicates that he added sufficient "oxygenated muriate of lime" to affect the starch as well as the colored impurities. The process was employed within a relatively short time (for that period) of Scheele's discovery of chlorine (1774), Tennants' first preparation of bleaching powder in England

(1799), and Sir Humphrey Davey's proof that chlorine is an element (1810) (*2*).

Liebig is generally given credit for the first scientific investigation of starch oxidation with a chlorine compound (1829) (*3*).

However, it was not until 1896 that Schmerber treated starch with a hypochlorite for the purpose of obtaining a starch having new properties (*4*). Since that time the patents and publications relating to the action of hypochlorite on starches and the uses of the resulting products have become so numerous that they cannot all be listed here. Earlier reviews by Newton and Peckham (*5*) and Degering (*6*) have discussed many of these. Furthermore, much of the literature on hypochlorite action refers to oxidation under acidic conditions and is not particularly applicable to the alkaline hypochlorite oxidation used for starches of commerce. Consequently, this chapter will be limited primarily to a discussion of current methods of manufacture, properties, and uses of alkaline hypochlorite-modified starches.

II. Manufacture

1. The Starting Material

The oxidized starches of commerce consist of granules whose molecules have been attacked in a heterogeneous, topochemical fashion. Variations in the starch molecular structure and, thus, in the organization of the granule must of necessity result in variations in mode of attack of the oxidizing agent and lead to variations in molecular structure and properties of the oxidized starch.

The origin of the starting material, raw or unmodified starch, thus has a considerable effect on the properties of the resulting oxidized starch. Although dent corn is the source of most starch for oxidation, in recent years other crops have supplied a minor portion of the need. Grain sorghum (milo) is now wet-milled in considerable quantity, and the properties of its starch are in general very similar to those of dent corn starch (this Volume, Chapter I). Waxy maize is also a relatively important crop, and, while the setback properties of its pastes are such that oxidation affords little improvement in this characteristic, hypochlorite treatment can be used for bleaching and for reduction of paste viscosity. Sago starch has been commercially modified with hypochlorite (*7*), and potato, wheat, and tapioca starches are also so treated for specialized uses. The advent of high-amylose corns as commercial crops (*8*) raises the possibility that new oxidized starches with interesting properties may result from them, although at first glance oxidation would seem to nullify some of the advantages of these special starches. One effect of oxidation is to increase the dispersibility of high-amylose corn granules, which normally have very high gelatinization temperatures. Solution viscosities can also be reduced and controlled in this way.

It is evident that the properties of the finished oxidized starch can vary widely, depending on the source of the starting starch; there is some indication that variations within a single crop such as dent corn can lead to slight variations in the oxidized starch made from it. Manufacturing conditions such as length of steeping, sulfur dioxide levels, and removal of fine-granule starch in the process can also affect the results. In spite of the difficulties, however, present control methods permit routine production of many grades of oxidized starch of uniform quality.

2. Preparation of Sodium Hypochlorite Solutions

Since relatively large quantities of specially formulated sodium hypochlorite solutions are used in the manufacture of oxidized starches, all processors are equipped with installations for their compounding. These installations and their operation have been described in some detail by the various manufacturers of chlorine.

Essentially, sodium hypochlorite is made by diffusing chlorine into a solution of cool sodium hydroxide. The reaction proceeds as follows:

$$2NaOH + Cl_2 \rightarrow NaCl + NaOCl + H_2O + 24,650 \text{ calories}$$

For starch oxidation, a stable, and therefore mild, oxidant is desirable. Thus a limited amount of chlorine is used with an excess of sodium hydroxide. The heat evolved during reaction of chlorine with the alkali must be controlled as temperatures in excess of $30°$ favor the formation of undesirable chlorate.

A typical installation for the preparation of alkaline sodium hypochlorite solution is shown in Figure 1. Caustic soda (50% sodium hydroxide) is supplied in tank cars and is usually stored in steel or iron tanks which may be equipped with heating coils depending on the location of the tanks. Dilute sodium hydroxide solution may be prepared by proportional pumping of caustic soda and water through a mixing tee. The heat evolved is dissipated by means of a heat exchanger located in the line to the chlorination tank. This tank may be constructed of concrete, ceramics, or steel lined with rubber or plastic. Cooling coils may be used in this tank; however, since the corrosion of most metals that are useful for coils is very high during chlorination of the caustic, it is generally more economical to precool the dilute caustic to about $4°$. Chlorine, supplied in cylinders or tank cars, is introduced to the cool dilute caustic in the tank through a Duriron, lead or silver diffuser immersed below the surface. The diffusion provides ample agitation, and if liquid chlorine is used some additional cooling effect is obtained. Every precaution for safety is taken. Automatic valves in the chlorine line prevent excessive temperature rise during chlorination of the caustic. Alarms and gas masks for personnel are positioned throughout the danger area. In this system, the hypochlorite solution strength can be determined approximately by the amount of caustic and chlorine used coupled with liquid volume increase. Accurate control is achieved by following the reaction with analyses of the available chlorine. Modification of the above system may be made by the installation of electrometric devices which control caustic dilution by conductivity sensing and avail-

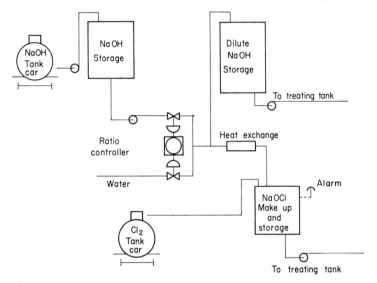

FIG. 1.—Process for preparing sodium hypochlorite solution.

able chlorine by redox potential detection (9). This automation eliminates the time required for analytical tests and consequently reduces operating costs.

Among the variables involved in starch oxidation, certainly none is as important as the hypochlorite formulation. The concentration of available chlorine and the amount of excess sodium hydroxide give a hypochlorite solution its unique capacity for a particular oxidative modification of a starch.

3. The Starch–Hypochlorite Reaction

Hypochlorite-oxidized starches are made by treating a suspension of starch granules with a solution of an alkaline hypochlorite such as described above. After the reaction is finished, the suspension is neutralized with acid, and the starch is washed to remove salts and then dried. Properties of the oxidized starch are related to the degree and type of treatment and these in turn are determined by the reaction conditions. Among the variables in the reaction are temperature, pH, hypochlorite, and starch concentrations, organic and inorganic impurities, and reaction by-products (10, 11).

Other variables in the reaction may also be important. There is a reduction in the pH as oxidation occurs, and, if compensation is not made, the course of the oxidation will be affected. Naturally, the reaction is influenced by temperature, and, since it is exothermic, some means of dissipating the heat evolved is mandatory, not only for control of the actual oxidation but also for curtailing the formation of undesirable hypochlorite decomposition compounds. With the random oxidation action that occurs, some of the molecules within the granule are attacked to excess, are degraded and dissolve (12). Aside from the economic loss involved, the accumulations of these degradation products will influence the further course of the oxidation. Partial solubilization cannot be eliminated, but it can be reduced by careful selection of reaction conditions.

Additional factors that must be considered or controlled are the quantity and concentration of the starch to be oxidized, the degree of agitation, and the presence of metal ions such as those of cobalt, copper, and nickel that catalyze the decomposition of hypochlorite. The molecular structure of the starch as determined by botanical origin and genetic variation also plays a major role (10).

The schematic in Figure 2 represents a generalized system for the hypochlorite oxidation of starch. Since each manufacturer uses conditions peculiar to his own plant and to the type of product desired and since the exact details are confidential, precise figures cannot be given for the many variables. However, the process may be described as follows:

A 20–24°Bé slurry of refined starch containing 20,000 to 100,000 lbs. of dry substance is introduced into the treating tank. This tank is constructed of materials reasonably resistant to the corrosive action of the chemicals added and formed in the process. To insure rapid mixing of the chemicals with starch, the tank is equipped with motors and impellers designed to conform to the volume of starch being treated. The pH of the slurry is adjusted with dilute sodium hydroxide to a value usually within the range of 8–10. Higher pH gives slower oxidation (10, 11), The hypochlorite solution, containing 5 to 10% available chlorine is then added at a rate dependent on the quantity to be added and the time. allotted for the addition. Ordinarily, several hundred gallons of hypochlorite may be added within a few hours. Automatic controllers can be used to proportion the hypochlorite addition during the required reaction period. As the oxidation proceeds, the pH shifts downward; it can be readjusted by automatic alkali addition. It is necessary to maintain the temperature within a desired range, usually 21° to 38°. Since the reaction is exothermic, cooling must be effected by controlling the rate of hypochlorite addition or by the use of a mechanical cooling system.

When the desired amount of oxidation has been achieved, as determined primarily by chemical and physical methods (13), the treated starch is neutralized or made slightly acidic, pH 6.0–6.5. Any free chlorine present is removed by the use of sodium bisulfite solution or sulfur dioxide gas. For removal of other impurities and by-products of the reaction, the

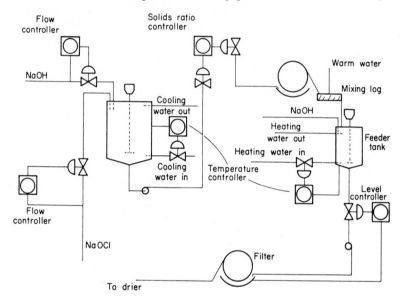

FIG. 2.—Alkaline hypochlorite process.

treated starch is diluted and washed on continuous vacuum filters or in centrifugal devices such as Dorrclones. After washing, the starch is recovered by means of a vacuum filter and dried in a continuous hot air drier to a moisture content of 10–12%.

By variation of the procedure outlined, each manufacturer is able to produce a wide range of oxidized starch products for specific uses.

III. CHARACTERISTICS OF HYPOCHLORITE-OXIDIZED STARCHES

1. Physical Properties

Finished hypochlorite-oxidized starch is supplied to the consumer in the same granular form as other starches. The most noticeable characteristic of this starch is its whiteness; within limits, the bleaching effect increases with the degree of oxidation. In general, the oxidized starches are very sensitive to heat, and, if they are dried at too high a temperature, browning will occur.

Microscopically the granules closely resemble those of unmodified starch. They stain blue with iodine and show typical polarization crosses. Closer scrutiny of the granules reveals the presence of radial fissures and fragmentation; the amount of fragmentation increases with degree of oxidation. Wheat starch granules are increased in size by the treatment while waxy maize starch granules are not altered in size (10). Presumably any starches containing amylose will exhibit swelling in proportion to their amylose content.

The presence of the polarization crosses, coupled with an unchanged x-ray diffraction pattern, gives strong evidence that most of the oxidation occurs in the amorphous regions of the granule (10, 12). Fissures may represent portions of the granule that were dissolved by excessive localized attack during treatment (12).

Hypochlorite-oxidized starch granules strongly absorb certain dyes such as methylene blue, and this absorption is related to the ionic charge associated with the molecules (14). Since methylene blue is a positively charged dye, it is absorbed by the oxidized starch whose negative charge is the result of carboxyl groups. The intensity of absorption is related, within limits, to the degree of oxidation. This staining phenomenon is observed with all negatively charged starches and cannot be used for the specific identification of hypochlorite-oxidized starch. However, its use in conjunction with other tests makes identification possible in many instances.

The most outstanding characteristics of the hypochlorite-oxidized starches are to be seen during and after gelatinization. The granules lose birefringence at temperatures several degrees lower than those of unmodified starch. Pasting occurs more rapidly and at a lower temperature, and the degree of thickening that occurs with unmodified starches is reduced. The cooled starch pastes exhibit a greater degree of fluidity and clarity than those of untreated starch. Furthermore, if the degree of oxidation is great enough, the granules disintegrate completely during cooking, yielding extremely clear solutions. Upon aging, the tendency toward setback or gel formation, so characteristic of most starches, is minimized to a very large extent because of the presence of functional groups that block the associative tendencies of starch chains (15). If a solution of an oxidized starch is spread in a thin layer on a glass plate and allowed to dry, a strongly adherent, continuous, and clear film results. By contrast, brittle, opaque, and flake-like films are obtained with unmodified and many modified starches. All these properties are the result of oxidation of hydroxyl groups in the starch molecules and of depolymerization that has occurred during the oxidation reaction (16).

2. Rheological Properties

Obviously, a single oxidized starch is limited to no more than a few of the numerous industrial applications; consequently, a wide range of starches having different visco-elastic properties in solution are required. Most manufacturers produce a series of starches ranging from a low to a high degree of hypochlorite oxidation. From these, the selection of a specific concentration of a starch having a specific degree of oxidation can be made for each application. Generally, classification is based on some type of fluidity or viscosity measurement, which only partially describes the intricate rheological properties that solutions of the starches will exhibit under various conditions (see Volume I, Chapter XVI). Numerous instruments and devices have been used in an attempt to measure quantitatively some of the specific properties and behavior of these colloidal solutions for a given application. These have been discussed in detail by Van Wazer and co-workers (17) and Myers (Volume I, Chapter XVI).

Figure 3 illustrates the concentration–viscosity relationships of some of the usual types of hypochlorite-oxidized corn starches offered by industry. Graphical representations such as these serve only as guides in selecting a product for a particular use.

3. Chemical Properties

The chemical structures responsible for the interesting and valuable physical properties of commercial oxidized starches are relatively unknown. The presence of alkali during oxidation leads to numerous degradative actions, making a definitive analysis very difficult. Superimposed upon the degradation is the oxidative action of atmospheric oxygen, which may be different from that of hypochlorite. In any case, there is no doubt that a number of carboxyl groups and carbonyl groups are formed on the starch molecules; their quantities and relative proportions are determined by the reaction conditions. Simultaneously, there is scission of some of the D-glucosidic bonds, which results in an over-all decrease in molecular size. Some of the starch is solubilized and is removed in the commercial process by filtration and washing.

The solubles include the major portion of the nitrogen-containing impurities of the starch, which are extensively solubilized in the early stages of hypochlorite treatment (7, 18). From 70 to 80% of the nitrogen is removed commercially depending on conditions of treatment. Coloring matter is also removed or decolorized in the early stages of treatment. Free fatty acid content, on the other hand, is reduced by only 15 to 20%

after prolonged treatment; most of this reduction occurs in the early stages of the reaction.

One of the best descriptions of the chemical properties of oxidized starches is given by Schmorak and co-workers (10), who did an extensive study of the oxidation of both wheat and waxy maize starches. For starches

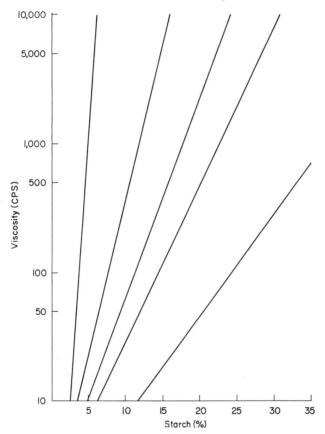

FIG. 3.—Viscosity data for pasted commercial oxidized starches. Each line represents a different starch, with degree of oxidation increasing from the most lightly oxidized (left) to the most highly oxidized (right).

that consumed oxygen amounting to approximately 0.05 moles per D-glucose unit (AGU), carboxyl groups were formed to the extent of one per 36 to one per 97 AGU depending on the pH. Higher pH gave more carboxyls. These values correspond with carboxyl levels in commercial oxidized starches.

Carbonyl groups were formed in somewhat lower quantity in wheat starch, ranging from one per 110 AGU to less than one per 200 AGU. For waxy maize starch, however, carbonyl group formation was about twice as great as for wheat starch and approximated the amount of carboxyl group formation. Here, too, the number of functional groups increased with increasing pH of oxidation.

On the basis of sedimentation experiments, combined with determinations of degree of polymerization (D.P.) by periodate oxidation, Schmorak and co-workers (10) concluded that the oxidized wheat amylopectin molecule must have a structure approaching that of Erlander and French's Model V (19), with weight average D.P. near 200. For waxy maize starch, the weight average D.P. was 550, and there was fair agreement of the ultracentrifugal results with those predicted for Model V.

Schmorak and co-workers also made an interesting calculation of the numerical relationships between D-glucosidic bond scissions, carboxyl groups formed, and carbonyl groups formed. They concluded that each scission in wheat starch was accompanied by the consumption of 4 to 5 atoms of oxygen and by the formation of nearly 2 carboxyl groups and up to one carbonyl. The corresponding figures for waxy maize starch appeared to be about 2 to 3 oxygen atoms and about 1.5 of each of the functional groups per scission.

Since the scission reaction results in the formation of two molecules from one, it can be expected to have more effect on the physical properties than oxidations within the D-glucose rings, although undoubtedly both are important.

Scission of amylose, catalyzed by alkali and oxygen, was discussed by Greenwood (20), who postulated "a random, catalytic, hydrolytic scission of 4 → 1-α-D bonds (which does not occur in the absence of oxygen)." He further noted that amylopectin (from potato) has no such oxygen-sensitive bonds. Dux, on the other hand, working with more rigorous conditions, found that potato amylopectin was cleaved in the presence of alkali and air and speculated that α-D-(1 → 6) bonds were preferentially split with simultaneous formation of carboxyl on carbon 6 (21). Both authors point out that oxidations at carbons 2, 3, and 6 are the most likely, since the others are involved in ring and chain formation. However, by analogy with known reactions of simple sugars, the single reducing end-group in each molecule may also undergo oxidation under alkaline conditions with the production of a carboxyl group (22), formation of saccharinic acids (20, 23–26), or loss of carbon dioxide to give an aldopentose (27) or aldonic acid (22) residue. (See also Volume I, Chapter XXI.)

Whether the oxidation with air differs in kind from the oxidation with hypochlorite cannot be decided on the basis of present evidence, but both must have an effect on the chemical properties of commercially oxidized starches. It is also impossible at the present time to estimate the relative importance of the nonoxidative alkaline degradation that takes place in conjunction with the oxidation. Greenwood (*20*) and BeMiller (Volume I, Chapter XXI) have discussed this for starch, and Corbett (*23*) has given an elegant presentation of the corresponding reactions for oxycellulose.

IV. Uses

The present yearly consumption of oxidized starches is about 200 million pounds (*28*). By far the largest user of this kind of starch is the industry primarily responsible for its development, the paper industry. Use of this starch in surface sizing and pigment coating of paper accounts for nearly 85% of the total production. The textile industry, the second largest user of hypochlorite oxidized starch, requires approximately 10 million pounds for finishing operations. The balance of the annual consumption goes into adhesives, the manufacture of building materials, laundry applications, and miscellaneous industrial uses.

1. In Paper

The principal use for oxidized starches in paper is in coating. Although their use for this purpose dates from the early part of the 1900's, it was not until the introduction of machine coating in 1930 that they gained their full importance (*29*). Since then, the yearly production of coated paper has increased from approximately 200,000 tons to over 3 million tons (*30*). As machine coating demanded greater speed and economy, new requirements were placed on coating adhesives. To effect quick and satisfactory drying on the steam-heated drums of the paper machine, coatings having high solids and workable flow properties were needed. The hypochlorite-oxidized starches of high fluidity were found to satisfy the adhesive and other colloidal requirements of these coatings without adverse effect on water retention and flow behavior. Today, they are the most widely used adhesives for this process (*29*).

Large amounts of oxidized starches are used in surface sizings applied at the size press, size tub, or in the case of heavier papers, at the calenders. This type of sizing results in the formation of a smooth, hard film which seals the pores of the paper and provides a better surface for writing and printing (*31*). The superior film-forming characteristics of the hypochlorite-oxidized starches play an important role in this process. Equally important for smooth and even application is the stability of their solutions toward thickening, that is, their lack of set-back. Furthermore, dilute solutions of these starches do not form sediments to the extent that is frequently found with other starches. The fluidity choices for surface sizing cover the entire range of products offered, as there are many variations involved in this aspect of paper manufacture.

Hypochlorite-oxidized starches are sometimes used in the internal sizing of paper. Frequently these starches are used in conjunction with a rosin size for more effective precipitation of the rosin–alum complex. This action results in increased ink and water resistance of the finished sheet. In some cases, because of the higher fluidity and better dispersion, these starches will penetrate the fibers more completely and may be used for imparting strength to high density paper (*32*).

Oxidized starch is sometimes added to the beaters in uncooked form. When the sheet containing these granules comes in contact with the heated drying rolls, the starch is easily gelatinized because of its modification.

2. In Textiles

It is well known that starches of various kinds are used in the textile industry for sizing warps of cotton, spun rayon, other synthetics, and various fiber blends (*33*, *34*, This Volume, Chapter VII). In addition, starches are used in the finishing of the woven fabrics made from these yarns. When it is considered that several hundred different types of cotton fabrics, each requiring different yarns, are processed by the textile industry, the complexity of the sizing requirement is at once recognized. Although the oxidized starches are not used as extensively in warp sizing as other starches, there are applications in which the additional cost of these starches is compensated for by their performance. Their high fluidity coupled with stable flow properties enables these starches to be used at high concentrations so that greater add-on may be obtained. In combed cotton weaving mills, which use fine yarns, the use of hypochlorite-oxidized starches permits the formation of a tough, elastic sheath that can withstand the abrasive action of the looms. The hypochlorite-oxidized starches are excellent sizes for a variety of spun rayon and synthetic blends. The requirements here are essentially the same, except that a more easily removed size is desirable. Since films of oxidized starches are relatively soluble, their usefulness in this operation is apparent. In some instances, worsted and woolen yarns are sized with hypochlorite-oxidized starches to provide added protection against the mechanical action of high speed looms.

Nearly every kind of starch has been used as a textile finish. This is especially true with the cotton fabrics. Finishes are applied to impart a certain amount of protection to the yarn as well as to give the fabric various characteristics such as firmness and draping quality. The hypochlorite-oxidized starches again find considerable use in some of these processes. In finishing printed fabrics, the less-opaque film obtained with oxidized starch is desirable to prevent dulling of the colors. With fabrics that need high strength with less firmness, oxidized starches can be used.

3. In Laundry Finishing

Closely allied to industrial textile finishing is the starching of laundered fabrics. Although many kinds of starch have been used as a laundry finish, not all impart the most desirable qualities of appearance and feel. The hypochlorite-oxidized starches give an ideal laundry finish. Within recent years there have been offered a number of laundry starch products especially prepared for convenience in home use. These do not require cooking, since they are supplied either as liquids or as dry, cold-water-soluble powders (35–37). More recently, another type of laundry starch has been introduced in a form that can be applied to the fabric as a spray (38). Many of these home laundry products have formulations based on the utilization of a hypochlorite-oxidized starch.

4. In Building Materials

The hypochlorite-oxidized starches are used to some extent in the fabrication of construction materials. Among such products are construction papers, insulation and wall boards, and acoustical tile. By definition, all these materials can be considered as paper board regardless of whether the fiber used is cellulose, mineral, or synthetic. They are made by typical paper-making processes and require adhesives and sizings derived from starches. Nearly 4 million pounds of oxidized starch are consumed by this industry annually (28).

5. Gelatinized Products

Recently two types of oxidized starches have been introduced in dry, gelatinized form. They vary in degree of oxidation, and are proposed for use in the food industry as thickeners and in the paper industry for wet-end addition, sizing, and pigment coating (39).

6. Intermediates

Several starch derivatives (esters, ethers) have found broad utility in many different fields. In order to provide the most general usefulness, these starch derivatives are supplied in a range of viscosities. One of the ways in which viscosity may be reduced is by oxidation, and a considerable amount of oxidized starch is now prepared for captive use as an intermediate for derivatization by the corn wet-millers. Since ester groups would be saponified under the conditions of hypochlorite oxidation, the oxidation step must be performed first. Even in the case of ether derivatives that are stable to alkali, oxidation is usually performed before derivatization in order to avoid complicating reactions.

There is every indication that the use of hypochlorite oxidation for the preparation of such starch derivatives will increase rapidly in the future. Furthermore, the present outlook is for a generally increased demand for oxidized starches in all of their many uses.

V. REFERENCES

(1) S. Hall, British Patent 4559 (1821).
(2) H. Remy, "Treatise on Inorganic Chemistry," Elsevier Publishing Co., Amsterdam, 1956, Vol. 1, pp. 778–805.
(3) J. Liebig, Ann. Phys. Chem. (Poggendorff's, Leipzig) (1829).
(4) O. Schmerber, Bul. Soc. Ind. Mulhouse, 238 (1896).
(5) J. Newton and G. Peckham, in "Chemistry and Industry of Starch," R. W. Kerr, ed., Academic Press Inc., New York, N.Y., 1950, pp. 325–343.
(6) E. F. Degering, in "Starch and its Derivatives," J. A. Radley, ed., Chapman and Hall, Ltd., London, 1953, Vol. 1, pp. 343–364.
(7) A. D. Fuller, U.S. Patent 1,942,544 (1934); Chem. Abstr., 28, 1888 (1934).
(8) Anon., Chem. Eng. News, 36, 54 (1958).
(9) D. J. Pye, J. Electrochem. Soc., 97, 245 (1950).
(10) J. Schmorak, D. Mejzler, and M. Lewin, Staerke, 14, 278 (1962); J. Schmorak and M. Lewin, J. Polymer Sci., A1, 2601 (1963).
(11) I. Potze and P. Hiemstra, Staerke, 15, 217 (1963).
(12) F. F. Farley and R. M. Hixon, Ind. Eng. Chem., 34, 677 (1942).
(13) D. E. Lucas and C. H. Fletcher, Paper Ind., 40, 812 (1959).
(14) T. J. Schoch and E. C. Maywald, Anal. Chem., 28, 382 (1956).
(15) T. J. Schoch, Tappi, 35, 4 (1952).
(16) G. A. Hull and T. J. Schoch, Tappi, 42, 438 (1959).
(17) J. R. Van Wazer, J. W. Lyons, K. Y. Kim, and R. E. Colwell, "Viscosity and Flow Measurement," Interscience Publishers Inc., New York, N.Y., 1963.
(18) G. Pollock and C. Campbell, Abstr. Papers, Am. Chem. Soc., 121, 8P (1952).
(19) S. Erlander and D. French, J. Polymer Sci., 20, 7 (1956).
(20) C. T. Greenwood, Advan. Carbohydrate Chem., 11, 335 (1956).
(21) E. F. W. Dux, Staerke, 6, 91 (1954).
(22) C. L. Mehltretter, Staerke, 15, 313 (1963).
(23) W. M. Corbett, in "Recent Advances in the Chemistry of Cellulose and Starch," J. Honeyman, ed., Heywood and Co., Ltd., London England, 1959, pp. 122 and 126.
(24) W. M. Corbett and J. Kenner, J. Chem. Soc., 1431 (1955).
(25) H. S. Isbell, J. Res. Natl. Bur. Std., 32, 45 (1944).
(26) J. C. Sowden, M. G. Blair, and D. J. Kuenne, J. Am. Chem. Soc., 79, 6450 (1957).
(27) J. W. Daniel, Tappi, 42, 534 (1959).
(28) Corn Industries Research Foundation, 1001 Connecticut Ave., N.W. Washington 6, D.C.
(29) F. H. Frost, "Starch and Starch Products in Paper Coating," Tappi Monograph No. 17, Tech. Assoc. Pulp Paper Ind., New York, N.Y., 1957, p. 1.
(30) C. E. Snook and R. B. Porter, Tappi, 42, 131A (1959).
(31) J. P. Casey, "Pulp and Paper," Interscience Publishers Inc., New York, N.Y. Vol. 3, 1960.
(32) Reference 31, Vol. 2, p. 959.
(33) P. V. Seydel, "Warp Sizing," W. R. C. Smith Pub. Co., Atlanta, Ga., 1958.

(34) "Cotton Warp Sizing Handbook," 2nd Ed., E. F. Houghton Co., Philadelphia, Pa., 1949.

(35) R. W. Kerr, U.S. Patent 2,732,309 (1956); Chem. Abstr., 50, 6824 (1956).

(36) W. J. Katzbeck, U.S. Patent 2,938,809 (1960); Chem. Abstr., 54, 20261 (1960).

(37) R. L. Curtin, E. A. Sowell, and B. L. Scallet, U.S. Patent 3,066,036 (1962).

(38) R. L. Curtin, E. A. Sowell, and B. L. Scallet, U.S. Patent 3,066,037 (1962).

(39) Anon., Chem. Eng. News, 42, 45 (1964).

CHAPTER XI

PRODUCTION AND USE OF STARCH DEXTRINS

By R. B. Evans and O. B. Wurzburg

National Starch and Chemical Corporation, Plainfield, New Jersey

I. Introduction

The term "dextrin" is used in its broadest sense to cover the degradation products of starch regardless of the manner in which they are produced. The exceptions are the mono- and oligosaccharides.

All dextrins belong to a large and varied group of D-glucose polymers from the purely linear, through highly branched structures, to cyclic compounds.

Dextrins may be classified by the general procedure used in their preparation into four major groups: first, those dextrins obtained by enzymic action, particularly by the action of the amylases on starch; second, the cyclic Schardinger dextrins produced by the action of *Bacillus macerans* on starch; third, dextrins produced by acid hydrolysis in aqueous media; and fourth, the pyrodextrins which comprise products prepared by the action of heat, or both heat and acid, on starch. It is these last mentioned products with which we will be concerned in this chapter. There are a large number of pyrodextrins manufactured, many of which are of considerable industrial importance.

II. Chemistry of Conversion

Although our knowledge of the details of the reactions involved in the dextrinization of starch are still incomplete, our understanding of these reactions has been considerably advanced by the recent papers published on this subject.

1. Early Work on Dextrinization

As early as 1934, Katz and co-workers (*1, 2*) studied the modifications taking place during the heating of starch to temperatures up to 200°. They showed that, as the starch was heated, water vapor was given off. The loss of water was irreversible as indicated by the gradual disappearance of the x-ray pattern at temperatures over 140°. They indicated that, at high temperatures, the dextrinization reaction was exothermic and that the pyrodextrins produced did not retrograde when dissolved in water. It was suggested that anhydride formation takes place during dextrinization at high temperatures which would lead to levoglucosan type structures in the products.

Microscopic studies of the granule during the heating of granular starch was investigated by Badenhuizen and Katz (*3*).

The first major study of the dextrinization process was undertaken by Brimhall (*4*) in 1944. She found that a dextrin having a D.P. of 60–70 D-glucose units produced by the action of heat on dry starch was water soluble, whereas an amylodextrin containing less than 20 D-glucose units, produced by the action of cold acid on granular starch, was cold water insoluble. The latter product was substantially linear in structure and retrograded readily from solution, whereas pyrodextrins did not, indicating a substantial difference in structure between the two products.

Methylation studies of a commercial British gum, having an average D.P. of 66 D-glucose units, indicated the presence of one nonreducing end-group for each 12 D-glucose residues in the molecule. From this it was deduced that there were 5 to 6 nonreducing end-groups or an average of 4 to 5 branches per molecule, the terminal branches being about 5 D-glucose units in length. This structure was further supported by the change in the digestibility of the sample by beta amylase, the dextrin producing only 22% maltose as against 55% for the original starch, and the complete loss of Schardinger dextrin formation by the action of *Bacillus macerans* on the pyrodextrin.

Dextrinization of the linear (amylose) and branched (amylopectin) components of starch as well as of amylodextrin, retrograded starch, and granular corn starch was followed by measurement of water solubility, reducing power and digestibility with beta-amylase. It was concluded from these tests that the linear components became branched during dextrinization and that there was in increase in the degree of branching in each case with continued conversion. It was suggested that two reactions were involved in the dextrinization of starch: (a) hydrolysis of the starch molecules to relatively low levels of molecular weight and (b) a recombination of these fragments primarily through $(1 \rightarrow 6)$ linkages to more highly branched structures.

From nitrogen contents of the nitrate derivatives prepared from a series of dextrins, Caesar (5) and co-workers found that, as dextrinization progressed, it became more difficult to introduce the anticipated theoretical nitrogen content. They considered that these results gave further support to the hypothesis that both levoglucosan and $(6 \rightarrow 6)$ ether linkages were produced, especially during the course of high temperature conversions.

The results recorded by Rüggeberg (6), who also studied the composition of the nitrate esters of a number of dextrins, substantiated the original work of Caesar.

However, Kerr and Cleveland (7), who made a more extensive study of the dextrinization of amylose, believed that the difference in the degree of nitration found by both Caesar and Ruggeberg was probably due to physical rather than chemical causes. It was shown that a full degree of acetylation of a British gum or pyrodextrin could be attained if the proper acetylation technique was applied. Heating amylose to 80° produced a decrease in the D.P. as determined by osmotic pressure measurements, intrinsic viscosity, and reducing values during the first hour. However, on prolonged heating these values remained substantially constant. There was no change in the acetyl content of amylose acetates prepared from the samples obtained after the first hour of conversion. Although these workers agree with the hypothesis that hydrolysis to shorter linear chains takes place followed by a repolymerization of the smaller molecules, they also hypothesized that a transglucosidation is involved in which the more labile $(1 \rightarrow 4)$ linkages in the amylose are exchanged for a more stable $(1 \rightarrow 6)$ linkage during dextrinization at high temperatures. This idea is supported by the fact that the reaction is exothermic.

These authors believe that since the D.P. or average viscosity, of the sample remains substantially constant during nearly 80% of the reaction period, it is unreasonable to assume that such close balance between the hydrolysis and repolymerization reactions could be maintained under these conditions. They prefer to interpret the results as due to trans-glucosidation which is said to predominate especially during the high temperature stages of dextrinization. Furthermore, the loss in the linear character of the amylose with the development of an increase in the number of nonreducing end-groups was demonstrated by the periodate oxidation technique, the reduction in the attack on the samples by beta-amylase, and the increase in the cold water solubility.

Another interesting aspect was the results for dextrinization of amylose in various physical forms. Samples in the crystalline and retrograded states appeared to dextrinize more rapidly than those in the amorphous or frozen gel states. These differences were explained on the basis that the molecules in the crystalline or retrograded states are in close proximity to each other. The reactions are thus more complex than a simple hydrolysis–repolymerization reaction. It is assumed that there is also a direct interaction involving an exchange of D-glucosidic link-ages. Such interactions would involve no change in the D.P. of the sample. There was little evidence to support the idea of the formation of D-glucosan structures or inner ether linkages.

Frey and Lottner (8) studied the degradation of pyrodextrins with acids, malt, and fungal amylase and measured the extent of degradation by determining the quantity of ethanol produced by fermentation with yeast. They tentatively concluded that white dextrins consist of starch fragments containing $(1 \rightarrow 4)$ and some $(1 \rightarrow 6)$ linkages, the latter pos-sibly formed by reversion, while canary dextrins are more complex in character as shown by their increased resistance to degradation by amylases. While containing the predominant $(1 \rightarrow 4)$ and $(1 \rightarrow 6)$ link-ages of starch, canary dextrins also contain structures of the levoglucosan type; however, the formation of $(6 \rightarrow 6)$ and $(4 \rightarrow 6)$ ether linkages cannot be excluded.

In a series of recent papers, Wolfrom and co-workers have examined the dextrinization of amylose (*9, 10*), starch (*9*), and levoglucosan (*11, 12*) under various conditions.

2. Fragmentation Studies

Thompson and Wolfrom (*10*) made a fragmentation analysis of an acid hydrolyzed amylose British gum. In addition to the α-D-$(1 \rightarrow 4)$ linkages present in the original amylose, α-D-$(1 \rightarrow 6)$, β-D-$(1 \rightarrow 6)$, and β-D-$(1 \rightarrow 2)$ linkages were detected as well as 1,6-anhydro-β-D-gluco-

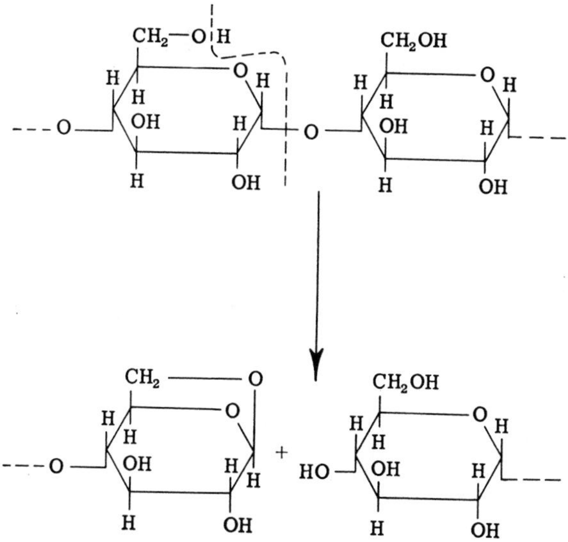

Fig. 1.—Proposed mechanism for the formation of levoglucosan from starch (*10, 13*).

pyranose end groups. Other linkages, especially α-D-$(1 \rightarrow 2)$ linkages, were probably also present.

Under dry rotating conditions, the authors believed that little hydrolysis took place. Based on the mechanism for the thermal decomposition of cellulose (*13*), they postulated that the primary hydroxyl group on C-6 attacks the D-glucosyl linkage of the same D-glucose unit in the manner shown in Figure 1. The identification of levoglucosan in the products of hydrolysis is evidence for this mechanism. This is in agreement with the actual pyrolysis of starch at somewhat higher temperatures in which levoglucosan is the primary product, although Dimler and co-workers (*14*) have also isolated 1,6-anhydro-β-D-glucofuranoside from the products of the distillation of starch. In agreement

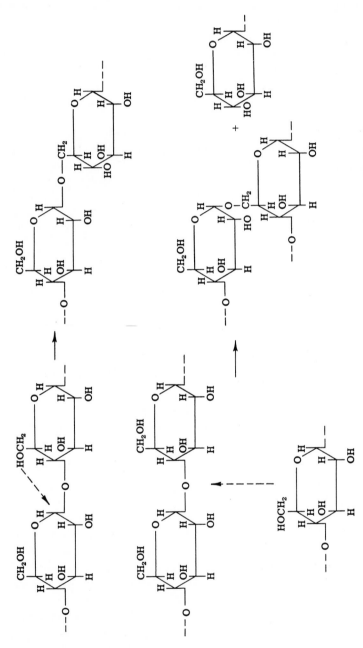

Fig. 2.—Proposed mechanism for the formation of (1 → 6) linkages during dextrinization (4, 10).

with Brimhall (4), Thompson and Wolfrom (10) suggested that other hydroxyl groups, preferably the primary hydroxyl of the adjacent D-glucose unit, may also attack the glycosyl linkage in the way shown diagrammatically in Figure 2.

3. Polymerization of Levoglucosan

Later (11) it was shown that levoglucosan (1,6-anhydro-β-D-glucopyranose) under dextrinizing conditions, polymerized to produce the usual D-glucosidic linkages in a pyrodextrin according to the mechanism shown in Figure 3. Fragmentation studies of the polymers produced established the presence of α- and β-D-(1 → 6), α- and β-D-(1 → 4), and

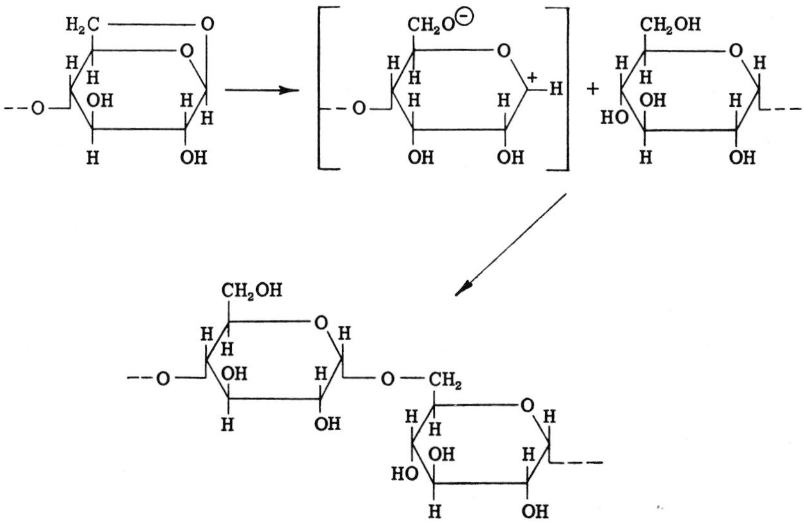

FIG. 3.—Proposed mechanism for the polymerization of levoglucosan (11).

β-D-(1 → 2) linkages and 1,6-anhydro-β-D-glucose end-groups in the polymer. This path to the dextrinization of starch may be important in the absence of acid and at high temperatures.

Furthermore, Carvalho and co-workers (15) polymerized levoglucosan in the presence of monochloracetic acid catalyst with or without solvent (tetramethylenesulfone) and obtained polymers with molecular weights from 4,325 to 309,000 as determined by the light scattering technique. Periodate oxidation studies indicated that highly branched polymers were produced containing D-glucosidic linkages attached to the hydroxyl groups of C-2, C-3, C-4, or C-6 of another D-glucose residue.

Further work by Wolfrom and co-workers (12) on several low-molecular-weight thermal polymers (ethanol soluble portion) of levoglucosan showed it was possible after partial hydrolysis to isolate by carbon chromatography and refractionation on a silicate column the hexaacetates of the following sugars: 4-O-α-D- and 4-O-β-D-, 2-O-α-D- and 2-O-β-D-glucopyranosyl-1,6-anhydro-β-D-glucopyranose. 4-O-(2,3,4,6-Tetra-O-acetyl-β-D-glucopyranosyl)-2,3-di-O-acetyl-1,6 anhydro-β-D-glucopyranose (1,6-anhydrocellobiose hexaacetate) was also isolated in two crystalline forms. The anhydrodisaccharide acetates were identified by ring cleavage with titanium tetrachloride followed by anomeric inversion with mercuric acetate and reacetylation. It should be pointed out that no 3-O-D-glucopyranosyl-anhydrodisaccharides were encountered, nor had any 3-O-D-glucosyl-linked substances been found in the previous fragmentation studies. Three anhydrotrisaccharides were also isolated in this work.

Continuing the study of dextrinization, Wolfrom and co-workers (9) converted both acidified as well as anhydrous amylose. They expressed the view that, in the presence of moisture and acid, opposing hydrolytic and reversion reactions occur with a shift to reversion as the moisture disappears. This view is supported by the fact that reducing values of samples taken during extensive dextrinization rise to a peak and then decrease. The term reversion is used by these authors for those reactions involving the liberated reducing end groups and is illustrated by the equation in the upper part of Figure 4. It is also proposed that various recombinations take place. This term is applied to the utilization of anhydro end groups in which the molar loss in reducing value is much less than the molar loss in periodate oxidizable groups. This reaction is illustrated by the lower equation in Figure 4. Carbon atoms 2, 3, or 4 may be involved in such recombinations.

A number of mechanisms may be involved in the roasting of acidified starch. With unacidified starch, the hydrolysis reversion mechanism probably plays a minor role and the 1,6-anhydro-D-glucose mechanisms, in which linkages in the polymer shift by degradation to 1,6-anhydro end-groups and reform at another position by reacting with another hydroxyl, are more important.

4. Polymerization of D-Glucose

Pursuing the study of dextrin formation from another point of view, Mora and co-workers (16, 17) examined the polymerization of D-glucose. D-Glucose was polymerized, with and without solvent, in vacuum by heating to predetermined temperatures (140°–170°) for various times in the presence of phosphorus acid as catalyst. Without acid, considerable decomposition and low degrees of polymerization were obtained. Phosphorus acid was considered the most effective catalyst being highly nucleophilic, nonvolatile, and nonoxidative in properties. Products having number average molecular weights of from 5,000 to 30,000 were produced.

Fractionations indicated that the solubility of the dextrin polymers in water–ethanol apparently varied with both the molecular weight and

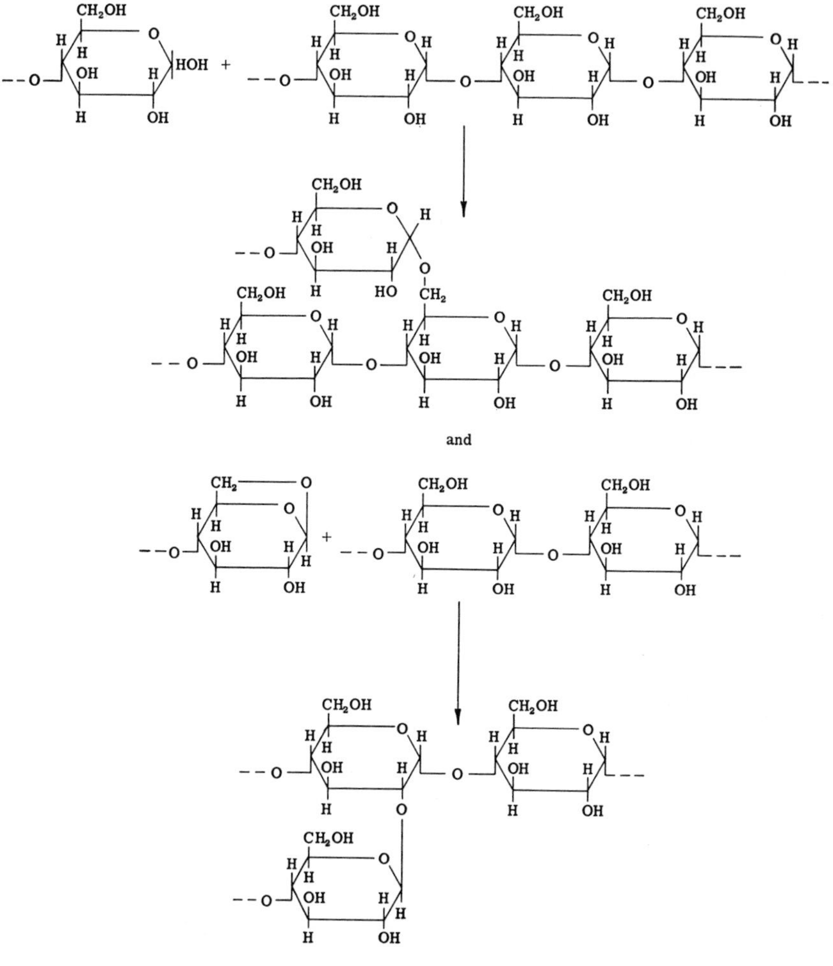

FIG. 4.—Two possible recombination reactions.

variation in structure (degree of branching). Higher polymerization temperatures increased the degree of branching which also increased with increasing molecular weight. These workers were unable in some instances to get the full degree of acetylation by standard procedures with certain polymers indicating the possibility of some (6 → 6) type ether linkages.

5. Fractionation of Dextrins

Several commercial corn and wheat dextrins were fractionated and their compositions studied by methylation and periodate oxidation by Smith and co-workers (18–20). In the analysis of the corn dextrin (18), it was found that the D-glucose units stable to periodate oxidation were 5% higher than in the original starch. Analysis of the hydrolyzed methylated dextrin shows the complexity of the dextrin structure (Table I).

Table I
Hydrolysis Products from Methylated Corn Starch Dextrin (18)

Methyl derivative of D-glucose	Yield	
	%	Mole ratio
2,3,4,6-Tetra-O-	16.5	35
2,3,6-Tri-O-	57.3	123
2,3,4-Tri-O-	2.6	6
2,4,6-Tri-O-	1.2	3
2,3-Di-O-	6.3	14
2,6-Di-O-	10.0	21
3.6-Di-O-	3.2	7
2-O-	1.5	3
3-O-	0.8	1.7
6-O-	0.5	1

These authors consider that transglucosidation is a major mechanism in the development of the highly branched products used in this work.

In a similar manner, a canary wheat dextrin (19) was subjected to periodate and methylation studies. The results are tabulated in Table II.

Table II
Hydrolysis Products from Methylated Wheat Starch Dextrin (19)

Methyl derivative of D-glucose	Yield	
	%	Mole ratio
2,3,4,6-Tetra-O-	12.2	31.5
2,3,6-Tri-O-	74.8	208
2,3-Di-O-	3.9	11.5
2,6-Di-O-	7.9	23
2-O-	0.9	3
3-O-	0.3	1

Periodate oxidation studies indicated that the molecule has an average repeating unit of 8-D-glucose residues. This dextrin also contains about 10% D-glucose stable to periodate oxidation, leading to the conclusion that it, too, is a highly branched polymer in which the units are joined together by a wide variety of glycosidic bonds.

6. Summary

As a result of the work to date, it is apparent that in the early stages of dextrinization, hydrolysis is the major reaction. It is during this period that the viscosity of the starch is substantially reduced to near the level of the finished dextrin. Although some reversion is possible during this phase, the repolymerization reaction becomes a major factor in the mechanism as the temperature rises. As the reaction progresses, an equilibrium viscosity is approached, and at increasing temperatures, it appears that a transglucosidation reaction predominates. The detailed mechanism, as well as the exact nature of the linkages present in various types of dextrins and British gums, is not completely understood at this time.

III. Basic Technology of Process

The manufacture of dextrin in the dry state is practiced to obtain products which are partially or entirely cold water soluble and which have lower viscosities than the native starch. These products have a combination of specific properties especially suitable for industrial applications.

There are four major steps in the production of pyrodextrins: acidification, predrying, dextrinization, and cooling.

1. Acidification

Basically, acidification is accomplished by spraying powdered starch, which should contain at least 5% of moisture to minimize danger of specking with a dilute solution of acid, usually hydrochloric acid, salts or other chemicals.

Due to the variations in the purity of some starches, it is necessary to predetermine the ease with which they may be expected to convert. Determination of the pH in a 1:2 suspension, the acid factor, and the ash of the starch is usually sufficient, although the fiber content is sometimes determined on tapioca samples. The acid factor is that quantity of 0.1N hydrochloric acid necessary to bring a 1:2 suspension of 25.0 grams of dry starch to a pH of 3.0. From these three tests it can be determined whether the sample is what is known in the trade as a "soft" or "hard" flour. A "soft" flour (starch) is one that will convert to a given degree with relatively little treatment. Tapioca starch, which dextrinizes easily, would have a pH of 4.5–5.5, a low acid factor, and an ash of less than 0.1%.

The primary concern in acidification is the uniform distribution of the catalyst in the starch. For this reason, a volatile acid is generally employed. The time of mixing, the moisture content, and the temperature of the starch are also important factors in this operation.

Although the acid (0.05% to 0.15%) is generally sprayed into starch agitated in a horizontal or vertical mixer, there are patents claiming advantages in the use of gaseous hydrogen chloride as recommended by several workers (21–24). Lenders (25) acidified the starch in suspension and removed the excess water in vacuum, while Gore (26) added a small quantity of dextrin to the acid and produced starch pellets which were dextrinized.

Oxidative catalysts have also been employed in the hope of obtaining more stable dextrins by the introduction of carboxyl groups during the dextrinization process. The use of chlorine is exemplified in the processes of Berquist (27), Fuller (28, 29), and Kerr (30) in which superior products are claimed. Bulfer and Gapen (31) treated starch with monochloroacetic acid and later with chlorine gas, which is said to be especially effective in producing white dextrins of improved smoothness, tack, and adhesiveness. Their films are said to have greater luster and whiteness.

Although hydrochloric acid is generally used in dextrinization, nitric acid is also employed (32). In addition to acting as an acid, it also acts as an oxidizing agent serving to alter the color, particularly when used in making potato dextrins.

Kerr (33) recommends the use of aluminum chloride as a converting agent. This catalyst is added to the starch slurry to the extent of 0.05% to 0.50% on the weight of the starch at a pH of 2.8 to 3.4. It is claimed that improved products are produced in a shorter converting period. Staerkle and Meier (34) used both formaldehyde and acid and converted in vacuum to produce acetal derivatives while dextrinizing. Bloede (35) suggested the use of calcium chloride, which acts both as a catalyst and a modifying agent.

It is also possible to add alkaline reagents such as sodium phosphate, sodium bicarbonate or triethanolamine to the starch before dextrinization. These products act as buffers, particularly in the production of British gums in which some acidity develops at high temperatures. Clegg (36) added ammonium hydroxide, and Caesar (37) converted with urea after heating the starch to 132°.

2. Predrying

Depending upon the specific operation and type of dextrin desired, the acidified starch may or may not be dried prior to conversion. Moisture promotes hydrolytic reactions and is particularly deleterious to conversions such as yellow dextrinizations where products having high cold water solubility and good solution stability or resistance to pasting are desired. The predrying operation may be done in the regular dextrin cooker or in some other unit designed to remove moisture rapidly with minimal total heating. In this step the moisture may be lowered to about 1–5%.

3. Converting

The actual conversion usually is made in vertically or horizontally mounted mixers which may be heated by steam or oil jackets or by direct heat. They may hold anywhere from a few hundred to several thousand pounds of starch.

The number of dextrins produced commercially is comparatively large, many of these are made for a specific purpose and some to customer specifications. Acidity, time, and cooking temperature schedule are critical factors determining the viscosity of the product.

The rate at which the temperature is raised and the residual moisture content during the heating period are somewhat critical in a bulk type converter generally referred to as a "cooker." If the moisture content is high and the temperature is brought up slowly, low viscosity products having high reducing sugar contents are produced. The rate of heating, however, is limited by the maximum temperature differential which can be tolerated without charring the starch against the walls of the heating elements. A stream of air is sometimes used to reduce the moisture content more rapidly. Staerkle and Meier (34) suggest the use of vacuum during this phase of the heating period.

If the starch is brought up to a final temperature of 95° to 120° at certain acidifications, white products are obtained; at higher temperatures (150° to 180°) a series of low viscosity canary dextrins are produced. The maximum temperatures used industrially in the manufacture of British gums are about 170° to 195°; these products are held in the cooker for 7 hours or more.

Brindle (38) and Horesi (39) sprayed an acidified starch suspension into hot air to produce the dry starch, then heated the starch to produce dextrin; Stutzke (40) and Singer (41) conducted a similar operation producing the dextrin during the drying stage.

4. Cooling

The dextrin, as it leaves the converter, is at temperatures of from 90° to 205°. It is in an active state of conversion and, therefore, must be cooled as rapidly as possible to prevent overconversion. This is accomplished by transferring the hot dextrin to a cooling mixer or conveyer where it is agitated and cooled by means of a cold water jacket. At this time the acid may be neutralized if desired.

In some operations, the dextrin is then rehumidified by allowing it to regain moisture from the air or by exposure to moist air while falling through a shaft.

IV. CHANGES TAKING PLACE DURING DEXTRINIZATION

It is obvious that, because of the nature of the dextrinization process and the molecular complexity of the starch, an almost unlimited number of dextrin structures are possible. Complications, however, are considerably reduced by the fact that all the variations in structure lead to only two major characteristic changes. One is the molecular size of the dextrin molecule, the other is essentially a change in the degree of linearity. Each of these changes has a specific effect on the physical and chemical characteristics of the dextrin. Variation in the average molecular weight influences the viscosity of the dextrin, while the change in linearity greatly influences the solution stability characteristics.

There are numerous parameters by which a dextrin may be characterized and which may be used to follow the progress of the conversion. A hypothetical series of curves have been set up in Figure 5 to illustrate the changes taking place during dextrinization.

1. Moisture

As would be expected, the moisture content of the starch, which initially may be as high as 20%, is gradually reduced during the dextrinization process. The final moisture content ranges from about 3 to 5% for white dextrins and is usually less than 2% for canary dextrins. In contact with the normal humidity of the atmosphere, however, dextrin may regain moisture up to a final content of 8–10%.

2. Granule

Little or no change takes place in the superficial appearance of the starch granule during commercial dextrinization. For this reason the botanical origin of the dextrin may be identified from its microscopic appearance in glycerol. When examined in water the granules may show signs of exfoliation and structural weakening depending upon the extent of dextrinization.

3. Viscosity

The change in the viscosity of a starch during dextrinization is shown graphically in Figure 5. As the acidified starch is heated, there is a rapid drop in the viscosity during the early stages of heating. This is confirmed by the work of Kerr and Cleveland (7) in which amylose was dextrinized, the major change in viscosity taking place during the

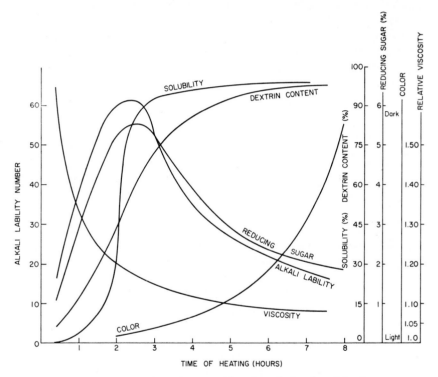

TIME OF HEATING (HOURS)

Fig. 5.—Characteristic changes taking place during dextrinization.

first hour of heating. The rate of hydrolysis is a function of the acidity and can become very rapid at high acidities. There is, however, a limit beyond which the viscosity will not fall. It is apparently the result of an equilibrium between two simultaneous reactions, hydrolysis and repolymerization. At very high temperatures there is a tendency for the equilibrium to shift to slightly higher viscosities.

The viscosity of dextrins is usually measured by special pipets or by the use of standard instruments which measure the viscosity in centipoises. Fetzer and co-workers (42) suggest the use of a special funnel for the determination of the viscosity of dextrin pastes.

4. Solubility

In the early stages of dextrinization there is little change in the cold water solubility of the starch, but as the temperature reaches 130°–145° under acidic conditions the solubility rapidly approaches the 100% level (Figure 5). Cooked pastes of these products, however, are unstable and set back to thick gels on cooling. The rise in solubility is due primarily to the shortening of the chain lengths of the starch with a corresponding weakening of the hydrogen bonds holding the granule together. This at first allows some parts of the granule to be dispersed in cold water, and later the entire granule becomes cold water soluble.

Many white dextrins have partial solubility in cold water, while all fully converted dextrins are practically 100% soluble. British gums, depending on their level of conversion, may vary in solubility from only a few percent to nearly 100 percent.

5. Reducing Sugar

The reducing sugar content or dextrose equivalent (D.E.) of starch during the initial heating period is a function of the change in viscosity and, therefore, reaches a maximum figure at about the time the viscosity reaches a minimum value (Figure 5). During this period saccharides including D-glucose, maltose and oligosaccharides are formed which give a white dextrin an exceptionally high reducing value.

Repolymerization of these low-molecular-weight compounds at high temperatures results in a corresponding decrease in the reducing sugar content of the dextrin; the final reducing sugar content of a canary dextrin is as low as 1%. Industrially, reducing sugars are generally determined by one of the copper reducing procedures, such as the reduction of Fehling solution.

6. Alkali Lability

Schoch and Jensen (43) devised a procedure to determine the sensitivity of a starch product to the action of hot sodium hydroxide solution. The resulting alkali number is the milliliters of $0.1N$ sodium hydroxide consumed by 1 gram of starch sample after a 1-hr. heating period in a boiling water bath. Under these conditions, amylose gives values of 20–30 ml. per gram, while amylopectin gives figures as low as 8–10 ml. per gram; ordinary starches are in the range of 11–15 ml. per gram.

During the course of conversion, as the chain lengths become shorter, there is an increase in the alkali number of the product; the maximum figures are about 60–70 ml. per gram. On continued roasting with a change to the more branched type structures, the alkali numbers of the canary dextrins are gradually reduced to values of 15–20 ml. per gram (Figure 5).

7. Specific Rotation

During the early stages of conversion, when the products are white, the specific rotation of the sample remains high and is between $+180°$ and $+195°$, but, as repolymerization and transglucosidation predominate, these figures fall to as low as $+150°$. This drop in specific rotation is due to the formation of many new β-D bonds which have a lower inherent rotation.

8. Dextrin Content

In some patent literature, identification of the dextrin is limited by the use of the term "dextrin content." This is an arbitrary term in which the "dextrin content" is that portion of a given product which is soluble in one-half saturated barium hydroxide solution at a dextrin concentration of 1%. This evaluation has been considered in a paper by Caesar and Cushing (44) which shows that the dextrin content varies with the degree of conversion. A number of curves point out the relationship between the various parameters and the dextrin content. It is pointed out that "except at relatively low temperatures and times of conversion the barium hydroxide method of evaluating 'dextrin' is in reasonably close accord with the solubility values for high acid types of converted starch products." There are, however, other types of conversion giving products in which the "dextrin content" tends to parallel the viscosity.

9. Solution Characteristics

The solution stability of dextrins varies over a wide range. Stable solutions of white dextrins can be obtained by the addition of borax in an alkaline solution or by the use of certain stabilizers such as urea. The well-known library pastes are made from various grades of white dextrin and plasticizers.

Solution stability of canary dextrins is generally of more importance since there are many operations in which complete stability at high solids and under acidic conditions is required. Dextrins derived from various starches, when well converted, have different stability characteristics. Those made from the waxy starches, tapioca, and potato starch tend to be stable, while canary corn dextrins, although not unstable, are highly thixotropic at high solids. Thixotropy is that property of a corn dextrin which prevents a solution of the product from flowing freely when not agitated. The thixotropic effect shown by corn dextrins appears to be due primarily to the presence of the fatty acids in the corn starch granule. This impurity appears to interfere with the normal reactions taking place during dextrinization, resulting in complexes with some starch fragments which set up the thixotropic character.

10. Color and Response to Beta Amylase Action

The color of a dextrin is influenced by the acidity and the temperature during conversion. Those products made at low temperatures are substantially white in color, while those made at increasingly higher temperatures become darker and darker shades of brown. The greater the acidity at a given temperature, the darker the color.

When white dextrins are subjected to the action of β-amylase, the degree of conversion to maltose is very similar to that found for the original starch. As the conversion temperature is increased, there is a decrease in the action of the amylase, as has been pointed out by Brimhall (4) and Kerr and Cleveland (7). Highly converted canary dextrins, as well as British gums, convert only to the extent of 12–15% maltose.

V. RELATIONSHIP BETWEEN CONVERSION CONDITIONS AND PROPERTIES

1. White Dextrins

The first step in the dextrinization of starch is one of hydrolysis. This reaction takes place at low temperatures in the presence of the moisture in the starch and gives rise to a series of polymer fragments of varying molecular sizes. Depending upon the quantity of acid used, white dextrins varying from thin boiling starches to products of minimum viscosities can be produced. If made at low temperatures, these dextrins vary in solubility in cold water from 0% to about 90%.

Fractionation of white dextrins reveal their heterogeneity. They contain a wide range of molecular species down to and including D-glucose. The presence of low-molecular-weight oligosaccharides and D-glucose accounts for the high reducing sugars usually associated with these dextrins.

Assuming that the composition of starch is a mixture of linear and branched chain material in the ratio of 25:75, it can be calculated that the average degree of branching of these dextrins will be about 3% unless there is some preferential hydrolysis of the (1 → 6) linkages in the amorphous regions of the starch granule. The latter possibility has been suggested by Kerr (45) and would lead to somewhat lower degrees of branching. White dextrins can then be considered to be a series of products having an average degree of branching of about 3% and covering a wide range of polymerization depending upon their viscosity. Products which may be considered as white dextrins by color can also be produced by slightly increasing the conversion temperatures and thereby increasing somewhat the solubility of the product at a given viscosity. Such highly converted white dextrins will still set back after cooking, although they will have a somewhat higher degree of branching and correspondingly greater stability than the true white dextrins.

2. Canary Dextrins

When the temperatures used in converting the acidified starch are considerably increased over those used in the manufacture of white dextrins, the product takes on a tan color and has considerable solubility. The product is more tacky and gum-like when dissolved in water.

It is now well established (4, 7, 10, 18, 19) that, during this phase of the conversion, a considerable degree of branching develops because of repolymerization and transglucosidation. The results of various workers indicate that the average degree of branching in these products may be as high as 20% as compared with the 2–3% of branching in a white dextrin. This modification accounts for the major change in the character of the dextrin.

Fractionation of a tapioca dextrin of this type shows a high percentage of the material concentrated in the intermediate fraction. Both the high- and low-molecular-weight products have substantially disappeared from the mixture. With canary corn dextrin, there is a small quantity (about 10%) of a high-molecular-weight fraction which is believed to be associated with the fatty acids (about 0.65%) and is responsible for the thixotropic character of these dextrins.

Products of different viscosities can be obtained by varying the acidity and temperature during conversion; the colors vary from pale amber to dark brown. If the conversions are stopped short of full dextrinization, products of intermediate characteristics can be produced. A number of starches give canary dextrins of very high solution stabilities at solids concentrations as high as 70%.

3. British Gums

Although both white dextrins and canary dextrins are made from acidified starch, British gums are made by heating untreated or buffered starch to a high temperature. Due to the absence of acidic catalyst, there is little hydrolytic breakdown and the transglucosidation reaction is very slow. It is, therefore, necessary to convert British gums over long periods of time (up to as long as 18 hours) to produce the necessary rearrangements in the molecules of the product. The resulting high-molecular-weight structures can be considered as highly branched glucans (4) similar to canary dextrins, the degree of branching again being in the order of 20–25%.

British gums give cooked sols which are more stable than white dextrins of comparable viscosities. Because of their high molecular weight, British gums generally tend to set back more than the lower molecular weight yellow dextrins.

The general relationship existing among the dextrins is shown diagrammatically in Figure 6. High viscosity products are represented at the top of the chart as thin boiling starch on the left and British gum

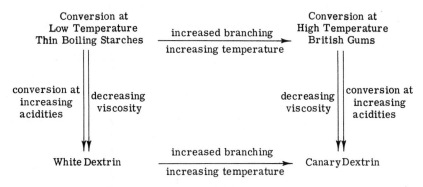

FIG. 6.—Relationship between various starch degradation products.

on the right. Increasing the acidity at which the dextrinization is conducted results in products of lower viscosity, while increasing the temperature increases the degree of branching (reduces linearity) and improves the stability. The lowest viscosity white dextrins and the fully converted canary dextrins are shown at the bottom of the chart.

VI. EQUIPMENT TECHNOLOGY

There have been many types of converters in use in the manufacture of dextrin. In 1907, Fielding (46) introduced acid and steam into starch in a rotating cylinder mounted on trunnions. Merrill (47, 48) has patented the use of a vertical circular vessel in which the sides and bottoms are heated, the heating elements extend up from the bottom in the center of the vessel. Countercurrent agitation is used together with hot air to dry the starch.

Conversions have also been made by suspending the acidified starch in an immiscible liquid and heating (49) and by forcing the starch suspension at high pressure into a hot air chamber (50). Horesi (39) converted acidified starch, containing 45% of moisture, by passing it through three mills containing air at the proper temperature. The first mill dried the starch; the second converted it at 149°, and the third cooled the product which was then collected in a dust collector. Neuman (51) has patented the use of dielectric heating, between the plates of a condenser, as a means of dextrinizing starch.

Common equipment for the manufacture of dextrin is the bulk-type converter in which up to several thousand pounds of starch is converted at one time. In these roasters, the mass of acidified starch is stirred slowly by a gear-driven, horizontal or vertical ribbon agitator. Heating is effected in one of four ways: (a) by the use of steam coils in the side and bottom wall, (b) by the circulation of hot oil at high temperatures, (c) by the circulation of the products of gas combustion or (d) by maintaining of steam under pressure in the jacket.

Disadvantages of this type of cooker are the difficulty of producing a uniform temperature throughout the mass of starch and the slow rate at which it can be heated. At 205° the starch scorches; for this reason the best quality products are made at lower temperatures. The rate of heat transfer is dependent upon the agitation.

Rowe and Hagen (52) have patented an improved steam-jacketed cooker containing a vertical agitator. The jacket is divided into a plurality of circular steam ducts, each containing a steam inlet and condenser outlet so arranged that the steam must flow in a continuous stream throughout the length of the ducts.

Phillips (53) developed a continuous conversion process in which a thin layer of acidified starch is carried on a belt moving through heated ovens at a uniform speed.

More recently, Staerkle and Meier (54) patented a process in which the starch is dextrinized in a nonoxidizing environment to avoid discoloration. These conditions are obtained by the use of vacuum or an atmosphere of nitrogen, sulfur dioxide, carbon dioxide, or the like. The acid is applied to the starch as a vapor after partial vacuum drying. It is stated that other chemicals may be added as desired and that derivatives of the products may be prepared during dextrinization.

Ziegler and co-workers (55) devised a method for roasting dextrin in which the starch is passed through a heated spiral tube conveyer. The starch is moved through the tube by means of vibrations of a frequency of 1250 per minute and an amplitude of 2–4 mm. The dextrinized starch is discharged from an opening at the end of the conveyer.

In another recent development, Fredrickson (56) converted starch in a fluidized bed. By the addition of 1% of calcium phosphate, the starch is readily fluidized (57). Claims are made for considerable improvement in the dextrinization with regard to time, control, and quality. It is stated that, when a gas is passed through the fluidized bed, the vapors can be adjusted to all variables including acidity, humidity, and temperature. Since the gas is recycled, adjustments can be made at any time during the operation, or the dextrinization may be run continuously. By this procedure the starch may be dried, acidified, dextrinized, neutralized, cooled, and conditioned with respect to moisture content all in one operation. The dextrin also may be blended with any other agents at the same time.

Goerner (58) describes a complete plant for the continuous manufacture of dextrin which is in operation in Germany. The starch is stored in silos from which it is carried pneumatically to the acidifiers in which acid is sprayed through turbo nozzles. The thoroughly mixed, acidified starch is pumped to a predryer in which the moisture content is reduced to 2–3% under vacuum. It is then conveyed pneumatically to a kiln-type dextrinizer which is about 3 feet in diameter and about 20 feet long, rotates at 3 to 12 rpm., and operates at a steam pressure of 8–10 atmospheres. After dextrinization, the product is again conveyed pneumatically into a cooling tower in which it is allowed to fall through cool air. The dextrin then is mixed, sifted, and passed through a remoistening tower several times wherein it comes in contact with a fog of moist air. After resifting it is put into storage containers.

VII. Applications

Most uses for dextrins are dependent upon the ability of their aqueous solutions to form films capable of bonding similar or dissimilar surfaces. In general, raw starches provide the strongest films and have the best adhesive strength. Dextrins, while lacking the inherent film strength of native starches, often have characteristics essential in coating, binding, and adhesive applications which are lacking in raw starches. Their relatively lower viscosities allow their use at high concentrations; as a result their films dry faster and provide much faster tack than those of native starch. Solution stability at high concentrations is much better than that of the parent starch. Consequently, they are more readily formulated in adhesives, and the resulting adhesive has much better working properties than one made with native starch. The solubility of dextrins in cold water is greater than that of native starch; this permits using them in applications requiring partially or totally soluble binders.

The adhesive industry uses substantial amounts of white dextrins, British gums, and yellow dextrins in the preparation of liquid and dry adhesives. These products are used as back seam and front seam gums for envelopes, as bottle labeling adhesives, as adhesives for remoistening gummed tape, postage stamps, lined cardboard boxes, and in many other applications. Many of these adhesives contain additives to modify the solution or film properties of the dextrin. Borax (sodium tetraborate) is one of the most common additives used with dextrins. Depending upon the application and the nature of the dextrin, the amount of borax may range up to 20% of the weight of the dextrin. The presence of borax in this range increases the viscosity of the dextrin solution, stabilizes it, and makes it more cohesive. The addition of borax lowers the concentration at which a dextrin film loses free water and forms a hydrogel. Borax increases the rate at which a dextrin sol develops tack.

The effects of borax are usually most marked at low levels of addition. However, the borax effect may be further increased by the addition of sodium hydroxide which converts the borax to sodium metaborate. With the addition of sodium hydroxide, there is a further increase in viscosity, stability, and tack until all the borax has been converted to metaborate. Additions of sodium hydroxide beyond this point will cause the viscosity to drop. Besides increasing the viscosity and tack of borated dextrins, addition of sodium hydroxide also increases the penetration and bite of dextrin adhesives.

Sugar, corn syrup, glycerol, and other polyhydroxy compounds are used in dextrin adhesives to plasticize their films and reduce the tendency of the film to become brittle at low humidities. Urea and dicyandiamide sometimes are used to reduce the viscosity of a dextrin or British gum solution and to stabilize it against set-back.

Intermediate and high viscosity dextrins and gums are also used in the manufacture of paper, primarily to bind pigments such as clay to paper in the paper coating process. Oxidized starches, acid-modified starches, hydroxyethylated starches, and enzyme-converted starches are also used in the manufacture of coated papers. The choice of the particular binder will depend upon the economics and specific requirements of the operation. Pyrodextrins are used in high solids machine coatings in which the low viscosity and high binding strength of their coating colors permit use at higher solids than other types of starch binders. Kerr and Schink (59) demonstrated the superiority of certain pyrodextrins over other types of converted starches in high solids coatings.

Dextrins are used in the glass fiber industry as sizes for glass fiber immediately after it has been formed by extrusion of the molten glass through a plantinum orifice. The dextrin forms a film which acts as a sheath for the fiber to protect it against abrasion. White dextrins are used in textile finishing in order to impart stiffness to certain types of interlining fabrics. Dextrins are preferred in such applications because their low viscosity permits application at high solids.

There are many other industrial uses in which dextrins or British gums act as binders. These include core binders in foundary operations, binders for water colors, binders for mineral aggregates, insecticides, briquettes, and so on.

Dextrins and British gums are also used as thickeners for textile printing pastes, which consist of aqueous solutions of chemicals and dyestuffs or pigments. British gums not only function to thicken the paste, but also to modify its rheological properties so that it will flow readily into the printing roll engravings or through a printing screen. They also prevent the paste on the cloth from flowing.

Cold-water-soluble dextrins are used as carriers for active ingredients such as food flavors where their low viscosity and solubility are of advantage. They are also used as diluents and carriers for dyestuffs.

The pharmaceutical industry uses white dextrins as carbohydrate nutrient sources in the preparation of certain antibiotics by fermentation. They are used in situations in which a slowly assimilable polysaccharide is needed in contrast to a readily assimilable carbohydrate such as D-glucose. Johnson, Koepsell, and Churchill (60) mention an example of such a use in a neomycin fermentation medium. Dextrins are preferred over native and thin-boiling starches in situations where the carbohydrate is used at high solids and the high viscosity of starches would interfere with the agitation and aeration of the nutrient medium.

While traditional uses for dextrins continue, the number of uses is expanding as new products and applications develop. In many cases, these demand entirely new types of dextrins and combinations of properties. To meet these needs, there is continuing research directed toward the development of new products and new markets.

VIII. REFERENCES

(1) J. R. Katz, Rec. Trav. Chim., **53**, 555 (1934).
(2) J. R. Katz and A. Weidinger, Z. Physik. Chem., A., **184**, 100 (1939).
(3) N. P. Badenhuizen and J. R. Katz, Z. Physik. Chem., A, **182**, 73 (1938).
(4) B. Brimhall, Ind. Eng. Chem., **36**, 72 (1944).
(5) G. V. Caesar, In "Chemistry and Industry of Starch," R. W. Kerr, ed., Academic Press Inc., 2nd Ed., 1950, p. 353.
(6) H. Rüggeberg, Staerke, **4**, 78 (1952).
(7) R. W. Kerr and F. Cleveland, Staerke, **5**, 261 (1953).
(8) A. Frey and E. Lottner, Staerke, **5**, 56 (1953).
(9) M. L. Wolfrom, A. Thompson, and R. B. Ward, Ind. Eng. Chem., **53**, 217 (1961).
(10) A. Thompson and M. L. Wolfrom, J. Am. Chem. Soc., **80**, 6618 (1958).

(11) M. L. Wolfrom, A. Thompson, and R. B. Ward, *J. Am. Chem. Soc.*, **81,** 4623 (1959).
(12) M. L. Wolfrom, A. Thompson, and R. B. Ward, *J. Org. Chem.*, **26,** 4617 (1961).
(13) W. G. Parks, R. M. Esteve, Jr., M. H. Gollis, R. Guercia, and A. Petrarca, *Abstr. Papers, Am. Chem. Soc.*, **127,** 6E (1955).
(14) R. J. Dimler, H. A. Davis, and G. E. Hilbert, *J. Am. Chem. Soc.*, **68,** 1377 (1946).
(15) J. S. Carvalho, W. Prins, and C. Schuerch, *J. Am. Chem. Soc.*, **81,** 4054 (1959).
(16) P. T. Mora and J. W. Wood, *J. Am. Chem. Soc.*, **80,** 685 (1958).
(17) P. T. Mora, J. W. Wood, P. Maury, and B. G. Young, *J. Am. Chem. Soc.*, **80,** 693 (1958).
(18) J. D. Geerdes, B. A. Lewis, and F. Smith, *J. Am. Chem. Soc.*, **79,** 4209 (1957).
(19) G. M. Christensen and F. Smith, *J. Am. Chem. Soc.*, **79,** 4492 (1957).
(20) G. M. Christensen, Ph.D. Thesis, Univ. of Minnesota, St. Paul, Minn., 1957; *Dissertation Abstr.*, **19,** 2450 (1959).
(21) L. E. Smith and S. G. Morris, *Ind. Eng. Chem.*, **36,** 1052 (1944).
(22) S. G. Morris, U.S. Patent 2,359,378 (1944); *Chem. Abstr.*, **39,** 832 (1945).
(23) W. Browing and J. S. Barlow, U.S. Patent 773,469 (1904).
(24) A. Fielding, Brit. Patent 22,455 (1910).
(25) A. W. H. Lenders, U.S. Patent 1,305,291 (1919); *Chem. Abstr.*, **13,** 2143 (1919).
(26) H. C. Gore, U.S. Patent 1,335,162 (1920); *Chem. Abstr.*, **14,** 1617 (1920).
(27) C. Berquist, U.S. Patent 1,851,749 (1932); *Chem. Abstr.*, **26,** 3135 (1932).
(28) A. D. Fuller, U.S. Patent 1,937,752 (1933); *Chem. Abstr.*, **28,** 1214 (1932).
(29) A. D. Fuller, U.S. Patent 1,942,544 (1934); *Chem. Abstr.*, **28,** 1888 (1934).
(30) R. W. Kerr, U.S. Patent 2,108,862 (1938); *Chem. Abstr.*, **32,** 3188 (1938).
(31) A. J. Bulfer and C. C. Gapen, U.S. Patent 2,287,599 (1942); *Chem. Abstr.*, **37,** 280 (1943).
(32) C. O'Neill, Brit. Patent 1,861 (1858).
(33) R. W. Kerr, U.S. Patent 2,503,053 (1950); *Chem. Abstr.*, **44,** 6180 (1950).
(34) M. A. Staerkle and E. Meier, U.S. Patent 2,698,937 (1955); *Chem. Abstr.*, **49,** 4315 (1955).
(35) V. G. Bloede, U.S. Patent 536,260 (1895).
(36) J. E. Clegg, U.S. Patent 2,127,205 (1938); *Chem. Abstr.*, **32,** 8183 (1938).
(37) G. V. Caesar, U.S. Patent 2,131,724 (1938); *Chem. Abstr.*, **32,** 9341 (1938).
(38) R. G. Brindle, U.S. Patent 1,505,696 (1924); *Chem. Abstr.*, **18,** 3290 (1924).
(39) A. C. Horesi, U.S. Patent 2,274,789 (1942); *Chem. Abstr.*, **36,** 4366 (1942).
(40) R. W. G. Stutzke, U.S. Patent 1,320,719 (1919); *Chem. Abstr.*, **14,** 231 (1920).
(41) P. A. Singer, U.S. Patent 1,564,979 (1925); *Chem. Abstr.*, **20,** 516 (1926).
(42) W. R. Fetzer, E. K. Crosby, and R. E. Fullick, *Anal. Chem.*, **24,** 1671 (1952).
(43) T. J. Schoch and C. C. Jensen, *Ind. Eng. Chem., Anal. Ed.*, **12,** 531 (1940).
(44) G. V. Caesar and M. I. Cushing, *Ind. Eng. Chem.*, **31,** 921 (1939).
(45) R. W. Kerr, *Paper Trade J.*, **115,** 30 (1942).
(46) A. Fielding, Brit. Patent 20,488 (1907).
(47) J. J. Merrill, U.S. Patent 1,428,604 (1922); *Chem. Abstr.*, **16,** 3771 (1922).
(48) J. J. Merrill, U.S. Patent 1,425,497 (1922); *Chem. Abstr.*, **16,** 3410 (1922).
(49) H. E. Bode, U.S. Patent 2,156,488 (1939); *Chem. Abstr.*, **33,** 6084 (1939).
(50) R. W. G. Stutzke, U.S. Patent 1,516,512 (1924); *Chem. Abstr.*, **19,** 416 (1925).
(51) S. Neuman U.S. Patent 2,494,191 (1950); *Chem. Abstr.*, **44,** 2780 (1950).
(52) W. J. Rowe and C. Hagen, U.S. Patent 2,332,345 (1943); *Chem. Abstr.*, **38,** 1660 (1944).
(53) N. C. Phillips, U.S. Patent 1,894,570 (1933); *Chem. Abstr.*, **27,** 2599 (1933).
(54) M. A. Staerkle and E. Meier, U.S. Patent 2,698,818; *Chem. Abstr.*, **49,** 4314 (1955).

(55) C. Ziegler, R. Köhler, and H. Rüggeberg, U.S. Patent 2,818,357 (1957); *Chem. Abstr.*, **52,** 12438 (1958).

(56) R. E. C. Fredrickson, U.S. Patent 2,845,368 (1958); *Chem. Abstr.*, **53,** 2658 (1959).

(57) R. E. C. Fredrickson, U.S. Patent 3,003,894 (1961); *Chem. Abstr.*, **56,** 2624 (1962).

(58) A. Goerner, *Staerke*, **12,** 365 (1960).

(59) R. W. Kerr and N. F. Schink, *Paper Trade J.*, **120,** 145 (1945).

(60) L. E. Johnson, H. J. Koepsell, and B. W. Churchill, U.S. Patent 2,957,810; *Chem. Abstr.*, **52,** 9526 (1958).

CHAPTER XII

MODIFICATION AND USES OF WHEAT STARCH

By J. W. Knight

Corn Products Company, Ltd., Trafford Park, Manchester, England

I. Introduction

In some parts of the world where wheat is grown in large quantities, flour is the main source of starch. For example, in Australia and New Zealand, wheat starch is produced in much larger quantities than maize or sorghum starches.

Starch is usually extracted from wheat flour by a modified Martin process (*1*; This Volume, Chapt. II). The starch is used in the unmodified state or further processed into many different forms. These special starches each have particular properties which are required for many uses in widely differing industries.

II. Unmodified Wheat Starch

Commercial wheat starch, which is purer and whiter than most starches, has a moisture content of about 12% and a protein content of about 0.2% (N × 5.7). When this starch is squeezed or pressed, a decided "crunch" can be detected as the granules grind against each other. The granules in wheat starch fall into two distinct sizes, the smaller being as small as 2 μ in diameter and the larger measuring up to the 30 μ range. Granules intermediate in size are few. A photomicrograph of wheat starch granules is given in this volume, Chapter XXVII.

If a sample of wheat starch is compared with the starch present in the original flour, it will be found that the proportion of small granules is less in the extracted starch because the small granules are retained in the wheat gluten.

When wheat starch is added to water at room temperature, a slurry or suspension is formed from which the granules quickly settle. When the temperature of the slurry is raised to about 50°, the larger granules commence to swell because of the penetration of water through the weakened starch structure. Above 50°, the smaller granules also begin to swell although some of the smallest are very resistant to enlargement. At about 65°, the starch slurry begins to form a paste; when 70° is reached, most of the granular form of the starch has disappeared. Thus, the thin slurry has become a thick, semi-opaque paste and the viscosity is high because of the crowding effect of the swollen granules; or, stated in another way, because of the hydrodynamic force of the balloon-like granules in aqueous suspension.

If this cooked starch is subjected to high mechanical shear, the paste becomes thin and fluid because the fragmented granules are no longer elastic. Wheat starch, however, is less susceptible to thinning by shear than potato and waxy maize starches.

When cooked wheat starch paste is allowed to cool and age, the soft texture changes to a rigid gel and, finally, separation of free water occurs.

Like most of the common starches, wheat starch contains two types of molecules: linear, unbranched chains of D-glucopyranose units joined by α-D$(1 \rightarrow 4)$ linkages, and highly branched, structures in which most of the D-glucopyranose units are joined as in the linear type but at frequent points a D-glucopyranose unit is joined by an α-D$(1 \rightarrow 6)$ linkage.

Wheat starch contains about 30% of the amylose (linear) fraction and 70% of the amylopectin (branched) fraction. The long linear amylose molecules associate by hydrogen bonding producing bundles of molecules, and cause wheat starch pastes to form rigid gels. This behavior is in contrast to that of waxy sorghum or waxy maize starch pastes which do not form gels at normal concentrations since they do not contain amylose.

Unmodified wheat starch is used in a wide variety of industries. Examples of its use in foods are as a component of dried soups, as a thickener in canned foods, soups, and sauces, as an inert diluent in baking powder, as a custard powder when colored with an edible yellow dye, as an improver in cookie doughs to give increased spread and crispness, and, when mixed with edible oils, as a molding starch for gum candies. Its use as a replacement for 30% of the flour in angel food cake recipes increases the volume of the finished cake by about 10%, improves the grain and texture, and prolongs the shelf life. In pie pastry, it imparts better working and handling characteristics to the dough and a better appearance and more flakiness to the finished pastry; it also reduces the shortening requirement because the protein content of the dough has been reduced.

The non-food applications of wheat starch include its use as a beater additive in the manufacture of paper to increase the dry strength of the paper sheet, as an adhesive in the manufacture of corrugated boxes, as a sedimentation agent in the refining of bauxite, with borax as a laundering starch in institutions such as hospitals, and as a component of printing pastes, pharmaceutical tablets, and some types of cake soap.

III. Crystal Starch

This product is an old favorite in the domestic laundry. It is called crystal starch because the lumps or nuggets give the appearance of a crystalline structure. The product is made from a thick slurry of good quality wheat starch containing about 1% of borax and a whitener. The mixture is pressed into 6- or 12-in. cubes which are wrapped in brown paper and air dried at about 45° for 2 weeks. The blocks are then removed and gently broken up into the familiar hard nuggets.

Recently, a similar type of starch has been manufactured by continuously compacting starch between rolls (2). This process involves feeding warmed dry starch into the nip between two rolls under high mechanical pressure. Vacuum is applied at the nip to remove discharged air. The product comes from the rolls as a starch board which can be broken into dust-free nuggets.

IV. Precooked Wheat Starch

For some applications, a cold water pasting starch is required. This starch, normally prepared by cooking and drying on heated drums, hydrates in cold water to form a thick, viscous paste which undergoes some retrogradation or setback. Although wheat starch is not particularly sensitive to viscosity breakdown, as shown by a conventional pasting curve, some of its natural viscosity is lost when it is commercially drum pasted and dried. The reconstituted paste exhibits a lower viscosity because of greater granule fragmentation on the drums.

When precooked wheat starch is required for use in a food product, it is often desirable to remove the "wheaty" taste which is normally present. Storage of wheat starch in air-tight packages tends to intensify its mild taste which can become objectionable. These flavors (3, 4) are overcome by the use of trisodium phosphate or a sequestering agent during the cooking process.

Invariably some of the smaller sized wheat starch granules are not effectively swollen during most commercial precooking operations, so the final product is not fully precooked. Consequently, a precooked wheat starch is sometimes less satisfactory than precooked starches from other sources. Removal of the small granules from wheat starch should provide a more acceptable product.

However, in the manufacture of some canned soups, differential swelling of the large and small wheat starch granules is a valuable property. During manufacture, cooking conditions are regulated so that the large granules swell and thicken the soup to the consistency desired for easy processing while the small granules remain intact. When the canned soup is diluted with water and heated for serving, the small granules gelatinize and provide the desired consistency for serving. Of the common starches, only wheat starch has this unique property of double gelatinization.

When a fine powdered, precooked starch is added to water, immediate swelling of the particles occurs. Lumps are formed unless the starch is slowly sifted into water under vigorous agitation. These lumps, which have a layer of hydrated starch on the outside and dry starch in the center, are very difficult to disperse. The finer the precooked starch, the greater the rate of hydration and the greater the problem of lumping. This problem can be overcome by the use of a surfactant during manufacture which suppresses the rate of hydration and permits even wetting of the dry starch. An added effect of the surfactant is to give quick release of the dried film from the steam rolls. Borax can be used in conjunction with the surfactant when use in food is not involved. However, the technique of drum drying must be altered since the borax tends to form a "glass" on the drum surface that reduces the rate of drying. There is a tendency for flakes rather than a continuous film to be formed, although these effects depend on the amount of borax present.

Another method for drying precooked starches is by means of a spray dryer. The starch slurry is first cooked, either batchwise or continuously, and then dried by spraying, usually under pressure, into a drying chamber. Rapid evaporation of the water keeps the temperature of the solid particles low. Therefore, it is possible to use fairly high temperatures in the drying air without overheating the product. The dried product from a spray dryer is finely divided, and consists of hollow spheres. Its large surface area gives added lumping problems during rehydration unless special additives are used. Precooking offers the advantage of controlled cooking, which is not always obtained when the starch is cooked and dried on heated drums. Precooking can be continuous, as with a Votator, and continuous cooking equipment can be used in conjunction with a drum dryer as well as with a spray dryer. Drum drying capacity can be increased by as much as 25%.

In a comparison of costs for precooked starches produced by drum drying or spray drying, it must be remembered that heat efficiency and actual cost of drying are only a part of the over-all considerations. Spray drying of precooked starch offers good process control, high yields, and less grinding requirements for the finished product. On the other hand, the material is dusty, very low in bulk density, and may lump when dispersed in water.

Today more use is being made of precooked foods. A good example is the instant pudding which can be prepared rapidly and easily without cooking. A typical formula consists of sugar, anhydrous sodium pyrophosphate and anhydrous disodium phosphate, precooked wheat starch, and various coloring and flavoring agents.

Another product of interest to the housewife is instant laundry starch. This starch, when added to cold water, gives a slurry which is immediately suitable for starching fabrics. The older practice of preparing a cooked starch paste is thereby eliminated. A suitable instant laundry starch must disperse easily and rehydrate quickly without lumping. The paste must not thicken at the bottom of the container or starch will be deposited unevenly and the result is particularly objectionable on a colored garment. The starch shall not dull the color of the fabric but give "slip" to the iron and impart stiffness to the cloth.

All these requirements can be met by wheat starch that has been cooked in the presence of various additives, dried, and finely ground.

Many people do their own interior decorating using instant wallpaper paste. A good product can be made by precooking a borated wheat starch ether together with additives for good dispersion.

Another small but interesting domestic use of precooked wheat starch is in the manufacture of "finger paints" for young children. The precooked starch, colored with edible dyes, is easily mixed with cold water to form a paint that can be used by children.

Wheat starch is used, in some parts of the world, as a beater additive in the manufacture of paper. Sometimes wheat flour is used, but for better grades of paper the pure starch is required. It is either cooked continuously by the papermaker or used in the more expensive but convenient precooked form. The precooked wheat starch must be free-flowing for easy addition into the beater. Rate of hydration in the starch particle must be slow enough to prevent lumping before dispersion, because lumps will produce "fish eyes" or "windows" in the finished paper. These lumps can also clog the felts, Dandy roll, and suction boxes and cause sticking on the presses. To aid dispersion, surfactants, vegetable oils, hydrogenated phenols, and various inorganic salts, such as silicates, can be used.

In comparison with potato starch, which is widely used as a beater additive, slurried wheat starch tends to settle more quickly, but this does not adversely affect its utility as a beater additive. The basic merit of starch for this use lies in its ability to improve strength and surface properties of the finished paper. Properly processed wheat starch gives results comparable to those obtained with potato starch in most types of paper.

Another important outlet for the use of precooked wheat starch is the foundry. Sand cores are shaped in molds from a moistened mixture of sand and a binding agent and then baked. These baked cores are used for the production of hollow castings. The binding agent must give "green" strength to the wet core for handling before baking and provide "dry" strength after baking and "hot" strength during the pouring of the molten metal. It must not produce excessive gas during and after the pouring process since this weakens the casting by blow-hole formation. At the same time it should burn away evenly so that the sand can be recovered for re-use.

A good cereal core binding is made by precooking a mixture of flour and wheat starch; the ratio is about 80:20, respectively, but may vary for individual users. The binder should be high in protein and pentosan (pentoglycan) content since this imparts very high "green" bond strength. The bulk density of the cereal binder should be constant because it is measured in the foundry by volume instead of by weight. A slightly borated mixture, up to 1% borax, produces a more stable binder; the addition of sugar in the form of molasses also helps to stabilize the product. The flour–starch mixture is cooked on drums at a low steam pressure. The feed may be applied as a thin dough which permits a high rate of production.

Precooked starch is used extensively in the formulation of oil well drilling muds. These muds are used in the drilling operation to lubricate and cool the cutting bit, seal cavities, and carry the cuttings to the surface. Starch improves the viscosity and water-retaining characteristics of the mud. Precooked wheat starch for this purpose should be cooked under alkaline conditions and dried as a thin film for maximum viscosity.

A dry powdered mixture consisting of unmodified wheat starch, precooked wheat starch, and borax is often used as an adhesive for manufacture of corrugated paperboard. The precooked starch is included to provide the required viscosity in the aqueous mix and to keep the raw starch in suspension. The raw starch is cooked by the hot rolls in the corrugating machine and is the bonding substance. The aqueous mixture is made up with 2% caustic soda solution, which functions to disperse the precooked starch efficiently and to reduce the pasting temperature of the raw starch.

When a moisture resistant bond in the corrugated board is wanted, a phenol is added to the dry mix, and paraformaldehyde is added later to the liquid mix.

Wheat Starch can be usefully employed in the manufacture of roll dried adhesives and liquid adhesives. The roll dried adhesive is a convenient product which forms a paste when added to water while the liquid adhesive is ready for use. These two products are widely used in all the fields in which adhesives are required. Wheat starch is usually mixed with a waxy starch and pasted in the presence of caustic soda and other additives. After a period of heat treatment, the resulting thinned starch paste is dried on steam heated rolls and the film is ground and sieved. For the liquid adhesive, the drying operation is omitted.

Precooked wheat starch has been used as a flocculating agent. Varying degrees of success have been obtained in the treatment of coal wash water and uranium ores and in the clarification of river water.

V. Oxidized Wheat Starch

Oxidation of wheat starch with sodium hypochlorite introduces carboxyl and carbonyl groups into the starch to modify some of its characteristic properties. Products may be made ranging from super-thick to very low viscosity by varying the degree of oxidation. The oxidized starch pastes have improved paste stability, good film forming and adhesive properties, high clarity, and good color. These properties make oxidized wheat starches particularly useful in the paper (5) and textile industries. Low viscosity products can be used to prepare high solids pigmented coatings for paper having excellent printing characteristics.

For manufacture of oxidized wheat starch, a slurry is prepared in a suitably lined tank at a concentration so that the volume of water will dissipate the heat produced by the exothermic oxidation reaction and keep the temperature below 32°. Sodium hypochlorite solution is added, and the pH of the slurry is adjusted until it is definitely alkaline. When the oxidation is complete, sodium metabisulfite is added and the pH adjusted to about 4. The starch is then dewatered and washed, dewatered, and dried. The pH of the finished starch is between 6 and 7.

Oxidized wheat starch is used to prepare a convenient liquid laundry starch for consumer uses. This product can be mixed into water and used directly. For preparation, oxidized starch of the correct viscosity is thoroughly cooked in water with a preservative, dispersing agent, and a dye if the final product is to be colored. After cooling to about 35°, a solution of borax and sodium salts is added. Perfume and further preservatives are also added. After homogenizing, the liquid product is packaged.

A paste of oxidized wheat starch, containing various additives, has been used in the preparation of starch aerosols for laundry application.

VI. ACID-MODIFIED WHEAT STARCH

When wheat starch is treated with dilute acid at temperatures below its pasting temperature, the hot-paste viscosity is reduced to form a product known as a thin-boiling starch. The principal effect of the acid treatment is hydrolysis with increased tendency for gel formation. The starch granules appear unchanged by the treatment, but when the starch is pasted, the granules disintegrate and give a dispersion of low viscosity.

The usual manner of manufacture is to acidify a starch slurry with hydrochloric acid up to concentration of about 0.2N and then to heat the mixture to about 55° and maintain this temperature for several hours with stirring. When the desired thinning has taken place, the slurry is neutralized, washed, dewatered, and dried.

Acid-modified wheat starch may also be produced by a dry method that provides a low viscosity dextrin-type of product. The content of water solubles in this starch ranges from 2 to 10%.

The pronounced setback character of acid-modified wheat starch makes it very useful in confections such as gum candies. The starch can be used with sugar, color, and flavor; other colloids such as gelatin may also be included in the formula. The starch mixture is cooked and then poured into molds. After setting, the gums are removed from the molds and polished or given a sugar coating. The consistency of the finished gum can be varied by the degree of cooking which regulates the final moisture content. Sometimes the cooking is done on continuous as opposed to batch equipment.

Acid-modified wheat starch is also used in papermaking (5) and for warp sizing of textiles.

VII. WHEAT STARCH ETHERS

The introduction of a relatively small proportion of hydroxyalkyl groups into wheat starch gives a product still in granular form but having markedly different properties. Derivatives produced from ethylene or propylene oxide gelatinize at a lower temperature and undergo a more rapid viscosity increase than the original starch. The pastes are long bodied and cohesive and have an increased capacity to hold water. As a result, they penetrate less and form a more continuous film when used as a surface size for paper. The films have greater transparency, flexibility, and water solubility than those from the unmodified wheat starch. The ethers are more reactive toward borax, which thickens the pastes, and toward various synthetic resins, which render the paste insoluble.

Wheat starch hydroxyethyl ethers can be manufactured in a wide range of viscosities and with varying degrees of substitution. First, a wheat starch slurry is acid-modified to the desired viscosity and sodium chloride and sodium hydroxide are added to the resulting slurry. Sodium hydroxide catalyzes the etherification reaction and sodium chloride suppresses the swelling of the starch granules in the alkaline medium. The temperature of the slurry is raised to 50°, and the system is flushed with nitrogen. The required weight of ethylene oxide gas is fed into the slurry with efficient stirring. When the reaction is complete, the pH is adjusted to 6.5 and the starch is washed, dewatered, and dried. Impurities, particularly protein, interfere with the substitution; therefore, the original wheat starch should be very pure.

The paper industry in Australia and various other parts of the world uses these starch ethers as a surface size. Because of their excellent water holding and film forming properties, the hydroxyethyl ethers are used extensively for improving the surface and strength properties of paper. Their films are resistant to greases and waxes and they can sometimes be used in place of natural gums. They can be used at the size tub or press and also at the calender stacks. The flow, filming, and aging characteristics of the wheat starch ethers make them adaptable to a wide variety of general adhesive uses. A very good adhesive for the single lining of board, for example with glassine, can be prepared from the hydroxyalkyl ether mixed with clay, sugar, and sodium nitrate. Dextrinized wheat starch ethers can be used for case glues, label glues, and envelope adhesives.

The textile industry uses large amounts of wheat starch hydroxyalkyl ethers for warp sizing, finishing, and printing of fabrics, and polishing and glazing of threads and cords.

VIII. TORREFACTION DEXTRINS FROM WHEAT STARCH

A wide range of dextrins can be made from wheat starch by the application of heat, with or without a catalyst. In a typical method of manufacture, commercially dry wheat starch is acidified with a mineral acid, usually hydrochloric acid. The acid, diluted with water, is often sprayed on to the starch which is continuously mixed or recirculated. Inefficient distribution of the acid may result in black specks in the final product. An ideal way to obtain perfect acid distribution is to add an excessive quantity of the acid to a starch slurry and then to dewater by centrifugation.

The wet cake is reduced to 6% moisture for manufacture of a white dextrin and to 3% for colored dextrins. This step is usually considered essential for subsequent control in the dextrinization process although some manufacturers omit it.

The dried, acidified wheat starch may be converted in a fluidized bed reactor or in a dextrin kettle. The fluid bed reactor is a cone shaped vessel fitted with a stirrer and heating coils or steam jacket. Air, passed up from the apex of the cone, serves as the fluidizing medium. The air can be either cold or treated. Some variations of this equipment are patented (6). The iron kettle type of dextrinizer has been used for many years and must be designed to minimize local overheating. Circulated oil heating in the jacket has some advantages over steam heating.

The course of dextrinization may be followed by measuring reduction in paste viscosity, increase in water-soluble substances, color change, and level of reducing sugars. The rate and course of the conversion is influenced by temperature, time, acid concentration, and starting moisture. When the required properties are obtained, the conversion is stopped by cooling. The dextrin pH can now be adjusted with lime or gaseous ammonia, or the product can be left in the acid state. A neutral product is more stable during storage. The dextrins are remoistened by spraying with water and mixing until the moisture content is about 12%. Remoistening gives better dispersibility in water.

One way of making a good quality wheat dextrin is to predry wheat starch to 4% moisture and to convert it in a fluid bed reactor. Dry hydrogen chloride gas is fed in with the fluidizing hot air. When the desired degree of conversion is obtained, the supply of hydrogen chloride is stopped and the dextrin is cooled by fluidizing with cold air.

The finished wheat dextrins are much lower in viscosity than the parent starch and range from 2 to 99% solubility in cold water. Dextrose equivalent ranges from 1 to 8%. Some of the properties of the unmodified wheat starch persist in the low modification white dextrins; for example, retrogradation is still apparent in the pastes. In the more colored dextrins this retrogradation tendency is lowered to the extent that stable fluid syrups can be prepared. These syrups possess excellent adhesive properties because of the polymeric nature of the dextrins. Some of the highly soluble colored dextrins may be manufactured to retain a degree of setback.

Dextrins are used primarily as adhesives. A liquid adhesive that consists of dextrin and water, together with caustic soda, borax, and a wetting agent, is prepared at the dextrin factory and sold in drums that are to be cooked at the point of application. This adhesive is often sold in dry form to avoid the transportation of water. Sometimes, the dry mix is precooked on drum rolls, ground, and sieved. This product is very popular since it requires no processing at the point of usage.

IX. Enzymic Dextrins

When a slurry of wheat starch is heated to its pasting temperature and held in the presence of an alpha-amylase, it is rapidly converted into a mixture of dextrins and sugars. A mixture suitable for a liquid adhesive is prepared by converting at pH 6.5 and 70° for about 4 hours. The starch slurry must be heated to pasting temperature before the starch granule can be effectively hydrolyzed by the enzyme. After conversion, the enzymes are destroyed by boiling for about 20 min. The converted liquid is mixed with caustic soda and borax or both and dried to form a useful adhesive.

It is a common practice for paper manufacturers to enzyme-convert low-cost raw starches for paper coatings rather than buy the specialty starches from starch manufacturers. Here, a fungal or bacterial alpha-amylase is used to produce a low viscosity adhesive.

To facilitate enzyme conversion, wheat starch must be buffered to the pH that is best for the particular enzyme used. Calcium ions, usually in the form of calcium carbonate, are added to provide heat stability to the enzyme. Modification of the wheat starch, either by mechanical damage between rolls or chemically through etherification or esterification, renders the wheat starch more susceptible to enzyme hydrolysis.

X. Glucose Syrups and Dextrose Monohydrate

Starch for dextrose or syrup production should be as pure as possible to minimize formation of color bodies and off-tastes during the reaction. Wheat starch is inferior to most starches for production of sugars and syrups because it invariably contains pentosan (pentoglycan) slimes which make the purification and filtration of the reaction liquors more difficult. The total lipid content of wheat starch, which also causes problems during conversion, is higher than in the other starches. Some manufacturers pre-purify the wheat starch by alkaline treatment and enzyme treatment or both to remove protein.

1. Glucose Syrups

These products are clear, colorless syrups in which the conversion has been carried to an intermediate stage. In addition to D-glucose (dextrose), the syrups contain maltose, higher sugars, and dextrins. The glucose syrups are manufactured by acid hydrolysis of the starch to a desired D.E. (dextrose equivalent), usually to about 40 D.E.; by acid hydrolysis of the starch to a D.E. of about 40 followed by enzyme hydrolysis to about 60 D.E. to give a syrup rich in maltose; and by acid hydrolysis of the starch to about 15 D.E. followed by hydrolysis with enzymes to D.E. values ranging from 40 to 60. In the last method a range of products can be obtained and it is probably the method of the future for all glucose syrups.

Glucose syrups are used to a large extent in the confectionery trade, particularly to prevent the crystallization of sugar, to add bulk and chewiness, to reduce sweetness, and to retain moisture in the candy. Products made with sucrose alone dry out quickly; and glucose, being hygroscopic, retains the moisture.

Varying amounts of glucose syrups are used in bread, pastry, beer, soft drinks, canned foods, glacé fruits, toppings, ice cream, jams, jellies, pickles, sauces, leather tanning agents, adhesives, and tobacco.

2. Dextrose Monohydrate

Dextrose (D-glucose) monohydrate is a fine, white, crystalline powder having no odor. It has a sweet taste, but not as intense as sucrose. As usually produced, it contains one molecule of water for each dextrose molecule. As with glucose syrups, dextrose monohydrate is manufactured from wheat starch by acid, acid–enzyme, or enzyme–enzyme hydrolysis. Acid hydrolysis, which is declining in favor, gives a final D.E. of about 90. Acid hydrolysis to about 15 D.E. and completion of the conversion by amyloglucosidase gives a final D.E. of about 94 for wheat starch. In the enzyme–enzyme process, gelatinized starch is dextrinized first with an alpha-amylase to a D.E. of between 5 and 15. The conversion is then continued with an amyloglucosidase to give a D.E. of 98 and over.

Dextrose monohydrate is widely used in the confectionery and food trades as well as in several pharmaceutical applications. It is often preferred to cane sugar because of its reduced sweetness. There is a considerable usage of dextrose in the bread industry because it ferments rapidly and completely. It also imparts a golden brown color to the crust and gives a longer shelf life to the loaf. The crust coloration is caused by the Maillard reaction, which is a combining of nitrogenous compounds with dextrose at elevated temperatures that produces brown compounds. This reaction also makes dextrose useful in the manufacture of caramel color, and produces the caramelized flavor in many food products.

3. Crude Sugars

The preparation of dextrose involves the crystallization of the dextrose monohydrate crystals from the converted liquors. The mother liquor is known as hydrol. To produce a cheaper type of dextrose, the converted liquors may be concentrated after some degree of purification, and crystallized into blocks or a powdered product. If the D.E. of the converted liquors is lower than 95, the low melting point of the dextrose can cause difficulties during grinding and storage.

A crude product has been made from whole wheat as well as from the isolated wheat starch. It can be used in industries that use dextrose, provided a small amount of color and protein can be tolerated.

XI. References

(1) J. W. Knight, "The Chemistry of Wheat Starch and Gluten and their Conversion Products," Leonard Hill Books, London, 1965.
(2) A. Kott and R. M. Olson, U.S. Patent 3,119,719 (1964).
(3) J. W. Evans, U.S. Patent 2,806,026 (1957); *Chem. Abstr.*, **52**, 612 (1958).
(4) J. A. Korth, U.S. Patent 2,884,346 (1959); *Chem. Abstr.*, **53**, 12719 (1959).
(5) W. M. Honsch, *Staerke*, **14**, 58 (1962).
(6) R. E. C. Fredrickson, U.S. Patent 2,845,368 (1958); *Chem. Abstr.*, **53**, 2658 (1959).

CHAPTER XIII

STARCH DERIVATIVES

By Hugh J. Roberts
Krause Milling Company, Milwaukee, Wisconsin

I. Introduction

This chapter serves two purposes. The first is to introduce the subject of starch derivatives, their preparation, properties and uses. As such, it is an introduction to six succeeding chapters which, in turn, discuss the preparation and uses of starch phosphate, starch acetate, cationic starches, hydroxyethylstarch, dialdehyde starch, and cross-bonded starches. The second purpose of this chapter is to provide a bibliography of the remaining starch derivatives, those that have not achieved such widespread commercial significance. Since starch chemistry did not become of age until about 1940, more emphasis has been placed on the literature, especially the patent literature, of the past 25 years. These seven chapters, therefore, might be viewed as a starch derivatives section, with the present chapter predominantly introductory and miscellaneous. For a more detailed discussion of the chemistry of starch reactions, the reader is referred to Volume I, Chapter XIX.

What is a starch derivative? One definition is "a chemically modified starch in which the chemical structure of some of the glucose units has been altered." Such a definition excludes acid-modified starches but includes all oxidized starches. In common usage, however, the hypochlorite-oxidized starches are excluded because they have been used commercially for many years prior to the introduction of other starch derivatives.

Starch derivatives are characterized by the nature of their chemical modification, degree of modification, degree of polymerization and physical form. Substitution of the hydrogen atoms of starch hydroxyl groups yields starch esters, both organic and inorganic, and starch ethers; oxidation at C-2, C-3 or C-6 produces oxidized starches; attachment of polymeric chains to the starch molecule leads to graft copolymers; and treatment of starch with molecules having more than one reactive group usually results in intermolecular derivatives known as cross-linked or cross-bonded starches.

The degree of chemical modification may be expressed in several ways. If the modification involves substitution at the hydroxyl groups, the average number of substituents per D-glucose unit is the *degree of substitution* (*D.S.*). A D.S. of 1.0 indicates an average of one substituent for each D-glucose unit; maximum possible D.S. is 3.0. An alternative expression of degree of substitution, sometimes found in the German and Russian literature, is D.S. multiplied by 100, abbreviated as γ. Oxidation is usually limited to a single site per D-glucose unit, and may be expressed as *degree of oxidation* (*D.O.*) on a scale from 0 to 1.0. For graft copolymers, D.S. indicates frequency of occurrence of side-chains attached to the starch backbone; *molar substitution* (*M.S.*) is the average number of grafted monomer molecules per glucose unit, and specifies the chemical composition of the copolymer more precisely than D.S. The ratio M.S./D.S. gives the average number of repeating units per side-chain in a graft copolymer. Because of the small number of chemical groups introduced into most cross-linked starches, these derivatives are generally characterized in terms of such properties as viscosity, solubility, or susceptibility to swelling rather than by their composition. However, in one determination of the actual number of cross-links, the results were expressed as D-glucose units per cross-link (A.G.U./C.L.)[1] (1). For the most part, the starch derivatives described in the literature may be classified as either low (less than 0.2) D.S. or high (over 2.0) D.S. The low D.S. group includes most of the starch derivatives of commerce: starches which have been slightly derivatized to improve their performance in some traditional or new starch application. The high D.S. group consists primarily of laboratory products prepared for purposes of physical or chemical characterization. Notable exceptions are 2.7 D.S. starch nitrate, a commercially-available explosive; 2.0–2.5 D.S. allyl starch, once studied extensively for use as a curable surface coating resin; and some hydroxyalkyl starches that are sold in Europe.

Applied to unmodified starch or to starch derivatives, degree of polymerization is a term usually without meaning because most starches (except waxy varieties) contain linear amylose and branched amylopectin components that differ widely in degree of polymerization. Strictly speaking, the term should be applied to the isolated fractions. Nevertheless, starch derivatives are sometimes prepared from partially degraded starches, and chain degradation can be effected both during and after derivatization. The starch technologist then expresses the extent of degradation of starch derivatives in terms of viscosity or fluidity as he does with acid-modified and hypochlorite-oxidized starches.

Finally, starch derivatives are characterized by their physical form: granular or pregelatinized. Almost all the starch derivatives manufactured today maintain the granular form of the parent starch. A common method of preparation of low D.S. derivatives is to add a limited quantity of the derivatizing agent to uncooked starch slurried in water containing an alkaline catalyst and an inorganic salt to inhibit granule swelling, and to hold the slurry at some temperature below the gelatinization point until the reaction is completed. Alternatively, the dry unmodified starch may be heated together with the derivatizing agent at temperatures up to 150° to produce low to intermediate D.S. derivatives with their granule structures still intact. In such a roasting operation, the presence of 5–20% moisture based on starch is often essential; this process, therefore, is sometimes termed a "semidry" reaction. High D.S. granular derivatives are not readily prepared. With increasing degrees of substitution, the starch granule often swells in the reaction medium,

---

[1] The term anhydro-D-glucose unit, abbreviated A.G.U., has often been used to refer to the $C_6H_{10}O_5$ repeating unit of starch. In view of the use of the prefix anhydro- to refer to an oxygen bridge between two carbon atoms in a monosaccharide molecule (2), the simpler term D-glucose unit is preferred for the $C_6H_{10}O_5$ unit of starch and its fractions.

and may become completely soluble. If a nonswelling solvent is chosen as the reaction medium, substitution does not reach high levels unless the starch is activated first by some technique which destroys the granule structure. Consequently, most high D.S. starch derivatives are in gelatinized form. Low D.S. gelatinized derivatives may also be prepared by the use of a gelatinizing medium, by gelatinizing low D.S. granular derivatives, or by passing a slurry of unmodified starch, reagent and catalyst over steam heated rolls (3, 4). The cost of pregelatinized starch derivatives is much lower if their use does not require them to be separated from salts and other by-products of the derivatizing reaction.

Starches are derivatized to modify their physical or chemical properties so that they will function better in specific applications. With monofunctional reagents, little effect on starch properties is detectable until about one D-glucose unit in fifty is substituted (D.S. 0.02). Cross-linking with polyfunctional reagents, however, is readily detectable by an increase in paste viscosity at levels as low as one cross-link per thousand D-glucose units. Increasing the degree of cross-linking gives granular starches which may be completely resistant to cooking, even in an autoclave. Contamination of a monofunctional reagent by a bifunctional impurity can lead to unexpected and undesirable properties in a starch derivative as a result of cross-linking.

The principal effect on starch properties of low degrees of substitution by monofunctional agents is that retrogradation (setback) of the pasted product is retarded or prevented. This improvement in paste property has led to the annual consumption of millions of pounds of low D.S. starch derivatives in surface sizing and pigment coating of paper, and in processed foods subject to storage at temperatures near or below freezing. At low degrees of substitution, the effect of derivatization on starch properties is generally independent of the nature of the substituent group, provided that the group is nonionic. Ionic substituent groups, at low D.S. levels, convert starch into a polyelectrolyte. Starch then acquires the typical polyelectrolyte properties of increased water solubility and increased solution viscosity in the absence of added electrolyte. As charged macromolecules, ionic starch derivatives are attracted to surfaces of opposite charge; consequently, they find use as flocculating agents for suspended particles and as strengthening agents in paper.

At higher degrees of substitution, starch derivatives acquire properties characteristic of the substituent groups. Hydrophilic groups increase the water solubility of the starch; hydrophobic groups impart solubility in solvents such as acetone and chloroform. High D.S. starch derivatives are often thermoplastic. A more detailed treatment of the properties and uses of derivatives of starch and its fractions is presented in the discussions of the individual derivatives in this and the next six chapters.

II. STARCH ESTERS

Several reviews of the early history of starch esters are available (5–7). Although high D.S. starch acetates had been extensively investigated before 1945 and have continued to receive attention, only the low D.S. granular starch acetates have achieved commercial importance. Starch acetates, high and low D.S., warrant a separate chapter (Chapter XV). This section discusses the preparation, uses and properties of the remaining carboxylic esters, the carbamates, the sulfonates, and the inorganic esters of starch and its fractions.

1. Formates

When granular starch is slurried in formic acid at room temperature, the starch slowly gelatinizes to form a semisolid mass. Simultaneously, the starch undergoes esterification, and the mass is transformed into a sirupy solution of starch formate (8). Amylose behaves similarly (9–11). The esterification is reversible, and at equilibrium the degree of substitution depends upon the amount of water present in the system (12). The formic acid concentration can vary from about 50% (13) to 99.3% (14); the corresponding degrees of substitution range from 0.4 to 2.3. Using air-dried corn starch and an excess of 90% formic acid, a monoformate is readily obtained in 4–5 hours (8, 11, 15, 16). Only about two-thirds of the ester groups in the monoformate are on primary hydroxyls (10, 17). At high ratios of starch to formic acid (less than three moles of acid per D-glucose unit), more primary hydroxyl groups may be esterified (18). Starch is severely degraded during 30 hours in 99% formic acid at 85° (19). At room temperature, degradation is not noticeable (20), but no exact measurements have been reported. Formamide is reported to condense with starch in boiling toluene to yield a starch monoformate and ammonia (21).

Formic acid has been used to activate granular starches for subsequent esterification (13, 22) or etherification (23), during which the formate ester groups were partially or completely replaced. However, under milder conditions, the formate ester groups can be retained, and mixed formate acetates (9, 10, 16), formate propionates, butyrates and benzoates (9), formate p-toluenesulfonates (16), and formate phenylcarbamates (12) have been prepared.

Low D.S. granular starch formates have been prepared by treating a slurry of starch in 5–6% sodium carbonate solution with vinyl formate

(*24, 25*). The use of 0.1 and 0.4 moles of vinyl formate was reported to give degrees of substitution of 0.1 and 0.35. The reaction apparently proceeds by transesterification. The products would seem to have no advantage over low D.S. acetates prepared by an analogous reaction.

2. Higher Aliphatic Carboxylic Esters

High D.S. starch propionates, butyrates, and caproates are usually prepared from the corresponding acid anhydrides by techniques identical to that used for acetylation. Esterification is sluggish unless a third component is present to promote penetration of the granules by the hydrophobic anhydride. Pyridine is the most frequently used promoter, and has been used with propionic anhydride (*5, 9, 26, 27*), butyric anhydride (*5, 9, 27, 28*), and caproic anhydride (*27, 29*). Flow sheets have been published (*29*) for conducting these reactions on a semicommercial scale. Formamide has been combined with pyridine in the preparation of the propionate and butyrate esters (*30*). A less desirable promoter, if degradation is to be avoided, is the corresponding carboxylic acid. The products of reactions of starch in mixtures of propionic acid and propionic anhydride were reported to be triesters (*31*), but they were not completely characterized. Partially formylated starches have been esterified with mixtures of either propionic acid and its anhydride or butyric acid and its anhydride; small amounts of sulfuric acid were used to catalyze the reactions (*13*). Sulfuric acid also catalyzed the superficial esterification of starch in a butyric anhydride–acetic acid–xylene system (*32*). No measure of degradation was given in either case of acid-catalyzed esterification. Recently, a new acylation technique was used to prepare undegraded high D.S. amylose acetates and propionates (*33*). The acylating agent was the acid anhydride, and a macroreticular styrenesulfonic acid-type resin was employed as a catalyst.

Acid chlorides can also be used to prepare the lower fatty acid esters of starch; but owing to their ready availability, the anhydrides are used almost exclusively. The acid chloride in pyridine and formamide was chosen for the preparation of starch 3-methylvalerate (*34*).

The predominant method for obtaining the higher fatty acid esters of starch has also been acylation with an acid chloride in a tertiary amine, although the palmitate has been prepared from the anhydride either in pyridine (*27*) or in fused monochloroacetic acid containing sulfuryl chloride as catalyst (*35*). High D.S. fatty esters prepared from the acid chloride in pyridine, picoline, or quinoline include starch undecanoate (*36*), laurate (*35, 37*), myristate (*35*), palmitate (*35, 36, 38–40*), and stearate (*35, 36, 40*). Benzene or toluene is commonly used as a solvent in these reactions, and the technique has been applied in the preparation of saturated fatty esters of amylose (*41*), and in the esterification of partially allylated starch (*42, 43*). Stearoyl chloride reacts with starch in a mixture of acetic acid and xylene containing a little sulfuric acid to give a partial stearic acid ester (*32*). Aqueous sodium hydroxide has been used in place of a tertiary amine with a benzene solution of both lauroyl and benzoyl chlorides to prepare the mixed ester of starch (*44*). Mixed esters of amylose prepared by the acid anhydride–pyridine method include the acetate propionate, acetate butyrate, and the formate butyrate (*9*).

The properties of the high D.S. aliphatic esters depend on both the nature of the starting material and the length of the alkyl chain (*27, 41, 45*). Amylose triesters melt at the highest temperatures (up to 300°), followed by starch triesters and amylopectin triesters. The melting range decreases steadily as the ester group increases in size. Aside from the effect of molecular weight upon viscosity, intrinsic viscosity decreases with increasing size of the ester group; but measured viscosity is affected by the solubility of the ester, and solubility depends to a large extent upon the physical condition of the polysaccharide prior to esterification. In general, these esters of starch and amylopectin do not form self-supporting flexible films, although the caproate appears to be an exception. Films of amylose triesters show decreased tensile strength, hardness, and density as the ester group is increased in size. Elongation is at a maximum in the caproate to laurate range. Permeability of the films to water vapor decreases sharply with increasing length of the alkyl groups. Mixed esters have a broader solubility range and, except for the mixed formate esters, form films of increased plasticity (*9*). Wettability of films of amylose and amylopectin propionates, butyrates, and caproates is independent of the structure of the polymer, depending only on the nature of the attached ester group (*46*).

Several methods have been used for the preparation of low D.S., granular starch esters. A propionate was prepared by adding concurrently propionic anhydride and sodium hydroxide solution to an aqueous starch slurry to maintain the pH between 9 and 10 (*47*). A starch butyrate resulted when starch containing 12% moisture was heated at 100° for 3 hours with 15 mole per cent of butyric anhydride (*48*). Under similar conditions, ammonium laurate served as the esterifying agent in the preparation of a low D.S. granular starch laurate (*49*). Transesterification of granular starch in an aqueous alkaline slurry with the appropriate vinyl ester has produced the propionate, butyrate, 2-ethylhexoate, and stearate (*25, 50*). Homogeneous acylation of amylose in dimethyl sulfoxide yielded low D.S., water-dispersible amylose propionates and butyrates (*11*); the acid anhydride was the acylating agent, and triethylamine was used as a catalyst. At low D.S., the lower aliphatic esters of starch show no advantage in properties over the cheaper starch acetates. The higher fatty esters, especially the partial stearates, have been proposed as additives to margarine to eliminate the need for hardening vegetable oils (51). They have also been recommended as flour additives for improving the structure of baked goods (52), as thickening and stabilizing agents in paints, oils, and cosmetics (53), and as components of photographic film (40). Starch 3-methylvalerate is reported to enhance the flavor of tobacco (34). Although the triesters of starch (29) and of amylose (9, 41, 45) have been investigated as potential ingredients of coatings, adhesives, and plastics, they have enjoyed no commercial acceptance.

3. Functionally Substituted Aliphatic Esters

A number of starch esters have been prepared in which the aliphatic ester group bears an additional chemical function. Of particular interest are the unsaturated, carboxylated, and chlorinated esters. Starch esters substituted with hydroxyl, amino, cyano, phenyl, thiocyanato, and sulfonic acid groups are also known.

a. Unsaturated Aliphatic Esters

These starch esters are prepared in the same manner as their saturated analogs. Starch trimethacrylate, proposed as a thermosetting resin, was prepared from pyridine-pretreated starch by reaction with methacrylic anhydride in pyridine and benzene (54). A low D.S. granular starch methacrylate, capable of insolubilization by free radical catalysts, has been prepared from the anhydride in an aqueous system at pH 8–9 (55). Alkenoic acid chlorides have been used to prepare starch linoleate (56), the oleic and linoleic esters of partially allylated starch (43), and amylose oleate (41); dimethylaniline (56) or pyridine was used as the base. A low D.S. granular starch crotonate was prepared from vinyl crotonate in an aqueous alkaline slurry, but there was some evidence that cross-linking accompanied the esterification (25). The maleic, itaconic, and alkenylsuccinic half esters of starch are considered with the carboxyl-substituted esters in the following paragraph.

b. Carboxyl-Substituted Alpihatic Esters

In general, the esterification of starch with the anhydride of an aliphatic dibasic acid results in the half-ester; that is, the ester group is carboxyl-substituted. Methods of preparation are similar to those already described. Succinic anhydride in pyridine produces the fully esterified starch acid succinate (29), and the same technique has been used to introduce succinic, glutaric, and maleic half-ester groups into partially acylated starches (30). A D.S. of 0.7 was obtained by heating starch with succinic anhydride at 100° for 3 days in glacial acetic acid containing sodium acetate (57). Low D.S., granular, acid esters have been prepared by treating an aqueous alkaline starch slurry with succinic, adipic, or maleic anhydrides (47, 58); by roasting at 50°–140° a slightly moist, acidic mixture of starch and succinic, maleic, or itaconic anhydride (59); or by roasting at 110°–120° a similar mixture of starch and ammonium maleate or dibasic ammonium citrate (49). In the second method, the solid anhydrides are preferably dissolved in dimethylformamide or a high-boiling ketone to improve their distribution in the mixture. The homogeneous reaction of amylose in dimethyl sulfoxide with maleic anhydride and triethylamine also gives a low degree of substitution (11).

Introduction of carboxyl-substituted ester groups increases the hydrophilic character of starch esters, particularly in alkaline systems. As a consequence, sodium starch acid succinate, for example, shows improved freeze-thaw stability (58). High D.S. starch esters containing a minor percentage of carboxyl-substituted ester groups are soluble in 5% sodium or ammonium hydroxide solution, but insoluble in 5% sodium carbonate solution, artificial gastric fluid, or artificial intestinal fluid (30); they have been suggested as enteric tablet coating materials. However, if the dicarboxylic acid anhydride is substituted with a higher alkyl group (I), the alkali salts of the low D.S. half-acid esters of starch become surface-active, possessing both hydrophilic and hydrophobic properties (60). Examples of the hydrocarbon groups substituted on succinic or glutaric anhydrides are heptyl, octenyl, nonenyl, decenyl, triisobutenyl, caproyloxy, benzyloxy, and the 1,1-dimethyl-2-cyclohexenyl ring (II) (60). The polyvalent metal salts of these particular starch

I   II

R = Higher alkyl group

half esters, on the other hand, are extremely hydrophobic (61). Their lack of wettability by water has suggested their use (61) as mold release agents, substitutes for talcum powder, and bases for pest control dusts.

They have also been proposed as components of tobacco smoke filters (62). Under intense mechanical shear they can be dispersed in water sufficiently to permit gelatinization on cooking, and in this form they can be used as encapsulating agents for oils or water-insoluble flavors (63). Another hydrophobic half ester is that prepared from the Diels-Alder adduct of maleic anhydride and an ester of abietic acid (29).

Geurden (64) recently disclosed that the addition of maleic anhydride to a 0.6 D.S. hydroxyethylstarch film could effect an insolubilization of the starch ether. After applying an aqueous solution of hydroxyethyl-starch containing maleic anhydride to a cotton swatch, drying, and iron-ing, he found that the increased stiffness of the fabric was not reduced by repeated laundering. Treatment of the maleic half ester of amylo-pectin with a polyfunctional amine also results in a water-insoluble product (65).

c. *Aliphatic Chloroesters*

Starch esters of mono-, di-, or trichloroacetic acid may be prepared by direct esterification, either in excess acid in the same manner as the formate ester (15), or in refluxing benzene (66). A D.S. of approximately one is readily attained. Degradation becomes increasingly serious as the esterification temperature is raised (67). Monochloroacetic anhydride has been employed with a sulfuric acid catalyst to obtain the fully sub-stituted ester of a partially degraded starch (68). It has been reported that the corresponding acid chlorides fail to give the desired esters (68), but the failure may have been due to the extreme sensitivity of these compounds to hydrolysis by traces of moisture. The reaction of starch triacetate with phosphorus pentachloride can yield either the tri-(tri-chlororoacetate) (68) or an acetylated octasaccharide containing a single chlorine atom (69). The course of that reaction may depend upon the choice of solvent, but more probably it is determined by the nature of impurities in the system. Starch triacetate has also been converted to a tri-(dichloroacetate) by treatment with liquid chlorine (70).

Low D.S., granular chloroesters of starch have been prepared from chloromaleic anhydride in aqueous alkaline slurry (47), and in low moisture roasting reactions with either dichloromaleic anhydride (48), chloroacetic anhydride buffered with disodium phosphate (48), or am-monium or trimethylammonium chloroacetate (49).

d. *Other Substituted Aliphatic Esters*

In starch lactate, the ester group possesses a substituent hydroxyl group. It has been claimed that lactic acid esterifies starch in an anhydrous ammonium acetate–acetamide system (71).

Certain lactones react with starch, but whether the products are hydroxyalkyl esters, carboxyalkyl ethers, or both, appears to depend upon reaction conditions. Caldwell and Wurzburg (72) treated starch with β-propionolactone and with β-butyrolactone in aqueous alkaline slurry. They stated that, under these conditions, a starch ester of the β-hydroxy aliphatic acid is formed, and that under neutral or acid conditions the starch ether is formed. Lolkema and Moes (73) also described the product of the alkali-catalyzed reaction of starch with β-propionolactone as an ester. Kerr and Faucette (74), on the basis of experiments with β-propionolactone and γ-valerolactone, concluded that under semidry conditions, etherification and esterification take place simultaneously but at different rates, yielding partially cross-linked derivatives. They found that the slower esterification reaction could be minimized by low reaction temperatures, short reaction times, low concentrations of lactone, and control of pH by the addition of a buffer such as ammonium carbonate. Under these conditions, their products were almost entirely the carboxyalkyl ethers. Unfortunately, no analytical data were reported for any of these reaction products of starch with lactones.

Heating slightly moist starch at 110°–125° with ammonium cyanoacetate, or ammonium aminoacetate for 3–5 hours gives a low D.S. starch cyanoacetate or aminoacetate (49). A phenylacetic ester has been prepared by treating alkali-gelatinized starch with a benzene solution of the acid chloride (44).

Sulfonic acid groups may be introduced into aliphatic ester substituents on starch by the addition of bisulfite to the double bond in an unsaturated ester (75). This reaction has been accomplished with starch crotonate and with the citraconate, itaconate, and maleate half esters of starch. The latter derivatives possess both sulfonic and carboxylic acid groups, and display a markedly increased capacity for water absorption. They have been proposed as additives to green molding sand (76) and to foam rubber (77), and as components of electrolyte pastes (78) and of pastes for printing on glass fiber textiles (79).

4. Aromatic Carboxylic Esters

a. *Benzoates*

If suitably activated, starch is readily benzoylated in pyridine by benzoyl chloride (27, 29, 80–84) or benzoic anhydride (26, 27) to any desired degree of substitution. Amylose and amylopectin tribenzoates are similarly obtained (27); starch formates (9), allyl starch (43), and starch S-benzylxanthate (85) have been benzoylated in the same way. High D.S. starch benzoates may also be prepared by treating starch with benzoyl chloride and relatively large amounts of an alkali hydroxide (86–88). A similar technique has been used with a mixture of benzoyl and lauroyl chlorides (44). Properties of the tribenzoates of starch, amylose, and amylopectin resemble those of the aliphatic esters (27, 29, 45, 46); however, they display greater solubility in organic solvents than do most of the aliphatic esters (27).

A low D.S. starch benzoate, capable of emulsifying a hexane–water system, was prepared by heating a mixture of starch and benzoic anhydride at 110° for 2 hours (48). Benzoic anhydride has also been employed in the preparation of low D.S. amylose benzoates in dimethyl sulfoxide containing triethylamine (11).

b. *Other Aromatic Carboxylic Esters*

Starch is esterified in pyridine with aroyl chlorides other than benzoyl chloride. The D.S. of starch cinnamates prepared in this manner ranges from 2 to 3, depending upon the pretreatment of the starch (82, 89). A triester of nicotinic acid (3-carboxypyridine) was similarly prepared from soluble starch; when the ester was fed to rats, nicotinic acid and its methyl ester were isolated as metabolic products (90).

A Schotten–Baumann reaction between starch in aqueous potassium hydroxide and acetylsalicylyl chloride in chloroform produced an aspirin ester of starch having a D.S. of 0.85 (91). The substituent ester groups were reported to be entirely on the primary hydroxyls. No significant hydrolysis to acetylsalicylic acid was detected after intramuscular injection of the derivative (92). A 0.8 D.S. starch O-methoxybenzoate was similarly prepared (91).

Phthalic anhydride in pyridine readily yields the water-soluble pyridinium salt of a fully esterified starch acid phthalate (29). The product is precipitated from aqueous solution by acidification. Partial acetates of starch or amylose have been esterified by phthalic anhydride in pyridine to give mixed esters of interest for enteric tablet coating (30, 93). Low D.S. starch acid phthalates are prepared from the anhydride either in an aqueous alkaline slurry (47) or by heating at 140° for 1 hour in the presence of a small amount of water and N,N-dimethyl-formamide (59). Heating with ammonium phthalate also produces a low D.S. ester (49). Phthaloyl chloride was probably the acylating agent in an esterification involving phthalic acid and p-toluenesulfonyl chloride in pyridine (94); with slightly more than a stoichiometric amount of the acid, a 0.2 D.S. amylose phthalate was prepared and phthalate groups were introduced into a 1.2 D.S. starch acetate to a D.S. of 0.43.

Aromatic sulfonic acid groups may also be introduced into starch by means of ester linkages. Low D.S., granular starch sulfobenzoate and starch sulfophthalate were prepared from the corresponding anhydrides by the aqueous alkaline slurry technique (75).

5. Carbamates

If an intimate blend of urea and starch containing 5–10% moisture is heated at 90°–120°, a low D.S., nitrogen-containing starch derivative is produced (95, 96). No proof of structure has been reported, but the product is assumed to be a starch carbamate, starch–O–CO–NH$_2$ (96). The reaction is promoted by addition of potassium acetate (96). Incorporating mono- and disodium phosphates (97) or phosphoric acid with excess urea (98, 99) into the reaction mixture results in some phosphorus being bound as well, although it is not clear whether the phosphate is bound in phosphate ester or phosphoramide groups. Hjermstad (97) observed that heating starch at 135° with phosphate salts and formamide or other alkyl amides in place of urea also resulted in both nitrogen and phosphorus being bound, and he proposed that the nitrogen was bound to the starch through phosphate ester groups.

Boiling water is reported to be a solvent for the reaction of starch with urea (100), but the product has not been characterized. Boiling toluene is also said to promote the condensation of urea wtih starch yielding ammonia and high D.S. starch carbamates containing up to 14% nitrogen (21, 101); however, most of the nitrogen is readily extracted from such products by water or alcohol.

Low D.S. starch carbamates gelatinize at temperatures below the gelatinization temperature of the parent starch. They show increased reactivity toward formaldehyde and other aldehydes, particularly in slightly alkaline solutions (96, 98, 102). Consequently, they have been proposed as binders for pigmented paper coatings; glyoxal, added to the coating, cross-links the starch to give some degree of water resistance (98). The high D.S. starch carbamates swell in cold water and disperse in hot water to give viscous sols which dry to clear, tough films (21, 101).

Substitued carbamates, starch–O–CO–NHR, are prepared by the reaction of starch with isocyanates. Aryl isocyanates have been used most frequently, and the resulting starch, amylose, and amylopectin aryl carbamates have also been called carbanilates (103–108). Anhydrous pyridine is the usual reaction medium at 80°–100°. Fully substituted aryl carbamates are generally obtained within 24 hours (108). The rate of the reaction depends upon the isocyanate chosen; the following isocyanates are listed in order of decreasing reactivity (105): m-chlorophenyl > phenyl > m-tolyl > 2,5-dichlorophenyl > o-chlorophenyl > p-bromophenyl > p-tolyl > o-tolyl > 1-naphthyl. Under similar reaction conditions, hexamethylene diisocyanate and toluene 2,4-diisocyanate yield cross-linked products (104, 106). A partial allyl ether of starch has been similarly converted to the mixed derivative, allyl starch phenylcarbamate (43); and 6-O-trityl-2,3-di-O-phenylcarbamylamylose was prepared from the monotrityl ether (109, 110).

Ethyl isocyanatoacetate, $C_2H_5OCOCH_2NCO$, is a monofunctional aliphatic isocyanate that has been used to derivatize amylose, starch, and partially acetylated amyloses (111). A D.S. of 3.0 is obtained in 16–20 hours at 100° in anhydrous pyridine; a pyridine–formamide system gives partially substituted products. The derivative, amylose-$OCONHCH_2$-$COOC_2H_5$, is amylose carbethoxymethylcarbamate or amylose carboxymethylcarbamate ethyl ester. If the ethyl ester group is removed by mild saponification, the free carboxyl group reacts with ammonia or hydrazine to give the amide or hydrazide (111).

Pyridine is not essential to the reaction of starch with aryl carbamates. Anhydrous dimethyl sulfoxide was the solvent in the preparation of a series of starch and amylose aryl carbamates (112). The isocyanates used were prepared by blocking one of the isocyanate groups of toluene 2,4-diisocyanate through urethane formation. Selective conversion of the isocyanate groups in the para position is possible owing to their tenfold greater reactivity than the isocyanate groups in the ortho position. The following urethane groups were substituted in the C-5 position of the aryl group in the series of starch 2-methylphenylcarbamates: isopropyl, ethyl 95% and methyl 5%, octadecyl, nonyl-phenyl, and urethanes from soybean oil alcohols and soybean oil diglycerides. It is claimed that any D.S. may be obtained by this procedure, but analytical data were presented only for water-soluble products up to 0.2 D.S.; with increasing amounts of isocyanate, water-insoluble products were obtained that were presumably of higher D.S.

In a water slurry at pH 9, hexamethylene diisocyanate or toluene 2,4-diisocyanate cross-links granular starch (113). Atomization of 1.3% toulene 2,4-diisocyanate onto a dry, pregelatinized starch, however, did not reduce its cold water solubility (114). On the other hand, heating granular corn starch that had been wet with a carbon tetrachloride solution of hexamethylene diisocyanate or stearoylethyleneurea at 120° for 30 min. gave a cross-linked product (115). A diisocyanate terminated, polyester-based polyurethane prepolymer is reported to react with starch during molding at 130° (116).

The ease of preparation under mild conditions of fully substituted aryl carbamates of starch and its fractions has encouraged investigations of their solution behavior in organic solvents. Wolff, Watson, and Rist

(*117*) have published rotatory dispersion data for the tricarbanilates of starch, amylose, and amylopectin. Burchard and Husemann (*107*) have given light scattering data and a viscosity–molecular weight relationship for amylose tricarbanilate. A similar viscosity–molecular weight relationship was determined for amylose tris-(carbethoxymethylcarbamate) (*109*). Wolff and Rist (*103*) reported some fractionation of starch tricarbanilate into the corresponding amylose and amylopectin derivatives using ethyl acetate.

Related to starch carbamate are the N,N-disubstituted starch iminocarbamates, starch–OC(=NH)NR$_2$ (*118*). Since these substituted pseudoureas behave as polycations, they are discussed in Chapter XVI.

6. Sulfonates

Starch esters of arylsulfonic acids are readily prepared from the corresponding sulfonyl chloride in anhydrous pyridine. With p-toluene sulfonyl chloride (tosyl chloride), partial (*119*) or full tosylates of starch (*80, 120, 121*) and partial tosylates of amylose (*121–123*) have been prepared. The primary hydroxyl group is tosylated preferentially, and with amylose a primary tosyl D.S. of about 0.7 can be attained before secondary tosylation is detected (*122*). Starch monoformate (*16*), and the 2,3-di-*O*-benzoate (*124*), 2,3-di-*O*-phenylcarbamate (*110*), and the 6-*O*-trityl ether of amylose (*125*) have been tosylated similarly. Partially acetylated amylopectin has been esterified with p-chlorosulfonylbenzoic acid in pyridine to introduce p-carboxyphenylsulfonate groups (*126*).

Starch tosylates of 1–1.5 D.S. may be prepared by treating a dispersion of starch in aqueous alkali with tosyl chloride in benzene (*127, 128*), or in the absence of an organic solvent (*26*). Under the latter conditions, a large excess of 3,4-dichlorobenzenesulfonyl chloride (*128*), benzenesulfonyl chloride, or p-acetamidobenzenesulfonyl chloride (*26*) has also yielded the corresponding starch monoester.

The ease with which primary tosyloxy groups are displaced by various nucleophilic agents has permitted the introduction into the starch or amylose molecule of iodo (*80, 120, 124*), thiocyanato (*119*), hydrazido (*123*), and azido (*110*) groups, and of 3,6-anhydro rings (*122, 124*). Displacement of secondary tosyl groups in amylose has yielded 2,3-anhydro rings (*125*). Introduction of amino groups by this technique is discussed in Chapter XVI. The preparation and reactions of sulfonate esters of carbohydrates has been reviewed by Tipson (*129*).

7. Inorganic Esters

Starch phosphate is the subject of a separate chapter (Chapter XIV) and will not be discussed here. This section includes the sulfate, nitrate, and xanthate esters of starch. The only starch monocarbonate which appears to have been described was prepared by treating granular starch in alkaline aqueous slurry with allyl chloroformate (55).

a. *Sulfates*

Starch is esterified by concentrated sulfuric acid, but the reaction is accompanied by degradation (130, 131). However, only a small decrease in intrinsic viscosity was observed during the sulfation of a dextrin with oleum in formamide at 0° (132).

Chlorosulfonic acid and certain organic complexes of sulfur trioxide are milder sulfating agents than sulfuric acid. Starch sulfates of approximately 2 D.S. have been prepared using chlorosulfonic acid in pyridine (133), in picoline (134), or in a mixture of chloroform and pyridine (135). Amylose (136), corn starch dextrin (137), and sodium carboxymethylstarch (138) have been similarly sulfated. The sulfates are formed initially as the tertiary amine salts, but are generally converted to the alkali metal salts by treatment with sodium or potassium hydroxide. The free acid form is subject to rapid autohydrolysis.

Starch is also sulfated to a low D.S. with sodium chlorosulfonate in pyridine and benzene (139); or, it may be gelatinized in alkali, the alkaline paste dried, and the dry alkali-starch treated with chlorosulfonic acid in chloroform (4). Formamide has been used with chlorosulfonic acid in the sulfation of starch (140), amylose (141), dextrin (142), and a number of derivatives of a carboxyl-containing starch prepared by oxidation with fuming nitric acid (142–146). No tertiary amine or strong base is necessary when formamide is used, and reaction temperatures of 20°–40° are sufficient to produce high degrees of sulfation.

The complexes of sulfur trioxide with tertiary amines or with certain ethers are excellent sulfating agents for starch. A 0.66 D.S. starch sulfate was prepared using pyridine–sulfur trioxide in an equimolar mixture of benzene and pyridine (147). The same complex gave a higher degree of sulfation when formamide was the solvent (148). A methyl ester of a nitric acid oxidized starch (149) and an amino derivative of a similar oxidized starch (150) have been sulfated with pyridine–sulfur trioxide complex in excess pyridine. A dextrin sulfate was prepared from dimethylaniline–sulfur trioxide complex in a picoline–hexane system (147). Triethylamine–sulfur trioxide in dimethylformamide has been used to prepare 0.38 D.S. starch sulfate and 1.4 D.S. amylose and amylopectin sulfates (151, 152).

Certain of the sulfur trioxide complexes are sufficiently stable to be used to prepare low D.S. granular starch sulfates in an aqueous alkaline slurry. Complexes with trimethylamine, triethylamine, tributylamine,

N-methylmorpholine, N,N-dimethylbenzylamine, and pyridine have been effective (153, 154). The trimethylamine–sulfur trioxide complex has been used together with sodium trimetaphosphate to prepare cross-linked granular starch sulfates (58, 155), or with acrylonitrile to give a cyanoethylstarch sulfate (155). Sulfation of wheat flour with trimethylamine–sulfur trioxide in an aqueous alkaline system has also been investigated (156). The sulfur trioxide complex of poly(2-vinylpyridine) has recently been used in an aqueous medium to prepare low D.S. starch sulfates from gelatinized starches (157, 158). Granular starch was not effectively sulfated by this agent.

Two semidry processes have been described in the patent literature for the preparation of low D.S. granular starch sulfates. One involves heating starch at $100°-120°$ with a mixture of three to five parts of sodium bisulfite and one part of sodium nitrite (159). In the other (160), a mixture of four parts of urea and one part of sulfamic acid is the sulfating agent, and a temperature of $130°-150°$ is used. Acetamide may replace urea in the latter method, and ammonium sulfamate may be used in place of the acid.

Starch sulfates form highly hydrophilic sols. For this reason, they have been suggested as water retention agents in oil well drilling muds (139) and in various hydraulic cements (140, 161). The excellent stability of starch sulfate sols toward storage at temperatures below freezing suggests their use as thickening agents in frozen foods (58). Although starch sulfate is reported to be nontoxic in large oral doses (162), its use in food was not permitted in the United States as of December 1966.

Far more interest has been shown in the physiological properties of starch sulfates than in the physical properties of their aqueous dispersions. The search for a low-cost substitute for the natural anticoagulant, heparin, has led to a number of investigations of the sulfate esters of starch (134, 148, 162–167), amylose (167, 168), amylopectin (168), and various chemically modified starches (138, 143–146, 149, 150). It is believed that these polysaccharide sulfates, like heparin, inhibit the enzyme thrombin. They also appear to possess the antilipemic activity of heparin (169, 170), and retain antilipemic activity at low degrees of polymerization while losing most of their anticoagulant activity (137, 142). More recently, it has been found that pepsin is inhibited by sulfate esters of starch (133, 171, 172) and amylose (136, 173), and it has been suggested that these derivatives be used in treating peptic ulcer. Amylose sulfate is also an inhibitor of pancreatic ribonuclease (174). Starch sulfate causes a reversible agglutination of thrombocytes (175), and has been used to precipitate serum β-lipoproteins (176). The rapid rate of passage of amylose sulfate into the lymphatic system suggests its use as a carrier for basic antibiotics or drugs (*177*). Prior to the development of extensive knowledge of the physiological effects of polysaccharide sulfates, a calcium starch sulfate was proposed as a blood serum substitute (*131*).

The osmotic molecular weight of corn amylose disulfate has been measured, and the limiting viscosity numbers of amylose and amylopectin sulfates have been determined (*151*). Periodate oxidation of amylose monosulfate indicates that about 50% of the sulfate groups are on primary hydroxyls (*151*). Starch sulfate is less susceptible than starch to hydrolysis by malt amylase, but is readily hydrolyzed by acid to reducing sugars and inorganic sulfate (*178*).

b. *Nitrates*

Starch nitrate is the oldest known derivative of starch, and is the only highly substituted starch to have gained commercial importance (*179*). Statistics relating to the volume of starch nitrate produced for explosives are not available publicly, since the sole producer for many years has been the Trojan Powder Company. During the construction of the Panama Canal, that company supplied large amounts of explosives based on starch nitrate.

The commercial product contains about 13.2% nitrogen (*179*), equivalent to a D.S. of 2.65. It is manufactured by treating starch with a mixture of concentrated sulfuric and nitric acids. The process probably does not differ greatly from that patented by Holmes over 50 years ago (*180*). He treated starch with four parts of a mixed acid having the composition 32.5% nitric acid, 64.5% sulfuric acid, and 3% water. He stabilized the product by boiling it for 75–100 hours in water containing calcium carbonate. Many of the improvements in Holmes' process have been concerned with stabilization, a step that apparently removes a small number of nitroso-sulfuric ester groups.

Starch trinitrate (13.9–14.0% nitrogen; calculated 14.14%) is prepared in the laboratory using dinitrogen pentaoxide in chloroform containing sodium fluoride (*181, 182*). By complex formation, the sodium fluoride removes nitric acid from the system as rapidly as it is formed. At temperatures in the range 0°–15°, the reaction is complete in less than 30 minutes. As a result of the mild, anhydrous conditions, degradation of the starch does not occur; consequently, the nitrate esters of starch, amylose, and amylopectin prepared by this method are suitable for molecular weight and intrinsic viscosity measurements (*183*).

Caesar (*179*) has written an excellent historical review covering more than a century of starch nitrate literature (1833–1954). The few references that might be added to those cited by Caesar relate to the comparative stabilities of amylose and amylopectin nitrates (184), to the explosive properties of starch nitrate (185), and to the nitration of starch with mixtures of nitric acid, phosphorous acid, and phosphorus pentaoxide, or nitric acid, acetic acid, and acetic anhydride (186). In 1958 Urbanski and Hackel (187) described in English their work on starch nitration, the earlier publication of which is mentioned by Caesar.

Since Caesar's review, two patents have been issued describing modified processes for nitrating starch; one employs mixed nitric acid and sulfuric acids (188), the other (189) nitric acid alone. An investigation˙ of the nitration of starch with mixed acids in carbon tetrachloride showed that, in the absence of water, the esterification reaction was almost instantaneous and not very exothermic (190). Stabilization of starch nitrate with boiling aqueous methanol has been patented (191). Stabilities of nitrates of starch, amylose, and amylopectin prepared from nitric acid containing phosphorus pentaoxide were found to decrease in the order amylose nitrate > starch nitrate > amylopectin nitrate; but after prolonged boiling in slightly alkaline water, all samples possessed similar stability properties (192). Amylose and amylopectin nitrates have also been studied under controlled thermal decomposition (193). Recent patents on uses for starch nitrate relate to its inclusion in ignition delay compositions (194), in dynamite (195, 196), and in blasting explosives displaying delayed sensitivity (197).

c. *Xanthates*

Starch xanthate was prepared first by Cross and Bevan (198) shortly after their development of the cellulose xanthate (viscose) process for rayon. Their simple process of adding aqueous sodium hydroxide to a mixture of starch and carbon disulfide is still considered to be the best laboratory method (199), although the alternative of adding carbon disulfide to the alkaline starch paste permits the use of higher starch to carbon disulfide ratios (200–202). The reaction proceeds readily at 15°– 25° (203), and the rate appears to be greater when potassium hydroxide is used in place of sodium hydroxide (204). Recently, a continuous process has been developed for the large-scale xanthation of starch (205).

Starch xanthate is water soluble and may be precipitated by alcohol (200, 201). The crude precipitate is purified by washing it in 5% acetic acid (199). Cupric ions precipitate a starch cuproxanthate (206) that is probably a mixture of cuprous starch xanthate and starch xanthide, the xanthide arising from the oxidation of xanthate by the cupric ion (199):

$$4 \text{ Starch–O·CS·S}^- + 2 \text{ Cu}^{++} \rightarrow 2 \text{ Starch–O·CS·S·Cu} + \text{Starch–O·CS·S·S·SC·O–Starch}.$$

Cross-linked starch xanthides are also prepared by treating starch xanthate with iodine (198, 199), diazonium salts (207), nitrous acid (199, 208), or any of a number of oxidants including oxygen, chlorine and iron salts (199, 209, 210). Zinc salts precipitate insoluble zinc starch xanthate (199).

Aqueous solutions of starch xanthate are unstable (200), and even the isolated derivatives contain enough moisture to permit hydrolytic and oxidative reactions during storage. On the other hand, starch xanthides appear to be stable (199), and starch S-methyl xanthates have been tritylated and acetylated without loss of xanthate groups (202). Similarly, starch S-benzyl xanthates have been benzoylated (85).

Probably because of their instability, starch xanthates have not achieved commercial importance. A number of patents have been issued, however, describing their use as adhesives (211), additives to viscose rayon (212, 213), soil conditioners (214) and soil stabilizers (215), and as flotation aids in ore beneficiation (201, 216, 217). More recent investigations suggest the use of starch or flour xanthides as additions for improving the wet and dry strength of paper and insulating board (199, 218).

III. STARCH ETHERS

The low D.S. ethers are probably the most important starch derivatives of commerce today. Millions of pounds of hydroxyalkylstarches and cationic ethers are consumed each year by the paper and textile industries. Many other starch ethers have been prepared and evaluated for a wide variety of uses, and there is an extensive body of literature relating to alkyl, carboxyalkyl and allyl derivatives. Those starch ethers have yet to gain commercial acceptance; although in recent years, products have been marketed that appear to be low D.S. carboxyalkyl and cyanoethyl ethers.

Hydroxyalkyl, aminoalkyl, and quaternary ammonium ethers are discussed in detail in Chapters XVI and XVII. This section includes alkyl ethers, carboxyalkyl and other substituted alkyl ethers, allyl ethers, and a few miscellaneous etherified starches.

1. Alkyl Ethers

Some of the earliest preparations of alkylstarches appear in the patent literature (219–221). But the major force behind the development of alkylation techniques was the interest of academic workers in determining the structure of starch by methylation followed by hydrolysis and identification of the methylated sugars (222–224).

a. *O-Methylstarch*

Starch has been methylated by variations of four distinct techniques: dimethyl sulfate in alkali (Haworth reagents), methyl iodide and silver oxide (Purdie reagents), sodium in liquid ammonia followed by methyl iodide, and diazomethane. Of the four, the dimethyl sulfate–alkali technique would appear best for commercial use, especially for low D.S. methyl ethers of starch (*4, 225, 226*) and of amylose (*11, 227, 228*). Early attempts to methylate starch and its fractions completely with the Haworth reagents showed that several methylations were necessary to attain a D.S. of 2.0–2.5, and that considerable degradation usually occurred (*229–231*). Twenty-four treatments with dimethyl sulfate and sodium hydroxide were necessary to achieve a D.S. of 2.85 (*230*). By starting with starch triacetate and conducting the methylation in acetone, Haworth and co-workers obtained a 90% yield of an almost 2.9 D.S. product with only six treatments (*232; see also 233*). Then, Hess and Lung showed that a single treatment of native starch could give a D.S. of 2.7–2.8 with little degradation if a 40% solution of sodium hydroxide was used as solvent and oxygen was excluded from the system (*234*). At temperatures above 100°, methyl chloride can replace dimethyl sulfate (*235, 236*); even at lower temperatures, methyl chloride can be used to introduce very low degrees of substitution into granular starch (*237, 238*) and amylose (*227*). Methyl bromide is somewhat more reactive (*239*), and methyl iodide readily methylates amylose in solutions containing 18–40% sodium hydroxide (*240*).

The Purdie reagents, methyl iodide and silver oxide, are most useful for increasing the degree of methylation of starch that has been made soluble in methyl iodide by some other method of methylation (*224, 230*). Karrer and Naegeli, however, prepared a degraded monomethyl ether using these reagents on an autoclaved aqueous starch paste (*229*).

The preferred laboratory method for complete methylation of starch and its fractions utilizes methyl iodide and sodium in liquid ammonia (*224, 241, 242*). Amylose and amylopectin are methylated directly, but granular starch requires pretreatment (*242*). In this method, alternate additions of small portions of sodium and methyl iodide are made to the dispersion of the polysaccharide in liquid ammonia. To prevent degradation, the amount of excess sodium is kept to a minimum, and the product is separated from sodamide by filtration and washing with liquid ammonia part way through the operation. Starch sodium alkoxides obtained by refluxing starch with sodium hydroxide in a non-aqueous solvent have also been converted to methyl ethers by excess methyl iodide (*240, 243–246*).

Diazomethane has found occasional use as a methylating agent for starch. Ether is used as solvent, and the introduction of up to 26% methoxyl (about 1.5 D.S.) has been achieved (*247, 248*).

Recently dimethyl sulfoxide has been used as solvent in the methylation of a canary dextrin and a soluble starch with dimethyl sulfate (*249, 250*), of a soluble starch with methyl iodide and silver oxide (*251*), and of a native corn starch with methyl iodide and barium oxide (*252*). None of these techniques gives a tri-*O*-methylstarch in a single methylation. With methyl iodide in dimethyl sulfoxide, for example, one obtains an approximately 1.5 D.S. product (*249*). A unique feature of that method is that the solvent serves as the acid acceptor:

$$2 \text{ HI} + (\text{CH}_3)_2\text{SO} \rightarrow (\text{CH}_3)_2\text{S} + \text{H}_2\text{O} + \text{I}_2$$

Anhydrous calcium sulfate is used to maintain anhydrous conditions.

The properties of low D.S. methylstarches are similar to those of any starch derivative lightly substituted with small, nonionic groups. These properties include lowered gelatinization temperature, increased water solubility, and reduced tendency toward retrogradation. At high D.S., the properties depend upon both the degree and method of methylation, since the extent of starch degradation varies widely from one methylation technique to another. Relatively undegraded methylstarch is soluble in cold water at a D.S. of 1, but insoluble in chloroform and in boiling water. As the methoxyl content is increased, chloroform solubility increases and water solubility decreases. Tri-*O*-methylstarch is purified by extraction with boiling water, dissolution in chloroform, and precipitation with petroleum ether (*224*).

The distribution of methyl groups in partially methylated amylose has been investigated by several workers using methyl iodide and aqueous alkali (*240*), dimethyl sulfate in aqueous alkali (*253*), and a methyl iodide–sodium alkoxide technique (*240, 254*) that was previously reported (*243–246*) to give selective methylation at C-2. All the results were similar: methylation occurs at all three positions, but predominantly at C-2 and C-6. The ratio of secondary to primary methyl groups in approximately monomethyl derivatives varies from 1:1 to 2:1 depending upon alkali concentration; in cupralkali solutions, the ratio is reported to rise to 4.5:1 (*240*).

Methylstarch has been studied in the ultracentrifuge (*255*) and the wettability of films of methylamylose and methylamylopectin has been measured (*46*). Among the uses suggested for methylstarches are protective colloid in emulsions (*256*), soil suspending agent in detergents (*257*), flocculant for pigments (*258*), thickener in paper screening (*259*), and component of the photographic transfer layer in the direct production of positive images (*260*). Methylamylose is said to be superior to starch ethers for sizing textile yarns (*228*), and methylamylopectin has been listed as a blood volume expander (*261*).

Fully methylated starch may be acid hydrolyzed to give predominantly 2,3,6-tri-*O*-methyl-α-D-glucopyranose, or converted to the corresponding methyl glycosides by methanolysis in acidic methanol (*223*, *262–264*). Bromoacetolysis followed by methanolysis also yields the methyl glycosides (*265*), and it has been shown that this technique liberates the tetra-*O*-methyl-α-D-glucopyranose end groups rapidly and completely before a significant amount of the trimethyl sugars has been produced (*266*).

It is claimed that heating methylstarches in liquid chlorine results in chlorination (*267*). Methylstarch has also been used as a substrate for graft polymerization of acrylonitrile (*268*).

b. *Higher Alkyl Ethers*

The methods for preparing the higher alkyl ethers of starch are generally the same as those used for methylation. A common technique involves dissolving the starch in at least 10% aqueous alkali, adding more alkali and heating with part of the alkylating agent, then treating with additional alkali and heating with the balance of the alkylating agent. In this way, 0.5–2.8 D.S. starch ethers have been prepared from diethyl sulfate, ethyl chloride and iodide, propyl bromide, butyl chloride and iodide, amyl chloride and bromide, and hexyl, heptyl and dodecyl iodides (*220*, *269*, *270*). Variations can be made in the ratios of alkali to carbohydrate to water (*236*); at very low water to starch ratios, cold-water-soluble granular ethers are obtained (*271*). Higher temperatures, 100°–170°, have been used to promote etherification with alkyl chlorides (*235*, *236*, *272*), but degradation is increased by the combination of excess alkali and high temperatures. If the ethers are sufficiently substituted and relatively undegraded, they are isolated by filtration and washing (*269*); otherwise, they are precipitated from boiling water (*269*) or salted out (*273*).

The higher alkylstarches may also be prepared in nonaqueous systems. Pretreatment with formic acid to "activate" the starch, and heating with diethyl sulfate and solid sodium hydroxide in toluene at 85° yields a 1.9 D.S. *O*-ethylstarch (*23*). *O*-Ethylstarch has also been prepared from ethyl iodide and sodium in liquid ammonia (*242*). Treating the sodium alcoholate of starch with butyl chloride or with ethyl, propyl, isopropyl, butyl, isobutyl or isoamyl bromide yields the corresponding monosubstituted alkyl ethers (*244–246*).

Low D.S. O-ethylamylose is prepared by treating a solution of amylose in 5% sodium hydroxide with ethyl bromide at room temperature (11). Similarly, granular alkylstarches are obtained at low D.S. by adding the alkylating agent to an aqueous alkaline starch slurry (225, 226, 237, 238). With granular corn starch, temperatures up to about 55° are possible if sufficient salt is added to the slurry to prevent gelatinization. In this manner, granular starch has been alkylated with ethyl, propyl and amyl chlorides (237, 238), diethyl sulfate, tetraethyl silicate, tris-isopropyl borate and tributyl phosphate (226). Reaction of starch with diethyl sulfate in an aqueous alkaline slurry can also be effected by passing the slurry over heated rolls to simultaneously derivatize, gelatinize, and dry the starch (3).

The properties of the high D.S., gelatinized, higher alkyl ethers of starch have been described by Degering (7) and by Hamilton and Yanovsky (269). Solubility in cold water is observed up to 0.5 D.S. for the butyl ether and perhaps to 1.5 D.S. for the ethyl ether. Above 0.5 D.S. all the ethers are insoluble in hot water, and the lauryl ether is insoluble in cold water as well. Chloroform solubility occurs above 2 D.S. with the ethyl ether, and at a D.S. as low as 0.9 for the heptyl and lauryl ethers. The specific gravity of these derivatives decreases with increasing length of the alkyl group. It is claimed that the alkyl ethers are chlorinated at 30°–90° in liquid chlorine (267).

O-Ethylstarches are useful as protective colloids (256), and they have been suggested as components of detergent formulations (257). O-Ethylamylose of sufficient D.S. to be organic solvent soluble has been proposed as a binder for tobacco sheet (274). Lower D.S. ethyl and propyl ethers of amylose are claimed to be superior textile warp sizes for hydrophobic yarns (228).

2. Substituted Alkyl Ethers

a. *Sodium O-Carboxymethylstarch*

Like dimethyl sulfate, sodium chloroacetate ($ClCH_2CO_2Na$) is an effective alkylating agent for starch in aqueous alkali (275–285). Unlike the methyl ether, however, the sodium carboxymethyl ether (the word "sodium" is omitted throughout the rest of this section, but should be understood) is highly water soluble. Consequently, much effort has been directed toward methods of isolation and purification from residual salts. Alcohol precipitation and exhaustive alcohol extraction of the precipitate was the earliest method used (275). Salting out with sodium sulfate eventually yields a product from which a large part of the salt can be removed by grinding and screening (273). Precipitation with alum gives the insoluble aluminum salt, which can be resolubilized with alkali (286). Alternatively, aluminum soaps have been incorporated in the reaction mixture (287).

A major improvement in carboxymethylation technique involves conducting the reaction in a water-miscible solvent containing minor amounts of water (288–295). Isopropanol is probably the solvent of choice (293), although both methanol and ethanol have been widely used. This technique has been successfully applied to high-amylose corn starches (296, 297). In a related process, a carboxymethyldextrin was prepared by treating the sodium alcoholate of the dextrin with sodium chloroacetate in anhydrous butanol (246).

Low D.S. carboxymethylstarches may be obtained in the original granule form using an aqueous alcohol reaction medium (288, 290). Up to about 0.1 D.S., the granular derivatives are not cold water soluble. Hence, they may also be obtained by conducting the reaction in an aqueous alkaline slurry containing added salts (237, 238, 298). Granular products at slightly higher D.S. can be obtained if the granule is cross-linked before etherification (239). At low degrees of cross-linking, the carboxymethyl ethers are gelatinizable in hot water, but extensive cross-linking results in intractable granules that have been proposed as ion-exchange materials (299). An alternative approach to a granular product is to blend starch with sodium chloroacetate and sodium or barium hydroxide, adding little or no moisture beyond that naturally present in the starch, and to store the blend at room temperature (271, 300), or to heat it either in a jacketed blender (271) or in a fluid bed (301).

The carboxymethylation of high-amylose corn starch was mentioned above. Carboxymethylamylose is also readily prepared in aqueous alkali (11, 302); under these conditions, the secondary hydroxyl groups react preferentially (302). In 1942, Höppler reported that methanol fractionation of a carboxymethyl potato starch, incorrectly called sodium starch glycolate, gives an 85% yield of "sodium amylopectin glycolate" or "ultraamylopectin", a product of remarkably high viscosity (303–305). Later, Moe described similar products from potato and mandioca [sic] starches (276).

The viscosity of carboxymethylstarches may be increased by the incorporation of various cross-linking agents in the reaction mixture (73, 306, 307). Exclusion of air by means of an inert gas blanket increases viscosity by inhibiting oxidative degradation in reactions conducted in aqueous alkali. Degraded products are obtained by adding hydrogen peroxide or sodium hypochlorite during the etherification (308), or by thermal degradation of ordinary carboxymethylstarches (309).

Treatment of carboxymethylstarch with ethylene oxide is said to produce the ethyl ester (*310*). The mixed allyl carboxymethyl (*311, 312*) and benzyl carboxymethyl (*313*) ethers of starch and its fractions have also been described.

The carboxymethyl ethers of starch and its fractions are anionic polyelectrolytes; as such, their salt-free aqueous solutions are highly viscous, but marked viscosity losses occur in the presence of added electrolytes. Senti and co-workers (*296, 297*) have investigated the viscosity of solutions of carboxymethyl high-amylose starch and found that, at equivalent D.S. and concentration, they were more viscous than solutions of carboxymethylamylose. Carboxymethylstarch solutions were still more viscous, and carboxymethylcellulose gave solutions of the highest viscosity. Carboxymethylamylose is a typical, linear polyelectrolyte, and has been the basis of a number of theoretical investigations of polyelectrolyte solution behavior (*314–317*). A solution property of carboxymethylstarch that is of practical significance is its compatibility with solutions of poly(vinyl alcohol), a property also possessed by starch half esters of dicarboxylic acids (*318*).

The physiological effects of carboxymethylstarch are of interest in view of the common use of carboxymethylcellulose in foods, and the reported similar use in Europe of Höppler's "sodium amylopectin glycolate" (*319*). When fed to humans, a 0.4–0.5 D.S. carboxymethyl ether of starch causes diarrhea at the 60 g. per day level (*320*). When fed to rats in the amount of 45% of the diet weight, the same derivative caused death; but a 0.03 D.S. carboxymethylstarch caused only mild diarrhea when fed at 45% of the diet weight. Used as a blood volume expander in dogs, carboxymethylstarch was found to be only moderately toxic (*321*). Since carboxymethylcellulose has been used clinically for its laxative effect (*322*), it would seem that there is little difference in the physiological effects of these polysaccharide derivatives. The use of carboxymethylstarch as an ice cream stabilizer has been patented (*323*).

Recently, carboxymethylamylose has been used as the anion of a polymeric salt in which the cation is a basic drug, such as an alkaloid, anesthetic or antibiotic; the resulting polysalts show increased ability to enter the lymphatic system (*324*). Other pharmaceutical uses for carboxymethylstarch, and particularly for Höppler's "sodium amylopectin glycolate," depend upon its thickening ability (*304, 325–329*).

A potential major industrial consumer of carboxymethylstarch is the textile industry. Its use in textile finishing and dyeing has been demonstrated (*279, 330, 331*); and because of its resistance to biological degradation, it has been considered as a warp size that would not contribute to the biological oxygen demand of the waste stream from a desizing operation (*332–334*). Carboxymethylamylose is said to be superior to starch ethers for sizing hydrophilic yarns (*228*).

Other major industrial applications proposed for carboxymethylstarch are as soil suspending agents in detergents (*257, 297*) and as flocculants (*335–337*). Benzylcarboxymethylstarch has been patented as a foaming agent for use in detergents (*313*).

The insolubility of polyvalent metal salts of carboxymethylstarch is the basis for a number of patents describing the preparation of water-resistant coatings (*338–340*), fibers (*341*), and binding agents (*342*). Precipitation of carboxymethylstarch with alum is useful in suspending pulp for screening paper (*259*). Insoluble films have also been prepared by polymerization of allylcarboxymethylstarches (*311, 312*).

One of the oldest miscellaneous uses for carboxymethylstarch is as an indicator in iodometric titrations due to its superiority over starch (*343–346*). Other uses include soil conditioner (*347, 348*), component of latex-based paint (*349*) and of a paint remover (*350*), binder for kaolin castings (*351*), replacement for gum arabic in lithography (*352*), component of photographic film emulsion (*353*), and additive to impart free-flowing characteristics to granular explosives (*354*).

b. *Other Carboxyalkylstarches*

Salts of α-halocarboxylic acids other than chloroacetic have been used to prepare higher carboxylalkylstarches by the same general techniques. Sodium α-chloro- (*276*) or α-bromopropionate (*288*) gives sodium O-(1-carboxyethyl)starch, and sodium α-bromoisovalerate yields O-(1-carboxy-2-methylpropyl)starch (*288*).

Recently, it has been shown that low D.S. granular carboxyethylstarches can be prepared by adding almost any ester of acrylic acid to an alkaline starch slurry (*355*). The properties of the products indicate that cross-linking occurs with most of the esters; ethyl and butyl acrylate appear to give relatively noncross-linked products. In a similar manner, a low D.S. granular O-(1-methyl-2-carboxyethyl)starch was prepared from ethyl crotonate. Dimethylitaconate gave a cross-linked derivative.

Methyl propiolate, $HC{\equiv}CCO_2CH_3$, reacts with starch and sodium hydroxide to yield the sodium 2-carboxyvinyl ether, Starch-OCH$=$CHCO$_2$Na (*356*). The reaction is analogous to that of starch with acrylates, and these derivatives are conveniently considered with the carboxyalkylstarches. Much higher alkali concentrations are used in reactions of starch with methyl propiolate than in the corresponding acrylate reactions; slightly aqueous *tert*-butanol is the preferred reaction medium. Degrees of substitution up to 0.95 are reported. A mixed hydroxyethyl carboxyvinyl ether has also been described (*356*).

The reactions of starch with β-propionolactone, β-butyrolactone, and γ-valerolactone were discussed earlier in this chapter. Products of these reactions have been described as hydroxyalkyl esters, carboxyalkyl ethers, or mixtures of both (*72–74*). Formation of low D.S. carboxyalkyl ethers appears to be favored by low reaction temperatures, short reaction times, and a relatively low pH.

Carboxyethyl groups are also introduced into starch by alkaline hydrolysis of cyanoethyl or carbamylethyl groups. These reactions are discussed later. Carboxyethylstarch is reported to be useful for preventing the formation of lumps in hygroscopic crystals such as ammonium chloride (*357*).

c. *Sulfoalkyl Ethers*

Like the carboxyalkyl ethers of starch, the sulfoalkyl ethers are anionic polysaccharides. The halogen atoms in sodium β-haloalkyl-sulfonates are sufficiently reactive to enable these compounds to function as alkylating agents. Cold-water-soluble, granular 2-sulfoethylstarch has been prepared from sodium 2-chloroethanesulfonate in 90% isopropanol containing sodium hydroxide (*358*), and from sodium 2-bromoethanesulfonate and alkali at 100°–105° in the absence of solvent (*271*). Low D.S. granular sulfoalkylstarches are also prepared from sodium 3-chloro-2-hydroxypropanesulfonate, the reaction product of sodium bisulfite and epichlorohydrin (*75, 359*).

Sultones, the cyclic intramolecular esters of hydroxyalkylsulfonic acids, are also excellent alkylating agents for starch. Since this reaction is one of ring opening rather than displacement, only a slight excess of base is required over that necessary to neutralize the sulfonic acid group. Hence, gelatinized sodium sulfoalkylstarches, prepared in aqueous alkali and dried without purification, contain little salt (*360*). Sulfo-alkylstarches have been prepared from propane sultone, γ-butane sultone, and tolyl sultone (*360*). A 3-sulfopropyl ether of amylose was found to have more secondary than primary hydroxyl groups etherified (*302*).

A series of nonionic starch ethers related to the sulfoalkylstarches may be prepared from monovinyl sulfones, $RSO_2CH:CH_2$ (*361*). The reaction is base catalyzed and may be conducted in water or in an organic solvent.

d. *O-(2-Cyanoethyl)starch*

Alkali-catalyzed reactions of starch with acrylonitrile proceed rapidly to form 2-cyanoethyl ethers (*362, 363*). The reaction can be conducted in an aqueous alkaline starch paste from which cyanoethyl-starches precipitate in the D.S. range 1.5–2.5 (*364*). With less than sufficient alkali to cause gelatinization of the starch, granular products up to 0.8 D.S. have been obtained (*365*). The nature of these granular products varies markedly with the manner in which they are prepared. With short reaction times and a large excess of acrylonitrile, highly water-insoluble products are obtained (*366, 367*). A 0.05 D.S. cyano-ethylstarch prepared in that way withstands steam sterilization condi-tions without caking, suggesting that the granule surface is highly derivatized (*367*). On the other hand, if the amount of acrylonitrile is limited and the reaction allowed to proceed until all of the acrylonitrile is consumed, granular products are obtained that are readily gelatinized at 100° in water at pH 10–11, even at 0.8 D.S. (*365*). Although a loss of 10–20% of the bound nitrogen occurs during gelatinization at pH 10–11, no carboxyethyl groups are formed.

Amylose is similarly cyanoethylated in aqueous alkaline solution; the products are water soluble in the D.S. range of 0.02–0.15 (*11*). Retrograded amylose may be cyanoethylated in water suspension in the same manner as granular starch; products in the D.S. range 0.19–0.88 are insoluble in cold water, but dissolve in water at 125°–200° (*368*). β,β'-Oxybispropionitrile also cyanoethylates starch in alkaline solution (*369*).

Dispersions of 1.5–2.0 D.S. cyanoethylstarch in solvents such as acetone, methyl ethyl ketone, cyclohexanone, aqueous acetonitrile, or aqueous dimethyl sulfoxide have been used to impart microbiological resistance to cloth and to paper (*370*). The resistance of cyanoethyl-starches to microorganisms has also suggested their use as stabilizers in water-based paints (*371*). Other patented applications for cyanoethyl-starches include their use as drilling mud adjuncts (*372*), as flocculants (*373*), in the separation of aromatic from aliphatic hydrocarbons (*374*), in dry cell manufacture (*375*), and as additives to improve the dyeing properties of poly(acrylonitrile) (*376*).

It has been mentioned that aqueous alkali is capable of removing cyanoethyl groups from starch, the base-catalyzed reaction with acrylonitrile being reversible. Hydrolysis of the cyanoethyl groups to carboxyethyl groups usually occurs concurrently (*377–379*). Carboxy-ethylcyanoethylstarches prepared in this manner show excellent water solubility and have been proposed as flocculants (*379, 380*). Carbamyl-ethyl groups, the intermediate hydrolysis product in the conversion of cyanoethyl to carboxyethyl, are not found in alkali-hydrolyzed cyano-ethylstarches because carbamylethylgroups hydrolyze more rapidly than cyanoethyl groups. The conversion of cyanoethylstarch to carbamyl-ethylstarch is discussed in the following section.

e. *O-(2-Carbamylethyl)starch*

The reactivity of acrylamide with alkaline starch is less than that of acrylonitrile; nevertheless, 2-carbamylethyl ethers of starch (sometimes called propionamide ethers) are readily prepared up to a D.S. of 1.0 or slightly higher. The lower D.S. granular products are obtained by adding acrylamide to an aqueous alkaline starch slurry that usually contains a gelatinization inhibitor, such as an alcohol or a neutral salt (*381–383*). Similar products result when a damp mixture of starch, acrylamide and sodium hydroxide are held at 35°–40°. As the D.S. rises above 0.2, it becomes increasingly difficult to wash the granular products with water without causing some gelatinization. In such cases, washing is facilitated by adjusting the pH of the wash water to pH 2–3 (*381*). Above 0.4 D.S., carbamylethylstarches are prepared by heating starch in water with alkali and excess acrylamide above the gelatinization temperature of the product (*384*).

At alkali concentrations significantly greater than those required to catalyze the etherification, carbamylethyl groups are hydrolyzed to carboxyethyl groups. Mixed carboxyethyl carbamylethyl derivatives prepared in this manner are claimed to be effective flocculants (*385*) and wet-end additives for improving the dry strength of paper (*386*).

Treatment of 2-cyanoethyl ethers of starch with slightly alkaline hydrogen peroxide yields 2-carbamylethyl ethers with no production of carboxyethyl groups (*387*); some degradation of the starch accompanies the reaction, however. The amide groups of 2-carbamylethylstarches react with formaldehyde under alkaline conditions to give methylol-amides (*382, 388*). Films cast from pastes of these methylolated derivatives show reduced moisture sensitivity, and such products have been suggested for sizing textiles, binding pigmented paper coatings, and for formulation into waterproof adhesives (*388*).

3. *O*-Allylstarch

Among the unsaturated ethers of starch, *O*-allylstarch is by far the most thoroughly investigated. In the years immediately following World War II, it appeared that a 1.8 D.S. solvent-soluble allyl ether of starch would become an item of commerce. Its ability to cure to a solvent resistant resin suggested a number of practical applications. But while the starch manufacturers hesitated over marketing a new product so unlike starch, the completely synthetic vinyl polymers usurped many of the potential markets. Interest in its potential still exists, however, as indicated by the continued appearance of publications concerning its application.

Initially, starch was allylated to a D.S. of 0.5 with excess allyl bromide in 10% sodium hydroxide solution at 100° (*389*). Under these conditions, the D.S. is limited by the extensive conversion of allyl bromide or chloride to allyl alcohol and allyl ether. As the alkali concentration is increased, hydrolysis of the etherifying agent is decreased; use of 40–50% sodium hydroxide or 65–70% potassium hydroxide, together with a ketone to dissolve the product as it is formed, makes 1.5–2.5 D.S. allyl ethers readily available (*390–393*). Such a reaction takes place in two stages: an exothermic etherification that is relatively rapid, followed by a slow degradation of the starch molecule permitting solution of the ether to take place. The time required to solubilize the product is reduced by adding acid after etherification is complete (*394–398*). Etherification time is shortened by conducting the reaction in a medium of excess allyl chloride and controlling the consumption of allyl chloride by using limited amounts of alkali (*398*), or by starting with an acid-modified or enzyme-hydrolyzed starch (*399*).

Variations of these methods include pretreating the starch with formic acid prior to etherification in a completely anhydrous medium (*23*), and pretreatment of the starch with sodium hydroxide in aqueous isopropanol prior to reaction in excess allyl chloride (*398*) or bromide (*400*). Addition of small amounts of sodium iodide appears to improve the reaction with allyl chloride (*394, 396*). Use of acetylated starch as starting material was originally believed to give a solvent soluble product without the need for degradation with acid (*390, 401*). Later work showed, however, that an undegraded starch acetate gives products resembling those obtained from unmodified starch (*402*), indicating that the earlier starch acetates were partially degraded during acetylation.

Methallyl ethers of starch are prepared from methallyl bromide and 50% sodium hydroxide solution in methyl ethyl ketone (*403*). Low D.S., granular *O*-allylstarches are prepared from allyl chloride or allyl bromide in an aqueous alkaline slurry (*55, 237, 238*).

At 1.5–2.5 D.S., allylstarches become gummy, but not truly soluble in water. They are insoluble in aliphatic hydrocarbons, and readily soluble in alcohols, ketones and aromatic hydrocarbons. For the less degraded preparations, dioxane or pyridine is an effective solvent. Solutions of these derivatives are stable, but on exposure to oxygen of the air, or to other oxidizing agents, they undergo polymerization through the formation of hydroperoxide groups at the allylic carbon atom (*390*). The mechanism is similar to that by which drying oils are cured. In fact, insolubilization of films of allylstarch is promoted by the cobalt and lead driers used in oil-based paints (*404*). Insolubilization is also effected by sulfur (*405*); sulfur dioxide (*312*), sulfur chlorides (*406*), peroxygen compounds (55, 311, 399, 407), and dimethyl itaconate (408). Treatment of an allylstarch in ethanol with hydrogen peroxide gives a product that is sensitized by dichromates to photo-induced polymerization (400). Ultraviolet radiation also induces curing of allylstarch films (409).

The most obvious application for allylstarches is their use in lacquers or varnishes. Addition of a plasticizer improves flexibility of the coating and eliminates crazing (410–413). Stable emulsions of allylstarch have been prepared and used for coating paper or textiles (414, 415). Its use in printing inks has been suggested (416), and it has been considered as a finishing agent for wool (417) and an additive to acrylic resins (418). A series of mixed allyl alkyl ethers of starch was prepared for the same reason by allylating ethyl, propyl, butyl, amyl, hexyl, heptyl, lauryl, and several benzylstarch ethers (269, 270). The benzyl groups appeared to be the most effective in reducing water sensitivity. A carboxymethylstarch has been etherified with allyl bromide (311, 312); and allylstarch has been etherified with propylene oxide (419) and copolymerized with styrene (420). The early literature relating to allylstarch and other allyl carbohydrates was reviewed by Yanovsky in 1953 (409).

4. Benzyl Ethers

Development of methods for the preparation of starch benzyl ethers followed a pattern very similar to that of allyl ethers. Initially, starch was benzylated with excess benzyl chloride in 9% sodium hydroxide solution to give 1.0 D.S. corn starch ethers and 0.5 D.S. potato starch ethers (421). Subsequent workers did not confirm a difference in reactivity among starch species, however (422). Use of 30–40% sodium hydroxide to reduce hydrolysis of the benzyl chloride was the next development (423, 424). It was followed by the use of limited amounts of alkali, first in excess benzyl chloride, then with the excess benzyl chloride replaced by an inert solvent (425). Later, formic acid pretreated starch was etherified with benzyl chloride and sodium hydroxide in an anhydrous medium (23). The reactivity of benzyl chloride is such that pyridine can be used both as the base and the solvent to prepare high D.S. starch benzyl ethers, provided that the starch is activated by pretreatment with hot aqueous pyridine (83). Low D.S., granular starch benzyl ethers may be prepared in aqueous alkaline slurry (237, 238), or by heating anhydrous starch with benzyl chloride and sodium hydroxide (271).

Benzylstarches are said to be useful as molding powders (426) and as additives to acrylic resins (418). They have also been suggested as components of detergents (257) and adhesives (426). Emulsions of benzylstarches are suitable for finishing textiles (426).

A partial benzyl ether of starch has been further etherified with allyl chloride to give a mixed allyl benzyl ether (270). The same derivative has also been prepared by simultaneous derivatization with mixed etherifying agents (270), as have benzyl carboxymethyl and benzyl 2-hydroxypropyl ethers (313). The last two derivatives carry both hydrophilic and hydrophobic substituents, and are effective foaming agents in aqueous systems (313). Benzylethylamylose is reported to be useful as a textile size (228).

Several ring-substituted benzyl ethers of starch have been prepared following methods used for benzylstarches. Etherifying agents used are o- and p-chlorobenzyl chlorides (270), sodium α-chloro-p-toluenesulfonate (75, 427), and p-nitrobenzyl chloride (428). Reduction of the nitro group on the last derivative gave a p-aminobenzylstarch capable of undergoing diazotization and coupling to give colored starches (428).

5. Miscellaneous Ethers

a. O-Triphenylmethylstarch

Etherification of starch or amylose with triphenylmethyl chloride in pyridine yields an approximate 6-O-triphenylmethyl (6-O-trityl) ether (122, 429, 430). The reaction is not completely restricted to primary hydroxyl groups, but is sufficiently specific to permit its use in estimating the number of free primary hydroxyl groups in partially substituted polysaccharides. Examples of this use involve the tritylation of amylose acetates (10, 431), starch acetate (10), starch S-methylxanthate (202), methyl ethers of amylose (240), and carboxymethyl, 2-hydroxyethyl, and 3-sulfopropyl ethers of amylose (302). Tritylation is also used to block primary hydroxyl groups in the synthesis of fully substituted polysaccharides; subsequent removal of trityl groups by acid hydrolysis or reduction leaves the primary hydroxyls available for further reaction. Mixed derivatives of amylose prepared for subsequent removal of trityl groups include 2,3-di-O-acetyl-6-O-tritylamylose (122, 432), 2,3-di-

O-benzoyl-6-*O*-tritylamylose   (*124*),   2,3-di-*O*-phenylcarbamyl-6-*O*-tritylamylose (*109, 110*), and 2-*O*-tosyl-6-*O*-tritylamylose (*125*).

b. *O-Vinylstarch*

A recent investigation of the alkali-catalyzed, high-pressure reaction of acetylene with starch and its fractions resulted in the preparation of vinyl ethers up to about 1.0 D.S. (*433–435*). Optimum conditions were determined by use of response surface designs. Subsequent examination of vinylamylose and -amylopectin showed that the C-2 position is the predominant site of substitution (*435*).

c. *Substituted Hydroxyalkyl Ethers*

The hydroxyalkyl ethers of starch are discussed in detail in Chapter XVII, which also mentions phenylhydroxyethylstarch and several other substituted hydroxyalkyl ethers. To make the bibliography of the present chapter as complete as possible, reference is made here to reported reactions of starch and amylose with styrene oxide (*227, 436–440*), butadiene monoxide (*55, 441, 442*), glycidyl allyl ether (*441, 442*), glycidyl isopropyl ether (*436*), glycerol monochlorohydrin (*443*), and expoxidized fatty acids and their derivatives (*444*).

IV. OXIDIZED STARCHES

The commercially important oxidized starches are those prepared by dilute alkaline hypochlorite oxidation and by periodate oxidation. Discussion of the production and uses of these starches appears in Chapters X and XVIII, respectively. Nitrogen dioxide-oxidized starch has been the subject of a number of recent Japanese patents and publications, and is considered here as probably the next most important oxidized starch. Since Liebig's observation in 1829 of the action of chlorine and chlorous acid on starch (*445*), a wide variety of oxidizing agents have been investigated. Most of these oxidations resulted in extensive degradation, and the products were no longer starch derivatives as the term is defined early in this chapter. For that reason, and because several excellent bibliographies of starch oxidation are available (*7, 446–448*), only a few recent examples of starch oxidation other than with nitrogen dioxide are included here. Yields and specific viscosities of oxidized starches obtained by steeping granular starch in 1% solution of the following oxidants decreased in the order given: $FeCl_3 > Na_2S_2O_3 >$ $NaBO_3 > K_2Cr_2O_7 > H_2O_2 > Na_2O_2 > 1\%$ $H_2O_2 + 0.1\%$ $FeCl_3 >$ $NaOCl > KMnO_4 >$ bleaching powder $> 1\%$ $NaOH + 0.5\%$ $NaOCl$ (*449*).

1. Nitrogen Dioxide-Oxidized Starch

The C-6 hydroxyl groups of starch are oxidized preferentially by nitrogen dioxide (N_2O_4). The reaction may be conducted by adding liquid N_2O_4 to starch in carbon tetrachloride at room temperature (*450, 451*), or by exposing starch to N_2O_4 vapors (*451, 452*). In the latter case, the reaction is promoted by traces of moisture (*452*). Up to 90% apparent conversion of primary hydroxyl groups to uronic acid groups is obtained (*451, 452*), although some carboxyl groups are generated by oxidation of a small number of reducing-end groups formed by hydrolysis.

The same reaction can be effected in fuming nitric acid or in nitric acid of any concentration above 50%, provided that it contains some nitrous acid (*453–457*). The nitrous acid may be introduced by adding sodium nitrite (*453, 457*), may be generated *in situ* by adding para-formaldehyde (*455*), or may be present as a result of diluting fuming nitric acid to 72% nitric acid (*453, 454, 457*). With 72% nitric acid, no weight loss occurs if the oxidation proceeds at 0°–5°, but only about 50% oxidation is achieved (*453, 454*).

Nitrogen dioxide-oxidized starch is almost completely decarboxylated in 15 minutes at 255° (*458*). Acid hydrolysis yields D-glucuronic acid (*453, 454, 459*), but never in amounts greater than 60% based on the carboxyl content. D-Glucuronic acid is also present in boiled alkaline solutions of the oxidized starch (*460*). Reduction of nitrogen dioxide-oxidized starch with sodium borohydride has no effect on the carboxyl content, but increases the yield of uronic acid formed on acid hydrolysis and decreases the amount obtained on treatment with alkali (*459–461*). These results are explained by the presence of carbonyl groups at C-2 and C-3 in the oxidized starch. Additional evidence for secondary hydroxyl oxidation has been provided by periodate oxidation studies (*462*), and by the isolation of other hexuronic acids from the acid hydrolyzate of borohydride reduced, nitrogen dioxide-oxidized starch (*463*).

Comparison has been made of the products of the oxidation performed at 0°–5° in 72% nitric acid, at 20° in 67% nitric acid, and at 50° in 50% nitric acid (*457*). Low temperature oxidation with a high concentration of nitric acid promotes carbonyl group formation, while the opposite conditions promote hydrolysis and non-uronyl carboxyl group formation.

Methyl esters of nitrogen dioxide-oxidized starch have been prepared both before and after borohydride reduction (*464*). Reagents used were methanolic solutions of mineral acids, or methyl halides with the sodium salts of the oxidized starches. Sodium borohydride has no effect on amylose that has not been oxidized, other than to convert the reducing end group to a nonreducing end group (465).

2. Other Oxidized Starches

a. Chlorine

In addition to the well-known aqueous hypochlorite oxidation of starch, the reaction of corn starch with chlorine in methanol has received recent attention (466). The products resemble commercial thin-boiling starches in viscosity and in pasting temperatures, but have lower alkali numbers, lower paste clarities, and show more paste setback.

Oxidation of wheat starch with chlorine gas results primarily in depolymerization, with the formation of small amounts of carbonyl groups and D-gluconic acid (467, 468). The reaction is promoted by light and moisture.

Chlorous acid-oxidized starches have been reported to be carboxylated and to show increased viscosity (469). They may be useful as textile sizing agents (470). Similarly useful starches are prepared by heating starch with N,N-dichlorohydantoins that probably act as oxidizing agents (471). More study of these products is necessary to determine the nature of the oxidation.

b. Permanganate

Permanganate oxidation of starch results in some depolymerization and decrease in stability toward pasting (472). The maximum number of carbonyl and carboxyl groups are introduced at pH 10 (473).

c. Dichromate

Chromic anhydride, either in acetic acid–acetic anhydride or in 0.2M sulfuric acid, introduces aldehyde, ketone, and carboxyl groups into starch (474). Potassium dichromate at pH 0.7, on the other hand, yields a product containing 60% of 2,3-dialdehyde groups and only 4–5% of carboxyl groups (475). Like periodate-oxidized starches, dichromate-oxidized starch imparts wet strength to paper when used as a beater additive (476).

d. Ozone

Carbonyl groups, mostly aldehyde, are introduced into starch upon exposure to ozone in water or in other solvents (477, 478). Ozone-treated starches are also capable of initiating graft polymerization of vinyl monomers (479–482), suggesting that hydroperoxide groups are formed as well. Unfortunately, the solution properties of ozone-oxidized starch have not been described.

V. GRAFT COPOLYMERS OF STARCH

The principal mechanisms by which starch graft copolymers are produced are chain transfer, physical activation, and chemical activation as discussed in Volume 1, Chapter XIX. Examples of chain transfer grafting are the polymerization of acrylonitrile in solutions of starch (268), starch methyl ether (268), and amylose (483); and the polymerization in the presence of allylstarch of styrene (420), acrylic acid, acrylonitrile, and acrylamide (399).

Physically activated grafting includes gamma (Co^{60}) irradiation induced copolymerization of acrylamide onto amylose (484) and of acrylonitrile and methyl acrylate onto wheat starch (485). Mechanical degradation of starch by freezing and thawing produces terminal radicals that initiate block copolymerization of monomers such as acrylonitrile (486–488). Similar results are obtained by ball milling starch with acrylamide (489), or by mastication of starch with monomers such as styrene or methyl methacrylate (490–493).

Chemical activation of grafting involves the production of free radicals on starch through a chemical reaction. One method is to subject the starch to any free radical oxidation; systems which generate hydroxyl radicals, such as hydrogen peroxide–ferrous ion and persulfate–bisulfite, have been used with many monomers (494, 495). Another technique utilizes a single electron transfer oxidation, such as that obtained with ceric ion (496, 497). A third method, involving the introduction of hydroperoxide groups with ozone, has been used to graft butadiene (479), styrene (479, 480), methyl methacrylate (481, 482), acrylonitrile (482) and vinyl chloride (482) onto starch. Methacrylonitrile has been grafted onto starch ethers by a process referred to as anionic polymerization (498), but peroxides may have been involved. The alkali-catalyzed reaction of 1-deoxy-1-acrylamido-D-glucitol with amylose resulted in a graft copolymer through polyether formation (499).

Few uses for graft copolymers of starch have been reported, although patents have been issued covering the use of starch–acrylonitrile graft copolymers as depressants in ore flotation (500), starch–acrylate copolymers as sizing agents for hydrophobic yarns (501, 502), and starch–acrylamide grafts as electrolyte-holding materials in dry cells (503). Graft copolymerization of styrene or styrene–acrylonitrile with hydroxyethyl starch or amylose gives thermoplastic resins of high impact strength (504).

VI. Other Starch Derivatives

1. Starch–Aldehyde Reaction Products

In 1950, Kerr (505) noted that the widely studied action of formalde-hyde and other low molecular weight aldehydes on starch was no longer thought to be unique. Rather it was believed to be representative of the general class of starch cross-linking reactions. Subsequent work has confirmed this belief, and the reader will find aldehyde cross-linked starches discussed in Chapter XIX. In addition, however, the stabiliza-tion of amylose solutions by chloral (506) and by formaldehyde (507–510) is apparently the result of an intermediate equilibrium formation of amylose hemiacetals. The hemiacetal bonds appear to be most stable at pH 5–7 (510), being converted to cross-linked acetals as the pH is lowered and dissociating to a mixture of amylose and free aldehyde at higher pH values. Recognition of the effect of pH on cross-linking has led to the development of a series of pregelatinized cold-water-soluble starch–formaldehyde compositions, prepared under neutral or slightly alkaline conditions, capable of giving water-resistant coatings or adhesives when cured under neutral or slightly acid conditions (511–513). Other aqueous starch compositions have been patented incorporat-ing butyraldehyde (514), glyoxal (515), and benzaldehyde (516).

A noncross-linked, full acetal of starch has been prepared in an acid-catalyzed addition reaction with 3,4-dihydro-2H-pyran (517).

Low D.S. granular products are obtained in aqueous solution and are water soluble. High D.S. products require the use of dimethyl sulfoxide as solvent; at D.S. values of 0.7, 1.1, and 1.5 they become soluble in dioxane, chloroform, and benzene, respectively. Reaction of a dextrin with hexyl or lauryl chloromethyl ether in dimethylformamide contain-ing sodium carbonate also gives a noncross-linked, full acetal (518). Such products are surface active agents. The product obtained by evaporating a starch paste with 3-hydroxyphthalide is said to have an acetal structure (519).

2. Starch Alkoxides

In a series of patents (243–246), Gaver and co-workers describe the preparation of "sodium starchates" by refluxing a mixture of starch and alcoholic sodium hydroxide. Analogous compounds are obtained using quaternary ammonium bases (520). Although these products give characteristic x-ray diffraction patterns, it is not clear whether they are true alkoxides of starch, or alkali complexes similar to the amylose–alkali complexes, $3C_6H_{10}O_5 \cdot MOH \cdot 3H_2O$, obtained by deacetylation of amylose triacetate in alcoholic alkali (521). Regardless of their structure, the sodium in the "starchates" is readily displaced by other metals, and the copper and mercury derivatives are claimed to be useful as mildewproofing agents (244). As might be expected of true alkoxides, the "sodium starchates" also react easily with alkylating agents to form ethers (243–246). Starch complexes with inorganic compounds, such as those formed with titanyl sulfate or TiO_2 (522), are discussed in Volume I, Chapter XIII.

3. Deoxy Starches

In all of the starch derivatives discussed so far, the hydroxyl group oxygen atoms have formed part of the derivative group. Either a substituent group has been attached to the D-glucopyranose ring through one of its hydroxyl oxygens, or hydrogen has been removed to give an oxidized hydroxyl group. It is possible, however, to form certain derivatives in which one or more of the hydroxyl group oxygens is displaced.

Heating starch with phosphorus pentachloride at 170° gives a chlorinated starch in which all three hydroxyl groups and two additional hydrogen atoms are reported to be replaced by chlorine (523). Although both oxidation and chlorination occur in liquid chlorine at 55°–100°, mono-, di-, and trichlorides of starch have been isolated (524, 525).

In recent years, there have been attempts to utilize the well-known displacement of p-toluenesulfonyloxy (tosyloxy) groups to synthesize deoxyamyloses. Treatment of 2,3-di-O-benzyl-6-O-tosylamylose (124) or 2,3-di-O-acetyl-6-O-tosylamylose (122) with strong base introduces 3,6-anhydro rings. Displacement of the primary tosyloxy groups in 2,3-di-O-benzyl-6-O-tosylamylose with iodide ion gives the corresponding 6-deoxy-6-iodo derivative which, in turn, yields a 6-deoxyamylose by lithium aluminum hydride reduction (124). Lithium aluminum hydride reduction of similarly prepared 6-deoxy-2,3-di-O-phenylcarbamyl-6-thiocyanoamylose and 6-azido-6-deoxy-2,3-di-O-phenylcarbamylamylose gives the corresponding 6-deoxy-6-thio and 6-amino-6-deoxy derivatives (110). Aminodeoxy groups are introduced in both the C-2 and C-6 positions of amylose by treating a di-O-tosylamylose with hydrazine and reducing the product with hydrogen and Raney nickel (123). Acetylation of the amine groups gives an acetamidodeoxyamylose (123).

4. Miscellaneous Derivatives

Xylopyranosyl groups are attached to amylose by an alkali-catalyzed transglycosidation from phenyl β-D-xylopyranoside (*526*). Acid-catalyzed transglycosidation has been used to introduce 13.5% D-galactose into the amylopectin molecule, but rearrangement of the D-glucose units undoubtedly occurred concurrently (*527*). A more sophisticated method for the introduction of mono- and oligosaccharide branches into amylose involves the silver perchlorate catalyzed displacement of trityl groups by poly-*O*-acylglycosyl bromides (*109*). By that method, up to 0.5 D.S. D-glucosylamylose has been prepared; maltosylamylose, cellobiosylamylose and amylose substituted with side chains of three or more D-glucose units are also reported.

Chlorosilanes react with starch to give substituted silyl derivatives (*528*). The reaction is performed in anhydrous formamide at room temperature, with or without pyridine. Trimethylchlorosilane, diphenyl-*n*-butoxychlorosilane, di-*tert*-butoxymethoxychlorosilane, and di-*tert* butoxy-*n*-butoxychlorosilane give products up to 2.0 D.S. The methoxy-silyl groups are readily removed by hydrolysis, but the larger butoxy groups appear to stabilize the silicon–oxygen–starch linkage. Treatment of granular starch in water with up to 2% sodium methylsiliconate imparts hydrophobic properties to the starch granules (*529, 530*).

VII. ANALYSIS OF STARCH DERIVATIVES

Determination of the average degree of substitution of a starch derivative is only a matter of calculation based upon analysis for an element in the substituted group, or for the group itself. The derivative, Starch-OZ, can be formulated as $C_6H_7O_2(OZ)_n(OH)_{3-n}$, where n is the D.S.; its unit molecular weight is $162 + n(z\text{-}1)$, where z is the molecular weight of the substituent Z. Obviously, the percentage of Z by analysis must equal $100nz/[162 + n(z\text{-}1)]$, and n is directly calculable. Consequently, if Z contains an element other than carbon, hydrogen and oxygen, determination of D.S. is straightforward (*531*). Otherwise, an analysis for the specific functional group is needed.

Formate and acetate groups are determined by saponification (*8, 532*). The lower alkyl ethers, as well as hydroxyethyl and hydroxypropyl starches, can be analyzed by a modified Zeisel procedure (*533, 534*). Carboxyl groups, such as those in *O*-carboxymethylstarch, can be titrated after conversion to the free acid form (*535*). High D.S. *O*-allyl-starches are analyzed by a modification of the Wijs iodine number determination (536). Infrared spectroscopy is useful for the qualitative identification of some starch derivatives (537), and perhaps this technique will be improved by the application of differential infrared spectroscopy.

A more complete discussion of the analysis of chemically modified starches is presented in Chapter XXV.

VIII. F.D.A. APPROVED STARCH DERIVATIVES

Under the regulations of the Federal Food, Drug, and Cosmetic Act, administered by the U.S. Food and Drug Administration, two types of modified starches are recognized. "Food starch–modified" may be safely used in food within specified legal limits; "industrial starch–modified" may be used as a component of articles intended for use in processing or packaging food.

As of this writing (538), "food starch–modified" includes starches esterified with (maximum limits) 5% acetic anhydride, 0.12% adipic anhydride with 5% acetic anhydride, vinyl acetate up to 2.5% acetyl groups in the product, 4% succinic anhydride, 3% 1-octenylsuccinic anhydride, 2% 1-octenylsuccinic anhydride with 2% aluminum sulfate, 0.1% phosphorus oxychloride, sodium trimetaphosphate up to 0.04% phosphorus in the product, and sodium tripolyphosphate with sodium trimetaphosphate up to 0.4% phosphorus in the product. Etherifying agents permitted for food starch–modified include up to 0.6% acrolein, 0.3% epichlorohydrin, and 25% propylene oxide. Also approved are combinations of acrolein with vinyl acetate, epichlorohydrin with acetic anhydride, epichlorohydrin with succinic anhydride, and phosphorus oxychloride with propylene oxide. The mixed derivatives that are cross-linked esters or cross-linked ethers are used as thickening agents in foods that demand stability toward acid-thinning and low temperature storage.

"Industrial starch–modified" (539) includes starch derivatives prepared by reaction of starch with (maximum limits) 5.5% sodium hypochlorite, 0.3% epichlorohydrin, 4% β-dimethylaminoethyl chloride, 3% dimethylaminoethyl methacrylate, 5% 2,3-epoxypropyltrimethylammonium chloride, and ethylene oxide up to 3% in the product. Up to 0.375% dimethylol ethylene urea may be used to modify starch for internal sizing only. All the derivatives permitted for food use are, of course, permitted for use in food packaging material. Certain surface active agents are also approved as adjuncts for use with "industrial starches–modified."

IX. References

(1) G. E. Hamerstrand, B. T. Hofreiter, and C. L. Mehltretter, *Cereal Chem.*, **37**, 519 (1960).

(2) Anon., *J. Org. Chem.*, **28**, 281 (1963).

(3) J. Lolkema, French Patent 874,436 (1942); U.S. Patent Reissue 23,443 (1951); *Chem. Abstr.*, **46**, 2830 (1952).

(4) J. Lolkema, Neth. Patent 55,779 (1944); British Patent 601,374 (1948); *Chem. Abstr.*, **41**, 3988 (1947); **42**, 7060 (1948).

(5) J. W. Mullen II and E. Pacsu, *Ind. Eng. Chem.*, **34**, 1209 (1942).

(6) R. L. Whistler, *Advan. Carbohydrate Chem.*, **1**, 279 (1945).

(7) E. F. Degering, in "Chemistry and Industry of Starch," R. W. Kerr, ed., Academic Press Inc., New York, N.Y., 2nd Ed., 1950, p. 262.

(8) H. J. Roberts, in "Methods in Carbohydrate Chemistry," R. L. Whistler, ed., Academic Press Inc., New York, N.Y., Vol. 4, 1964, p. 289.

(9) I. A. Wolff, D. W. Olds, and G. E. Hilbert, *Ind. Eng. Chem.*, **49**, 1247 (1957).

(10) R. L. Whistler and H. J. Roberts, *J. Am. Chem. Soc.*, **81**, 4427 (1959).

(11) M. W. Rutenberg, W. Jarowenko, and L. J. Ross, British Patent 871,634 (1961); U.S. Patent 3,038,895 (1962); *Chem. Abstr.*, **57**, 1139 (1962); **57**, 10086 (1962).

(12) I. A. Wolff, D. W. Olds, and G. E. Hilbert, *J. Am. Chem. Soc.*, **79**, 3860 (1957).

(13) O. A. Moe, U.S. Patent 2,462,210 (1949); *Chem. Abstr.*, **43**, 4038 (1949).

(14) B. L. Browning and L. O. Sell, *Textile Res. J.*, **23**, 939 (1953).

(15) A. G. Kldiaschwili, *Zh. Russ. Fiz. Khim. Obschch.*, **36**, 905 (1904); *J. Chem. Soc. Abstr.*, **86**, Part 1, 798 (1904).

(16) D. Gottlieb, C. G. Caldwell, and R. M. Hixon, *J. Am. Chem. Soc.*, **62**, 3342 (1940).

(17) O. A. Moe, S. E. Miller, and M. I. Buckley, *J. Am. Chem. Soc.*, **73**, 4185 (1951).

(18) H. Tarkow and A. J. Stamm, *J. Phys. Chem.*, **56**, 266 (1952).

(19) J. Traquair, *J. Soc. Chem. Ind.*, **28**, 288 (1909).

(20) R. F. Nickerson, *Textile Res. J.*, **21**, 195 (1951).

(21) K. M. Gaver, E. P. Lasure, and L. M. Thomas, U.S. Patent 2,538,903 (1951); *Chem. Abstr.*, **45**, 3629 (1951).

(22) J. R. Whinfield and G. G. Ritchie, British Patent 535,949 (1941); *Chem. Abstr.*, **36**, 1518 (1942).

(23) P. L. Nichols, Jr., and R. M. Hamilton, U.S. Patent 2,405,973 (1946); Fr. Patent 961,458 (1949); *Chem. Abstr.*, **40**, 7676 (1946).

(24) C. E. Smith and J. V. Tuschoff, U.S. Patent 2,928,828 (1960); *Chem. Abstr.*, **54**, 13703 (1960).

(25) J. V. Tuschoff and C. E. Smith, U.S. Patent 3,022,289 (1962); British Patent 912,387 (1962); *Chem. Abstr.*, **56**, 14520 (1962); **58**, 5875 (1963).

(26) W. Ciusa and G. Adamo, *Ann. Chim. (Rome)*, **41**, 733 (1951); *Chem. Abstr.*, **46**, 8401 (1952).

(27) I. A. Wolff, D. W. Olds, and G. E. Hilbert, *J. Am. Chem. Soc.*, **73**, 346 (1951).

(28) R. L. Lohmar, Jr., U.S. Patent 2,627,516 (1953); *Chem. Abstr.*, **47**, 5146 (1953).

(29) J. W. Mullen II and E. Pacsu, *Ind. Eng. Chem.*, **35**, 381 (1943).

(30) Upjohn Co., British Patent 810,306 (1959); *Chem. Abstr.*, **53**, 18401 (1959).

(31) D. E. Mack and R. N. Shreve, *Ind. Eng. Chem.*, **34**, 304 (1942).

(32) J. T. Lemmerling, Belgian Patent 619,380 (1962); French Patent 1,334,113 (1963); *Chem. Abstr.*, **58**, 8553 (1963).

(33) H. P. Panzer, *Abstr. Papers, Am. Chem. Soc.*, **144**, 16C (1963).

(34) S. O. Jones, U.S. Patent 2,766,145 (1956); *Chem. Abstr.*, **51**, 3941 (1957).

(35) E. Lorand, *Cellulosechemie*, **13**, 185 (1932); U.S. Patent 1,959,590 (1934); *Chem. Abstr.*, **27**, 2574 (1933); **28**, 4432 (1934).
(36) I. G. Farbenindustrie, German Patent 484,242 (1923); French Patent 699,217 (1930); *Chem. Abstr.*, **24**, 962 (1930); **25**, 3482 (1931).
(37) H. Gault, *Compt. Rend.*, **177**, 592 (1923).
(38) P. Karrer and Z. Zega, *Helv. Chim. Acta*, **6**, 822 (1923).
(39) P. Berthon, U.S. Patent 1,651,366 (1927); *Chem. Abstr.*, **22**, 881 (1928).
(40) Gevaert Photo-producten N.V., Belgian Patent 615,411 (1962); *Chem. Abstr.*, **58**, 9790 (1963).
(41) A. T. Gros and R. O. Feuge, *J. Am. Oil Chemists' Soc.*, **39**, 19 (1962).
(42) J. Chadapaux, G. Champetier, and E. Savostianoff, *Bull. Soc. Chim. France*, 594 (1950); *Chem. Abstr.*, **44**, 9357 (1950).
(43) J. H. Schwartz, C. A. Brown, and E. A. Talley, *U.S. Dept. Agr., Bur. Agr. Ind. Chem., Mimeo. Circ. Ser.*, **AIC-339** (1952).
(44) M. Hagedorn, French Patent 668,686 (1929); U.S. Patent 1,994,608 (1935); *Chem. Abstr.*, **29**, 3157 (1935).
(45) I. A. Wolff, D. W. Olds, and G. E. Hilbert, *Ind. Eng. Chem.*, **43**, 911 (1951).
(46) J. J. Scholz, B. R. Ray, and J. R. Anderson, *J. Phys. Chem.*, **62**, 1227 (1958).
(47) C. G. Caldwell, U.S. Patent 2,461,139 (1949); *Chem. Abstr.*, **43**, 3222 (1949).
(48) E. F. Paschall, U.S. Patent 2,914,526 (1959); *Chem. Abstr.*, **55**, 25306 (1961).
(49) W. H. Minkema, U.S. Patent 2,868,780 (1959); *Chem. Abstr.*, **53**, 6662 (1959).
(50) J. V. Tuschoff and C. E. Smith, Belgian Patent 616,364 (1962); French Patent 1,323,122 (1963); *Chem. Abstr.*, **58**, 8128 (1963).
(51) Rootry Exploitatie Maatschappij N.V., Neth. Patents 93,354, 93,355 (1960); *Chem. Abstr.*, **55**, 9718 (1961).
(52) Rootry Exploitatie Maatschappij N.V., Neth. Patent 93,357 (1960); *Chem. Abstr.*, **55**, 9719 (1961).
(53) Rootry Exploitatie Maatschappij N.V., Neth. Patent 93,356 (1960); *Chem. Abstr.*, **55**, 6736 (1961).
(54) R. H. Treadway, U.S. Patent 2,492,203 (1949); *Chem. Abstr.*, **44**, 3016 (1950).
(55) C. G. Caldwell and O. B. Wurzburg, U.S. Patent 2,668,156 (1954); *Chem. Abstr.*, **48**, 10365 (1954).
(56) L. Rosenthal and W. Lenhard, German Patent 478,127 (1924); U.S. Patent 1,739,863 (1929); *Chem. Abstr.*, **24**, 980 (1930).
(57) F. C. McIntire, U.S. Patent 2,505,561 (1950); *Chem. Abstr.*, **44**, 6550 (1950).
(58) R. W. Kerr and F. C. Cleveland, Jr., U.S. Patent 3,021,222 (1962); *Chem. Abstr.*, **56**, 10653 (1962).
(59) E. F. Paschall and W. J. Katzbeck, U.S. Patent 2,891,947 (1959); *Chem. Abstr.*, **53**, 19421 (1959).
(60) C. G. Caldwell and O. B. Wurzburg, U.S. Patent 2,661,349 (1953); British Patent 691,364 (1953); *Chem. Abstr.*, **47**, 10256 (1953); **48**, 1720 (1954).
(61) C. G. Caldwell, U.S. Patent 2,613,206 (1952); *Chem. Abstr.*, **47**, 899 (1953).
(62) G. P. Touey, U.S. Patent 3,008,473 (1961); *Chem. Abstr.*, **56**, 7565 (1962).
(63) O. B. Wurzburg and H. M. Cole, U.S. Patent 3,091,567 (1963); *Chem. Abstr.*, **59**, 11661 (1963).
(64) R. M. Geurden, U.S. Patent 3,077,468 (1963); *Chem. Abstr.*, **58**, 14282 (1963).
(65) M. N. Vrancken, British Patent 860,632 (1961); *Chem. Abstr.*, **55**, 14978 (1961).
(66) J. N. Borglin, U.S. Patent 2,392,359 (1946); *Chem. Abstr.*, **40**, 2262 (1946).
(67) A. Kldiashwili, *Zhur. Russ. Fiz. Khim. Obshch.*, **37**, 421 (1905); *J. Chem. Soc. Abstr.*, **88**, Part 1, 634 (1905).

(68) H. Rudy, *Cellulosechimie*, **13**, 49 (1932).

(69) E. Peiser, *Z. Physiol. Chem.*, **161**, 210 (1926); **167**, 88 (1927); *Chem. Abstr.*, **21**, 668, 2881 (1927).

(70) H. N. Barham, U.S. Patent 2,562,883 (1951); *Chem. Abstr.*, **45**, 9863 (1951).

(71) M. G. Groen, Neth. Patent 56,009 (1944); U.S. Patent 2,412,213 (1946); British Patent 599,066 (1948); *Chem. Abstr.*, **41**, 2265, 4169 (1947); **42**, 5700 (1948).

(72) C. G. Caldwell and O. B. Wurzburg, U.S. Patent 2,654,736 (1953); *Chem. Abstr.*, **48**, 1040 (1954).

(73) J. Lolkema and G. Moes, British Patent 787,153 (1957); U.S. Patent 2,853,484 (1958); Swiss Patent 370,729 (1963); *Chem. Abstr.*, **52**, 7750 (1958); **53**, 1797 (1959).

(74) R. W. Kerr and W. A. Faucette, U.S. Patent 2,660,577 (1953); *Chem. Abstr.*, **48**, 3052 (1954).

(75) C. G. Caldwell, U.S. Patent 2,825,727 (1958); *Chem. Abstr.*, **52**, 8601 (1958).

(76) B. P. Wallace and R. E. Melcher, U.S. Patents 3,086,784, 3,086,785 (1963); Can. Patent 666,617 (1963).

(77) T. H. Rogers, U.S. Patent 3,107,225 (1963); *Chem. Abstr.*, **60**, 3180 (1964).

(78) B. Agness and F. B. Finan, U.S. Patent 2,674,642 (1954); *Chem. Abstr.*, **48**, 8683 (1954).

(79) J. M. O'Flahavan, German Patent 957,835 (1957); *Chem. Abstr.*, **53**, 6640 (1959).

(80) K. Hess and R. Pfleger, *Ann.*, **507**, 48 (1933); *Chem. Abstr.*, **28**, 114 (1934).

(81) A. F. Damansky, *Compt. Rend. Soc. Biol.*, **114**, 1051 (1933); *Chem. Abstr.*, **28**, 1886 (1934).

(82) W. S. Reich and A. F. Damansky, *Bull. Soc. Chim. Biol.*, **19**, 158 (1937); *Chem. Abstr.*, **31**, 5200 (1937).

(83) E. Pacsu and J. W. Mullen II, U.S. Patent 2,372,337 (1945); *Chem. Abstr.*, **39**, 4250 (1945).

(84) A. Guilbot and R. Drapron, *Intern. Inds. Agr. Aliment. Madrid, 10th Congr.*, 2379 (1954); *Chem. Abstr.*, **50**, 16146 (1956).

(85) W. M. Doane, C. R. Russell, and C. E. Rist, *Abstr. Papers, Am. Chem. Soc.*, **145**, 10E (1963); *Staerke*, **17**, 77 (1965).

(86) W. Ciusa, *Ann. Chim. Applicata*, **33**, 127 (1943); *Chem. Abstr.*, **40**, 7675 (1946).

(87) W. Ciusa and N. Zattoni, *Ann. Chim. Applicata*, **35**, 123 (1945); *Chem. Abstr.*, **40**, 7675 (1946).

(88) W. Ciusa and G. Adamo, *Ann. Chim. (Rome)*, **40**, 295 (1950); *Chem. Abstr.*, **45**, 10631 (1951).

(89) W. S. Reich and A. F. Damansky, *Compt. Rend.*, **197**, 275 (1933); *Chem. Abstr.*, **27**, 5572 (1933).

(90) C. Dumazert, D. Picard, and A. el Ouachi, *Compt. Rend. Soc. Biol.*, **146**, 470 (1952); *Chem. Abstr.*, **47**, 1280 (1953).

(91) K. Kratzl and E. Kaufmann, *Monatsh.*, **92**, 371 (1961); *Chem. Abstr.*, **55**, 27777 (1961).

(92) K. Kratzl, E. Kaufmann, O. Kraupp, and H. Stormann, *Monatsh.*, **92**, 379 (1961); *Chem. Abstr.*, **55**, 27653 (1961).

(93) J. G. Wagner, T. W. Brignall, and S. Long, *J. Am. Pharm. Assoc.*, **48**, 244 (1959); *Chem. Abstr.*, **53**, 11763 (1959).

(94) Gevaert Photo-producten N.V., Belgian Patent 613,575 (1962); *Chem. Abstr.*, **57**, 16729 (1962).

(95) H. Winter, *Brauwissenschaft*, 113 (1951).

(96) E. F. Paschall, U.S. Patent 2,935,509 (1960); *Chem. Abstr.*, **54**, 20261 (1960).

(97) E. T. Hjermstad, U.S. Patent 3,069,411 (1962); *Chem. Abstr.*, **58**, 5874 (1963).

(98) G. Moes and A. H. Zijderveld, Belgian Patent 613,242 (1962); *Chem. Abstr.*, **58,** 1625 (1963).

(99) W. A. Scholten's Chemische Fabrieken N.V., Belgian Patent 618,620 (1962); *Chem. Abstr.*, **58,** 8139 (1963).

(100) V. J. Shapiro and M. I. Mazurina, *Byumash. Prom.*, **23,** 37 (1948); *Chem. Abstr.*, **46,** 6860 (1952).

(101) K. M. Gaver, E. P. Lasure, and L. M. Thomas, U.S. Patent 2,621,174 (1952); *Chem. Abstr.*, **47,** 9354 (1953).

(102) K. M. Gaver, E. P. Lasure, and L. M. Thomas, U.S. Patent 2,725,362 (1955); *Chem. Abstr.*, **50,** 4555 (1956).

(103) I. A. Wolff and C. E. Rist, *J. Am. Chem. Soc.*, **70,** 2779 (1948).

(104) I. A. Wolff, U.S. Patent 2,562,978 (1951); *Chem. Abstr.*, **45,** 10632 (1951).

(105) I. A. Wolff, P. R. Watson, and C. E. Rist, *J. Am. Chem. Soc.*, **74,** 3061 (1952).

(106) I. A. Wolff, P. R. Watson, and C. E. Rist, *J. Am. Chem. Soc.*, **76,** 757 (1954).

(107) W. Burchard and E. Husemann, *Makromol. Chem.*, **44/46,** 358 (1961); *Chem. Abstr.*, **55,** 27099 (1961).

(108) I. A. Wolff, in "Methods in Carbohydrate Chemistry," R. L. Whistler, ed., Academic Press Inc., New York, N.Y., Vol. 4, 1964, p. 301.

(109) E. Husemann and M. Reinhardt, *Angew. Chem.*, **71,** 429 (1959); *Makromol. Chem.*, **57,** 109 (1962); *Chem. Abstr.*, **54,** 1332 (1960); **58,** 9215 (1963).

(110) R. L. Whistler and D. G. Medcalf, *Arch. Biochem. Biophys.*, **104,** 150 (1964).

(111) E. Husemann, R. Resz, and R. Werner, *Makromol. Chem.*, **47,** 48 (1961).

(112) C. E. Brockway and H. R. Ready, U.S. Patent 3,065,223 (1962); *Chem. Abstr.*, **58,** 3593 (1963).

(113) I. A. Wolff and P. R. Watson, U.S. Patent 2,668,169 (1954); *Chem. Abstr.*, **48,** 5535 (1954).

(114) Sichel-Werke A.-G., German Patent 967,880 (1957); *Chem. Abstr.*, **53,** 14560 (1959).

(115) C. Schoeller, German Patent 909,569 (1954); *Chem. Abstr.*, **52,** 8597 (1958).

(116) F. W. Boggs, U.S. Patent 2,908,657 (1959); *Chem. Abstr.*, **54,** 12666 (1960).

(117) I. A. Wolff, P. R. Watson, and C. E. Rist, *J. Am. Chem. Soc.*, **74,** 3064 (1952).

(118) E. F. Paschall, U.S. Patent 2,894,944 (1959); *Chem. Abstr.*, **54,** 2794 (1960).

(119) J. F. Carson and W. D. Maclay, *J. Am. Chem. Soc.*, **70,** 2220 (1948).

(120) C. Dumazert, *Bull. Soc. Chim. Biol.*, **32,** 983 (1950); *Chem. Abstr.*, **45,** 9904 (1951).

(121) H. J. Roberts, in "Methods in Carbohydrate Chemistry," R. L. Whistler, ed., Academic Press Inc., New York, N.Y., Vol. 4, 1964, p. 299.

(122) R. L. Whistler and S. Hirase, *J. Org. Chem.*, **26,** 4600 (1961).

(123) M. L. Wolfrom, M. I. Taha, and D. Horton, *J. Org. Chem.*, **28,** 3553 (1963).

(124) B. J. Bines and W. J. Whelan, *Chem. Ind. (London)*, 997 (1960).

(125) B. J. Bines, Z. H. Gunja, and W. J. Whelan, *Chem. Ind. (London)*, 1358 (1960).

(126) Gevaert Photo-producten N.V., Belgian Patent 623,091 (1963); Jap. Patent 23,500 (1963); *Chem. Abstr.*, **59,** 13011 (1963).

(127) I. Fukushima and Y. Takamatsu, *J. Soc. Chem. Ind. Japan*, **32,** 130 (1929); *Chem. Abstr.*, **23,** 5058 (1929).

(128) A. A. Houghton, British Patent 493,513 (1938); U.S. Patent 2,206,354 (1940); *Chem. Abstr.*, **33,** 2626 (1939); **34,** 7648 (1940).

(129) R. S. Tipson, *Advan. Carbohydrate Chem.*, **8,** 107 (1953).

(130) Ref. 7, p. 259 ff.

(131) K. Ueno, Jap. Patent 177,162 (1948); *Chem. Abstr.*, **45,** 5370 (1951).

(132) K. Vogler, Swiss Patent 329,205 (1958); *Chem. Abstr.*, **53,** 9084 (1959).

338   HUGH J. ROBERTS

(*133*) O. Nemecek, Z. Roubal, and Z. Placer, Czech. Patent 100,274 (1961); *Chem. Abstr.*, **57**, 8669 (1962).

(*134*) I/S Solusol, Danish Patent 65,269 (1946); *Chem. Abstr.*, **41**, 6281 (1947).

(*135*) R. Tamba, *Biochem. Z.*, **141**, 274 (1923).

(*136*) Z. Roubal, Z. Placer, and V. Vokac, Czech. Patent 88,330 (1959); Brit. Patent 859,278 (1961); Danish Patent 91,064 (1961); *Chem. Abstr.*, **54**, 2201 (1960); **55**, 11771 (1961).

(*137*) F. J. Petracek and M. D. Draper, U.S. Patent 3,017,407 (1962); French Patent 1,325,603 (1963); *Chem. Abstr.*, **56**, 11722 (1962).

(*138*) F. Hoffmann-La Roche & Co. A.-G., Swiss Patent 235,228 (1945); *Chem. Abstr.*, **43**, 3978 (1949).

(*139*) R. V. Jones, U.S. Patent 2,686,779 (1954); *Chem. Abstr.*, **49**, 11697 (1955).

(*140*) K. E. Heumann, F. E. Freitig, and H. Berndt, German Patent 1,132,044 (1962); *Chem. Abstr.*, **57**, 5593 (1962).

(*141*) Dr. A. Wander A.-G., Swiss Patent 305,572 (1955); *Chem. Abstr.*, **50**, 15110 (1956).

(*142*) Chugai Seiyaku K.K., Belgian Patent 612,153 (1962); French Patent 1,714M (1963); *Chem. Abstr.*, **58**, 11176 (1963).

(*143*) Y. Nitta, M. Yikikata, and K. Nawata, Jap. Patent 17,748 (1961); Belgian Patent 606,326 (1961); French Patent 1,315M (1962); *Chem. Abstr.*, **56**, 15620 (1962).

(*144*) Chugai Seiyaku K.K., Jap. Patent 16,700 (1960); *Chem. Abstr.*, **56**, 2520 (1962).

(*145*) Chugai Seiyaku K.K., Jap. Patent 13,549 (1963); *Chem. Abstr.*, **60**, 3079 (1964).

(*146*) Y. Nitta, M. Yukikata, and K. Nawata, Jap. Patent 22,750 (1963); *Chem. Abstr.*, **60**, 4241 (1964).

(*147*) R. V. Jones, U.S. Patent 2,697,093 (1954); *Chem. Abstr.*, **49**, 2766 (1955).

(*148*) K. Vogler, Swiss Patent 326,792 (1958); British Patent 796,737 (1958); *Chem. Abstr.*, **52**, 18245 (1958); **53**, 7041 (1959).

(*149*) Y. Nitta, M. Yukikata, and E. Tomita, Jap. Patent 12,200 (1963); *Chem. Abstr.*, **60**, 649 (1964).

(*150*) Y. Nitta, M. Yukikata, and E. Tomita, Jap. Patent 23,050 (1963); *Chem. Abstr.*, **60**, 4242 (1964).

(*151*) R. L. Whistler and W. W. Spencer, *Arch. Biochem. Biophys.*, **95**, 36 (1961).

(*152*) R. L. Whistler and W. W. Spencer, in "Methods in Carbohydrate Chemistry," R. L. Whistler, ed., Academic Press Inc., New York, N.Y., Vol. 4, 1964, p. 297.

(*153*) O. B. Wurzburg, M. W. Rutenberg, and L. J. Ross, British Patent 755,461 (1956); U.S. Patent 2,786,833 (1957); *Chem. Abstr.*, **51**, 8460 (1957); **51**, 10936 (1957).

(*154*) R. W. Kerr, E. F. Paschall, and W. H. Minkema, British Patent 807,070 (1959); U.S. Patent 2,967,178 (1961); *Chem. Abstr.*, **55**, 7705 (1961).

(*155*) R. W. Kerr, E. F. Paschall, and W. H. Minkema, British Patent 847,669 (1960); *Chem. Abstr.*, **55**, 109321 (1961).

(*156*) H. E. Smith, C. R. Russell, and C. E. Rist, *Cereal Chem.*, **39**, 273 (1962).

(*157*) H. E. Smith and C. R. Russell, U.S. Patent 3,057,855 (1962); *Chem. Abstr.*, **58**, 652 (1963).

(*158*) H. E. Smith, C. R. Russell, and C. E. Rist, *Cereal Chem.*, **40**, 282 (1963).

(*159*) E. F. Paschall, U.S. Patent 2,775,586 (1956); *Chem. Abstr.*, **51**, 4746 (1957).

(*160*) I. Martin and O. B. Wurzburg, U.S. Patent 2,857,377 (1958); British Patent 823,073 (1959); *Chem. Abstr.*, **53**, 7041 (1959); **54**, 7192 (1960).

(*161*) R. V. Jones, U.S. Patent 2,896,715 (1959); *Chem. Abstr.*, **53**, 19348 (1959).

(162) T. Astrup, I. Galsmar, and M. Volkert, *Acta Physiol. Scand.*, **8**, 215 (1944); *Chem. Abstr.*, **39**, 4976 (1945).

(163) J. Piper, *Acta Pharmacol. Toxicol.*, **2**, 317 (1946); *Chem. Abstr.*, **41**, 3866 (1947).

(164) S. Bergstrom, *Naturwissenschaften*, **23**, 706 (1935); *Z. Physiol. Chem.*, **238**, 163 (1936); *Chem. Abstr.*, **30**, 1073, 2637 (1936).

(165) E. Husemann, K. N. v. Kaulla, and R. Kappesser, *Z. Naturforsch.*, **1**, 584 (1946); *Chem. Abstr.*, **41**, 5983 (1947).

(166) J. Piper, *Acta Pharmacol. Toxicol.*, **2**, 138 (1946); *Chem. Abstr.*, **40**, 7415 (1946).

(167) E. Husemann, P. Pannemueller, H. Schill, and W. Hertlein, *Z. Naturforsch.*, **12b**, 427 (1957); *Chem. Abstr.*, **51**, 18318 (1957).

(168) W. M. Doane and R. L. Whistler, *Arch. Biochem. Biophys.*, **101**, 436 (1963).

(169) P. Constantinides, A. Cairns, and A. Werner, *Arch. Intern. Pharmacodynamie*, **99**, 334 (1954); *Chem. Abstr.*, **49**, 6453 (1955).

(170) J. Hladovec, Z. Roubal, and V. Mansfield, *Experientia*, **12**, 190 (1957).

(171) Z. Placer and Z. Roubal, *Cesk. Gastroenterol. Vyziva*, **14**, 422 (1960); *Chem. Abstr.*, **55**, 4795 (1961).

(172) L. J. Ravin, J. G. Baldinus, and M. L. Mazur, *J. Pharm. Sci.*, **51**, 857 (1962); *Chem. Abstr.*, **57**, 16761 (1962).

(173) V. Vokac, Z. Placer, and Z. Roubal, *Cesk. Gastroenterol. Vyziva*, **11**, 266 (1957); *Chem. Abstr.*, **52**, 4033 (1958).

(174) J. Fellig and C. E. Wiley, *Arch. Biochem. Biophys.*, **85**, 313 (1959).

(175) J. Piper, *Acta Physiol. Scand.*, **9**, 28 (1945); *Chem. Abstr.*, **39**, 4977 (1945).

(176) W. H. Florsheim and C. Gonzales, *Proc. Soc. Exptl. Biol. Med.*, **104**, 618 (1960); *Chem. Abstr.*, **55**, 662 (1961).

(177) M. Herold, J. Hofman, P. Malek, J. Capkova, M. Hermansky, M. Vondracek, and J. Kolc, Czech. Patent 90,981 (1959); *Chem. Abstr.*, **54**, 14594 (1960).

(178) P. Karrer, H. Koenig, and E. Usteri, *Helv. Chim. Acta*, **26**, 1296 (1943).

(179) G. V. Caesar, *Advan. Carbohydrate Chem.*, **13**, 331 (1958).

(180) F. B. Holmes, U.S. Patents 779,421 (1905), 779,422 (1905), 875,913 (1907), 875,928 (1907); cited in Ref. *179*.

(181) G. V. Caesar and M. Goldfrank, *J. Am. Chem. Soc.*, **68**, 372 (1946).

(182) M. Goldfrank, in "Methods in Carbohydrate Chemistry," R. L. Whistler, ed., Academic Press Inc., New York, N.Y., Vol. 4, 1964, p. 291.

(183) G. V. Caesar, N. S. Gruenhut, and M. L. Cushing, *J. Am. Chem. Soc.*, **69**, 617 (1947).

(184) W. R. Ashford and H. Hibbert, *Can. J. Research, B*, **25**, 151 (1947).

(185) A. Le Roux, *Mem. Poudres*, **33**, 211 (1951); *Chem. Abstr.*, **47**, 10229 (1953).

(186) E. Berl, U.S. Patent 2,384,415 (1945); *Chem. Abstr.*, **40**, 206 (1946).

(187) T. Urbanski and J. Hackel, *Tetrahedron*, **2**, 300 (1958).

(188) I. A. Grageroff, U.S. Patent 2,883,376 (1959); *Chem. Abstr.*, **53**, 13598 (1959).

(189) W. Zimmermann, G. A. Sieper, and L. Reinhardt, British Patent 815,280 (1959); U.S. Patent 2,995,549 (1961); *Chem. Abstr.*, **53**, 18487 (1959); **55**, 26448 (1961).

(190) A. Kunz and I. Toth, *Magyar Kem. Folyoirat*, **63**, 201 (1957); *Chem. Abstr.*, **52**, 11755 (1958).

(191) W. Zimmermann, G. A. Sieper, and L. Reinhardt, German Patent 1,031,300 (1958); *Chem. Abstr.*, **54**, 18996 (1960).

(192) A. Mustafa, A. F. Dawoud, and S. El-Shourbani, *Can. J. Chem.*, **40**, 2072 (1962).

(193) M. L. Wolfrom, A. Chaney, and K. S. Ennor, *J. Am. Chem. Soc.*, **81**, 3469 (1959).

(194) T. Toshima, K. Honma, K. Nakai, and H. Yoshitomi, Jap. Patent 8,498 (1955); *Chem. Abstr.*, **51**, 18612 (1957).

(*195*) E. J. Russell, U.S. Patent 2,821,466 (1958); *Chem. Abstr.*, **52**, 6795 (1958).

(*196*) Iroda A.-G., Belgian Patent 613,336 (1962); *Chem. Abstr.*, **57**, 14045 (1962).

(*197*) G. L. Griffith, Jr., and D. G. Samuel, Jr., U.S. Patent 2,860,041 (1958); *Chem. Abstr.*, **53**, 3697 (1959).

(*198*) C. F. Cross, E. J. Bevan, and J. F. Briggs, *J. Chem. Soc.*, **91**, 612 (1907); *Proc. Chem. Soc.*, **23**, 90 (1907).

(*199*) C. R. Russell, R. A. Buchanan, C. E. Rist, B. T. Hofreiter, and A. J. Ernst, *Tappi*, **45**, 557 (1962).

(*200*) H. Ost, F. Westhoff, and L. Gessner, *Ann.*, **382**, 340 (1911); *Chem. Abstr.*, **5**, 3574 (1911).

(*201*) E. H. Brown, U.S. Patent 2,629,493 (1953); *Chem. Abstr.*, **47**, 5341 (1953).

(*202*) E. G. Adamek and C. B. Purves, *Can. J. Chem.*, **38**, 2425 (1960).

(*203*) M. Wronski, *Lodz. Towarz. Nauk. Wydzial III*, No. 4, 47 (1960).

(*204*) E. G. Adamek and C. B. Purves, *Can. J. Chem.*, **35**, 960 (1957).

(*205*) C. L. Swanson, T. R., Naffziger, C. R. Russell, B. T. Hofreiter, and C. E. Rist, *Ind. Eng. Chem., Prod. Res. Devel.*, **3**, 22 (1964).

(*206*) T. Lieser and A. Hackle, *Ann.*, **511**, 128 (1934); *Chem. Abstr.*, **28**, 5411 (1934).

(*207*) J. H. Holberger, German Patent 562,180 (1932); *Chem. Abstr.*, **27**, 841 (1933).

(*208*) W. Harrison, British Patent 264,261 (1927); *Chem. Abstr.*, **22**, 164 (1928).

(*209*) R. Wolffenstein and E. Oeser, *Kunstseide*, **7**, 27 (1925).

(*210*) W. Harrison, British Patents 286,331, 286,332 (1926); German Patent 497,240 (1927); *Chem. Abstr.*, **23**, 155 (1929).

(*211*) E. Stern, U.S. Patent 1,412,020 (1922); *Chem. Abstr.*, **16**, 2014 (1922).

(*212*) J. A. V. Bourgeois, French Patent 730,698 (1932); *Chem. Abstr.*, **27**, 3076 (1933).

(*213*) R. Elssner, U.S. Patent 2,000,887 (1935); *Chem. Abstr.*, **29**, 4175 (1935).

(*214*) G. W. Meadows, U.S. Patent 2,761,247 (1956); *Chem. Abstr.*, **51**, 1518 (1957).

(*215*) G. W. Meadows, U.S. Patent 2,801,933 (1957); *Chem. Abstr.*, **51**, 17057 (1957).

(*216*) E. H. Brown and T. A. Cecil, U.S. Patent 2,699,255 (1955); *Chem. Abstr.*, **49**, 7820 (1955).

(*217*) C. S. Chang, *Mining Eng.*, **6**, 922 (1954).

(*218*) T. R. Naffziger, C. L. Swanson, B. T. Hofreiter, C. R. Russell, and C. E. Rist, *Tappi*, **46**, 428 (1963).

(*219*) L. Lilienfeld, British Patent 3,370 (1916); U.S. Patent 1,350,820 (1920); Austrian Patent 82,866 (1921); German Patent 360,415 (1922); Can. Patent 222,377 (1922); *Chem. Abstr.*, **16**, 4087 (1922); **17**, 1803 (1923).

(*220*) L. Lilienfeld, British Patents 163,017, 163,018 (1920); Can. Patents 248,226, 248,228 (1925); German Patent 475,884 (1929); *Chem. Abstr.*, **15**, 3207 (1921); **19**, 3491 (1925).

(*221*) I. G. Farbenindustrie A.-G., French Patent 676,344 (1929); *Chem. Abstr.*, **24**, 2914 (1930).

(*222*) K. H. Meyer, *Advan. Colloid Sci.*, **1**, 154 (1942).

(*223*) F. Smith and R. Montgomery, *Methods Biochem. Anal.*, **3**, 158 (1956).

(*224*) G. W. Hay, B. A. Lewis, and F. Smith, in "Methods in Carbohydrate Chemistry," R. L. Whistler, ed., Academic Press Inc., New York, N.Y., Vol. 4, 1964, p. 306.

(*225*) O. R. Kreimeier and R. W. Maxwell, British Patent 454,963 (1936); U.S. Patent 2,116,867 (1938); *Chem. Abstr.*, **31**, 1523 (1937); **32**, 5108 (1938).

(*226*) R. W. Kerr, U.S. Patent 2,858,305 (1958); *Chem. Abstr.*, **53**, 4786 (1959).

(*227*) Cooperative Verkoop- en Productievereniging van Aardappelmeel en Derivaten "Avebe" G.A., Italian Patent 603,804 (1960); British Patent 869,192 (1961); *Chem. Abstr.*, **55**, 22878 (1961).

(228) J. Lolkema, G. Moes, and W. F. Vogel, Italian Patent 606,839 (1960); French Patent 1,204,376 (1960); German Patent 1,118,151 (1961); British Patent 895,429 (1962); Chem. Abstr., 56, 14501 (1962).

(229) P. Karrer and C. Naegeli, Helv. Chim. Acta, 4, 185 (1921).

(230) J. C. Irvine and J. Macdonald, J. Chem. Soc., 1502 (1926).

(231) K. H. Meyer, M. Wertheim, and P. Bernfeld, Helv. Chim. Acta, 23, 865 (1940); 24, 378 (1941).

(232) W. N. Haworth, E. L. Hirst, and J. I. Webb, J. Chem. Soc., 2681 (1928).

(233) O. Fernandez, R. Olalla, E. Martinez, and R. L. Larraneta, Ion, 8, 381 (1948); Chem. Abstr., 43, 4036 (1949).

(234) K. Hess and K.-H. Lung, Ber., 70, 1259 (1937); 71, 815 (1938).

(235) G. Young, British Patent 184,825 (1921); Chem. Abstr., 17, 878 (1923).

(236) L. Lilienfeld, British Patent 427,387 (1935); Chem. Abstr., 29, 5856 (1935).

(237) E. T. Hjermstad and C. C. Kesler, U.S. Patent 2,773,057 (1956); Chem. Abstr., 51, 4746 (1957).

(238) E. T. Hjermstad and C. C. Kesler, U.S. Patent 3,062,810 (1962); Chem. Abstr., 58, 3593 (1963).

(239) L. O. Gill and J. A. Wagoner, U.S. Patent 3,014,901 (1961); Chem. Abstr., 56, 7564 (1962).

(240) G. S. Smirnova, V. A. Derevitskaya, and Z. A. Rogovin, Vysokomolekul. Soedinen., 4, 80 (1962).

(241) K. Freudenberg and H. Boppel, Ber., 71, 2505 (1938).

(242) J. E. Hodge, S. A. Karjala, and G. E. Hilbert, J. Am. Chem. Soc., 73, 3312 (1951).

(243) K. M. Gaver, E. P. Lasure, and D. V. Tieszen, U.S. Patents 2,572,923 (1951); 2,609,370 (1952); Chem. Abstr., 46, 1786 (1952); 47, 9353 (1953).

(244) K. M. Gaver, U.S. Patents 2,397,732 (1946); 2,518,135 (1950); 2,609,368 (1952); Chem. Abstr., 40, 3620 (1946); 44, 11142 (1950); 47, 898 (1953).

(245) K. M. Gaver, D. V. Tieszen, and E. P. Lasure, U.S. Patents 2,671,780 2,671,781 (1954); Chem Abstr., 48, 8569 (1954).

(246) K. M. Gaver, E. P. Lasure, and D. V. Tieszen, U.S. Patent 2,671,779 (1954); Chem. Abstr., 48, 8569 (1954).

(247) L. Schmid, Ber., 58, 1963 (1925); L. Schmid and M. Zentner, Monatsh., 49, 111 (1928); Chem. Abstr., 22, 3395 (1928).

(248) L. Hough and J. K. N. Jones, Chem. Ind. (London), 380, (1952).

(249) H. C. Srivastava, S. N. Harshe, and P. P. Singh, Indian J. Chem., 1, 304 (1963).

(250) R. Kuhn and H. Trischmann, Chem. Ber., 96, 284 (1963).

(251) K. Wallenfels, G. Bechtler, R. Kuhn, H. Trischmann, and H. Egge, Angew. Chem., Internat. Ed., 2, 515 (1963).

(252) H. C. Srivastava, S. N. Harshe, and P. P. Singh, Tetrahedron Letters, 1869 (1963); Chem. Abstr., 60, 6915 (1964).

(253) I. Croon, Acta Chem. Scand., 13, 1235 (1959).

(254) B. J. Bines and W. J. Whelan, J. Chem. Soc., 4232 (1962).

(255) C. M. Worstall, Dissertation Abstr., 13, 19 (1953); Chem. Abstr., 47, 4638 (1953).

(256) L. Lilienfeld, U.S. Patent 1,444,257 (1923); Chem. Abstr., 17, 1310 (1923).

(257) J. Vallee, Rev. Franc. Corps Gras, 3, 112 (1956); Chem. Abstr., 50, 6816 (1956).

(258) L. L. Balassa, U.S. Patent 2,941,896 (1960); Chem. Abstr., 54, 25884 (1960).

(259) M. Yoshimura, Jap. Patent 6,248 (1953); Chem. Abstr., 48, 12408 (1954).

(260) E. Weyde, German Patent 1,013,965 (1957); U.S. Patent 3,043,691 (1962); Chem. Abstr., 54, 10614 (1960).

(261) M. Wiedersheim, W. Hertlein, E. Husemann, and R. Loetterle, Arch. Exptl. Pathol. Pharmakol., 217, 107 (1953); Chem. Abstr., 47, 4495 (1953).

(262) M. L. Wolfrom and D. R. Meyers, *J. Am. Chem. Soc.*, **63**, 1336 (1941).

(263) G. W. Hay, B. A. Lewis, and F. Smith, in "Methods in Carbohydrate Chemistry," R. L. Whistler, ed., Academic Press Inc., New York, N.Y., Vol. 4, 1964, p. 79.

(264) T. R. Ingle and R. L. Whistler, in "Methods in Carbohydrate Chemistry," R. L. Whistler, ed., Academic Press Inc., New York, N.Y., Vol. 4, 1964, p. 83.

(265) W. N. Haworth and E. G. V. Percival, *J. Chem. Soc.*, 1342 (1931).

(266) S. Peat and J. Whetstone, *J. Chem. Soc.*, 276 (1940).

(267) H. N. Barham, U.S. Patent 2,562,884 (1951); *Chem. Abstr.*, **45**, 9863 (1951).

(268) E. I. Jones, L. B. Morgan, J. F. L. Roberts, and S. M. Todd, British Patent 715,194 (1954); *Chem. Abstr.*, **49**, 2748 (1955).

(269) R. M. Hamilton and E. Yanovsky, *Ind. Eng. Chem.*, **38**, 864 (1946); U.S. Patent 2,463,869 (1949); French Patent 954,702 (1949); British Patent 653,798 (1951).

(270) E. A. Talley, J. H. Schwartz, A. S. Hunter, and C. A. Brown, *U.S. Dept. Agr., Bur. Agr. Ind. Chem., Mimeo Circ. Series*, **AIC-261** (1950).

(271) C. G. Caldwell and I. Martin, British Patent 713,750 (1954); Can. Patent 526,990 (1956); U.S. Patent 2,802,000 (1957); *Chem. Abstr.*, **49**, 7880 (1955); **51**, 17215 (1957).

(272) D. Rankin and E. F. Degering, *Proc. Indiana Acad. Sci.*, **54**, 114 (1945); *Chem. Abstr.*, **40**, 1791 (1946).

(273) L. Balassa, U.S. Patent 2,588,463 (1952); *Chem. Abstr.*, **46**, 4830 (1952).

(274) E. B. Hotelling and T. E. Kelly, U.S. Patent 2,984,244 (1961); *Chem. Abstr.*, **55**, 20342 (1961).

(275) J. K. Chowdhury, *Biochem. Z.*, **148**, 76 (1924); *Chem. Abstr.*, **19**, 640 (1925).

(276) O. A. Moe, U.S. Patent 2,523,709 (1950); *Chem. Abstr.*, **45**, 4474 (1951).

(277) K. Sarui and Y. Akiyama, Jap. Patent 697 (1953); *Chem. Abstr.*, **48**, 2093 (1954).

(278) Sichel-Werke A.-G., German Patent 920,780 (1954); *Chem. Abstr.*, **52**, 14204 (1958).

(279) A. Z. Pelizzari, Spanish Patent 233,326 (1957); *Chem. Abstr.*, **52**, 1645 (1958).

(280) K. Hayashi, Jap. Patent 92 (1959); *Chem. Abstr.*, **53**, 10818 (1959).

(281) Y. Sakaguchi and I. Ishizu, *Sen-i Gakkaishi*, **14**, 814 (1958); *Chem. Abstr.*, **53**, 1796 (1959).

(282) J. P. Feliu, Spanish Patent 250,609 (1959); *Chem. Abstr.*, **55**, 9920 (1961).

(283) Ajinimoto K.K., Jap. Patent 3,699 (1961).

(284) K. Hayashi, Jap. Patent 5,298 (1961); *Chem. Abstr.*, **55**, 27930 (1961).

(285) J. Toth, *Budapesti Moszaki Egyetem Mezogazdasagi Kem. Technol. Tanszekenek Evkonyve*, **3–8**, 202 (1952–1954); *Chem. Abstr.*, **49**, 14356 (1955).

(286) Sichel-Werke A.-G., French Patent 895,422 (1944).

(287) P. Landmann, German Patent 1,044,056 (1958); *Chem. Abstr.*, **55**, 3459 (1961).

(288) A. Schrodt, German Patent 717,275 (1942); *Chem. Abstr.*, **38**, 2520 (1944).

(289) M. Laurent, French Patent 949,474 (1949); *Chem. Abstr.*, **45**, 4070 (1951).

(290) W. F. Filbert, U.S. Patent 2,599,620; *Chem. Abstr.*, **46**, 11732 (1952).

(291) K. Sarui, *et al.*, Jap. Patent 5,295 (1952); *Chem. Abstr.*, **48**, 394 (1954).

(292) R. S. Apple and O. U. Nichols, Brit. Patent 781,209 (1957); *Chem. Abstr.*, **52**, 2408 (1958).

(293) H. Suzuki, Y. Tadokoro, and N. Taketomi, *Denpun Kogyo Gakkaishi*, **9**, 33 (1961); *Chem. Abstr.*, **57**, 8784 (1962).

(294) S. Hashimoto and I. Furukawa, *Sci. Eng. Rev. Doshisha Univ.*, **3**, No. 2, 43 (1962); *Chem. Abstr.*, **58**, 7016 (1963).

(295) S. M. Cantor and L. M. Cooke, French Patent 975,387 (1950).
(296) F. R. Senti and C. R. Russell, Tappi, 43, 343 (1960).
(297) J. W. Sloan, C. L. Mehltretter, and F. R. Senti, J. Chem. Eng. Data, 7, 156 (1962).
(298) L. M. Cooke, French Patent 975,322 (1950).
(299) A. L. Bullock and J. D. Guthrie, U.S. Patent 3,065,222 (1962); Chem. Abstr., 58, 4723 (1963).
(300) J. Lolkema and F. A. Möller, Neth. Patent 56,340 (1944); Chem. Abstr., 41, 3988 (1947).
(301) W. A. Scholten's Chemische Fabrieken N.V., British Patent 815,358 (1959), Chem. Abstr., 53, 18523 (1959).
(302) E. Husemann and M. Kafka, Makromol. Chem., 41, 208 (1960).
(303) F. Höppler, Kolloid-Z., 101, 305 (1942); Chem. Abstr., 38, 2232 (1944).
(304) F. Höppler, Chem.-Ztg., 67, No. 7–8, 72 (1943); Chem. Abstr., 37, 5553 (1943).
(305) F. Höppler, East German Patent 4,390; cited in Ref. 329.
(306) T. Takata and J. Yamada, Jap. Patent 8,092 (1955); Chem. Abstr., 51, 18666 (1957).
(307) N. Yasumuru, T. Ajichi, and H. Kitabayashi, Jap. Patent 8,738 (1955); Chem. Abstr., 51, 18666 (1957).
(308) T. Hayashi, Jap. Patent 2,296 (1955); Chem. Abstr., 51, 14796 (1957).
(309) M. Staerkle, E. Meier, and C. Christoffel, Swiss Patent 289,057 (1953); M. Staerkle and E. Meier, U.S. Patent 2,698,936 (1955); Chem. Abstr., 48, 10366 (1954); 49, 4314 (1955).
(310) R. Koehler, H.-H. Grun, and H. Kosche, U.S. Patent 3,092,619 (1963); Chem. Abstr., 59, 15490 (1963).
(311) W. Klendauer and J. Voss, German Patent 1,125,645 (1962); French Patent 1,291,066 (1962); British Patent 916,571 (1963); Chem. Abstr., 57, 2413 (1962).
(312) H.-H. Grun, German Patent 1,102,715 (1961); Chem. Abstr., 56, 6168 (1962).
(313) J. Lolkema and P. J. A. Beersma, British Patent 699,530 (1953); German Patent 931,593 (1955); Chem. Abstr., 48, 6720 (1954); 52, 21178 (1958).
(314) M. Roger, Dissertation Abstr., 14, 1550 (1954); Chem. Abstr., 49, 4313 (1955).
(315) A. G. Scott, Dissertation Abstr., 16, 250 (1956); Chem. Abstr., 50, 8291 (1956).
(316) S. S. Winter and C. O. Beckman, J. Phys. Chem., 60, 883 (1956).
(317) T. Inoue, Aichi Gakugei Daigaku Kenkyu Hokoku, No. 9, 69 (1960); Chem. Abstr., 54, 20420 (1960).
(318) H. C. Olsen and R. A. Weidener, U.S. Patent 2,808,380 (1957); Chem. Abstr., 52, 2438 (1958).
(319) E. Letzig, Z. Lebensm.-Untersuch. -Forsch., 94, 227 (1952); Chem. Abstr., 46, 7243 (1952).
(320) C. C. Wang, M. I. Grossman, and A. C. Ivy, J. Nutrition, 40, 471 (1950).
(321) W. L. Thompson, J. J. Britton, and R. P. Walton, J. Pharmacol. Exptl. Therap., 136, 125 (1962); Chem. Abstr., 57, 3983 (1962).
(322) J. Fittipoldi and P. L. Davis, Gastroenterol., 10, 667 (1948); cited in Ref. 320.
(323) J. Lolkema, U.S. Patent 2,590,077 (1952); Neth. Patent 70,443 (1952); Chem. Abstr., 46, 5223 (1952); 47, 2903 (1953).
(324) J. Hoffman, P. Malek, M. Herold, J. Capkova, M. Hermansky, M. Vondracek, and J. Kolc, Czech. Patent 90,980 (1959); Chem. Abstr., 55, 3014 (1961).
(325) W. Voelksen, Staerke, 3, 196 (1951).
(326) H. Dorn and H. Pfanz, East German Patent 9,491 (1955); Chem. Abstr., 52, 11364 (1958).

(327) H. Naumann, *Pharm. Praxis, Beil. Pharmazie*, **No. 4**, 29 (1957); *Chem. Abstr.*, **51**, 17096 (1957).

(328) H. L. Rohn and H. E. Schwarzkopf, East German Patent 11,595 (1956); German Patent 955,807 (1957); *Chem. Abstr.*, **53**, 4665, 16480 (1959).

(329) W. Kempf, *Staerke*, **9**, 235 (1957).

(330) H. Schoenefeld, *Deut. Textiltech.*, **13**, No. 1, 28 (1963).

(331) W. Schnupp, C. Vorck, and R. Hoffman, British Patent 788,369 (1958); *Chem. Abstr.*, **52**, 9614 (1958).

(332) J. A. McCarthy, *Sewage Ind. Wastes*, **28**, 334 (1956); *Chem. Abstr.*, **52**, 7710 (1958).

(333) J. B. Batdorf, U.S. Patent 2,865,853 (1958); *Chem. Abstr.*, **53**, 6498 (1959).

(334) G. J. J. Nijhoff, Neth. Patent 89,835 (1958); U.S. Patent 3,001,884 (1961); *Chem. Abstr.*, **54**, 894 (1960).

(335) V. K. La Mer, R. H. Smellie, Jr., and P.-K. Lee, *J. Colloid Sci.*, **12**, 230 (1957).

(336) N. Shikazono, S. Sasaki, and K. Maeda, *Tokyo Kogyo Shikenso Hokoku*, **52**, 149 (1957); *Chem. Abstr.*, **52**, 808 (1958).

(337) N. Kazono, S. Sasaki, and T. Maeda, Jap. Patent 612 (1959); *Chem. Abstr.*, **53**, 20634 (1959).

(338) P. J. A. Beersma and J. Lolkema, Neth. Patent 65,275 (1950); U.S. Patent 2,622,997 (1952); *Chem. Abstr.*, **44**, 5117 (1950); **47**, 6165 (1953).

(339) J. Lolkema, U.S. Patent 2,657,155 (1953); *Chem. Abstr.*, **48**, 3040 (1954).

(340) M. Geiger, E. Usteri, and A. Ruperti, U.S. Patent 2,547,261 (1951); *Chem. Abstr.*, **45**, 6344 (1951).

(341) J. D. Reid and G. C. Daul, U.S. Patent 2,495,767 (1950); *Chem. Abstr.*, **44**, 6653 (1950).

(342) E. Mayer and E. A. F. Bolin, German Patent 928,725 (1955); *Chem. Abstr.*, **52**, 5888 (1958).

(343) S. Peat, E. J. Bourne, and R. D. Thrower, *Nature*, **159**, 810 (1947).

(344) A. J. Nutten, *Metallurgia*, **42**, 271 (1950); *Chem. Abstr.*, **45**, 1460 (1951).

(345) L. Deibner, *Chim. Anal.*, **33**, 207 (1951); *Chem. Abstr.*, **45**, 8936 (1951).

(346) W. Theilacker, *Z. Anal. Chem.*, **132**, 356 (1951); *Chem. Abstr.*, **45**, 6958 (1951).

(347) K. Tokubo and A. Okuda, *Nippon Dojohiryogaku Zasshi*, **27**, 321 (1956); *Chem. Abstr.*, **51**, 17041 (1957).

(348) F. A. Möller and J. Lolkema, Neth. Patent 91,383 (1959); U.S. Patent 2,957,834 (1960); *Chem. Abstr.*, **54**, 15802 (1960).

(349) K. A. Ramsay, Can. Patent 598,949 (1960); *Chem. Abstr.*, **54**, 21785 (1960).

(350) G. Mitschke, German Patent 1,052,609 (1959); East German Patent 18,446 (1960); *Chem. Abstr.*, **55**, 6736, 7710 (1961).

(351) O. B. Claren and F. Drexler, German Patent 1,098,430 (1961); *Chem. Abstr.*, **56**, 11254 (1962).

(352) W. H. Wood, U.S. Patent 2,589,313 (1952); *Chem. Abstr.*, **46**, 6024 (1952).

(353) W. K. A. Koerber and D. M. A. van Goethem, German Patent 810,105 (1951); *Chem. Abstr.*, **47**, 5829 (1953).

(354) G. W. C. Taylor, British Patent 836,410 (1960); *Chem. Abstr.*, **54**, 20209 (1960).

(355) K. G. Taylor, Belgian Patent 590,272 (1960); British Patent 884,696 (1961); U.S. Patent 3,071,573 (1963); *Chem. Abstr.*, **56**, 8984 (1962).

(356) L. A. Miller, U.S. Patent 3,022,288 (1962); Italian Patent 636,172 (1962); British Patent 941,044 (1963); *Chem. Abstr.*, **57**, 3553 (1962).

(357) Y. Ishikawa, Jap. Patent 7,573 (1954); *Chem. Abstr.*, **50**, 5950 (1956).

(358) M. F. Fuller, U.S. Patent 2,883,375 (1959); *Chem. Abstr.*, **53**, 20868 (1959).

(359) E. F. Paschall, U.S. Patent 2,806,857 (1957); *Chem. Abstr.*, **52**, 768 (1958).

(360) J. Strating, G. Moes, and W. F. Vogel, Belgian Patent 584,901 (1960); British Patent 879,133 (1961); U.S. Patent 3,046,272 (1962).

(361) D. L. Schoene and V. S. Chambers, U.S. Patent 2,539,704 (1951); *Chem. Abstr.* **45,** 5721 (1951).

(362) J. H. MacGregor and C. Pugh, *Proc. Intern. Congr. Pure Appl. Chem., 11th, London, 1947,* **5,** 123 (1950).

(363) J. H. MacGregor, *J. Soc. Dyers Colourists,* **67,** 66 (1951).

(364) L. H. Bock and A. L. Houk, U.S. Patent 2,316,129 (1943); *Chem. Abstr.,* **37,** 5873 (1943).

(365) E. F. Paschall and W. H. Minkema, U.S. Patent 2,965,632 (1960); *Chem. Abstr.,* **55,** 8906 (1961).

(366) C. Caldo, Italian Patent 559,402 (1957); *Chem. Abstr.,* **53,** 7041 (1959).

(367) Monsanto Chemical Co., Brit. Patent 808,290 (1959); *Chem. Abstr.,* **53,** 9708 (1959).

(368) E. E. Fisher and J. L. Harper, Belgian Patent 611,052 (1962); French Patent 1,314,552 (1962); British Patent 935,340 (1963); *Chem. Abstr.,* **57,** 14042 (1962).

(369) G. E. Journeay, U.S. Patent 2,842,541 (1958); *Chem. Abstr.,* **52,** 15908 (1958).

(370) T. E. Sample, Jr., U.S. Patents 2,836,511, 2,836,512, 2,837,438 (1958); *Chem. Abstr.,* **52,** 19199, 19200, 15085 (1958).

(371) A. R. Wilson, U.S. Patent 2,881,143 (1959); *Chem. Abstr.,* **53,** 15596 (1959).

(372) H. M. Walker, U.S. Patent 3,032,498 (1962); *Chem. Abstr.,* **57,** 6216 (1962).

(373) T. P. Malinowski, U.S. Patent 3,001,933 (1961); *Chem. Abstr.,* **55,** 27725 (1961).

(374) E. C. Makin, U.S. Patent 2,983,768 (1961); *Chem. Abstr.,* **55,** 21050 (1961).

(375) Maxcel Denki Kogyo K.K., Jap. Patent 6,714 (1963).

(376) D. Maragliano and C. Caldo, Italian Patent 572,919 (1958); *Chem. Abstr.,* **53,** 15640 (1959).

(377) A. L. Houk and L. H. Bock, U.S. Patent 2,316,128 (1943); British Patent 546,585 (1943); Can. Patent 434,619 (1946); *Chem. Abstr.,* **37,** 5812 (1943); **40,** 3634, 5280 (1946).

(378) Y. Sakaguchi, *Sen-i Gakkaishi,* **14,** 818 (1958); *Chem. Abstr.,* **53,** 1795 (1959).

(379) Union Chimique Belge S.A., Belgian Patent 554,348 (1957); *Chem. Abstr.,* **53,** 18349 (1959).

(380) Toyo Koatsu Kogyo K. K., Jap. Patent 878 (1962).

(381) E. F. Paschall, U.S. Patent 2,928,827 (1960); *Chem. Abstr.,* **54,** 12626 (1960).

(382) A. E. Staley Mfg. Co., British Patent 879,849 (1961); *Chem. Abstr.,* **56,** 6228 (1962).

(383) E. F. Paschall, U.S. Patent 3,033,852 (1962); *Chem. Abstr.,* **57,** 12776 (1962).

(384) J. R. Stephens and L. Rapoport, U.S. Patent 2,938,026 (1960); *Chem. Abstr.,* **54,** 20262 (1960).

(385) H. Watanabe, H. Matsunaga, and T. Inouye, Jap. Patent 25,981 (1963); *Chem. Abstr.,* **60,** 10244 (1964).

(386) M. Arakawa, B. Yamada, and A. Katanosaka, Jap. Patent 2,102 (1962).

(387) T. Minamiyama, T. Kondo, and A. Kato, Jap. Patent 16,598 (1960); *Chem. Abstr.,* **55,** 18150 (1961).

(388) E. F. Paschall, F. D. Thayer, Jr., and W. H. Minkema, U.S. Patent 3,101,330 (1963); *Chem. Abstr.,* **59,** 15469 (1963).

(389) C. G. Tomecko and R. Adams, *J. Am. Chem. Soc.,* **45,** 2698 (1923).

(390) P. L. Nichols, Jr., R. M. Hamilton, L. T. Smith, and E. Yanovsky, *Ind. Eng. Chem.,* **37,** 201 (1945).

346

(391) P. L. Nichols, Jr., P. E. Meiss, and E. Yanovsky, U.S. Patent 2,413,463 (1946); British Patent 656,249 (1951); *Chem. Abstr.*, **41**, 2266 (1947); **46**, 2830 (1952).

(392) J. Chadapaux, G. Champetier, and E. Savostianoff, *Bull. Soc. Chim. France*, 185 (1948); *Chem. Abstr.*, **42**, 4148 (1948).

(393) J. Chadapaux, *Congr. Tech. Intern. Ind. Peintures Ind. Assoc., 1er, Paris, 1947*, 526 (1947); *Chem. Abstr.*, **44**, 9710 (1950).

(394) E. A. Talley, R. M. Hamilton, J. H. Schwartz, C. A. Brown, and E Yanovsky, *U.S. Dept. Agr., Bur. Agr. Ind. Chem., Mimeo. Circ. Ser.,* **AIC-140** (1947).

(395) R. M. Hamilton and E. Yanovsky, U.S. Patent 2,524,792 (1950); *Chem. Abstr.*, **45**, 1800 (1951).

(396) E. A. Talley and E. Yanovsky, U.S. Patent 2,635,099 (1953); *Chem. Abstr.*, **48**, 2093 (1954).

(397) T. J. Dietz and J. E. Hansen, U.S. Patent 2,510,089 (1950); *Chem. Abstr.*, **44**, 8686 (1950).

(398) K. C. Hobbs, U.S. Patent 2,615,885 (1952); *Chem. Abstr.*, **47**, 899 (1953).

(399) C. A. Wilham, T. A. McGuire, A. S. Rudolphi, and C. L. Mehltretter, *J. Appl. Polymer Sci.*, **7**, 1403 (1963).

(400) W. T. Ritter, R. O. Ragan, and R. F. Trant, U.S. Patent 2.916,376 (1959); *Chem. Abstr.*, **54**, 6376 (1960).

(401) R. M. Hamilton and P. L. Nichols, Jr., U.S. Patent 2,406,369 (1946); French Patent 961,458 (1950); *Chem. Abstr.*, **41**, 153 (1947).

(402) G. Jacini and M. Ferrazzi, *Chim. Ind. (Milan)*, **31**, 1 (1949).

(403) P. L. Nichols, Jr., A. N. Wrigley, and E. Yanovsky, *J. Am. Chem. Soc.*, **68**, 2020 (1946).

(404) P. L. Nichols, Jr., and L. T. Smith, French Patent 960,651 (1949).

(405) P. L. Nichols, Jr., and R. M. Hamilton, U.S. Patent 2,449,816 (1948); French Patent 954,646 (1949); *Cnem. Abstr.*, **43**, 2028 (1949).

(406) A. N. Wrigley, E. Yanovsky, and P. L. Nichols, Jr., U.S. Patent 2,623,864 (1952); *Chem. Abstr.*, **47**, 3035 (1953).

(407) W. B. Hewson, U.S. Patents 2,682,481, 2,682,482 (1954); *Chem. Abstr.*, **48**, 14264 (1954).

(408) C. A. Brown, U.S. Patent 2,794,789 (1957); *Chem. Abstr.*, **51**, 13419 (1957).

(409) E. Yanovsky, *U.S. Dept. Agr., Bur. Agr. Ind. Chem., Mimeo. Circ. Ser.,* **AIC-362** (1953).

(410) P. L. Nichols, Jr., R. M. Hamilton, L. T. Smith, and E. Yanovsky, *Paint Ind. Mag.*, **60**, 84 (1945); *Chem. Abstr.*, **39**, 2428 (1945).

(411) T. J. Dietz, J. E. Hansen, and M. E. Gallagher, *U.S. Dept. Agr., Bur. Agr. Ind. Chem., Mimeo. Circ. Ser.,* **AIC-175** (1948).

(412) R. Nordgren, M. H. Baker, and L. Champlin, Jr., *Paint, Oil Chem. Rev.*, **114**, No. 2, 15, 36, 38 (1951); *Chem. Abstr.*, **45**, 3611 (1951).

(413) J. R. Roach and R. Nordgren, *Org. Finishing*, **11**, No. 4, 8 (1950); *Chem. Abstr.*, **44**, 5633 (1950).

(414) A. N. Wrigley, J. H. Schwartz, and J. Siciliano, *Paint, Oil Chem. Rev.*, **114**, No. 21, 40 (1951); *Chem. Abstr.*, **46**, 1266 (1952).

(415) J. H. Schwartz and A. N. Wrigley, *U.S. Dept. Agr., Bur. Agr. Ind. Chem., Mimeo. Circ. Ser.,* **AIC-351** (1953); U.S. Patent 2,740,724 (1956); *Chem. Abstr.*, **51**, 3168 (1957).

(416) Anon., *Am. Ink Maker*, **28**, No. 5, 27 (1950); *Chem. Abstr.*, **44**, 6655 (1950).

(417) H. E. Wilde, U.S. Patent 2,707,689 (1955); *Chem. Abstr.*, **49**, 13662 (1955).

(418) P. L. Nichols, Jr., and L. T. Smith, U.S. Patent 2,458,191 (1949); *Chem. Abstr.*, **43**, 2466 (1949).

(419) M. DeGroote, U.S. Patent 2,626,901 (1953); *Chem. Abstr.*, **47**, 5106 (1953).

(420) A. N. Wrigley, J. Siciliano, W. C. Mast, and C. H. Fisher, *U.S. Dept. Agr., Bur. Agr. Ind. Chem., Mimeo. Circ. Ser.*, **AIC-266** (1950).

(421) M. Gomberg and C. C. Buchler, *J. Am. Chem. Soc.*, **43**, 1904 (1921).

(422) T. Asahina and G. Nara, *Bull. Chem. Soc. Japan*, **9**, 530 (1934); *Chem. Abstr.*, **29**, 1784 (1935).

(423) B. V. Maksorov and K. A. Andrianov, *Plasticheskie Massy*, No. 6, 1 (1933); *Chem. Abstr.*, **28**, 7041 (1934).

(424) B. V. Maksorov and K. A. Andrianov, *Rev. Gen. Mat. Plastiques*, **11**, 336, 373, 375 (1935); *Chem. Abstr.*, **30**, 6083 (1936).

(425) E. Doerr, German Patent 683,568 (1939), 703,003 (1941); *Chem. Abstr.*, **36**, 903, 4236 (1942).

(426) Van Linges Chemische Fabrieken, Neth. Patent 44,994 (1950); *Chem. Abstr.*, **44**, 6199 (1950).

(427) R. V. Jones, U.S. Patent 2,555,469 (1951); *Chem. Abstr.*, **45**, 7783 (1951).

(428) F. Pancirolli, *Boll. Reparto Fibre Tessili Vegetali Regia Staz. Sper. Ind. Carta e Fibre Tessili Vegetali*, **32**, 314 (1937); *Chem. Abstr.*, **31**, 7247 (1937).

(429) B. Helferich and H. Koester, *Ber.*, **57**, 587 (1924).

(430) H. J. Roberts, in "Methods in Carbohydrate Chemistry," R. L. Whistler, ed., Academic Press Inc., New York, N.Y., Vol. 4, 1964, p. 311.

(431) E. Husemann, M. Reinhardt, and M. Kafka, *Makromol. Chem.*, **41**, 184 (1960); *Chem. Abstr.*, **55**, 27929 (1961).

(432) Y. Hirasaka, I. Matsunaga, K. Umemoto, and M. Sukegawa, *Yakugaku Zasshi*, **83**, 976 (1963); *Chem. Abstr.*, **60**, 4233 (1964).

(433) J. W. Berry, H. Tucker, and A. J. Deutschmann, Jr., *Ind. Eng. Chem., Process Design Devel.*, **2**, 318 (1963).

(434) I. Klein and D. I. Marshall, *Ind. Eng. Chem., Process Design Devel.*, **3**, 287 (1964).

(435) J. W. Berry, A. J. Deutschman, Jr., and J. P. Evans, *J. Org. Chem.*, **29**, 2619 (1964).

(436) K. C. Hobbs, U.S. Patent 2,801,241 (1957); *Chem. Abstr.*, **51**, 18666 (1957).

(437) H. Kuhn, British Patent 794,644 (1958); German Patent 1,050,546 (1959); *Chem. Abstr.*, **52**, 17810 (1958); **55**, 2199 (1961).

(438) Y. Merle, *Compt. Rend.*, **249**, 2560 (1959).

(439) Y. Merle, *J. Rech. Centre Natl. Rech. Sci. Lab. Bellevue (Paris)*, **No. 51**, 91 (1960).

(440) K. P. Satterly, U.S. Patent 3,037,017 (1962); *Chem. Abstr.*, **57**, 7504 (1962).

(441) R. W. Kerr and W. A. Faucette, U.S. Patent 2,733,238 (1956); *Chem. Abstr.*, **50**, 6824 (1956).

(442) W. Jarowenko, U.S. Patent 2,996,498 (1961); *Chem. Abstr.*, **56**, 1658 (1962).

(443) P. P. Shorygin, N. N. Makarova-Zemlanskaya, R. L. Bilenko, V. A. Derevitskaya, and V. T. Shematenkova, *Zh. Obshch. Khim.*, **8**, 1910 (1938).

(444) H. Wolff, U.S. Patent 2,923,707 (1960); *Chem. Abstr.*, **54**, 11525 (1960).

(445) J. Liebig, *Ann.*, **15**, 541 (1829); cited in Ref. *448*.

(446) R. P. Walton, "A Comprehensive Survey of Starch Chemistry," The Chemical Catalog Co., New York, N.Y., Part 2, 1928, p. 100.

(447) E. F. Degering, in "Starch and its Derivatives," J. A. Radley, ed., John Wiley & Sons, Inc., New York, N.Y., 3rd Ed., Vol. 1, 1954, p. 355.

(448) J. M. Newton and G. T. Peckham, in "Chemistry and Industry of Starch," R. W. Kerr, ed., Academic Press Inc., New York, N.Y., 2nd Ed., 1950, p. 342.

(449) K. Ohashi and T. Takahashi, *Gifu Norin Semmon Gakko Gakujutsu Hokoku*, **68**, 79 (1950); *Chem. Abstr.*, **46**, 2322 (1952).

(*450*) J. W. Mench and E. F. Degering, *Proc. Indiana Acad. Sci.*, **55**, 69 (1945); *Chem. Abstr.*, **41**, 5739 (1947).

(*451*) W. O. Kenyon and C. C. Unruh, U.S. Patent 2,472,590 (1949); *Chem. Abstr.*, **43**, 7244 (1949).

(*452*) R. W. Kerr, *J. Am. Chem. Soc.*, **72**, 816 (1950).

(*453*) G. Graefe, *Staerke*, **5**, 205 (1953).

(*454*) K. Heyns and G. Graefe, *Chem. Ber.*, **86**, 646 (1953).

(*455*) H. Nakajima and A. Momose, Jap. Patent 6,898 (1957); *Chem. Abstr.*, **52**, 10620 (1958).

(*456*) Y. Kozai, N. Horiguchi, T. Mizuno, and R. Nozu, *Kobunshi Kagaku*, **17**, 461 (1960); *Chem. Abstr.*, **55**, 21631 (1961).

(*457*) Y. Hirasaka and K. Yamamoto, *Yakugaku Zasshi*, **83**, 956 (1963); *Chem. Abstr.*, **60**, 4229 (1964).

(*458*) A. S. Perlin, *Can. J. Chem.*, **30**, 278 (1952).

(*459*) Y. Imai, *Yakugaku Zasshi*, **81**, 1109 (1961); *Chem. Abstr.*, **56**, 1656 (1962).

(*460*) Y. Imai and S. Owari, *ibid.*, **81**, 1221 (1961); *Chem. Abstr.*, **56**, 10259 (1962).

(*461*) M. Ishidate, Y. Imai, and Y. Hirasaka, Jap. Patent 17,747 (1961); *Chem. Abstr.*, **56**, 15620 (1962).

(*462*) Y. Imai, *Yakugaku Zasshi*, **81**, 1115 (1961); *Chem. Abstr.*, **56**, 1656 (1962).

(*463*) Y. Imai and Y. Hirasaka, *ibid.*, **81**, 1362 (1961); *Chem. Abstr.*, **56**, 10259 (1962).

(*464*) Y. Nitta, M. Ukikata, and E. Tomita, Jap. Patent 7,150 (1962); *Chem. Abstr.*, **59**, 11645 (1963).

(*465*) M. Abdel-Akher, J. K. Hamilton, and F. Smith, *J. Am. Chem. Soc.*, **73**, 4691 (1951).

(*466*) W. C. Schaefer, C. R. Russell, J. J. Maurice, and C. E. Rist, *Cereal Chem.*, **40**, 101 (1963).

(*467*) N. Uchino and R. L. Whistler, *Cereal Chem.*, **39**, 477 (1962).

(*468*) T. R. Ingle and R. L. Whistler, *Abstr. Papers Am. Chem. Soc.*, **144**, 7D (1963).

(*469*) G. Bernier, French Patent 1,127,509 (1956); *Chem. Abstr.*, **54**, 13017 (1960).

(*470*) H. Wagner and L. K. Schwoerzer, German Patent 1,051,835 (1959); *Chem. Abstr.*, **55**, 5000 (1961).

(*471*) H. Robinette, Jr., U.S. Patent 2,880,107 (1959); *Chem. Abstr.*, **53**, 12719 (1959).

(*472*) T. E. Yeates, G. E. Babcock, and C. L. Mehltretter, *Abstr. Papers Am. Chem. Soc.*, **144**, 7D (1963).

(*473*) H. Suzuki, M. Tamura, and N. Taketomi, *Kogyo Kagaku Zasshi*, **61**, 1008 (1958); *Chem. Abstr.*, **55**, 18148 (1961).

(*474*) A. C. Ellington and C. B. Purves, *Can. J. Chem.*, **31**, 801 (1953).

(*475*) I. Feher, *Bor-Cipotech.*, **11**, 33, 65 (1961); *Chem. Abstr.*, **55**, 25305 (1961).

(*476*) A. Meller, *Tappi*, **41**, 684 (1958).

(*477*) L. Mester and A. Major, *Chem. Ind. (London)*, 469 (1957).

(*478*) C. D. Szymanski, *J. Appl. Polymer. Sci.*, **8**, 1597 (1964).

(*479*) J. Borunsky, Can. Patent 549,110 (1957); *Chem. Abstr.*, **52**, 7768 (1958).

(*480*) V. A. Kargin, P. V. Kozlov, N. A. Plate, and I. I. Konoreva, *Vysokomolekul. Soedinen.*, **1**, 114 (1959).

(*481*) V. A. Kargin, N. A. Plate, and E. P. Rebinder, *ibid.*, **1**, 1547 (1959); *Chem. Abstr.*, **54**, 11524 (1960).

(*482*) S. Kimura, T. Takitani, and M. Imoto, *Bull. Chem. Soc. Japan*, **35**, 2012 (1962); *Chem. Abstr.*, **58**, 8124 (1963).

(*483*) H. J. Hagemeyer, Jr., U.S. Patent 2,763,627 (1956); *Chem. Abstr.*, **51**, 1657 (1957).

(484) A. Mishina, *Mem. Inst. Sci. Ind. Res., Osaka Univ.*, **18**, 93 (1961); *Chem. Abstr.*, **56**, 4947 (1962).

(485) R. L. Walrath, Z. Reyes, and C. R. Russell, *Advan. Chem. Ser.*, **34**, 87 (1962); *Chem. Abstr.*, **57**, 12773 (1962).

(486) A. A. Berlin and E. A. Penskaya, *Doklady Akad. Nauk SSSR*, **110**, 585 (1956); *Chem. Abstr.*, **51**, 14300 (1957).

(487) A. A. Berlin, E. A. Penskaya, and G. I. Volkova, *Mezhdunar. Simpozium po Makromolekul. Khim., Dokl., Moscow, 1960*, **3**, 334 (1960); *Chem. Abstr.*, **55**, 7898 (1961).

(488) R. J. Ceresa, *Polymer*, **2**, 213 (1961); *Chem. Abstr.*, **58**, 12755 (1963).

(489) R. L. Whistler and J. L. Goatley, *J. Polymer Sci.*, **62**, S123 (1962).

(490) D. J. Angier, R. J. Ceresa, and W. F. Watson, *J. Polymer Sci.*, **34**, 699 (1959).

(491) R. J. Ceresa, *J. Polymer Sci.*, **53**, 9 (1961).

(492) B. H. Thewlis, *Nature*, **190**, 260 (1961).

(493) B. H. Thewlis, *J. Appl. Chem. (London)*, **13**, 249 (1963).

(494) C. E. Brockway, R. R. Estes, and D. R. Smith, British Patent 869,501 (1961); U.S. Patent 3,095,391 (1963); *Chem. Abstr.*, **55**, 24062 (1961).

(495) C. E. Brockway and K. B. Moser, *J. Polymer Sci., A*, **1**, 1025 (1963).

(496) G. Mino and S. Kaizerman, *J. Polymer. Sci.*, **31**, 242 (1960); German Patent 1,082,408 (1960); *Chem. Abstr.*, **55**, 22915 (1961).

(497) S. Kimura and M. Imoto, *Makromol. Chem.*, **42**, 140 (1960); *Chem. Abstr.*, **55**, 14972 (1961).

(498) A. Zilkhar, B. A. Feit, and A. Bar-Nun, Israel Patent 15,962 (1962); *Chem. Abstr.*, **58**, 5803 (1963).

(499) R. L. Whistler and H. J. Roberts, *J. Org. Chem.*, **26**, 2458 (1961).

(500) S. M. Gurevich, A. K. Livshits, and V. K. Potapov, U.S.S.R. Patent 130,428 (1960); *Chem. Abstr.*, **55**, 5309 (1961).

(501) C. E. Brockway, D. W. Christman, and R. R. Estes, U.S. Patent 3,061,471 (1962); *Chem. Abstr.*, **58**, 5832 (1963).

(502) C. E. Brockway, U.S. Patent 3,061,472 (1962); *Chem. Abstr.*, **58**, 5832 (1963).

(503) A. Mishina and Z. Nikuni, *Nippon Nogei Kagaku Kaishi*, **37**, 389 (1963); *Nucl. Sci. Abstr.*, **18**, 8426 (1964).

(504) N. R. Segro and W. Hodes, U.S. Patent 3,044,972 (1962); *Chem. Abstr.*, **57**, 11401 (1962).

(505) R. W. Kerr, in "Chemistry and Industry of Starch," R. W. Kerr, ed., Academic Press Inc., New York, N.Y., 2nd Ed., 1950, p. 466.

(506) K. H. Meyer and C.-P. Feng, *Chem. Ber.*, **85**, 590 (1952).

(507) K. Seidel, German Patent 825,746 (1951); *Chem. Abstr.*, **49**, 6653 (1955).

(508) P. Hiemstra, J. M. Muetgeert, and W. C. Bus, *Staerke*, **10**, 213 (1958).

(509) Cooperative Verkoop- en Productievereniging van Aardappelmeel en Derivate "Avebe" G.A., British Patent 822,587 (1959); *Chem. Abstr.*, **54**, 6148 (1960).

(510) J. Muetgeert and W. C. Bus, *J. Chem. Eng. Data*, **7**, 272 (1962).

(511) J. Lolkema and W. A. van der Meer, Neth. Patents 60,861 (1948), 66,492 (1950), 67,265, 67,471 (1951); British Patents 632,785, 632,789 (1949); U.S. Patents 2,510,748 (1950), 2,542,933, 2,575,423 (1951); *Chem. Abstr.*, **42**, 3984 (1948); **44**, 8686 (1950); **45**, 4472, 4473, 4954, 10633 (1951); **46**, 2324 (1952).

(512) E. Meier, Swiss Patent 276,399 (1951); *Chem. Abstr.*, **47**, 1981 (1953).

(513) D. M. Gagarine, U.S. Patent 2,486,399 (1949); *Chem. Abstr.*, **44**, 9692 (1950).

(514) E. Wulken, U.S. Patent 2,581,741 (1952); *Chem. Abstr.*, **46**, 3306 (1952).

(515) R. L. Lehmann and L. Gandon, French Patent 1,120,163 (1956); French Addn. 68,060 (1958); U.S. Patent 2,867,615 (1959); *Chem. Abstr.*, **53**, 12718, 23019 (1959); **55**, 6002 (1961).

(516) G. A. Roscelli, U.S. Patent 3,036,936 (1962); *Chem. Abstr.*, **57**, 3684 (1962).

(517) O. Weaver, C. R. Russell, and C. E. Rist, *J. Org. Chem.*, **28**, 2838 (1963).

(518) M. J. Rosen and I. A. Kaye, U.S. Patent 3,092,618 (1963); British Patent 941,268 (1963); *Chem. Abstr.*, **60**, 1939 (1964).

(519) D. D. Wheeler and D. C. Young, U.S. Patent 2,809,965 (1957); *Chem. Abstr.*, **52**, 3862 (1958).

(520) K. M. Gaver, E. P. Lasure, and L. M. Thomas, U.S. Patent 2,563,526 (1951); Reissue 23,528 (1952); *Chem. Abstr.*, **45**, 10632 (1951); **46**, 10654 (1952).

(521) F. R. Senti and L. P. Witnauer, *J. Am. Chem. Soc.*, **70**, 1438 (1948).

(522) F. K. Signaigo, U.S. Patent 2,570,499 (1951); *Chem. Abstr.*, **46**, 3783 (1952).

(523) H. N. Barham, E. S. Strickley, and M. J. Caldwell, *J. Am. Chem. Soc.*, **68**, 1018 (1946).

(524) H. N. Barham and T. R. Thomson, *J. Am. Chem. Soc.*, **70**, 3321 (1948).

(525) H. N. Barham, U.S. Patent 2,448,510 (1948); *Chem. Abstr.*, **43**, 428 (1949).

(526) S. Haggroth and B. Lindberg, *Svensk Papperstidn.*, **59**, 870 (1956); *Chem. Abstr.*, **51**, 17157 (1957).

(527) G. M. Christensen, M. H. Fischer, and F. Smith, *Abstr. Papers Am. Chem. Soc.*, **138**, 7D (1960).

(528) R. W. Kerr and K. C. Hobbs, *Ind. Eng. Chem.*, **45**, 2542 (1953).

(529) I. A. Wolff, U.S. Patent 2,961,339 (1960); *Chem. Abstr.*, **57**, 1139 (1962).

(530) K. P. Satterly, U.S. Patent 3,071,492 (1963); *Chem. Abstr.*, **58**, 7022 (1963).

(531) A number of such analytical methods are described in "Methods in Carbohydrate Chemistry," R. L. Whistler, ed., Academic Press Inc., New York, N.Y., Vol. 4, 1964.

(532) O. B. Wurzburg, in "Methods in Carbohydrate Chemistry," R. L. Whistler, ed., Academic Press Inc., New York, N.Y., Vol. 4, 1964, p. 286.

(533) H. J. Lortz, *Anal. Chem.*, **28**, 892 (1956).

(534) I. Jullander and O. Lagerström, in "Methods in Carbohydrate Chemistry," R. L. Whistler, ed., Academic Press Inc., New York, N.Y., Vol. 3, 1963, p. 303.

(535) S. Ikeda, K. Takeichi, T. Furukawa, T. Yawata, and H. Kambara, *Denpun Kogyo Gakkaishi*, **9**, 42 (1961); *Chem. Abstr.*, **58**, 1623 (1963).

(536) H. M. Boyd and J. R. Roach, *Anal. Chem.*, **19**, 158 (1947).

(537) J. R. van der Bij and W. F. Vogel, *Staerke*, **14**, 113 (1962).

(538) Anon., *Federal Register*, **30**, 6837 (1965).

(539) Anon., *Federal Register*, **29**, 12460 (1964).

CHAPTER XIV

PRODUCTION AND USES OF STARCH PHOSPHATES

By R. M. Hamilton and E. F. Paschall

Moffett Technical Center, Corn Products Co., Argo, Illinois

I. Introduction

Starch phosphates may be divided into two general classes: (*a*) monoester of phosphoric acid in which a starch hydroxyl group is esterified with only one of the three acidic functions of phosphoric acid, and (*b*) mixtures of mono-, di-, and triesters of phosphoric acid in which more than one of the acidic functions of phosphoric acid are esterified. The monoesters have been referred to as monostarch phosphate, starch phosphate monoesters, or simply as starch phosphate, but are more properly starch dihydrogen (or disodium, etc.) phosphate. Similarly, the polyesters have been designated as distarch phosphate and starch phosphate diesters, although mixtures of the mono-, di- [distarch monohydrogen (or monosodium, etc.) phosphate], and triesters probably exist. The polyesters have also been described as inhibited or cross-bonded starches since the formation of a di- or triester bond gives a cross-bonded network in which two or three starch segments are bonded together. This inhibits or restricts granule swelling when the starch is cooked in water.

Starches which have been cross-bonded with phosphorus oxychloride or trimetaphosphate salts have achieved wide commercial success, particularly in applications in which it is desirable to maintain a high and stable viscosity in the cooked product. The starch phosphate monoesters are relatively new, but are expected to find wide use in food and non-food applications in which high viscosity, paste clarity, cohesive strength, and ionic charge are important factors.

This chapter gives a brief historical review of the early synthesis of starch phosphates, followed by a description of the preparation, properties, and uses of the starch phosphate monoesters and polyesters.

II. History

The first synthetic starch phosphate appears to have been prepared in 1919 by Kerb (1), who treated soluble starch with phosphorus oxychloride in the presence of calcium carbonate. The calcium salt of starch phosphate was water-soluble and gave a D-glucose phosphate upon treatment with "takadiastase."

In 1922, Samec and Mayer (2) reported the preparation of the phosphoric acid ester of "erythroamylose" (amylopectin) from phosphorus oxychloride using a procedure similar to that of Kerb; the resulting product contained 0.48% phosphorus.

Pringsheim and Goldstein (3), in 1923, treated a cold pyridine suspension of "polyamylose" (amylose) with phosphorus oxychloride to obtain a product which contained 13% phosphorus. Vogel (4) later employed a similar procedure to prepare a 1.0 D.S. amylose phosphate which was soluble in cold pyridine, but insoluble in hot pyridine and cold water. The product swelled to a viscous paste in hot water without dissolving. Karrer and co-workers (5), in their investigation of anticoagulant activity of various ionic polymers, also prepared a high D.S. phosphoric ester of starch. Starch was dried over phosphorus pentaoxide and then treated with phosphorus oxychloride in dry pyridine. A water-soluble product devoid of anticoagulant activity was obtained.

Starch heated with phosphorus pentachloride at 170° does not produce a phosphate ester, but gives a chlorinated starch in which all three hydroxyl groups and two additional hydrogen atoms are replaced by chlorine (6).

More recently, Lohmar and co-workers (7, 8) observed that a hot-water insoluble starch phosphate is obtained if granular or pregelatinized starch is activated with pyridine prior to reaction with phosphorus oxychloride in dry pyridine. Without pyridine activation, a water-soluble derivative is obtained. These workers also reported that the degree of phosphation of starch granules increases with decreasing size of the starch granules and that the effect of granule size is lost when the starch is gelatinized prior to phosphation. This behavior suggests that phosphation with phosphorus oxychloride occurs predominantly on the surface of the starch granule since the degree of phosphation increases with increasing surface area. Later, Whistler and Spencer (9) examined electron micrographs of sections of starch granules which had been phosphated with phosphorus oxychloride in pyridine and converted to the mercuric salt. They observed that esterification takes place in narrow layers near peripheral and cavital surfaces.

Phosphation of starch with phosphorus oxychloride gives mixtures of mono-, di-, and triphosphate esters. Lohmar and co-workers (7) calculated from titration data that the amounts of mono-, di-, and trisubstituted phosphate esters are 60, 30, and 10%, respectively, for a product with 12% bound phosphorus prepared from phosphorus oxychloride in pyridine. These workers also observed the presence of organically bound chlorine which increased in amount with increase in reaction temperature.

Sannella (10) employed two methods to prepare amylose phosphate from 2,3-di-O-acetylamylose. In one method, a pyridine solution of acetylated amylose was treated with dibenzyl phosphorochloridate to form the 2,3-di-O-acetylamylose 6-dibenzylphosphate. Removal of blocking groups by reduction and hydrolysis gave amylose 6-dihydrogen phosphate of 0.7 D.S. In another method, acetylated amylose was treated with β-cyanoethyl phosphate and dicyclohexylcarbodiimide in pyridine to form 2,3-di-O-acetylamylose 6-β-cyanoethyl phosphate. Treatment with dilute sodium methoxide in methanol gave amylose phosphate having a D.S. of 1.0. Electrometric titrations with barium hydroxide coupled with periodate oxidation indicated that the phosphate groups were doubly bound as the cyclic 3,6-phosphate diester group. At lower degrees of phosphation, both singly and doubly bound phosphate groups were present. Direct phosphation of amylose with β-cyanoethyl phosphate and dicyclohexylcarbodiimide and removal of the β-cyanoethyl group with mild alkali gave the same product (11).

Beyer (12) was among the first to modify starch by heating it with a phosphate salt. He obtained a highly degraded, water-soluble product by heating a mixture of sodium acid hexametaphosphate and starch moistened with alcohol. No degree of phosphation was given. More definitive methods using ortho- and tripolyphosphates have been developed in recent years.

Much of the work discussed above was of academic interest and did not result in products of commercial value. It was not until processes were developed for controlled phosphations in aqueous or dry systems that commercial utility was achieved. The remainder of this chapter is devoted to starch phosphates of commercial value.

III. STARCH PHOSPHATE MONOESTERS

1. Preparation

Starch phosphate monoesters [starch disodium (or dipotassium, etc.) phosphate] are prepared by heating a dry mixture of starch and a water-soluble phosphate salt, such as the acid salts of ortho-, pyro-, or tripoly-phosphorus acid. Commercial methods used for production of the mono-esters have not been disclosed; however, valuable information can be obtained from the patent literature.

Starch heated with the above salts forms the monoester exclusively as opposed to the formation of mixtures of mono-, di-, and triesters which are formed when starch is reacted with polyfunctional phosphorus compounds, such as phosphorus oxychloride. The latter compounds are used almost entirely as cross-bonding agents since their reaction with starch cannot be controlled to give the monoester alone or even the monoester with a controlled degree of cross-bonding to produce a cross-bonded monoester. Therefore, it is customary to monoesterify and cross-link the starch in separate reactions.

Solutions of orthophosphate salts, such as mono- or disodium phosphates, may be mixed with granular starch by slurring, spraying onto dry starch (13–16), or mixing with wet starch filter cake (16). In a typical procedure, the salt-starch mixture at about 40% moisture is dried to a moisture content of about 10%, then heated for about 1 hour at 120°–140°. These starch phosphates may be made in a wide range of fluidity grades by varying pH, temperature, and time of reaction.

The reaction with monosodium orthophosphate may be represented by equation 1.

$$\text{Starch-OH} + \underset{HO}{\overset{NaO}{\diagdown}}\!\!\!P\!\!\!\overset{O}{\diagup}\!\!\!\underset{OH}{} \longrightarrow \underset{HO}{\overset{NaO}{\diagdown}}\!\!\!P\!\!\!\overset{O}{\diagup}\!\!\!\underset{O\text{-Starch}}{} + H_2O \qquad (1)$$

Orthophosphate salts (mixtures of mono- and dihydrogen phosphates at pH 5–6.5) produce starch phosphate monoesters with degrees of sub-stitution (D.S.) up to 0.2, but some hydrolysis of the starch occurs. Methods (17–21) have been developed for increasing the viscosity of starch phosphate monoesters by fractionation with methanol or other oxygen-containing water-miscible organic solvents. As all polyelectrolytes, salts reduce the paste viscosity of starch phosphates. Consequently, the increase in viscosity obtained by the use of this methanol-water technique may be partially attributable to salt removal. Further increase in viscosity and reduction in color intensity is obtained by the incorporation of gaseous chlorine during the methanol treatment (*22*).

Starch phosphate monoesters are also formed by heating dry mixtures of starch and sodium tripolyphosphate (*23*). Sodium tripolyphosphate produces substantially undegraded starch esters with a low degree of substitution (about 0.02). Because of the ionic nature of the phosphate group, the product has a higher viscosity than the parent starch. For example, a 1.8% paste has about the same hot viscosity, as measured by the standard Scott test, as a 4.3% paste of the parent starch. The reaction of starch with sodium tripolyphosphate may be represented by equation 2.

$$
\begin{array}{c}
\text{NaO} \quad \text{O} \\
\diagdown \!\! P \!\! \diagup \\[-2pt]
\text{NaO} \quad \text{O} \\
\diagdown \\
\text{O=P—ONa} \;+\; \text{Starch-OH} \;\longrightarrow\;
\begin{array}{c}
\text{NaO} \quad \text{O} \\
\diagdown \!\! P \!\! \diagup \\[-2pt]
\text{NaO} \quad \text{O-Starch}
\end{array}
\;+\; \text{Na}_3\text{HP}_2\text{O}_7 \quad (2) \\
\text{NaO} \quad \text{O} \\
\diagdown \!\! P \!\! \diagup \\[-2pt]
\text{NaO} \quad \text{O}
\end{array}
$$

In a typical reaction, corn starch is slurried in water at a pH value of about 8.5 with sufficient sodium tripolyphosphate so that 5% of the salt is retained in the filtered and dried starch. Alternatively, a sodium tripolyphosphate solution may be sprayed onto dry starch and blended to assure uniformity. The wet starch–salt mixture, dried to 5–10% moisture, is then heated for about 1 hr. at 120°–130°. The product is cooled, washed with water, and dried in the usual manner. A typical product contains about 0.40% bound phosphorus, which is equivalent to a starch phosphate monoester with a degree of substitution of 0.02 as the orthophosphate group. When gelatinized by pasting in water, the starch forms a viscous, clear, non-gelling sol which has long, cohesive flow characteristics.

Methods for the laboratory preparation of starch phosphate monoesters from sodium tripolyphosphate and from orthophosphate salts have been described (*24*). These methods are essentially the same as outlined above.

The degree of substitution obtained by the above methods is generally less than 0.15. Higher degrees of substitution may be obtained by using larger concentrations of phosphate salts, higher temperatures, and longer reaction times. For example, Greidinger and Cohen (*25*) produced water-soluble amylaceous phosphates containing 6–12% of molecularly bound phosphate (0.4–1.0 D.S.).

Neukom (*26*) used a mixture of monosodium phosphate, disodium phosphate, and urea to esterify starch. The starch was impregnated with this mixture, dried, then heated to effect reaction. The resulting product had a higher viscosity and shorter paste than starch phosphates prepared in the absence of urea.

Hjermstad (*27*) produced starch esters having phosphate groups containing nitrogenous radicals by treating starch with various soluble amides and mono- and disodium phosphates. These products had improved paste clarity and viscosity.

2. Properties

Corn starch forms translucent and relatively short-bodied pastes when gelatinized in water. These pastes revert to solid, opaque gels upon cooling, particularly at higher starch concentrations. However, when corn starch is phosphated to a D.S. as low as 0.01, the colloidal properties of the gelatinized starch ester resemble those of a potato starch sol to which it is closely related in chemical structure by virtue of phosphate ester groups. It also resembles other non-cereal starches as well as waxy starches.

The granular starch phosphate monoester may be water-insoluble or water-soluble depending on the degree of phosphation and the manner of treatment. The granules become cold water swelling at a D.S. level of about 0.07, which is characteristic of most ionic starch derivatives. When 8–10% orthophosphate salts are used to phosphate starch, cold-water-soluble products are obtained. Some of these products may be used to replace vegetable gums such as gum arabic and locust bean gum in various food applications. They do not require cooking, but can be processed with some heat, if desired. Starch phosphates prepared by reacting corn starch with orthophosphate salts at a 5% level may have greater thickening power than the starch from which they were derived (*28, 29*). The viscosity can be controlled by changing the base starch, varying the pH and temperature of reaction, or cross-bonding the product. Starch phosphate monoesters, compared to their unmodified counterparts, have greater paste clarity, greater paste viscosity, and a marked reduction in the tendency of the cold paste to setback on standing. Starch phosphate monoesters produce a long cohesive paste.

Pastes of starch phosphate monoesters are compatible with gelatin, vegetable gums, and similar colloids, producing clear, flexible films. Pastes can be prepared which have excellent freeze-thaw stability and do not exhibit syneresis on long storage. However, these pastes may be thinned with salts of the alkali metals, and like most ionic materials, may be insolubilized with soluble salts of polyvalent metals, such as aluminum, zirconium, and titanium. Because of their polar characteristics, the starch phosphates are valuable in the formulation of emulsifying agents.

3. Uses

a. *Food Applications*

Although cooked starches represent an excellent source of dietary carbohydrate, most food processors consider that the main purpose of starch is aesthetic, to increase the eye appeal of the product, to prevent separation of ingredients, to impart better texture, and to provide a carrier for flavor.

Starch is used as a thickening agent in a wide variety of food products, such as gravies, cream soups, sauces, oriental foods, Harvard beets, salad dressings, prepared mustard, cream pie fillings, fruit pie fillings, cream-style corn, and baby foods. Gel formation in these foods is usually undesirable. Because the starch phosphates thicken without gelling, they are excellent for use in these products. Foods thickened with untreated starches, and subsequently frozen, exhibit considerable syneresis on thawing. This separation of water also occurs during low temperature storage above freezing temperatures. Phosphation of the starch to a very low degree of substitution greatly improves freeze-thaw stability and makes starch phosphate especially valuable as a thickener in gravies and white sauces for frozen foods, and in fillings for frozen pies.

Albrecht and co-workers (*30, 31*) studied the properties of several types of starch for use in precooked frozen foods such as meat pies, tray dinners, stews, and other foods containing gravies. They rate the thickening agents in decreasing order of freeze-thaw stability as follows: (*a*) starch phosphate, (*b*) ungelatinized regular corn starch, (*c*) pregelatinized, cross-bonded waxy maize starch, (*d*) all-purpose flour, and (*e*) regular corn starch (which is gelatinized prior to freezing as part of the cooking process).

Mixtures of starch phosphate, guar gum, and propylene glycol have been used (*32*) to emulsify and stabilize oil and vinegar-type salad dressings. A freeze-thaw resistant salad dressing with a mayonnaise base has been developed (*33*) using a waxy starch treated with a phosphate to form a starch phosphate monoester. In the manufacture of the emulsified salad dressing, the starch is cooked with water and mixed with a previously prepared mayonnaise emulsion.

Evans (*34*) made a pudding starch by partially cooking starch phosphate monoester in water and drying the slurry on heated rolls to a moisture content of approximately 4%. A pudding mix is made by pulverizing the starch and packaging it with sugar, salt, and flavoring.

While he did not claim ester formation, Korth (*35*) developed a bland starch suitable for the preparation of instant dessert powders and icings by pregelatinizing starch in the presence of 0.005% to 5.0% tetrasodium pyrophosphate, disodium pyrophosphate or mixtures thereof. Kerr and Cleveland (*36*) used starch phosphate in instant pudding, dessert and pie filling mixes, as well as in salad dressings and cream-style corn. The starch phosphate improved the flavors of these products without imparting the taste characteristic of cereal starches. Neukom (*13*) developed an instant pudding mix using starch phosphates containing 1–5% bound phosphorus. Ferrara (*37*) has developed a dry gravy base containing starch phosphate monoester, meat extract, and monosodium glutamate.

b. *Foundry*

Foundries use large quantities of starches as core binders in forming sand molds in which iron, steel, brass, aluminum, and other metals are cast. Molds, often in precise and intricate shapes, are filled with sand containing starch, oil, clay, and other ingredients. After compression in the mold, the wet core is removed and given a baking treatment. A suitable binding agent should disperse or rehydrate in cold water, blend well with the sand, and have high water absorption so that the wet sand will set into shape quickly. At this point, the starch should have developed sufficient "green bond strength" so that the sand core can be removed intact from the mold and handled without breaking. Sufficient strength should develop on baking so that the core can be transferred to racks or casting units and retain its strength during pouring of the metal. Thereafter, the binder should burn out evenly without producing excessive gases and permit the sand to be poured from the cast after the metal has solidified. Neukom (*38*) produced a core binding material by impregnating starch with a solution of monosodium orthophosphate and disodium orthophosphate in such proportions as to provide a pH between 6 and 7. The salt-treated starch was dried and then heated to a temperature between 120° and 175° to effect esterification. The product had greatly improved properties in comparison with untreated starch; for example, green strength could be markedly improved by adding small amounts of fine sand, silica flour, and the like, and both green and baked strengths were improved by addition of certain carbonaceous materials. The starch phosphate binder was much more versatile than untreated starch, performed equally well with various types of sands, and baked equally fast with either high or low proportions of binders.

Frieders (39) used Neukom's technique to prepare amylose phosphate, which, unlike amylose, gave superior results as a foundry core binder. It provided acceptable green strength, good baked strength, and superior hot properties. When the phosphate-modified amylose was used in combination with gelatinized amylopectin, it was found that the amylopectin contributed to the baked strength, while the amylose contributed to the hot strength. The core binder could, therefore, be tailored to produce desired properties.

Hogan and Sietsema (40) used starch phosphates in combination with glutamic acid end liquor and obtained superior core binding properties, especially from the standpoint of rendering the core baking time requirements less critical.

c. *Paper*

A special type of corn starch phosphate has been developed (41) for use as a wet-end paper additive. The product may be used on a wide range of paper furnishes to improve Mullen strength, wax pick, and filler retention. Best results were obtained when the starch phosphate was added to the fan pump or headbox. A minimum of 1% alum (dry fiber basis) must be present in the furnish, and the pH should be between 4.3 and 6.0. These conditions provide for maximum starch and pigment retention. It is reported that the use of starch phosphate as a wet-end additive results in savings in the following ways without loss of quality: by decreased use of starch at the size press, by increasing filler content, and by more efficient use of costly pigments such as titanium dioxide.

Yarber (42) prepared a cold-water-swelling starch product by mixing starch with a small amount of water containing monosodium phosphate, then using drying heat and pressure to produce a starch phosphate. The product is employed as a beater size to produce papers with low ink penetration, smooth surface, excellent fold strength, and improved Mullen strength.

Moes and Zijderveld (43) produced water-insoluble paper coatings by the use of starch phosphates with a D.S. of about 0.02. Paper is surface coated with a mixture of the starch phosphate and clay first, then treated with aluminum sulfate to give an excellent water-resistant print paper. For example, 100 parts of potato starch heated for 1 hour at 125° with 6% of phosphoric acid and 15% of urea is dispersed in 400 parts of water and added to a suspension of 500 parts of china clay, 1.5 parts of $(NaPO_3)_6$ and 500 parts of water to form a paste containing 40% dry material. It is applied on wood-free, off-set paper and treated with 5% aluminum sulfate to give a water-resistant print paper.

"Starch phosphates" prepared by hydrolyzing starch with phosphoric acid in the presence of urea were rendered essentially water-insoluble by treating with aldehydes such as formaldehyde, glyoxal or similar compounds (44, 45). Paper coatings prepared from this adhesive had excellent binding power for clay pigments, good plasticity, and excellent water resistance.

d. Textiles

A process has been reported (46) for preparing a sizing material for fibers which involves agitation of 1.0–2.0% of polymerized phosphate and wheat flour together with water, and heating the mixture to gelatinize the starch. A textile printing paste employing an alkali metal phosphate has been developed (47).

Bode (48) describes a process for warp sizing of textiles with starch phosphate monoester and reports that less sizing is required than when other starches are used to obtain equivalent weaving efficiencies. The warp is readily desized and the starch may be precipitated from the waste water with divalent cations. This should be of benefit in reducing stream pollution.

e. Ore Refining

An important use for starch in the field of mining and metallurgy is that of improving the recovery of aluminum from bauxite ores. The advantage of starch lies in its ability to coagulate and depress iron oxides and other impurities in alkaline digests of the ore. In the treatment of bauxite for aluminum extraction by the Bayer process, a red mud is sedimentated from the aluminate formed in solution. The efficacy of various starch-containing materials in accelerating the sedimentation process was investigated by Holló and co-workers (49). Starch phosphates were found more effective than natural starch, native amylose more effective than native amylopectin or natural starch, and rye starch more effective than rye protein.

Starch has long been used as a depressant for certain constituents of various finely divided ores in flotation processes. The concentration of iron oxides from a low-grade ore such as hematite has been extensively examined. The process consists essentially of fine grinding the ore, the addition of water to form a slurry, the incorporation of frothing agents and conditioners, and the addition of depressants followed by separation of the ore constituents in suitable flotation equipment. When the gangue consists principally of silica, and one desires to float the gangue and collect the iron oxide by settling, aliphatic amines, higher fatty acids, soaps, resin acids and the like are effective. Chang (50) studied the use of various starches and their derivatives as iron oxide depressants in amine flotation of iron ore. Corn starches in order of decreasing ability as depressants were: aminoethylstarch > starch phosphate > unmodified starch > starch sulfonate > starch xanthate > oxidized starch.

f. *Detergents*

Work (*51*) has been reported on the use of starch phosphate containing 6–12% of molecularly bound phosphorus as soil-redisposition inhibitors, detergent builders, and protective colloids for incorporation in detergent compositions. Starch is soaked in high concentrations of sodium orthophosphates, dried, and heated at 120°–170° for at least 2 hours. Cold-water-soluble, low-viscosity starch phosphates are produced. These products are claimed to be at least equivalent to sodium carboxymethylcellulose for these detergent applications.

IV. STARCH PHOSPHATE DIESTERS

Starch phosphate diesters [distarch monohydrogen (or monosodium, etc.) phosphate] contain an ester bridge or bridges connecting adjacent starch molecules. Commercially they represent a class of starch derivatives wherein the starch granule is inhibited from swelling and rupture. Such cross-bonded starches have greatly enhanced stability to heat, to agitation, and to acidity.

1. Preparation

A wide variety of polyfunctional chemicals are effective cross-bonding agents for starch. A general review of cross-bonded starches is given in Chapter XIX. The following discussion concerns only the use of various derivatives of phosphoric acid for preparing cross-bonded starches. The current commercial processes for the manufacture of cross-bonded starches have not been disclosed, but reviewing the most important patents in this field provides much valuable information.

Felton and Schopmeyer (*52*) used phosphorus oxychloride, phosphorus pentachloride, and thiophosphoryl chloride to cross-link starches in an aqueous medium. By careful control of reaction conditions, these workers obtained granular derivatives which formed thick-bodied pastes having stable viscosities during extended cooking periods. The granular structures of these starches were remarkably resistant to disintegration in water. These properties were obtained by using 0.15 to 0.25% of phosphorus oxychloride, based on the starch.

Better control of the cross-bonding reaction was achieved later by the addition of water-soluble alkali or alkaline metal salts, such as sodium chloride, to the reaction slurry (*53*). The function of the salts may be to retard the hydrolysis of the highly reactive phosphorus oxychloride, thus permitting greater penetration of the reagent into the granule and more uniform phosphation.

Kerr and Cleveland (54–56) used water-soluble trimetaphosphate salts to prepare cross-bonded starches. The reaction is believed to occur

$$
2\ \text{Starch-OH} + \underset{\substack{| \\ \text{ONa}}}{\underset{O=P}{}}\!\!-\!\!O\!\!-\!\!\underset{\substack{| \\ \text{ONa}}}{\underset{P=O}{}} \longrightarrow \underset{\text{Starch-O}}{\overset{\text{NaO}}{}}\!\!P\!\!\overset{O}{}\!\!\text{O-Starch} + \text{Na}_2\text{H}_2\text{P}_2\text{O}_7 \quad (3)
$$

in the manner shown in equation 3. Although the product is referred to as a distarch phosphate ester, it is probable that small amounts of the mono- and trisubstituted esters occur. Phosphorus oxychloride may also give mono-, di-, and triesters.

Esterification of starch with trimetaphosphate salts in aqueous medium requires more rigorous conditions than does esterification with phosphorus oxychloride. Alkaline materials, such as sodium hydroxide, calcium hydroxide, and sodium carbonate, catalyze the esterification. A starch phosphate with a maximum hot-paste viscosity in normal cooking, that is, 15 minutes at 95°–100°, may be prepared by heating a starch slurry at 50° with 2% sodium trimetaphosphate, based on starch, for 1 hour at pH 10–11.

A variety of chemically modified starches have been cross-bonded to obtain improved paste properties. For example, Kerr and Cleveland (54) used trimetaphosphates to cross-bond starch phosphate monoesters, hydroxyethylstarch, and oxidized starch. The cross-bonded waxy sorghum starch phosphate was an excellent starch for use in fruit pie fillings. It produced an exceptionally clear filling, which had good gloss and brilliance. These fillings had superior freeze-thaw resistance, stability, and freedom from syneresis. This type of starch maintains its viscosity even during long cooking periods at high temperatures and low pH.

Gramera and co-workers (57) studied the distribution and structural form of phosphate ester groups in sodium trimetaphosphate cross-bonded waxy sorghum starch phosphate monoester. Starch phosphate containing 0.016 phosphate ester groups per D-glucose unit was oxidized with periodate to the dialdehyde derivative, which was subsequently hydrogenated with sodium borohydride and hydrolyzed. Two phosphorylated components isolated from the hydrolyzate were identified as D-erythritol 4-phosphate and 2-O-(α-D-glucopyranosyl 2-phosphate)-D-erythritol. Another component, isolated in trace amount, was suggested to be

D-glucose 3-phosphate. From the total amount of phosphorylated compounds isolated, the percentage distribution of phosphate groups esterified in the C-2, C-3, and C-6 positions of the starch phosphate molecule was calculated to be 28%, 9%, and 63%, respectively. Phosphate ester groups chemically bound to the starch molecule exist in a dibasic structural form.

Wurzburg (58) used phosphorus oxychloride to cross-bond starch acetate and propionates. Other workers used phosphorus oxychloride to cross-bond starch acylates by using vinyl esters or anhydrides of aliphatic monocarboxylic acids (59). Phosphorus oxychloride has been used to esterify synthetic polysaccharides such as dextran (60–62).

2. Properties

In the early stages of the cross-bonding reaction, the paste viscosity of the starch increases significantly. However, in contrast to simple esterification, which also may produce increased paste viscosity, the clarity of the starch phosphate diester paste does not increase. Unlike the starch phosphate monoester pastes, starch phosphate diester pastes are short-bodied and less cohesive.

As the cross-bonding reaction progresses, the viscosity reaches a peak and then declines to very low values as the swelling of the starch granules becomes progressively more inhibited; at the same time, shortness and opacity of the paste both increase.

Rate and extent of starch gelatinization are a function of pH, concentration of sugar and other materials present in the paste, ratio of water to starch, and the total environment involved in the use for which the starch is intended. The optimum degree of cross-bonding must, therefore, be considered in terms of the conditions under which the particular starch is to be used.

Properly cross-bonded starches have remarkable stabilities to long cooking under conditions of high temperature, low pH, and the disruptive forces of mechanical agitation and shear. Starches can be custom-made to give maximum viscosities and stabilities for these conditions. However, if such products are pasted at neutral pH, the granules do not swell sufficiently to produce their maximum thickening powers.

As the degree of cross-bonding increases, the gelatinization of the starch granule becomes progressively more difficult and may be carried to the stage at which the granules are insensitive to boiling water. Both sodium trimetaphosphate (55) and phosphorus oxychloride (63) have been used to prepare starches that are useful as surgical dusting powders which resist significant swelling during steam sterilization.

3. Uses

a. Food

A disadvantage of starches in general, and waxy starches in particular, is their tendency to break down when subjected to severe processing conditions such as high temperatures or high speed agitation. This effect is accentuated in the presence of the acids usually found in food products. Starches treated with cross-bonding agents show greatly improved stability to heat, agitation, and acidity. These starches are now widely used in baby foods, fruit pie fillings, salad dressings, frozen dinners, cream-style corn, Harvard beets, processed canned foods, frozen oriental foods, and an extensive variety of foods requiring thickeners and stabilizers.

The Food Additives Regulations (64) were amended in 1964 to provide for the safe use of a food starch modified by treatment with not more than 0.1% of phosphorus oxychloride and not more than 10% of propylene oxide.

Sodium tripolyphosphate and sodium trimetaphosphate (65) have also been approved for use in food starches. The residual phosphate in the starch is not to exceed 0.4% calculated as phosphorus. Starch phosphate is included among the starches being recommended for food purposes in Germany (66).

The specific requirements for starch to be used as a thickener in fruit pie fillings are typical of the exacting demands made by the food uses mentioned above. The starch used in fruit pie fillings must have the following properties:

(a) It must have sufficient consistency to keep the fruit in suspension during cooling and after the filling is placed in the pie shell. The starch must not break down under acidic conditions, high temperature, and shear.

(b) The cooked filling must not set to a gel on standing at room temperature, but it also must not be so thin as to flow when the pie is cut.

(c) The liquid portion of the filling must be clear, brilliant, glossy, and of acceptable flavor.

(d) The filling must be freeze-thaw resistant and stable to storage at temperatures slightly above 0°.

(e) The filling must not exhibit syneresis on standing.

Unmodified starches do not meet these requirements. They are all broken down by high temperature cooking at fruit pie pH (3.2–3.6), by high rates of shear, and by subjecting them to freeze-thaw conditions. Regular starches and their derivatives produce pastes too opaque for widespread acceptance as fruit pie thickeners. The waxy starches produce clear pastes, but are especially subject to breakdown. Pastes of waxy starch phosphate monoesters are clear and have excellent flavor, gloss, and freeze-thaw stability, but poor viscosity stability when cooked under acid conditions. Cross-bonding these starch phosphates with trimetaphosphate salts confers excellent stability to the paste under conditions of high temperature, low pH, and high rates of shear. These cross-bonded products are also excellent thickeners for the other food products previously mentioned.

Wurzburg (58) suggests the use of phosphorus oxychloride cross-bonded starch acetates and propionates as thickeners in frozen soups, pie fillings and the like.

Minkema (67) describes a pie filling starch made by cross-bonding waxy sorghum starch with sodium trimetaphosphate then pregelatinizing and roll-drying. The product is a readily dispersible fine flake. Because it is pregelatinized, the time for preparing the pie filling is greatly reduced. It produces fruit pie fillings of good clarity, taste, and freeze-thaw stability.

Ducharme and co-workers (68) have developed a batter mix for deep-fried foods containing cross-bonded starch phosphates made with phosphorus oxychloride, metaphosphates, and polymetaphosphates.

b. *Non-food*

Highly cross-bonded starch phosphate diesters have been suggested for use as battery starches (69). Kerr and Cleveland (70) have described a process for adding mono- or distarch phosphates to paper pulp to improve the retention of titanium dioxide.

Hullinger and Carrasco (71) discovered that, when unsized paper having very little wet strength is treated with starch and an alkali metal salt of trimetaphosphoric acid and these two reagents are caused to react within the interstices of the paper, the resulting product has exceptionally high wet strength. It is hypothesized that phosphate cross-bonds the starch and the cellulose.

Wettstein and co-workers (72) have studied cation-exchange on cross-bonded starch phosphate prepared with phosphorus oxychloride in pyridine. The exchange capacity of this bifunctional exchanger, with 62% strong and 38% weak acid groups, was 5.5 meq./gram. By titration of the starch phosphate with alkali in the presence of small amounts of perchlorates of divalent cations, the following selectivity series was obtained: $Ca^{++} < Ni^{++} < Zn^{++} < Cu^{++}$. Cationic-exchange equilibria were studied by a batch method. The selectivity is $Na^+ < K^+$ for strong groups and $K^+ < Na^+$ for weak ones; an S-shaped equilibrium curve was obtained with divalent metal cations with H^+ as reference. The strong acid groups are more selective for the divalent cations, the weak ones for H^+. Calculations showed a much higher selectivity coefficient for dihydrogen phosphate groups than for monohydrogen phosphate groups.

Cowan and Evans (73) used cross-bonded starch phosphate, prepared by reacting starch with phosphorus oxychloride in dry pyridine at 40° to 115°, to stabilize cottonseed and soybean oils. This starch phosphate contained at least 2% phosphorus. The starch phosphate complexes with metals, such as iron, copper, nickel, cobalt and the like, which are frequently present in oils and tends to prevent the metal from catalyzing oxidative rancidity of the oil. The versatility of starch diesters is illustrated by their suggested use as pill binders for pharmaceutical products (74).

V. Conclusions

Starch phosphates are unique in their dual role of structural function and nutrition in foods, and in the physical and chemical effects they contribute to non-food products and processes. The current philosophies on the use of food ingredients make it imperative that the full potential values be developed in natural materials, such as starch. In non-food applications, starch phosphate esters can frequently replace more expensive synthetically derived chemical products. As yet, however, the production of specifically useful starch derivatives has not reached its zenith; this is especially true of the family of starch phosphate esters.

VI. References

(1) J. Kerb, *Biochem. Z.*, **100**, 3 (1919); *Chem. Abstr.*, **14**, 2341 (1920).
(2) M. Samec and A. Mayer, *Koll. Chim. Beihefte*, **16**, 89 (1922); *Chem. Abstr.*, **17**, 270 (1923).
(3) H. Pringsheim and K. Goldstein, *Ber.*, **56**, 1520 (1923); *Chem. Abstr.*, **18**, 80 (1924).
(4) H. Vogel, *Ber.*, **725**, 2052 (1938); *Chem. Abstr.*, **34**, 3242 (1940).
(5) P. Karrer, H. Koenig, and E. Usteri, *Helv. Chim. Acta*, **26**, 1296 (1943); *Chem. Abstr.*, **38**, 2933 (1944).
(6) H. N. Barham, E. S. Strickley, and M. J. Caldwell, *J. Am. Chem. Soc.*, **68**, 1018 (1946).
(7) R. Lohmar, J. W. Sloan, and C. E. Rist, *J. Am. Chem. Soc.*, **72**, 5717 (1950).
(8) R. L. Lohmar, U.S. Patent 2,575,352 (1951); *Chem. Abstr.*, **46**, 2324 (1952).
(9) R. L. Whistler and W. W. Spencer, *Arch. Biochem. Biophys.*, **87**, 137 (1960).
(10) J. L. Sannella, *Dissertation Abstr.*, **24**, 1403 (1963).
(11) J. L. Sannella and R. L. Whistler, *Arch. Biochem. Biophys.*, **102**, 226 (1963).
(12) A. Beyer, U.S. Patent 2,225,479 (1941); *Chem. Abstr.*, **35**, 7585 (1941).
(13) H. Neukom, U.S. Patent 2,865,762 (1958); *Chem. Abstr.*, **53**, 5538 (1959).
(14) H. Neukom, U.S. Patent 2,884,412 (1958); *Chem. Abstr.*, **53**, 15612 (1959).
(15) R. W. Kerr and F. C. Cleveland, Jr., U.S. Patent 2,961,440 (1960); *Chem. Abstr.*, **57**, 1138 (1962).
(16) F. Schierbaum and O. Börner, E. German Patent 36,806 (1965); *Chem. Abstr.*, **63**, 3150 (1965).

(17) R. Kodras, U.S. Patent 2,971,954 (1961); *Chem. Abstr.*, **56**, 6227 (1962).
(18) J. W. Sietsema and W. C. Trotter, U.S. Patent 2,993,041 (1961); International Minerals and Chemical Corp., British Patent 857,868; *Chem. Abstr.*, **55**, 13887 (1961).
(19) J. W. Sietsema, U.S. Patent 3,060,171 (1962); *Chem. Abstr.*, **58**, 651 (1963).
(20) R. Kodras, Can. Patent 660,962 (1963).
(21) International Minerals and Chemical Corp., French Patent 1,338,959 (1963).
(22) J. W. Sietsema, U.S. Patent 3,060,170 (1962); *Chem. Abstr.*, **58**, 651 (1963).
(23) R. W. Kerr and F. C. Cleveland, Jr., U.S. Patent 2,884, 413 (1959); *Chem. Abstr.*, **53**, 16569 (1959).
(24) E. F. Paschall, in "Methods in Carbohydrate Chemistry," R. L. Whistler, ed., Academic Press Inc., New York, N. Y., Vol. 4, 1964, p. 294.
(25) D. S. Gredinger and B. M. Cohen, French Patent 1,342,792 (1963).
(26) H. Neukom, U.S. Patent 2,824,870 (1958); *Chem. Abstr.*, **52**, 8601 (1958).
(27) E. T. Hjermstad, U.S. Patent 3,069,411 (1962); *Chem. Abstr.*, **58**, 5874 (1963).
(28) J. Voorhees, *Food Process.*, **21**, No. 8, 43 (1960).
(29) J. Voorhees, *Chemurgic Dig.*, **19**, No. 7, 3 (1960).
(30) J. J. Albrecht, *Dissertation Abstr.*, **19**, 1049 (1958); *Chem. Abstr.*, **53**, 5715 (1959).
(31) J. J. Albrecht, A. J. Nelson, and M. P. Steinberg, *Food Technol.*, **14**, 57, 64 (1960).
(32) R. H. Klostermann, U.S. Patent 3,108,004 (1963); *Chem. Abstr.*, **60**, 1041 (1964).
(33) National Dairy Products Corporation, British Patent 938,717 (1963).
(34) J. W. Evans, U.S. Patent 2,806,026 (1957); *Chem. Abstr.*, **52**, 612 (1958).
(35) J. A. Korth, U.S. Patent 2,884,346 (1959); *Chem. Abstr.*, **53**, 12719 (1959).
(36) R. W. Kerr and F. C. Cleveland, Jr., U.S. Patent 3,021,222 (1962); *Chem. Abstr.*, **56**, 10653 (1962).
(37) L. W. Ferrara, U.S. Patent 2,865,763 (1958); *Chem. Abstr.*, **53**, 5540 (1959).
(38) H. Neukom, U.S. Patent 2,977,236 (1961); *Chem. Abstr.*, **55**, 16377 (1961).
(39) J. W. Frieders, U.S. Patent 2,974,049 (1961); *Chem. Abstr.*, **55**, 14267 (1961).
(40) F. A. Hogan and J. W. Sietsema, U.S. Patent 2,988,453 (1961); *Chem. Abstr.*, **55**, 19726 (1961).
(41) Anon., *Paper Trade J.*, **145**, No. 28, 48, 51 (1961).
(42) C. J. Yarber, U.S. Patent 2,590,912 (1952); *Chem. Abstr.*, **46**, 5873 (1952).
(43) G. Moes and A. H. Zijderveld, Belgian Patent 618,620 (1962); *Chem. Abstr.*, **58**, 8139 (1963).
(44) Scholten's Chemische Fabrieken, The Netherlands, French Patent 1,332,677 (1963).
(45) Scholten's Chemische Fabrieken, The Netherlands, British Patent 977,682 (1964).
(46) A. Tanenaka and T. Fukumura, Japan. Patent Pub. No. 18,592 (1963).
(47) J. Tsujimura et al., Japan. Patent Pub. No. 25,783 (1963).
(48) H. E. Bode, U.S. Patent 3,093,504 (1963); *Chem. Abstr.*, **59**, 8931 (1963).
(49) J. Holló, J. Szejtli, E. László, G. S. Gantner, Z. Toth, J. Huszar, and A. Lux, *Staerke*, **16**, 118 (1964).
(50) C. S. Chang, *Mining Eng.*, **6**, 922 (1954).
(51) Chemicals and Phosphates, Ltd., British Patent 971,659 (1964).
(52) G. F. Felton and H. H. Schopmeyer, U.S. Patent 2,328,537 (1943); *Chem. Abstr.*, **38**, 889 (1944).
(53) H. L. Wetzstein and P. Lyon, U.S. Patent 2,754,232 (1956); *Chem. Abstr.*, **50**, 13490 (1956).
(54) R. W. Kerr and F. C. Cleveland, Jr., U.S. Patent 2,801,242 (1957); *Chem. Abstr.*, **51**, 18666 (1957).

(55) R. W. Kerr and F. C. Cleveland, Jr., U.S. Patent 2,938,901 (1960); *Chem. Abstr.*, **54,** 16886 (1960).

(56) R. W. Kerr and F. C. Cleveland, Jr., U.S. Patent 2,852,393 (1958); *Chem. Abstr.*, **53,** 1797 (1959).

(57) R. E. Gramera, J. Heerema, and F. W. Parrish, *Cereal Chem.*, **43,** 104 (1966).

(58) O. B. Wurzburg, U.S. Patent 2,935,510 (1960); *Chem. Abstr.*, **54,** 16886 (1960).

(59) A. E. Staley Manufacturing Company, British Patent 980,390 (1965).

(60) W. Dedek, E. German Patent 28,841 (1964).

(61) U. Behrens, M. Ringpfeil, and A. Gabert, German Patent 1,149,702 (1963); *Chem. Abstr.*, **60,** 650 (1964).

(62) A. E. Bishop and L. J. Novak, U.S. Patent 2,970,141 (1961); *Chem. Abstr.*, **57,** 9941 (1962).

(63) D. F. Smith, U.S. Patent 3,122,482 (1964); *Chem. Abstr.*, **60,** 10484 (1964).

(64) Anon., *Federal Register*, **29,** 15256 (Nov. 13, 1964).

(65) Anon., *Federal Register*, **29,** 14403 (Oct. 20, 1964).

(66) G. Graefe, *Staerke*, **16,** 158 (1964).

(67) W. H. Minkema, *Food Eng.*, **36,** No. 4, 94 (1964).

(68) J. F. Ducharme, H. S. Black, and S. J. Leith, U.S. Patent 3,052,545 (1962).

(69) J. W. Evans, *Cereal Sci. Today*, **7,** 132 (1962).

(70) R. W. Kerr and F. C. Cleveland, Jr., U.S. Patent 3,132,066 (1964); *Chem. Abstr.*, **61,** 2055 (1964).

(71) C. H. Hullinger and R. R. Carrasco, U.S. Patent 3,144,298 (1964); *Chem. Abstr.*, **61,** 9674 (1964).

(72) F. Wettstein, H. Neukom, and H. Deuel, *Helv. Chim. Acta*, **44,** 1949 (1961).

(73) J. C. Cowan and C. D. Evans, U.S. Patent 2,626,951 (1953); *Chem. Abstr.*, **47,** 4635 (1953).

(74) K. K. Sankyo, Japan. Patent Pub. No. 18,835 (1964).

CHAPTER XV

PRODUCTION AND USES OF
STARCH ACETATES

By L. H. Kruger and M. W. Rutenberg
Research Department, National Starch and Chemical Corporation, Plainfield, New Jersey

I. Introduction

Considerable information has accumulated on starch esters, particularly starch acetates, covering preparation, properties, and possible uses (1–5). A selection from this literature is reviewed in this chapter and discussed from a commercial viewpoint. Reference should be made to the cited literature for a more complete review and comprehensive bibliography.

Since starch is a natural polymeric material, an acetylated starch can be defined completely only if the type of starch used and the treatment it has received are described. Thus, a full description of a starch acetate will include: plant source; physical form of the starch; type of starch or starch fraction; degree of substitution (D.S.); degree of polymerization (D.P.) and molecular weight distribution; presence of admixed or associated materials such as protein, fatty acids, and phosphorus; and treatments other than acetylation such as oxidation or dextrinization. Unfortunately, complete data on a sample are not always available.

As indicated, acetylated starch is not a single, well-defined chemical entity, but a series of products with property variants. The degree of substitution (D.S.) can range up to a maximum of three moles of acetyl substituent per mole of D-glucopyranose unit (anhydroglucose, AGU), signifying that all three available hydroxyl groups on each unit are acetylated. Starch triacetate (D.S. 3), theoretically containing 44.8% of acetyl groups by weight on an anhydrous basis, comes close to being a well-defined chemical species. However, a triacetate can be made from whole starch or one of its fractions and may vary in other respects as mentioned above (5–8). Similar considerations hold for the monoacetate and the diacetate which contain 21.1% and 35.0% of acetyl groups, respectively.

The commercial importance of starch acetates rests mainly on the sol stability of their aqueous dispersions. Since the tendency of an aqueous starch dispersion to increase in viscosity on cooling and finally to gel is related to the association of amylose molecules, any treatment such as acetylation which retards or eliminates this crystallization or retrogradation phenomenon will effect stabilization of the starch sol (see Volume I, pp. 303 and 351). Acetylation will also prevent or minimize association of amylopectin outer branches. This is of practical value in many industrial and food applications because association can cause cloudiness and syneresis in aqueous dispersions of waxy starches. Since a relatively small proportion of acetyl groups by weight of the starch is adequate to achieve this sol-stabilization effect, commercially manufactured starch acetates are generally granular and less than 0.2 D.S. (5% acetyl). These low D.S. starch acetates sell at prices commensurate with their useful properties in competition with other materials with related properties such as other starch derivatives and gums.

Considerable interest has focused on the D.S. 2–3 starch acetates, particularly amylose acetate, because of their organic solvent solubility, thermoplasticity, and film properties. In contrast to the large volume production of cellulose acetates, high D.S. starch acetates have not been developed commercially. Despite their similarity in properties, there are no known advantages that would permit high D.S. amylose acetate to compete economically with cellulose acetate. If the edibility and digestibility of amylose and low D.S. amylose acetates were also properties of high D.S. amylose acetates, they would have a distinct advantage in terms of special packaging and coating applications in foods, cosmetics, and pharmaceuticals. These application areas have not been fully explored and may be a major area of development for starch acetates. Any drastic changes in the supply of cellulose pulp or in the demand for cellulose derivatives or discovery of new technology favoring this type of derivative could also stimulate commercial interest in high D.S. starch acetates.

II. PREPARATION

1. General Considerations

As in any process, the selection of a starch acetylation method for translation to a large scale manufacturing operation requires consideration of the physical and chemical properties of the raw materials, products, and by-products as well as the process technology and the economics of raw material supply, manufacture, and product marketing.

The type of starch to be acetylated is determined mainly by the properties desired in the product as well as by the cost of the starch, which reflects availability and ease of processing. Potato, tapioca, corn, or sorghum starches, the last two in regular or waxy varieties, are commonly used for commercial products. Some pretreatment of the native starch prior to acetylation might be desirable. For example, to obtain lower viscosity products, the raw material can be the oxidized or slightly hydrolyzed "thin-boiling" starches of commerce. Sometimes a cross-linked granular starch with slightly repressed or "inhibited" swelling properties is the best raw material for obtaining the desired final product characteristics. In other cases, an isolated starch fraction, amylose or amylopectin, may be required to provide an acetate with specific properties.

At present, in the United States, commercially produced low D.S. starch acetates are generally manufactured from regular or waxy corn starches. These starches can be acetylated "on stream" in the aqueous suspension or "starch milk" obtained in the corn wet-milling process. If desired, a dry starch such as imported tapioca or potato may be slurried in water and acetylated. The granular form of starch is the preferred raw material since it is insoluble in water at the normal temperatures ($<50°$) used and can be acetylated in water suspension at high solids contents (up to about 44%), washed free of salts, and recovered easily by filtration and drying. When a pregelatinized cold-water-swelling starch is desired, the washed starch acetate may be gelatinized and dried on heated drums or gelatinized in a continuous cooker and then spray-dried. If a precooked cold-water-swelling starch is used as a raw material, complications in processing are encountered because of the high viscosity of the aqueous solution, the difficulty in removing salts and by-products, and the relatively large amounts of water to be removed during the drying operation.

In choosing a reagent to be used in a commercial starch acetylation process, the reactivity of the reagent with starch and hence the reaction conditions required are of major importance. Closely involved with the reaction conditions are the catalysts and the reaction media required. A number of reagent–catalyst–solvent systems have been reported, mainly for laboratory preparation of D.S. 2–3 products. Reagents used include acetic acid (9, 10), acetic anhydride (5, 8, 11–14), vinyl acetate (15–17), and ketene (18–20). In many cases, the necessity for some type of "activation" treatment to improve the reactivity of the native starch is evident or included in the preparative procedure. All these treatments involve disruption of the starch granule from partial granular swelling to complete gelatinization (1–3, 5, 21). In the case of isolated amylose or amylopectin fractions, activation involves rupture of intermolecular hydrogen bonds. Reassociation of the disorganized molecular structure is prevented by insuring that drying does not take place from a hydrated state. Usually organic solvents such as acetic acid, alcohol, or pyridine are used to displace water by washing or by azeotropic distillation. This subject is discussed in Volume I on page 440. In all starch reactions, the effects of activation treatments, reaction conditions, reagents, and catalysts on the hydrolysis and degradation of the starch polymer must be considered. From the point of view of commercial applications, such depolymerization or modification might be desirable, acceptable, or intolerable depending upon the properties needed in the product.

Many factors are involved in selecting a reagent and preparative method for a large-scale industrial process. Mention should be made of some of these in connection with commercial acetylation of starch. When the starch acetates are intended for use in foods, the reagents and solvents used in the acetylation process must yield acceptable products. In the United States and in some European countries, approval by a governmental agency is required before a particular modified starch may be used. The United States Food and Drug Administration permits the use of acetic anhydride or vinyl acetate within specified limitations for the preparation of starch acetates used in foodstuffs (22). The use of different reagents, different reaction conditions, or higher levels of acetylation with approved reagents requires specific clearance by the Food and Drug Administration.

The problems of handling reagents and solvents are multiplied in large scale operations, and the properties of these materials are important factors in the choice of a process and in the design and operation of a plant. The volatility of the chemicals used must be considered in relation to the allowable concentrations in air in terms of toxicity, flammability, and explosibility. Coupled with this is the question of recovery or disposal of excess reagent, by-products, and solvents. If the acetylation medium is an organic solvent, its economic recovery and re-use is extremely important. When large amounts of by-products are produced, recovery is economically important as well as necessary to minimize pollution. For example, in the acetylation reaction, acetic anhydride yields roughly 60% of its weight as by-product acetic acid. In preparing a starch triacetate, the acetic anhydride required is at least twice the weight of the starch, which results in an amount of by-product acetic acid at least equivalent to the weight of the starch raw material.

2. Acetic Acid

Aqueous acetic acid has little effect on starch. Early workers (23) have shown that starch can be acetylated by heating with relatively small amounts of glacial acetic acid, the degree of acetylation increasing with reaction time and the weight ratio of acetic acid to starch (Table I).

Table I

Acetylation of Starch with Glacial Acetic Acid (23)

Acetic acid (g./100 g. starch)	Time[a] (hr.)	Acetyl content (%)
25	13	4.7
50	5	3.0
50	13	6.0
100	5	3.4

[a] At 100°.

These products are apparently granular and are therefore insoluble in cold water but dissolve upon heating to 95°–100°. Solutions yield transparent elastic films when dried on a glass plate.

When dry starch is heated in a large excess of glacial acetic acid, progressively larger amounts of acetyl groups are introduced with increasing reaction time; as shown in Figure 1, the rate of acetylation is greater at reflux temperature (118°) than at 90° (9, 10). In the reflux reaction, the starch dissolves in the reaction mixture after about 18 hr. Complete acetylation (44.8%) is not achieved by refluxing for 620 hr. Products obtained at 90° are all soluble in water and insoluble in alcohol at room temperature and are degraded (4, 9). Sodium acetate has a retarding effect (Fig. 1).

Early in this century, a series of products was manufactured and marketed in England under the trade name "Feculose" (9). These products, containing 0.7–2.9% of acetyl groups, were prepared by heating dry starch at 3–4% maximum moisture with glacial acetic acid, 10–100%

based on the starch, for a maximum of 8 hr. at 90° or 2–3 hr. at 120°. The reaction was controlled to yield a product insoluble in cold water so that excess acid could be washed out by decantation. When the granular starch acetate was dispersed by cooking in boiling water, clear stable sols were formed. Potato, tapioca, corn, rice, sago, and wheat starches were treated, varying time, temperature, and the amounts of mineral acids added to the glacial acetic acid to obtain a range of products differing in viscosity and film properties. The products were used as substi-

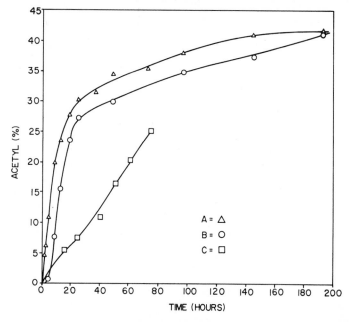

Fig. 1.—Effect of time and temperature on acetyl content in the acetylation of starch in glacial acetic acid (9, 10): A, Potato starch in 20 times its weight of glacial acetic acid. Water removed by distillation is replaced with equal volume of acetic acid. Reaction at reflux (118°). 44.0% Acetyl in 296 hr.; B, Same as A with 0.9% sodium acetate by weight based on starch. 43.3% Acetyl in 384 hr.; C, Dry starch in large excess of glacial acetic acid at 90°.

tutes for gelatin and polysaccharide gums in textile finishing, in paper sizing, and as a confectionery thickener.

Glacial acetic acid seems to be suitable for producing partially degraded low D.S. starch acetates but is not particularly efficient for the preparation of D.S. 2–3 acetates. The large scale preparation of products up to a D.S. of 1 (21% acetyl) is probably feasible since these may still be isolated by centrifugation (10). However, removal of the residual acetic acid could pose economic problems. The dry-heating procedure for "Feculose" probably could not compete today with other methods of preparing low D.S. acetates because drying is required before and after the acetylation reaction and control of degradation is difficult.

3. Acetic Anhydride

Acetic anhydride has generally been the reagent of choice in acetylating starch. It has been used alone or with catalysts (9, 24) as well as in conjunction with acetic acid (14, 19, 25, 26), pyridine (5, 8, 12, 13) and in aqueous alkaline solution (11, 12, 27).

a. Undiluted Acetic Anhydride

At room temperature, acetic anhydride does not acetylate native starch which has not undergone some type of activation treatment. At elevated temperatures, 90°–140°, acetylation accompanied by degradation takes place (4, 9). After 8 hr. at about 140°, only 1.8% acetyl content is obtained, rising to 8.7% in 15 hr. and 34% in 74 hr. In contrast, glacial acetic acid is a better acetylating agent when used alone on raw starch at reflux temperature (118°) (Fig. 1).

Acetic anhydride has been used with acid catalysts to acetylate starch (1, 4, 28). In most cases acetylation is accompanied by considerable degradation. Catalysts have included sulfuric acid and hydrogen halides. Differences in reactivity between activated and nonactivated starches were noted using acetic anhydride and 5% sulfuric acid catalyst (29). Potato starch, activated by gelatinization and alcohol precipitation, dissolves in the acetylation mixture in 1 day, yielding an alcohol-soluble product of 44.9% acetyl content. On the other hand, untreated potato starch is acetylated very slowly, approximately 80% being unchanged after 6 days. Rice, wheat, and corn starch behave similarly, except that the untreated starches dissolve in 3 days. Considerable degradation takes place in all cases. Sodium acetate has been used as a catalyst in refluxing acetic anhydride to acetylate corn starch yielding a product containing 43.5% acetyl after 4 days; fractionation revealed nonuniform acetylation and some degradation (30).

Acetic anhydride with sodium acetate and acetamide catalysts is claimed to yield acetates of D.S. 2.5–2.8 (31). At 10°–15°, starch is acetylated by acetic anhydride in liquid sulfur dioxide under pressure; this process is claimed to give more rapid, uniform esterification (32). Heating starch at 10–12% moisture in acetic anhydride alone or in an admixture with an inert organic solvent within a critical pH range of 2.5–5 is claimed to yield useful granular acetates of D.S. below 0.1 (24).

b. Acetic Anhydride and Acetic Acid

The acetic anhydride–acetic acid mixture has received considerable attention as a starch acetylation system, with at least one claim to a commercially feasible process (21).

At low temperatures without a catalyst, the reaction with corn starch is slow, reaching 4.1% acetyl in 6 hr. at 50° (Table II) (2, 19). However,

Table II
Acetylation: Effect of Acid Catalyst and Temperature (19)

Temperature (°C)		Acetyl values (%)[a]			
	Sulfuric acid (%):	0	1	5	10
0		2.1	6.4	7.2	11.9
10		3.1	6.2	8.5	13.3
20		3.5	9.0	12.0	17.0
30		3.8	16.2	22.0	25.6
40		4.0	19.4	—	37.5
50		4.1	40.9	—	—

[a] Corn starch (25 g.) was treated with 25 ml. of acetic anhydride for 30 min., then 100 ml. each of acetic anhydride and glacial acetic acid was added followed by the sulfuric acid diluted with 45 ml. of glacial acetic acid. Reaction time was 6 hr.

with 1% sulfuric acid the reaction is much more rapid, reaching 40.9% acetyl under the same conditions. The rate of acetylation increases with increasing temperature and acid catalyst concentration. Additional experimental work shows that, after a short induction period, the rate is relatively rapid up to an acetyl content of 35–40% is reached, after which it begins to decrease. Degradation of the starch polymer occurs and increases with acid concentration, temperature, and time. This is noticeable after a 24-hr. reaction at 20°–40° with 1% sulfuric acid as the product has an acetyl content greater than the theoretical triacetate value of 44.8% acetyl. This indicates the presence of oligosaccharides with a high proportion of end groups containing more than three hydroxyl sites for esterification.

In contrast to the results at low temperature without catalyst (Table II), starch is acetylated rapidly in acetic anhydride–acetic acid at reflux temperature without a catalyst (19). Thus, when dried corn starch in glacial acetic acid containing 3 molar equivalents of acetic anhydride, based on starch, is refluxed for periods ranging up to 40 hours, the acetylation rate is slow until an acetyl value of about 4% is reached (1.5–2 hr.); then very rapid acetylation occurs (34.5% acetyl in 4 hr.), with a subsequent slow, uniform rate. The acetyl content reaches 44.2%

in 40 hours. The viscous reaction solution becomes clear when the acetyl value reaches approximately 36%. Products are isolated by precipitation and leaching in water. A large excess of anhydride is unnecessary. Using this system, sulfuric acid, sodium acetate, zinc chloride, and p-toluenesulfonic acid were evaluated as catalysts. Sulfuric acid is the most effective, followed by p-toluenesulfonic acid. Considerable degradation takes place in both cases as shown by the very high acetyl values, 52.2% and 53.0%, respectively. The other two compounds give less degradation and show some catalytic effect.

Treadway (25) claimed almost complete acetylation of starch in about 9 hours at approximately 95° using an acetic anhydride–acetic acid mixture containing 0.2% perchloric acid and 0.6% sulfuric acid, based on starch. The preferred ratio of acetic anhydride to acetic acid (compensated for the acetic acid produced by reaction of the acetic anhydride with the starch moisture) is 1:1, but may range from 1:1.5 to 1.5:1. Corn, potato, tapioca, wheat, and rice starches have been esterified in this manner. Caesar (26) used four parts of 85% phosphoric acid to disperse corn starch prior to reaction with a 60:40 acetic anhydride–acetic acid mixture containing a trace of sulfuric acid catalyst at elevated temperature (105°). He obtained an acetyl content of 43.9% in 5 minutes reaction time.

Recently, investigations aimed at a commercially feasible process for preparation of amylose and amylopectin triacetates were reported; these were based on an acid-catalyzed treatment of the activated polysaccharides with acetic anhydride–acetic acid by methods similar to those used with cellulose (21). The activation step involves swelling the starch fraction in cold water and then dehydration by washing it several times with acetic acid. Aqueous acetic acid containing at least 40% water may also be used for activation. This would be advantageous since the precipitation liquor from recovery of the triacetate could be employed in the activation step. For minimum degradation, acetylation is done at 28°–32° for 4 to 6 hr. to yield the triacetates of amylose or amylopectin. If the acetylation is carried out above 32°, even for a short time, considerable degradation occurs.

For native starches in granular form, cold water activation fails because of insufficient granule swelling. However, when warm water at a temperature slightly below the pasting temperature is used with potato starch and the rest of the procedure is unchanged, the potato starch is acetylated easily to the triacetate at 30°. This result using sulfuric acid-catalyzed acetic anhydride–acetic acid reagent is comparable to the work reported in Table II (19). Here, corn starch, pretreated with acetic anhydride, yields 10–20% acetyl in 6 hr. at 20°–30°; but, when this procedure is applied to potato starch, no acetyl groups are introduced in 5 hr. This points out the efficacy of the water-activation treatment, even though the granule is not gelatinized (21).

Commercial preparation of high D.S. starch acetates with acetic anhydride–acetic acid appears preferable to the use of acetic anhydride–pyridine described in Section II,3,c. Acetic acid is a less expensive reagent and is also less unpleasant to handle than pyridine. Although the pyridine method is faster, the recovery and reuse of acetic acid is probably less expensive. Despite passage of eight years since publication of this method, no commercial production of starch acetate is accomplished in this way.

Panzer (14) used polystyrenesulfonic acid resin catalysts to esterify potato amylose with acetic anhydride–acetic acid. Acetylation to a D.S. of 2.8 was reported, with no extensive degradation as concluded from a comparison of viscosity data for this product and one made by the acetic anhydride–pyridine method. Potato amylose was activated by suspension in water for 16 hr. at room temperature followed by displacement of the water with glacial acetic acid as described above (21). The amylose was then suspended in acetic anhydride–acetic acid solution; about 30% of ion-exchange resin based on starch weight was added, and the reaction was allowed to continue for 1 week at room temperature or for 3–4 hr. at 60°–90°. The reaction mixture containing dissolved amylose acetate was poured into ice and water to precipitate the product. The resin can be used repeatedly without regeneration.

c. Acetic Anhydride–Pyridine

The most common system for laboratory acetylation of starch, an acetic anhydride–pyridine mixture (12), gives high degrees of substitution with minimum degradation (1). It has been reported (5) that untreated starch granules kept in contact with acetic anhydride in pyridine for 5 months at 20° showed no noticeable reaction. Generally, starch should be treated to disrupt its granule structure, or the associative bonds in the case of isolated amylose, to obtain a finely divided, porous material. Refluxing pyridine (115° for 1 hr.) activates starch without gelatinization of the granule (33). Another method (5) involves gelatinization of the starch by heating it in 60% aqueous pyridine, distilling the pyridine–water azeotrope (b.p. 93°) from the mixture, and replacing the distillate with 100% pyridine as the azeotrope is removed. Sufficient gelatinization is obtained as the temperature reaches 80°–90° with the last traces of the azeotrope being removed when the temperature reaches 115°. At this point, acetic anhydride is added and the reaction is 95% complete in about 5 min. at 115° as shown by the formation of a clear, transparent, light straw-colored gel. A total reaction time of 1 hr. is reported to be sufficient to acetylate starch fully. Triacetates of potato, tapioca, wheat, corn, and rice starches as well as of corn starch amylose have been prepared in this way. The ratio of starch to liquid in this procedure is determined by the mechanical characteristics of the reaction apparatus. A 10% starch concentration is the maximum manageable in a glass laboratory apparatus; with heavy duty dough-kneading equipment, a concentration as high as 50% starch might be handled (5).

Another activation method (8, 12, 34) involves disintegration of the starch granules by cooking them at 95°–100° in water, rupture by high shear agitation, and recovery by alcohol precipitation, washing, and drying under reduced pressure. Preparation by this method is reported (8) to give a more easily esterified starch using the acetic anhydride–pyridine reagent system than that obtained by the method of Mullen and Pacsu (5).

Acetylation of disorganized starch in acetic anhydride–pyridine proceeds rapidly at 100°, reaching 44.8% acetyl in 1.5–3 hours (1, 34). A moisture content of about 3% is also recommended to conserve acetic anhydride and minimize hydrolysis. The preferred ratio of acetic anhydride to pyridine to starch is apparently 3.2:3.7:1. In the acetylation of amylose, too large an excess of pyridine exerts a retarding effect (8).

A modification of the acetic anhydride–pyridine system, namely dispersing the starch in formamide at 65° for 1 hour followed by addition of pyridine and acetic anhydride, has been suggested (35). Treatment of potato starch in this way with reaction at 40° for 5 hr. yields an alcohol-precipitated product containing 41.9% of acetyl groups. Amylopectin and amylose fractions have been treated similarly after activation in water or alkali, respectively, and alcohol precipitation (36). Amylopectin so treated had an acetyl content of 40% and required a second acetic anhydride–pyridine treatment to obtain the triacetate. Amylose acetylation by a similar treatment (single) yielded a product containing 39% acetyl (37); it also required a double treatment to yield the triacetate (36). Using this formamide dispersion technique with acetic anhydride–pyridine, amylose has been acetylated at 60° for 12 hr. to yield the triacetate or an acetate of D.S. 2.5 when treated at −10° for 16 hr. (38). Molecular weight determinations show that degradation definitely occurs when acetylation is effected above 0° in this system and even on reacetylation at 0°. Some degradation may occur on acetylation below 0°. A variation omitting pyridine (39) in which corn starch is dispersed at 70°–80° for 1 hr. in formamide containing potassium acetate and then treated with acetic anhydride at 70° for 2–3 hr. yields the diacetate (33.7% acetyl).

A two-step process has also been proposed (*10*). It involves a 24-hr. reaction in refluxing glacial acetic acid followed by addition of pyridine and acetic anhydride to complete the acetylation to the triacetate.

The acetic anhydride–pyridine system can be used to prepare starch acetates with a wide range of substitution by control of reaction time, temperature, and acetic anhydride concentration. Its use in a commercial manufacturing process, however, would necessarily be limited to the higher degrees of substitution because of the high cost of pyridine and pyridine recovery. The efficiency of pyridine recovery is the crucial economic factor. Mullen and Pacsu (*5, 13*) have proposed starch acetate preparation and pyridine recovery processes. These are based on pyridine-azeotrope activation of starch, acetic anhydride–pyridine acetylation to a D.S. 3 product, isolation of the starch acetate by precipitation and washing in water, and recovery of the pyridine from the dilute aqueous pyridine obtained from the precipitation and washing steps. Pyridine recovery involves treatment with lime to convert pyridine acid salts to pyridine, followed by distillation of the pyridine-water azeotrope which can be broken by salting out, solvent extraction, or ternary distillation with benzene. This process has not been used commercially to date since the cost of manufacture is too high in relation to the useful properties of the product.

d. *Acetic Anhydride–Dimethylsulfoxide*

Amylose dispersed in dimethylsulfoxide has been acetylated with acetic anhydride using triethylamine as an acid acceptor yielding products with a D.S. up to 0.08 (*40*).

e. *Acetic Anhydride–Aqueous Alkali*

Preparation of starch acetates in granular form by reaction of starch in aqueous suspension with organic carboxylic acid anhydrides under alkaline conditions has been described (*11, 12*). Successful acetylation depends upon maintenance of conditions that favor acetylation (equation 1) over anhydride hydrolysis (equation 2) without appreciable hydrolysis of the starch acetate (equation 3).

$$\text{NaOH} + \text{Starch—OH} + (\text{CH}_3\text{CO})_2\text{O} \rightarrow \text{Starch—O}\overset{\overset{\text{O}}{\|}}{\text{C}}\text{CH}_3 + \text{CH}_3\overset{\overset{\text{O}}{\|}}{\text{C}}\text{ONa} + \text{H}_2\text{O} \quad (1)$$

$$(\text{CH}_3\text{CO})_2\text{O} + 2\,\text{NaOH} \rightarrow 2\,\text{CH}_3\overset{\overset{\text{O}}{\|}}{\text{C}}\text{ONa} + \text{H}_2\text{O} \quad (2)$$

$$\text{Starch–O}\overset{\overset{\text{O}}{\|}}{\text{C}}\text{CH}_3 + \text{NaOH} \rightarrow \text{Starch—OH} + \text{CH}_3\overset{\overset{\text{O}}{\|}}{\text{C}}\text{ONa} \quad (3)$$

The desired balance of conditions is attained by careful control of pH between 7 and 11. This pH control may be accomplished by alternate additions of successive portions of alkali and anhydride to the aqueous starch suspension which alternately raises the pH to 11 and drops it to 7 until the desired amount of anhydride has been added. Another method involves concurrent additions of anhydride and alkali, regulating the addition rates of each of these to maintain a pH between 7 and 9. Although sodium hydroxide is the preferred alkaline reagent, other alkali metal hydroxides, sodium carbonate, trisodium phosphate, and calcium hydroxide are claimed to be suitable. The reaction is preferably done at room temperature (25°–30°), but may be effected at 10° or at temperatures above 30°. At higher temperatures, the rate of hydrolysis of the anhydride and ester may be increased so that it overshadows the acetylation reaction. With acetic anhydride at room temperature, the optimum pH for acetylation in aqueous alkaline medium is 8–8.4 (12). The optimum acetylation pH is temperature dependent: at 38°, the optimum pH is about 7; at temperatures below 20°, the optimum pH may be above 8.4. The pH is maintained by addition of 3% sodium hydroxide solution. Addition of a higher concentration of sodium hydroxide solution could cause local gelatinization of the starch granule making recovery by filtration difficult. Reaction efficiencies of about 70% are expected.

Since granular starches are usually produced, the degree of substitution is limited to prevent gelatinization in the alkaline reaction. Although the maximum D.S. level attainable without gelatinization will vary with the particular starch, a level of 0.5 D.S. (approximately 13% acetyl) is a rough limit. These high levels are attained by repeated treatments since dilution of the reaction mixture with continued addition of reagent and 3% sodium hydroxide solution causes a decrease in reaction efficiency. Hence, the starch is filtered from the reaction mixture and resuspended in about 1.25–1.50 parts of water per part of starch, and the reaction is continued until filtration is again necessary. When higher D.S. products are required, acetylation of gelatinized starch is preferred (12).

A granular starch is apparently less readily acetylated than a gelatinized starch and this, in turn, is acetylated less readily than sucrose as determined by reaction efficiency at 5% acetic anhydride treatment (81% vs. 90% vs. 96%). The acetic anhydride should be added at a moderate rate. If the reaction time is of long duration, some hydrolysis of the starch acetate already formed will occur. Very rapid addition of acetic anhydride results in poor uniformity of acetylation. Furthermore, difficulty in maintaining pH control with rapid anhydride addition results in decreased reaction efficiency. It is of interest that acetylation of sugars and alcohols has also been done by this method (41–43).

The aqueous alkaline treatment of starch with acetic anhydride may be used in conjunction with linear mixed anhydrides to obtain cross-linked granular starch acetates (11), with cyclic dibasic acid anhydrides to obtain increased hydrophilicity or hydrophobicity (11, 44), or with anhydrides containing unsaturated groups to obtain insolubilization, a base for graft polymerization (45), or a base for addition of hydrophilic groups (46).

As mentioned previously, acetylation of granular starch by this method is directly applicable to commercial preparation of starch acetates of low D.S. and is so employed.

4. Ketene

Acetylation of starch by reaction with ketene in glacial acetic acid in the presence of catalytic amounts of sulfuric acid has been claimed (18). Ketene has also been reacted with starch suspended in acetone or ether using sulfuric acid as the catalyst (19). In ether suspension, reaction at 25° for 30–60 minutes gives white products containing 3.7–9.4% of acetyl groups; whereas, in acetone at 25° or 56° for 2 hr., products of 2.2–3.5% acetyl are obtained. No quantitative information concerning the relative amounts of ketene used was given. Reaction with gaseous ketene at 25° in a Pyrex tube 2.5 feet long by 14 mm. in diameter has also been reported. In 30 min., a white product containing 3.1% acetyl was obtained; in 1.5 hr. a tan product of 9.1% acetyl. Tan products were also obtained in 2 hr. reactions in the presence of chlorine or hydrogen chloride catalysts giving 8.1 and 7.4% acetyl, respectively.

A more definitive study of the acetylation of starch by ketene was reported by Talley and Smith (20) who discussed the necessity for an activation pretreatment of the starch to obtain more complete acetylation without extensive degradation. Acetic acid is used as both the pretreatment agent and reaction medium. Acid catalysts are required since basic catalysts catalyze ketene polymerization more than starch acetylation. Sodium acetate gives a highly colored product of low acetyl value. Anhydrous pyridine acts similarly but gives somewhat better results in the presence of some water. Zinc chloride produces little acetylation. Mineral acids are the most effective catalysts, sulfuric acid being preferred. Perchloric, phosphoric, and hydrochloric acids also have considerable catalytic effect, but the volatility of hydrochloric acid is a drawback. Next in efficiency to sulfuric acid is p-toluenesulfonic acid. A temperature of 90° is more satisfactory than 60°, the products obtained at 60° giving only moderately soluble products. Extension of reaction time at 60° to increase acetyl content results in discoloration. At 90°, the acetates produced are more homogeneous and only slightly discolored. In addition to acetic acid, acetone, chloroform, methyl ethyl ketone, and tetrachloroethane have been used as the reaction medium. Benzene and toluene are unsatisfactory because the reaction mixture separates into two phases.

Best results were obtained when 20 g., dry basis, of air-dried white potato starch was treated at 90° with 13 ml. of glacial acetic acid containing 0.063 g. of concentrated sulfuric acid. Ketene, prepared by pyrolysis of acetone, was then passed into the reaction mixture. After about 30 min., 37 ml. of glacial acetic acid was added; and, in about an hour after this addition, the starch began to dissolve. After 4.25 hours at an output of approximately 0.3 mole/hour, the ketene generator was stopped. About 30 min. later, the reaction mixture was stirred vigorously with cold water, and the precipitated product was washed thoroughly and filtered. The oven-dried (100°) starch acetate (38.6 g.) had an acetyl value of 42.5%. The concentration of sulfuric acid must be regulated carefully to obtain good acetylation efficiency without extensive degradation. These products are comparable to those obtained using acetic anhydride in acetic acid at 90° with sulfuric acid catalysis. There is some indication that direct acetylation with ketene might occur as well as the reaction via formation of acetic anhydride.

At present ketene cannot compete with the aqueous acetic anhydride reaction for manufacture of low D.S. starch acetates. Large scale preparation of uniformly substituted high D.S. products with this reagent appears remote.

5. Vinyl Acetate

Acylation of aliphatic hydroxyl compounds by alkaline-catalyzed transesterification with vinyl esters in aqueous medium has been applied to starch (15). When the vinyl ester is vinyl acetate, starch acetate is formed (16) with acetaldehyde as a by-product of the reaction as shown in equation 4. Since vinyl acetate has a molecular weight of 86, 50% by weight of the reagent is theoretically available for acetylation. This compares with only 42% of acetic anhydride.

$$\text{Starch—OH} + \text{CH}_2\text{=CHO}\overset{\text{O}}{\overset{\|}{\text{C}}}\text{CH}_3 \rightarrow \text{Starch—O}\overset{\text{O}}{\overset{\|}{\text{C}}}\text{CH}_3 + \text{CH}_3\overset{\text{O}}{\overset{\|}{\text{C}}}\text{H} \qquad (4)$$

The reaction with either granular or gelatinized starch requires the presence of water; reaction efficiencies of only 2–5% are obtained with less than 10% moisture. In a reaction at 24° for 1 hr. in vinyl acetate using starch blended with sodium carbonate, the reaction efficiency increases rapidly with increasing water content: 43% at 15% moisture; 73% at 65% moisture, based on dry substance starch. Although the reaction may be effected over a pH range of 7.5 to 12.5 using alkali metal hydroxides, quaternary ammonium hydroxides, ammonium hydroxide, and aliphatic amines as catalysts, the preferred range is about pH 9 to 10 which may be obtained using sodium carbonate as a buffer. The reaction rate is relatively rapid at 24° to 46°. The reaction may be done by suspending 100 g. of corn starch at 12% moisture in an aqueous solution of 0.057 moles of sodium carbonate in 150 ml. water at 38°, adding vinyl acetate (10 g.), and stirring for 1 hr. at 38°. The product is isolated by neutralizing the reaction mixture to pH 6–7 with dilute sulfuric acid, filtering out the starch, washing it with water, and drying. The pH during the reaction ranges from 10.0 to 8.6. The product has an acetyl content of 3.6% and gives a stable sol on cooking at 6% solids in water at 90° for 15 minutes and holding the suspension at room temperature for 24 hours. At pH 8.6–10, reaction efficiencies of about 65–70% are expected. Sodium, potassium, or lithium hydroxides at pH 9.5–12.2 give poorer reaction efficiency (45–55%). Ammonium hydroxide, pH 10.1–11.4, also gives low efficiency (about 45%). Corn starch (100 g.) is claimed to be acetylated to a 25% acetyl content by five successive 45-min. treatments at 27° with 30 g. of vinyl acetate and 9 g. of sodium carbonate with neutralization, filtration, and washing steps between each treatment. The use of the liberated acetaldehyde to cross-link the granular starch at pH 2.5–3.5 is also claimed (17).

Vinyl acetate can be used to acetylate amylose in a continuous reactor (47). The amylose is suspended in water containing sodium carbonate; vinyl acetate is added, and the reaction mixture is heated at 166°–177° (330°–350°F; 100–140 psi.). The reaction mixture is collected continuously at a rate of 1 gallon of effluent per minute. Products obtained range up to 5–8% acetyl, dry basis, and give solutions that have much less tendency to gel. Vinyl acetate is being used in the preparation of commercial granular starch acetates of low D.S.

III. Low D.S. Starch Acetates

The useful properties of native starches include cold water insolubility of the granules and viscosity and film forming characteristics of cooked products (48). These inherent properties of the native starches have been modified in the low D.S. starch acetates, up to 0.2 D.S., to enhance the utility of these properties in specific applications.

1. Properties

a. *The Starch Granule*

Microscopic examination of the granules of a low D.S. starch acetate reveals no discernible difference from the granules of the native starch used to prepare the acetate. Since the acetate group is nonionic, staining with anionic or cationic dyes will not show any differences from the raw starch granule but will differentiate from starches containing anionic or cationic groups (49). A granular starch acetate containing 1.8% acetyl may be completely deacetylated by suspension in water at pH 11 for 4 hr., maintaining the pH by addition of 3% aqueous sodium hydroxide solution. The deacetylated starch granule will be practically identical to the original base starch.

When a starch in granular form is cooked by suspending it in water and gradually raising the temperature of the slurry, the viscosity in-

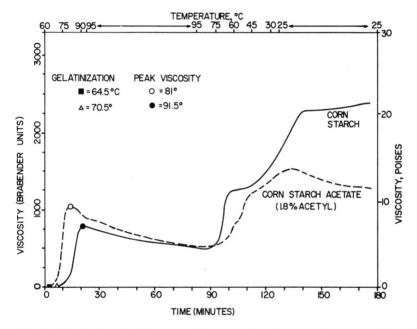

FIG. 2.—Brabender viscosity curves of corn starch and acetylated corn starch (1.8% acetyl). The concentration was 31.5 g. of dry starch suspended in 418.5 g. distilled water. The pH of the slurry was 5.9. Brabender 350 cm. g. cartridge used.

creases to a maximum then drops from this maximum and finally increases again on cooling. The Brabender Visco-Amylo-Graph (C. W. Brabender, South Hackensack, New Jersey) is a convenient instrument (50) for studying the changes in viscosity and thus the granule swelling and dispersion properties of the starch.

Figure 2 shows a comparison of viscosity curves of corn starch (dent maize) and the same starch when acetylated to 1.8% acetyl. The most obvious differences in the early stages of heating are the lower temperature of gelatinization and the higher hot peak viscosity for the acetylated product. The granule was weakened to such an extent that the gelatinization temperature was 6° lower, and the maximum hot viscosity was reached at a temperature 10° lower than that of the untreated starch. This reduction in gelatinization temperature on acetylation is common to all starches. An aqueous slurry of slightly cross-linked waxy maize starch at 5% solids has a gelatinization temperature of 71°, whereas the same starch with 1.8% acetyl gelatinizes at 64°, and with 3.5% acetyl, at 62°. Hence, acetylated starches are more readily dispersed by cooking. The effects of acetylation on lowering the gelatinization temperature (49) are given in Volume I, Chapt. XII, p. 294.

Lowering of the gelatinization temperature by acetylation is of value in connection with high-amylose starches. These starches, containing at least 50% amylose, are so highly associated that they do not gelatinize on cooking in boiling water but require temperatures as high as 160°. Thus, pressure cooking equipment is required to use these starches in aqueous dispersions. Furthermore, the sols produced by high temperature cooking are unstable and tend to gel as the temperature drops. Acetylation to a low D.S. (roughly 0.1–0.2, 2.5–5.0% acetyl) will lower the gelatinization temperature to the point that the starch disperses in boiling water and provides useable sol stability properties. Similar results can be obtained by acetylation of isolated amylose which is usually in retrograded form and hence requires cooking at superatmospheric pressure to effect solution. By regulation of the degree of acetylation, the temperature of dispersion and the degree of sol stability can be varied. Groups other than acetates produce similar properties (40).

As discussed in Volume I, Chapter XII, the increase in the viscosity of untreated starch dispersions on cooling is the result of the association of colloidally dispersed or dissolved starch molecules into larger units (retrogradation). Introduction of substituent groups, such as acetate, interferes with this association process; therefore the cooked acetylated starch increases in viscosity more slowly on cooling and, if sufficient acetyl groups are introduced, no gelling takes place. This gelling property can be demonstrated more dramatically by allowing the starch pastes to cool without stirring. On cooling, a firm gel, measurable by standard means (51), forms with cooked corn starch, whereas the acetylated corn starch does not gel but develops a "long" cohesive sol which is clearer than the opaque corn starch gel. Acetylation also improves sol clarity. This results from the effect of acetylation on increasing the degree of swelling and dispersion of the starch granule as well as reducing retrogradation. These clarity, viscosity, and stability properties of the acetylated starches are of value in food, paper, and textile applications.

b. *The Starch Film*

Starch acetate films, formed by drying thin layers of the colloidal solution, have greater clarity, higher gloss, more flexibility, larger elongation before rupture, less cracking tendency, and easier solubility in water than the unacetylated base starch (*4, 52*).

A low D.S. starch acetate film has about the same tensile strength as a corn starch film (4–5 kg./sq. mm., 22°, 50% relative humidity) and possibly a slightly higher elongation (8% compared to 6–7% for corn starch) (*53*). Films of acetylated high-amylose (70%) corn starch (3–5% acetyl) have elongations of 10–12% on breaking. A film of acetylated waxy maize starch (1.8% acetyl; 100% amylopectin) has low tensile strength (2.9 kg./sq. mm.) and a low elongation (4.1%). The increased elongation of high-amylose starch acetate and the decreased elongation of amylopectin acetate are predictable on the basis of the properties of the unacetylated films (*53*).

Film properties are of importance in finishing and sizing of textiles and paper.

2. Uses

a. *Foods* (See also Chapt. VIII.)

The major use of starches in foods is for thickening. Such starches should have a bland taste and should impart appealing texture; their sols should have clarity, high viscosity, and good stability. Stability is defined as the lack of change in viscosity and texture with time. The starch must retain these properties after exposure to processing, transportation, and storage. This may involve exposure to a pH as low as 3, to high temperatures in food preparation and sterilization; to high shear in mixing and pumping, to low temperatures in refrigerator (5°) and freezer (−18°) storage, and to moderately high temperatures in warehousing and transportation. Acetylation alone or in combination with other treatments such as cross-linking is used to prepare starches with the required properties.

Starch acetates containing 0.5–2.5% acetyl are used in foods primarily because of their stability and clarity. As discussed previously, the stability and clarity of starch acetate sols increase with increasing D.S. This stability is particularly important under low temperature conditions which foster congealing of starch sols. Even tapioca, waxy corn, and waxy sorghum starches, which have a high degree of stability under normal conditions, require acetylation for low temperature stability. This is important to prevent watering (syneresis) and development of cloudiness on prolonged storage at low temperatures (27, 54). Acetylation is usually combined with a cross-bonding treatment to improve textural properties, particularly in foods requiring a smooth, nongrainy, "short," and noncohesive character. Cross-bonding imparts resistance to viscosity breakdown by high temperature, shear, and low pH.

Cross-bonded acetylated starches are used in canned, frozen, baked, and dry foods. With these starches, baby foods and fruit and cream pie fillings in cans and jars meet the requirement of long shelf life under varying temperature conditions. Frozen fruit pies, pot pies, and gravies maintain their stability under low temperature storage. In baked goods, the pies, tarts, and filled cakes have greater "weeping" resistance. In addition, acetylated starches are pregelatinized for use in dry mixes where their more rapid absorption of water and smooth texture are advantageous. The same derivatives are used in areas in which cooking of the product is absent or minimal as in instant gravies and pie fillings.

Present F.D.A. regulations permit up to 2.5% acetyl content in starches used in foods. Acetylation in combination with certain other treatments is also permitted (22).

b. *Textile, Paper, and Other Uses*

Ready dispersibility, viscosity stability, and noncongealing character of their aqueous sols make low D.S. starch acetates convenient for preparation, storage, handling, and application in textile and paper manufacture. Acetylated starches are available in a number of viscosity grades so that solution concentrations can be adjusted for optimum machine operation and solution "pick-up" on the substrate (55). In textile and paper applications, the functional properties of the film are the basis for using starch acetates.

In textile applications, the major market for starch acetates is in warp sizing of synthetic fiber blends, cotton–dacron blends, and fancy cottons. Starch acetate acts as a film-forming material with sufficient adhesion to the yarn, tensile strength, and flexibility to protect the fibers from the abrasion of the weaving process. In addition, since the size should be easily removed from the cloth for finishing (52), the film solubility of the acetates is important.

Starch acetates are also used in combination with thermoset resins to produce inexpensive finishes. Here the starch acetate in the formulation gives weight and "hand" to the fabric. The viscosity stability of the starch acetate permits application at low temperatures.

The major use of starch acetates in the paper industry is in surface sizing where the size is applied to improve printability and functional properties by imparting low and uniform porosity, surface strength, abrasion resistance, oil holdout, and solvent resistance, as well as for adhering stray fibers to the substrate (52). Flexibility of the starch acetate size is important in reducing surface cracking of heavy weight papers on folding or scoring. The sol stability of the acetates improves compatibility with hydrophilic colloids in size formulations. In addition, when waste paper containing starch acetates is reintroduced into the papermaking system (by repulping), there is no adverse effect on the retention of fillers and pigments.

In gummed tape formulations, the flexibility, high gloss, and remoistenability of starch acetate films are useful.

IV. HIGH D.S. STARCH ACETATES

The objective of much of the work on high D.S. starch acetates was to find a substitute for cellulose acetate (56, 57). In general, starch and amylopectin acetates of high D.S. have limited commercial interest because their films, fibers, and molded products are weak and brittle (6, 13). Suggested uses are as coatings, adhesives, emulsions, and cellulose acetate diluents in molding compounds (13). Amylose triacetate, on the other hand, has generated greater interest because its films (6) and fibers (58, 59) appear comparable to those of cellulose triacetate. However, the decrease in use of cellulose acetate from 435 million pounds in 1950 to 280 million pounds in 1960 discouraged amylose triacetate development; since 1960 cellulose acetate use has been increasing and is expected to double by 1970 (60). If a cheap source of amylose is developed, interest in high D.S. amylose acetate may be renewed. However, based on raw material costs, the economics of producing amylose triacetate in competition with cellulose triacetate are not favorable. Dissolving pulp prices are about 9–11 cents per pound, while isolated amylose sells for 25 cents per pound as of July 1, 1966. A high volume market for isolated amylose would probably lead to price reductions, but the cost is not likely to be lower than 13–15 cents per pound even under the most favorable circumstances (including a substantial market for the concomitant fraction, amylopectin). Another major source of amylose might be the development of a hybrid corn yielding starch containing 100% amylose. If this high-amylose corn were processed in quantities comparable to the current milling of waxy corn, the price of the 100% amylose starch could be expected to be within the range of waxy corn starch, which was about 12 cents per pound on July 1, 1966.

1. Starch Acetates

Starch acetates have been made with acetyl values ranging from 5% to more than 44.8%. As shown in Table III, the specific gravity, specific rotation, and melting temperatures generally decrease with increasing acetyl content (57). The specific rotations of corn starch, corn amylose, and corn amylopectin triacetates in chloroform are very similar (8). In pyridine at 22°, the specific rotations of corn, potato, tapioca, wheat, and rice starch triacetates are similar (5). Corn amylose triacetate has a sharper melting point than corn amylopectin triacetate (7). However, it has been pointed out that melting or softening values obtained by the usual capillary tube techniques are subject to considerable variation (5,

Table III
Properties of Starch Acetates

| | | | | Melting point | | |
Product	Acetyl (%)	Specific gravity at 25°	$[\alpha]^{25}_D$ (circ. deg.)	First melting (°C)	Transparent (°C)	$\eta_{rel.}{}^k$
Starch[a]	5–7	1.6	+220–225[b]	235–268[d]	—	—
Starch[a]	9–10	1.6	+180–189[b]	238–260[d]	—	—
Starch[a]	41–43	1.2	+167–172[c]	175–188	195–215	—
Corn[e]	44.7	—	+171.5[c]	270–292[f]	—	—
Corn amylopectin[e]	44.8	—	+170.0[c]	205–265[f]	—	—
Corn amylose[e]	44.7	—	+174.5[c]	300–301[f]	—	—
Potato[g]	43.8[h]	—	+158.0[i]	—	—	3.87
Tapioca[g]	43.8[h]	—	+155.0[i]	—	—	3.50
Wheat[g]	43.8[h]	—	+151.0[i]	—	—	2.82
Corn[g]	43.8[h]	—	+156.5[i]	—	—	2.90
Rice[g]	43.8[h]	—	+157.9[i]	—	—	2.53
Cellulose acetate[g]	40 (approx.)	—	−28.2[i]	—	—	3.65

[a] Presumably corn starch. Reference 57.
[b] In water.
[c] In chloroform.
[d] Only decomposition observed.
[e] Reference 8.
[f] Reference 7.
[g] Reference 5.
[h] 43.3–44.3% acetyl.
[i] In pyridine at 22°.
[k] In pyridine at 25°; 1% solution.

7). Using pressure drop–temperature curves taken during molding experiments, it was estimated that the softening temperature of starch acetates is about 170° with clearing of the melt above 200° (5).

The solubility characteristics of starch acetates are dependent mainly upon the D.S. and the D.P. (1, 56). Whole starch acetates of up to 15% acetyl content are soluble in hot water (50°–100°) and insoluble in organic solvents (57). Water solubility is increased by degradation and has been reported for products containing as much as 25% of acetyl groups where degradation has occurred (9, 10). Starch acetates with an acetyl content of 40% or more are insoluble in water, ethers, aliphatic alcohols, and aliphatic hydrocarbons and soluble in aromatic hydrocarbons, halogenated aliphatic hydrocarbons (except carbon tetrachloride), ketones, glycol ethers, and nitroparaffins (57). The activation pretreatment given the starch prior to esterification affects solubility properties; the aqueous paste disruption technique (8) yields more soluble products than either the liquid ammonia or pyridine pretreatment methods (5). Products from the last two procedures are not completely soluble in any solvent while the acetates from the paste disintegration technique are soluble in chloroform, pyridine, and acetic acid and partially soluble in benzene, dioxane, ethyl acetate, acetone, and 2-nitropropane (8). The triacetates presumably do not form true solutions when prepared by the pyridine activation method but yield colloidal dispersions. Best dispersion is obtained with high energy transfer devices such as a colloid mill, homogenizer, or high speed blender (5, 13). Most common organic liquids have a swelling effect on the triacetates even though the esters are insoluble in these organic solvents (5, 8). Aromatic hydrocarbons, halogenated aliphatic hydrocarbons, and tertiary nitrogen bases are among the better dispersing agents (5).

Relative viscosity values of whole starch acetates in pyridine decrease in order of decreasing granule size, except for wheat starch, as shown in Table III (5). In tetrachloroethane, the potato starch acetate had a higher relative viscosity, 4.57 (5). Tetrachloroethane was considered a poorer solvent than pyridine because longer mixing in a blender was necessary to obtain a constant flow rate in the viscometer (5).

Unplasticized films made from the triacetates of whole starch or of amylopectin are clear, brittle, and very weak (6). Plasticizer retention by starch triacetate films is much less than that of cellulose acetate films, and the films become very brittle and opaque when leached with water (61).

2. Amylose Triacetate

Most of the interest in high D.S. starch acetates has centered on amylose triacetate because this acetate can be used for solution property studies, and its films and fibers have mechanical properties similar to those of cellulose triacetate. This interest was also fostered by the commercial availability of a potato amylose (21, 62). To focus attention on amylose as a material of possible commercial value, the properties are summarized in tabular form in the following sections.

a. Solution Properties

To study the size and shape of amylose and amylopectin, solutions of their triacetates have been employed. The acetates used for these studies must be prepared under conditions minimizing degradation. Measurements of the osmotic pressure, intrinsic viscosity, sedimentation, diffusion, and light scattering of solutions of amylose and amylopectin triacetates have been made to estimate molecular weight and molecular shape (63, see Volume I, Chapter XV).

As mentioned previously in connection with starch acetates, the solubility of amylose triacetates is influenced by the preparative treatment the sample has received (64). Corn amylose triacetates prepared by treatment with acetic anhydride–sodium acetate or acetic anhydride–formamide were soluble in acetone; those prepared with acetic anhydride–pyridine at 100° were not. All the corn amylose triacetates were soluble in chloroform and 1,1,2-trichloroethane (64). In general, acetic acid, pyridine, chlorinated hydrocarbons, and nitroparaffins are solvents for amylose triacetate.

b. *Film and Bulk Properties*

Corn amylose triacetate has reported capillary melting points of 290°–300° (6) and 300°–301° (7). However, the capillary melting point method is not considered suitable for determining the fusion points of cellulose and amylose acetates. Hence, the softening point of potato amylose triacetate was measured by a ring and ball method used for asphalts, tars, pitches, and resins (American Society for Testing Materials, ASTM method E28-51T), giving a value of 295° (65). This compares with a value of 306° for the melting point of a carefully characterized cellulose triacetate determined in a 4-mm. glass tube heated in a copper block (66); the ester charred at 315° (66). The softening point of a commercial cellulose triacetate is about 240° (67).

The hardness of a disk of solid potato amylose triacetate was determined by a modification of the Brinell Hardness Test (ASTM E10-54T), yielding a hardness index of 508. This is greater than the hardness index of Carnauba wax (65). The density of this amylose triacetate was 1.348 g./ml. at 30° (65).

Amylose triacetate forms pliable, transparent, lustrous, colorless films (6, 7). Films of amylose triacetate prepared by casting on a glass plate from chloroform solution and conditioning at controlled temperature and humidity are optically isotropic and have the same tensile strength in all directions (6). Amylose triacetate films swell and disperse in pyridine, acetic acid, chloroform, and tetrachloroethane. They are insoluble in water, alcohol, ether, and acetone (6).

Films are characterized readily by their stress–strain relationship. The stress–strain curve of an amylose acetate film is shown in Figure 3 (65). Here, the application of an increasing stress produces an elastic deformation which obeys Hooke's law. The load increases rapidly to a maximum (yield point) and then decreases as plastic flow begins and the film stretches. Elongation continues with applied stress until the film breaks at about 16.8% elongation. Plasticizers modify the stress–strain properties of these films. In the case of corn amylose triacetate, incorporation of dibutyl phthalate results in a decrease in film strength and an increase in elongation as shown in Table IV (6). The stress–strain

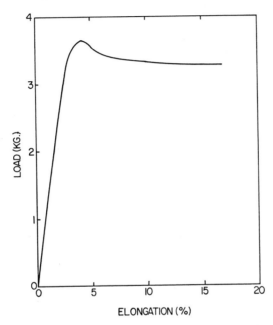

FIG. 3.—Typical stress–strain curve of potato amylose acetate using Instron Tensile Tester at a stretching rate of 0.5 in./min. and grip separation of 2 in. (ASTM Method D882-56T). Film 0.141 mm. thick, cast from chloroform, conditioned 10 days at 21°, 65% R.H. Original cross-sectional area, 0.895 sq. mm. (65).

curves of the plasticized films show a decreased yield value and, at 20% plasticizer, evidence that stretching 20–30% leads to increased strength as a result of partial orientation of the molecules (6). Many other plasticizers have been tried with amylose acetates (6, 61).

Some properties of amylose triacetate films are summarized and compared with those of cellulose triacetate films in Table V. The tensile strength values listed in both Tables IV and V show amylose triacetate films to be weaker than cellulose triacetate films (6, 7). There is some confusion concerning the relative elongation of amylose triacetate and cellulose triacetate. Early workers (6) give data showing unplasticized amylose triacetate to have greater elongation than the corresponding cellulose derivative. A later publication (7) reports that the percentage elongation is of the same order of magnitude. The data on plasticization

Table IV

Effect of Plasticizer on Tensile Strength and Elongation (6)

Plasticizer[a] (%)	Amylose triacetate[b]			Cellulose triacetate[c]		
	Tensile[d] (kg./sq. mm.)		Elongation[d] (%)	Tensile[d] (kg./sq. mm.)		Elongation[d] (%)
	A[e]	B[f]		A[e]	B[f]	
0	6.2	7.6[g]	22	8.7[i]	9.4[i]	8[i]
10	5.0	7.9	59	8.3	10.0	21
20	4.0	7.1	78	7.7	9.8	28
30	2.8	5.5	95	6.4	8.4	31
40	2.2	4.8[g]	120	4.0	5.7	42
50	1.0	2.2	116[h]	2.5	4.1	63

[a] Dibutyl phthalate.

[b] Corn amylose, butanol fractionation, 44.7% acetyl. Films cast from chloroform, conditioned at 21°, 50% R.H., for 12 days. Film 0.03–0.04 mm. thick.

[c] High grade commercial primary cellulose acetate, 44.2% acetyl.

[d] Estimated from stress–strain curves of Figure 2 of reference 6. Scott IP2 recording, inclined-plane serigraph at constant load rate of 36 g./sec.; clamp separation, 50 mm. at zero load.

[e] Tensile strength based on original film dimensions.

[f] Tensile strength based on film rupture dimensions calculated from A and elongation.

[g] Figure 3 of reference 6 gives B values at 7.9 and 4.2 for 0% and 40% plasticizer respectively. Table III of reference 7 also quotes these values.

[h] Figure 4 of reference 6 indicates 124% elongation which is also quoted by reference 7.

[i] Table II of reference 6 gives a tensile value of 8.6 and a 4% elongation. Assuming the 8.6 to be an A value, a B value of 8.9 can be calculated. Reference states 8.6 to be a B value.

shown in Table IV suggests that amylose triacetate has inherently greater plasticity and requires less plasticizer than cellulose triacetate (6). The data on folding endurance would tend to indicate a greater flexibility in amylose triacetate; this is, perhaps, related to its greater plasticity or lesser crystallinity as compared to the cellulose derivative. Certainly, good flexibility and elongation of films is of considerable value in developing commercial packaging films.

In connection with the discussion of plasticization of films (Table IV), the effect of stretching on increasing tensile strength was mentioned. Amylose triacetate film was stretched in a steam bath and an increase in tensile strength in the direction of the fiber axis was noted (Table V) (7). Transverse strength of the film was low. X-ray data suggest that the increase in tensile strength after stretching is the result of an alignment of the amylose triacetate molecules. This is indicated by

Table V

Unplasticized Film Properties of Triacetates[a]

Property	Amylose triacetate[b] Properties	References	Cellulose triacetate Properties	References
Tensile strength (kg./sq. mm.)[c]	6.2, 6.2, 4.4	6, 7, 65	8.6, 9–12, 7.3	6, 7, 66
Elongation at rupture (%)	22, 10–16, 16.1	6, 7, 65	4, 15–25	6, 7
Tensile after 100% stretch (kg./sq. mm.)[c]	10.5	7		
Folding endurance (Schopper double folds)	450–650,[e] 879[f]	6, 7	15–25	67
Bursting strength, Mullen (lb./sq. in.)	21	7		
Modulus of elasticity (kg./sq. mm.)	220	6		
Permeability × 10[12]	620[d]	65	44[h]	68
Electrical breakdown (volts/mil)	805–880	6	982	67
Refractive index	1.469	6	1.48, 1.472	6, 67
Hardness (Rockwell)	M60–65	6	M40–80	67
Density (g./ml.)	1.341, 1.348[g]	6, 65	1.4, 1.33, 1.52	6, 67, 66

[a] Numerical values and references are serially arranged.
[b] Corn amylose triacetate (*6, 7*); potato amylose triacetate (*65*).
[c] Calculated on original film dimensions.
[d] Permeability to water at 21°C, g./cm./sq. cm./sec./mm. Hg.
[e] Film 0.03 mm. thick.
[f] Film 0.025 mm. thick.
[g] At 30°.
[h] Permeability to water at 25° calculated from 550×10^{-8} cc. STP/sq. cm./sec./ mm./cm. Hg (*68*).

a change in the x-ray pattern from amorphous to a more "crystalline" form by stretching the film 400–600% in hot water (*69*) or 800% in glycerol at 160°–170° (*7*). The diffraction patterns indicate a high degree of orientation of the molecules in the stretched film. Corn and potato amylose acetate films give identical diffraction patterns (*69*). All stretched films show some birefringence (*69*). There is also a tendency for amylose acetate films to develop order on heating at 185° for 15 min.; the amorphous x-ray pattern changes to one having several clearly defined rings, indicating some "crystallinity." Compared to the original film, the heated film is more brittle, contracted by 20% in length and width, and increased in thickness (*7*).

The electrical breakdown value for amylose triacetate film given in Table V indicates that the film is comparable to cellulose triacetate. A plasticized amylose triacetate film did not break down when subjected to 200 volts of direct current for 3 weeks at 49° in a humidity cabinet. It was concluded that the film compares favorably with polymers used in electrical insulation tapes (6).

Mixed corn amylose esters were prepared and the film and solubility properties were tested (70). The acetate–butyrate and acetate–propionate esters gave somewhat weaker films than those of the triacetate, but they had somewhat more plasticity (Table VI). These materials appear to be good molding materials; they are strong and tough and easily released from the mold. The mixed esters are more soluble than the triacetate.

Table VI

Some Properties of Mixed Triesters of Corn Amylose Acetates (70)

Ester:	Butyrate		Propionate		Triacetate
Ester D.S.	0.45	1.4	0.4	1.6	—
Acetate D.S.	2.55	1.6	2.6	1.4	3.0
Acyl (% acetyl)	42.9	39.4	44.0	41.5	—
Tensile strength[a] (kg./sq. mm.)	5.8	5.1	5.6	5.4	6.2
Elongation at break (%)	14	18	18	20	13
Melting point[b] (°C)	239–42	226–229	280–282	247–258	300–301
Shrinking point[c]	150	212	169	220	—
Optimum molding (°C)	130	110–120	150	125	150

[a] Film cast from chloroform solution, tested on Scott IP2 inclined plane serigraph at constant load rate of 36 g./sec. Tensile calculated on original film dimensions.

[b] Capillary tube method to give clear melt.

[c] Point at which ester pulled away from sides of tube.

They are soluble in benzene, dioxane, acetone, nitropropane, and ethyl acetate.

The tabulated data on amylose triacetate and cellulose triacetate films were collected from several sources which varied in the methods used to obtain and present quantitative information. Thus, in compiling the tables, assumptions and interpretations were made where procedures, products, or experimental data were not clearly and completely defined. A major difficulty in making valid comparisons of films of cellulose and amylose triacetates is that the authors found no published experimental work in which both materials were prepared, cast into films, and evaluated at the same time under the same conditions. Usually the amylose triacetate was prepared under controlled conditions and carefully characterized; then films were cast and evaluated. Comparisons with cellulose triacetate were then made by preparing and evaluating films from commercial cellulose acetate, by evaluating commercial cellulose triacetate films, or by reference to published data on cellulose triacetate films. Since film properties are extremely dependent upon the characteristics of the film-forming material, the casting conditions, and the test conditions, there is an element of risk in drawing conclusions from the available data. There is a need for published data affording a direct comparison of the film properties of amylose and cellulose triacetates which have been prepared and fully characterized (including the original polysaccharides) in the same laboratory at the same time.

To provide some perspective on the comparisons, data on commercial cellulose triacetate is presented in Table VII (71). Although plasticized

Table VII
Properties of Commercial Cellulose Acetate Films (71)

	Cellulose acetate[a]	Cellulose triacetate[a]	ASTM Test numbers
Thickness range (mils)	0.88–2	0.8–2	
Specific gravity	1.29	1.29	D792–60T
Tensile strength (p.s.i.)	13,000–15,000[b]	12,000–15,000[c]	D882,
Elongation (%)	25–35	25–35	procedure B
Bursting Strength,[d] Mullen points (p.s.i.)	40–60	50–70	D774
Folding Endurance (Schopper double)	500–600[e]	1,000–2,000[e]	D643–63T
Permeability[f]	1200[g]	790[g]	D697
Dielectric strength (volts/mil)	3200	3700	

[a] These products are plasticized.
[b] Equivalent to 9.1–10.6 kg./sq. mm.
[c] Equivalent to 8.4–10.6 kg./sq. mm.
[d] 1 mil thickness.
[e] A 10-mil thick film of this secondary cellulose acetate gave only 5–10 double folds; the 10-mil film of the triacetate gave only 5–25 double folds.
[f] Water vapor permeability in g./24 hr./sq. m./mm. thickness/cm. Hg at 25°.
[g] Permeability depends greatly on film thickness. A 10-mil thick film of this secondary cellulose acetate had a permeability value of 210; a 10-mil film of cellulose triacetate had a value of 140.

films were used, the elongation figures are still relatively low. Therefore, one can again conclude that films of amylose acetates have greater elongation than those of cellulose acetates.

Amylose acetate, when tested as a coating, shows excellent fatty acid resistance, satisfactory hot and cold water resistance, and satisfactory accelerated weathering. The chief weakness is a lack of adhesion indicated by the fact that the film peels from metal test plates (7).

c. Fiber Properties

Fiber properties of amylose triacetate are given in Table VIII. In general, amylose acetate fiber is weaker and has a greater elongation than cellulose acetate fibers. The strength can be increased and the elongation decreased by appropriate stretching of the fiber (Table IX), although the elongation remains higher than that of cellulose triacetate. Amylose triacetate has less resistance to extension than cellulose triacetate. This is shown by a load of 0.39 grams/denier at 20% elongation for the amylose triacetate fiber versus 0.98 grams/denier for the cellulosic

Table VIII
Properties of Amylose Acetate Fibers[a]

	Amylose acetate[b]	Cellulose diacetate[c]	Cellulose triacetate[c]
Tensile (grams/denier)[d]	0.52	1.3	1.2–1.4, 2.1[e] *(58, 72)*
Elongation (%)	62	28	25–28, 25[e] *(58, 72)*
Young's modulus (grams/denier)	19.4, 15 *(58, 59)*	41, 29 *(58, 59)*	35–40, 49[e] *(58, 72)*
Knot strength (grams/denier)	0.53	1.1	1.1–1.2
Knot elongation (%)	64	22	
Loop strength (grams/denier)	0.54	1.23	1.5–1.2, 1.0[e] *(58, 72)*
Loop elongation (%)	63	—	26

[a] All references to reference *58* unless indicated otherwise.
[b] Corn amylose from butanol-fractionation; 44.9 acetyl; $[\eta]^{25}$ of 1.66 in chloroform. Filaments spun from methylene chloride.
[c] No data on spinning of cellulosics.
[d] 75 Denier, 20 filament yarn, 6-inch gage length, strain rate of 67%/min. at 65% R.H. and 21°.
[e] Celanese Corp. "Arnel 60."

fiber on stretching at 10%/min. at 21°, 60% R.H. (*59*). Data is also given in Table VIII for a commercial cellulose triacetate fiber (Celanese Corporation "Arnel") which has improved mechanical properties ascribed to increased orientation (*72, 73*). Amylose triacetate fibers spun without stretching are amorphous. Stretched fibers show typical crystalline x-ray diffraction patterns (*59*). Amylose triacetate fibers show no superior properties and hence no apparent advantages over the cellulose acetate fibers (*58, 59*).

High strength rayon (Celanese Corporation "Fortisan") (*75*) is made by orienting cellulose acetate fibers through stretching followed by deacetylation. A similar procedure has been suggested for amylose fiber production since deacetylated, unstretched amylose fibers are weak, having a tensile of 0.29 grams/denier and an elongation of 34% (*59*).

The digestibility and solubility of the amylose fibers may lead to special uses (58). Deacetylation of stretched amylose triacetate films (0.25 mm. thick and 2–4 mm. wide) has been used to prepare alkali amyloses having varied, well-defined fiber x-ray diffraction patterns (76, 77).

Table IX

Effect of Stretching on Amylose Acetate Fibers[a] (59)

	Stretching		After Stretching	
Amount (%)	Medium	Temp. (°C)	Strength[b] (grams/denier)	Elongation[b] (%)
0	—	—	0.52–0.63	76
25	Air	25	0.65 (58)	
50	Air	25	0.71 (58)	
100	Glycerol	170	0.9	47
200	Glycerol	170	1.1	56
400	Glycerol	170	1.35	45
600	Glycerol	170	1.8	40
200	Glycerol	140	1.0	36
100	Air	170	0.75	42
200	Air	170	1.6	45
200[c]	Steam		1.0	32

[a] Butanol-fractionated corn starch amylose acetate. Filaments spun from chloroform solution at 300–500 p.s.i. through spinneret orifices 3–5 mils in diameter into heated air at 250–450 ft./min.

[b] Measured on Scott IP2 inclined plane serigraph or electronically controlled single fiber balance. Fibers conditioned at 50% R.H., 72°F before testing.

[c] Cellulose diacetate when stretched 200% in steam had a strength of 2.6 grams per denier and an elongation of 4.1% (74).

V. Acetyl Analysis

Both high and low D.S. amylose acetates can be analyzed for acetyl content by measuring the alkali consumed in the hydrolysis of the ester (1, 12, 78). When identification of the acyl component is desired, trans-esterification in anhydrous methanol using a sodium methoxide catalyst can be used (79). This can be combined with gas chromatography of the methyl esters formed for a combined quantitative and qualitative analysis. The infrared carbonyl peak at 5.8 μ has been used to determine acetyl in starch acetate films, Nujol mulls, or potassium bromide preparations (80).

VI. References

(1) R. L. Whistler, *Advan. Carbohydrate Chem.*, **1**, 279 (1945).

(2) E. F. Degering, in "Chemistry and Industry of Starch," R. W. Kerr, ed., Academic Press Inc., New York, N. Y., 2nd Ed., 1950, p. 259.

(3) E. F. Degering, in "Starch and Its Derivatives," J. A. Radley, ed., John Wiley and Sons, Inc., New York, N. Y., 3rd Ed., 1954, Vol. 1, p. 298.

(4) J. Seiberlich, Rayon Textile Monthly, 22, 605, 686 (1941).

(5) J. W. Mullen II and E. Pacsu, Ind. Eng. Chem., 34, 1209 (1942); U.S. Patent 2,372,337 (1945); Chem. Abstr., 39, 4250 (1945).

(6) R. L. Whistler and G. E. Hilbert, Ind. Eng. Chem., 36, 796 (1944).

(7) I. A. Wolff, D. W. Olds, and G. E. Hilbert, Ind. Eng. Chem., 43, 911 (1951).

(8) I. A. Wolff, D. W. Olds, and G. E. Hilbert, J. Am. Chem. Soc., 73, 346 (1951).

(9) J. Traquair, J. Soc. Chem. Ind., 28, 288 (1909).

(10) H. T. Clarke and H. B. Gillespie, J. Am. Chem. Soc., 54, 2083 (1932).

(11) C. G. Caldwell, U.S. Patent 2,461,139 (1949); Chem. Abstr., 43, 3222 (1949).

(12) O. B. Wurzburg, in "Methods in Carbohydrate Chemistry," R. L. Whistler, ed., Academic Press Inc., New York, N. Y., Vol. 4, 1964, p. 286.

(13) J. W. Mullen II and E. Pacsu, Ind. Eng. Chem., 35, 381 (1943).

(14) H. P. Panzer, Abstr. Papers, Am. Chem. Soc., 144, 16C (1963).

(15) C. E. Smith and J. V. Tuschhoff, U.S. Patent 2,928,828 (1960); Chem. Abstr., 54, 13703 (1960).

(16) J. V. Tuschhoff and C. E. Smith, U.S. Patent 3,022,289 (1962); Chem. Abstr., 56, 14520 (1962).

(17) C. E. Smith and J. V. Tuschhoff, U.S. Patent 3,081,296 (1963); Belg. Patent 616,364; Chem. Abstr., 58, 8128 (1963).

(18) E. B. Middleton, U.S. Patent 1,685,220 (1928); Chem. Abstr., 22, 4536 (1928).

(19) C. A. Burkhard and E. F. Degering, Rayon Textile Monthly, 23, 340 (1942).

(20) E. A. Talley and L. T. Smith, J. Org. Chem., 10, 101 (1945).

(21) J. Muetgeert, P. Hiemstra, and W. C. Bus, Staerke, 10, 303 (1958).

(22) Code of Federal Regulations, Title 21, Food and Drugs, Chapter I, Part 121, Subpart D, Food Additives Permitted in Food for Human Consumption, Section 121.1031, Food Starch-Modified, U.S. Govt. Printing Off., Washington, D.C., Revised Jan. 1, 1966.

(23) C. F. Cross, E. J. Bevan, and J. Traquair, Chem. Ztg., 29, 527 (1905).

(24) E. F. Paschall, U.S. Patent 2,914,526 (1959); Chem. Abstr., 55, 25306 (1961).

(25) R. H. Treadway, U.S. Patent 2,399,455 (1946); Chem. Abstr., 40, 4238 (1946).

(26) G. V. Caesar, U.S. Patent 2,365,173 (1944); Chem. Abstr., 39, 3956 (1945).

(27) O. B. Wurzburg, U.S. Patent 2,935,510 (1960); Chem. Abstr. 54, 16886 (1960).

(28) C. A. Burkhard and E. F. Degering, Proc. Indiana Acad. Sci., 51, 173 (1941).

(29) G. K. Hughes, A. K. MacBeth, and F. L. Winzor, J. Chem. Soc., 2026 (1932).

(30) R. W. Kerr, O. R. Trubell, and G. M. Severson, Cereal Chem., 19, 64 (1942).

(31) M. G. Groen, U.S. Patent 2,412,213 (1946); Chem. Abstr., 41, 2265 (1947).

(32) A. Schmidt, G. Balle, and H. Lange, U.S. Patent 1,928,269 (1933); Chem. Abstr., 27, 5976 (1933).

(33) R. Lohmar and C. E. Rist, J. Am. Chem. Soc., 72, 4298 (1950).

(34) R. L. Whistler, A. Jeanes, and G. E. Hilbert, Abstr. Papers, Am. Chem. Soc., 104, 3R (1942); Reference 2, p. 270.

(35) J. F. Carson and W. D. Maclay, J. Am. Chem. Soc., 68, 1015 (1946).

(36) A. L. Potter and W. Z. Hassid, J. Am. Chem. Soc., 70, 3774 (1948).

(37) Upjohn Company, British Patent 810,306 (1959); Chem. Abstr., 53, 18401 (1959.)

(38) E. Husemann and H. Bartl, Makromol. Chem., 18/19, 342 (1956).

(39) Societa Nazionale Industria Applicazioni Viscosa, Belg. Patent 610,875 (1962); Chem. Abstr., 57, 11440 (1962).

(40) M. W. Rutenberg, W. Jarowenko, and L. J. Ross, U.S. Patent 3,038,895 (1962); Chem. Abstr., 57, 10086 (1962).

(41) V. Prey and A. Aszalos, Monatsh. Chem., 91, 729 (1960).

(42) A. Aszalos and V. Prey, *Staerke*, **14**, 51 (1962).

(43) F. Grundschober and V. Prey, *Staerke*, **15**, 225 (1963).

(44) C. G. Caldwell and O. B. Wurzburg, U.S. Patent 2,661,349 (1953); *Chem. Abstr.*, **48**, 1720 (1954).

(45) C. G. Caldwell and O. B. Wurzburg, U.S. Patent 2,668,156 (1954); *Chem. Abstr.*, **48**, 10365 (1954).

(46) C. G. Caldwell and O. B. Wurzburg, U.S. Patent 2,825,727 (1958); *Chem. Abstr.*, **52**, 8601 (1958).

(47) National Starch and Chemical Corp., Brit. Patent 969,711 (1964); *Chem. Abstr.*, **62**, 4203 (1965).

(48) O. B. Wurzburg, *Food Engineering*, **33**, No. 5, 95 (1961).

(49) T. J. Schoch and E. C. Maywald, *Anal. Chem.*, **28**, 382 (1956).

(50) R. J. Smith, in "Methods in Carbohydrate Chemistry," R. L. Whistler, ed., Academic Press Inc., New York, N. Y. Vol. 4, 1964, p. 114.

(51) E. T. Hjermstad, in "Methods in Carbohydrate Chemistry," R. L. Whistler, ed., Academic Press Inc., New York, N. Y., Vol. 4, 1964, p. 148.

(52) A. Harsveldt, *Chem. Ind. (London)*, 2062 (1961).

(53) I. A. Wolff, H. A. Davis, J. E. Cluskey, L. J. Gundrum, and C. E. Rist, *Ind. Eng. Chem.*, **43**, 915 (1951).

(54) R. W. Kerr and W. J. Katzbeck, U.S. Patent 3,061,604 (1962); *Chem. Abstr.*, **58**, 3593 (1963).

(55) "The Kofilm Manual," National Starch and Chemical Corporation, New York, N. Y., 1960.

(56) J. A. Radley, *Paint Manuf.*, **17**, 83 (1947).

(57) C. A. Burkhard and E. F. Degering, *Rayon Textile Monthly*, **23**, 416 (1942).

(58) R. L. Whistler and G. N. Richards, *Ind. Eng. Chem.*, **50**, 1551 (1958).

(59) I. A. Wolff, *Ind. Eng. Chem.*, **50**, 1552 (1958).

(60) L. F. Laun, *Oil Paint Drug Reptr.*, 5 (May 30, 1966).

(61) C. A. Burkhard and E. F. Degering, *Rayon Textile Monthly*, **23**, 676 (1942).

(62) P. Hiemstra, W. C. Bus, and J. M. Muetgeert, *Staerke*, **9**, 235 (1956).

(63) C. T. Greenwood, *Advan. Carbohydrate Chem.*, **11**, 335 (1956).

(64) A. Jeanes and R. W. Jones, *J. Am. Chem. Soc.*, **74**, 6116 (1952).

(65) A. T. Gros and R. O. Feuge, *J. Am. Oil Chemists' Soc.*, **39**, 19 (1962).

(66) C. J. Malm, J. W. Mench, D. L. Kendall, and G. D. Hiatt, *Ind. Eng. Chem.*, **43**, 684, 688 (1951).

(67) "Hercules Cellulose Acetate," Hercules Powder Co., Wilmington, Del., 1945.

(68) A. W. Myers, J. A. Meyer, C. E. Rogers, V. Stannett, and M. Szwarc, *Tappi*, **44**, 58 (1961).

(69) R. L. Whistler and N. C. Schieltz, *J. Am. Chem. Soc.*, **65**, 1436 (1943).

(70) I. A. Wolff, D. W. Olds, and G. E. Hilbert, *Ind. Eng. Chem.*, **49**, 1247 (1957).

(71) "Modern Plastics Encyclopedia for 1966," McGraw-Hill, New York, N. Y., 43, No. 1A, 537 (1955).

(72) B. S. Sprague, *Textile Res. J.*, **30**, 697 (1960).

(73) R. G. Stoll, *Textile Res. J.*, **25**, 650 (1955).

(74) B. S. Sprague and H. D. Noether, *Textile Res. J.*, **31**, 858 (1961).

(75) W. D. Paist, "Cellulosics," Reinhold Publishing Corp., New York, N. Y., 1958, pp. 4, 10, 39, 42.

(76) F. R. Senti and L. P. Witnauer, *J. Am. Chem. Soc.*, **68**, 2407 (1946).

(77) F. R. Senti and L. P. Witnauer, *J. Am. Chem. Soc.*, **70**, 1438 (1948).

(78) L. B. Genung and R. D. Mallott, *Ind. Eng. Chem., Anal. Ed.*, **13**, 369 (1941).

(79) R. L. Whistler and A. Jeanes, *Ind. Eng. Chem., Anal. Ed.*, **15**, 317 (1943).

(80) J. R. Van der Bij and W. F. Vogel, *Staerke*, **14**, 113 (1962).

CHAPTER XVI

PRODUCTION AND USES OF CATIONIC STARCHES

By E. F. Paschall

Moffett Technical Center, Corn Products Co., Argo, Illinois

I. Introduction

Since the commercial acceptance of hydroxyethylstarch in the early 1950's, numerous types of starch derivatives have been prepared to meet the needs of the paper, textile, and food industries. Impetus for the development of new derivatives with specific properties stems from: (*a*) intense competition within the wet-milling industry because of an over-abundance of starch, (*b*) the appearance of low cost synthetic polymers which have replaced conventional starch types in some uses, and (*c*) technological changes in the consuming industries which require more efficient performance or greater convenience in use.

Cationic starches represent a unique class of high performance starch derivatives which have recently gained commercial acceptance. Their industrial importance resides in their affinity toward negatively charged substrates, such as cellulose and some synthetic fibers, aqueous suspensions of minerals and slimes, and biologically active macromolecules. They have already found widespread use in paper manufacture in which

403

they function as internal binders and retention aids for various fillers and emulsions. They also appear to be useful as sizing agents for natural and synthetic fibers, as flocculating agents for aqueous suspensions of minerals and slimes, and in the separation and purification of biological materials.

This chapter describes in detail the preparations and properties of the more important cationic starches, and briefly reviews methods of preparation of less important cationic starches. An attempt has been made to provide a comprehensive review of the various uses of cationic starches as found in the published literature. Although details of manufacture are not disclosed by the starch companies, the procedures in patent examples usually give adequate descriptions for the preparation of most cationic starch types.

II. EARLY HISTORY

The early synthesis of cationic polysaccharides was directed almost entirely to the preparation of aminocellulose derivatives. Much of the initial work was done in the period 1925 to 1940 for the purpose of improving the dyeing characteristics of cellulose fibers. It was not until the early 1950's that serious efforts were made to synthesize cationic starch derivatives for industrial use. Since most of the methods applied initially for the synthesis of cationic cellulose derivatives have since been applied to starch, a brief survey of this early work on basic aminocellulose derivatives is given below.

Basic aminocellulose derivatives appear to have been reported first in 1926 (1, 2). Aryl sulfonate groups on cellulose or cellulose acetate were replaced with ammonia and amines, such as aniline and diethylamine, to give derivatives having sufficient basic character to improve the dyeing properties of the fiber.

Tertiary aminoalkylcelluloses were obtained at about the same time by direct treatment of alkali cellulose with haloalkyl tertiary amines, such as 2-chloroethyldiethylamine (3, 4). Haloalkyl tertiary amines were employed later in the preparation of amphoteric (5), high-D.S. acid-soluble (6), and quaternary ammonium (7, 8) cellulose derivatives. Use of monofunctional epoxyamines, such as N-(2,3-epoxypropyl)diethylamine, for the preparation of tertiary aminoalkylcelluloses was reported in 1938 (9). The synthesis of basic aminoalkyl derivatives by treatment of alkali cellulose with epichlorohydrin and ammonia was also described in 1938 (10). The derivative was undoubtedly cross-linked by unreacted epichlorohydrin as well as by di- and triepoxypropylamines formed by the reaction of epichlorohydrin and ammonia in the alkaline system.

Direct preparation of a primary aminoalkylcellulose, the 2-aminoethyl ether, from ethylenimine was reported in 1937 (11). The same ether of cellulose was obtained later by heating alkali cellulose with 2-aminoethyl sulfate (12). Reduction of cellulose nitrate with sodamide in liquid ammonia was also reported to give a primary amino derivative (13). The presence of the primary amine function in the reduced product was demonstrated by diazotizing and coupling with β-naphthol and resorcinol.

In 1937, cellulose derivatives bearing unsaturated radicals, such as crotonate and allyl, were treated with ammonia or amines containing at least one active hydrogen to give aminoalkylcellulose derivatives (14). The unsaturated derivative could be halogenated prior to treatment with the amine.

A more recent method for preparing nitrogen containing cellulose derivatives involves treating chloroacyl esters of cellulose with secondary amines to form cellulose N,N-dialkylaminoacylates (15). Substantially all the chlorine of the chloroacylated cellulose can be replaced with aminoalkyl groups by heating 5 hr. at 95° with an excess of amine in an inert organic solvent, such as 1,4-dioxane or acetone. A similar treatment of chloroacetyl cellulose with pyridine under anhydrous conditions was claimed to give the quaternary ammonium salt (16).

Pancirolli (17) was among the first to describe the preparation of aminoalkylstarch. The p-nitrobenzyl ester of starch was reduced to give the p-aminobenzyl derivative. Diazotizing and coupling with naphthol yielded colored starches. The aminostarches, however, were devoid of adhesive character.

A patent issued in 1938 (18) described the preparation of aminostarch derivatives by partial replacement of various aryl sulfonate groups on starch with amines such as monoethanolamine, amylamine, and ethylenediamine. Derivatives which were at least 0.5 D.S. with respect to amine were soluble in dilute acid, but insoluble in dilute alkali. The derivatives were claimed to be particularly useful for textile finishes because of their resistance to dilute alkaline solutions.

In 1952, Kerr and Neukom (19) reported the direct preparation of the 2-aminoethyl ether of starch by treatment of starch with ethylenimine. A cationic product of 0.26 D.S. was obtained by heating 180 g. of starch (10% moisture) with 1 mole (43 g.) of ethylenimine at 90°–100° for 4 hr. The product readily flocculated negatively charged colloids, such as algin, carboxymethylcellulose, and mineral suspensions.

Since then, a wide variety of cationic starch types, including tertiary amino, imino, quaternary ammonium, quaternary phosphonium, and tertiary sulfonium starches have been described, primarily in the patent literature. Preparation, properties, and uses of these are described below.

III. TERTIARY AMINOALKYL ETHERS OF STARCH

1. Preparation

Tertiary aminoalkylstarches were the first cationic starches to be marketed in the United States and have achieved wide commercial success, primarily as internal sizing agents in paper manufacture (20). They are prepared by treating an alkaline starch slurry or paste with a tertiary amine which contains a β-halogenated alkyl, a 2,3-epoxypropyl (glycidyl), or a 3-chloro-2-hydroxypropyl radical. In the presence of a strong base, such as sodium hydroxide, these radicals etherify starch hydroxyls to form tertiary amino ethers in free base form. Treatment with acid converts the free amine base to the cationic tertiary ammonium salt.

Beta-halogenated amines useful for preparing tertiary aminoalkylstarches include 2-dimethylaminoethyl chloride, 2-diethylaminoethyl chloride, 2-dimethylaminoisopropyl chloride, 2-diallylaminoethyl chloride, and 2-diisopropylaminoethyl chloride, (20, 21). These compounds etherify the hydroxyl groups of starch rapidly and efficiently with elimination of halide salts as illustrated in equation 1. Sufficient strong base is employed to maintain a pH above about 10 during reaction. With proper control of reaction conditions, about 80% of the added amine reacts with starch.

$$(C_6H_7O_2)_x(OH)_{3x} + a\ ClCH_2-CH_2-N(C_2H_5)_2 + NaOH \rightarrow$$
$$(C_6H_7O_2)_x(OH)_{3x-a}[O-CH_2-CH_2-N(C_2H_5)_2]_a + NaCl \quad (1)$$

Glycidyl tertiary amines useful for making tertiary aminoalkylstarches include N-(2,3-epoxypropyl)diethylamine, N-(2,3-epoxypropyl)-dibutylamine, N-(2,3-epoxypropyl)-N-methylaniline, N-(2,3-epoxypropyl)piperidine (19, 22, 23). Under the influence of an alkaline catalyst, such as sodium hydroxide or sodium carbonate, starch hydroxyls are readily etherified by the glycidyl function as shown in equation 2.

$$\overset{O}{\overbrace{}}$$
$$(C_6H_7O_2)_x(OH)_{3x} + a\ CH_2-CH-CH_2N(C_2H_5)_2 + NaOH \rightarrow$$
$$(C_6H_7O_2)_x(OH)_{3x-a}[O-CH_2-CHOH-CH_2-N(C_2H_5)_2]_a \quad (2)$$

Reaction efficiencies are generally somewhat lower than those obtained with the haloamines, particularly with glycidylamines which contain low-molecular-weight alkyl groups, such as methyl or ethyl. This results from both intermolecular and intramolecular quaternization of epoxide with the tertiary amino radical. Intermolecular quaternization may occur by the mechanism shown in equation 3. This reaction is minimized by use of

$$2 \overset{O}{\overset{\diagup\diagdown}{CH_2-CH}}-CH_2-N(CH_3)_2 + H_2O \rightarrow$$

$$\overset{O}{\overset{\diagup\diagdown}{CH_2-CH}}-CH_2-\overset{+}{N}(CH_3)_2CH_2CHOH-CH_2N(CH_3)_2 + OH^- \quad (3)$$

sterically hindered amines such as those containing butyl, aryl, or aralkyl radicals.

Glycidyl tertiary amines are conveniently prepared by treatment of epichlorohydrin with a secondary amine followed by addition of a strong base to epoxidize the chlorohydrin intermediate (24). The product is obtained in pure form by fractional distillation under high vacuum.

The 3-chloro-2-hydroxypropyl tertiary amines are equivalent to the glycidyl tertiary amines for preparation of aminoalkylstarches, except that the former requires conversion to the glycidyl form for reaction with starch. The conversion is readily accomplished by treating the aqueous starch–amine mixture with excess basic catalyst (equation 4).

$$(C_6H_7O_2)_x(OH)_{3x} + a\ Cl-CH_2-CH_2OH-CH_2-N(C_2H_5)_2 + NaOH \rightarrow$$
$$(C_6H_7O_2)_x(OH)_{3x-a}[O-CH_2-CH_2OH-CH_2-N(C_2H_5)_2]_a + NaCl \quad (4)$$

Although more stable than the glycidyl tertiary amines, the chlorohydrin species have been reported to form azelidinium salts by intramolecular quaternization (25) (equation 5).

$$ClCH_2-CHOH-CH_2N(C_2H_5)_2 \rightarrow (C_2H_5)\overset{+}{N}\overset{\displaystyle CH_2}{\underset{\displaystyle CH_2}{\diagup\diagdown\diagup}}CHOH + Cl^- \quad (5)$$

In the commercial preparation of low D.S. granular derivatives, which involves treating an alkaline suspension of granular starch with an epoxyamine or haloalkyl tertiary amine, a reaction time of 6–12 hr. at 40°–45° is usually sufficient to promote complete reaction. The product is then dewatered, and the filter cake is washed to remove soluble salts. The filter cake is dried by conventional methods.

Cold-water-soluble tertiary aminoalkylstarches have been prepared by gelatinizing the derivatives over revolving heated drums (26). High-D.S., cold-water-soluble, granular derivatives may be prepared by use of salts or inert organic solvents in the starch slurry to suppress granule swelling. A solution of methyl ethyl ketone (2-butanone) and water has been employed to prepare a granular diethylaminoethyl ether of starch which gelatinized instantly in cold water (27). High-D.S., cold-water-soluble, granular derivatives may also be prepared by etherification of alkaline semidry starch (15–20% moisture) with a haloalkyl tertiary amine or an epoxyamine. If an epoxyamine is used, only a catalytic amount of a strong base is required, and the product after neutralization contains only small amounts of salts.

Synthetic tertiary aminoalkylpolyglucose derivatives have been prepared with 2-chloroethyldiethylamine and 2,3-epoxypropyldiethylamine (28). The epoxyamine with sodium carbonate catalyst was preferred for preparing derivatives having a high and controlled D.S. Tertiary aminoalkyl ethers of polyglucose of 1.6 D.S. were prepared and converted to their quaternary ammonium salts by alkylation with ethyl iodide.

Using procedures previously employed for preparing insoluble aminoalkylcellulose derivatives (29), McKernan and Ricketts (30) prepared diethylaminoethyl ethers of dextran ranging up to 0.8 D.S. Examination of the sugars produced by acid hydrolysis of the derivative indicated substitution of amino groups on C-2, C-3, and C-4 of the D-glucose units. Titration with hydrochloric acid showed pK values of about 8.8. The derivatives were stated to be useful for separation of biological systems.

Vinyl heterocyclic amines, such as 2-vinylpyridine and N-vinyl-2-pyrrolidone, have been grafted to hypochlorite oxidized granular starch in an aqueous slurry using ferrous ion as the activator and tertiary butylhydroperoxide or hydrogen peroxide as the oxidizing catalyst (31). The copolymers contained 0.1–0.27% of nitrogen and possessed ion-exchange properties which could be enhanced by quaternizing the tertiary amine groups. Diethylaminoethyl methacrylate as well as the quaternary ammonium methacrylate salt has been similarly grafted to a variety of granular starches (31).

2. Properties

In common with aliphatic amines, the tertiary amino radicals are protonated with acids to form tertiary ammonium salts. Cationic activity in the starch derivative results from the positive charge on the ammonium ion. A typical amine titration curve is obtained when the basic aminoalkylstarch is titrated with acid or the amine salt is titrated with base. The titration data can be used to calculate D.S. if the alkali absorbed by a starch control is subtracted. The D.S. values are in close agreement with those calculated from nitrogen content.

The presence of tertiary amine groups on starch lowers the starch gelatinization temperature in direct proportion to degree of substitution. This behavior is common to starch derivatives that are not cross-linked. The cooked pastes remain fluid and relatively clear when held at ambient temperatures, even at low pH values. Paste stability is due to the forces of repulsion between the tertiary ammonium groups which are completely ionized at low pH. In contrast, pastes of sodium carboxymethylstarch develop turbidity as the pH is lowered because the undissociated acid is formed.

The hot paste viscosity of a tertiary aminoalkylstarch prepared from unmodified starch is somewhat higher than that of the parent starch, but not as high as for other ionic starch derivatives such as starch sulfate, carboxymethylstarch, or quaternary ammonium alkylstarch. Tertiary aminoalkylstarches may be prepared at lower viscosities by hydrolyzing the starch with acid either before or after etherification. In this connection, it has been observed that the rate of hydrolysis of the dimethylaminoethyl ether of starch is much slower with hydrochloric acid than with polystyrene sulfonic acid (*32*). The faster rate with the latter acid was attributed to counter-ion binding of tertiary amine groups to polystyrene sulfonic acid. Degree of hydrolysis, as measured by reducing sugar content, is greater with the polystyrene sulfonic acid and also increases with increasing tertiary amino D.S. (*33*). It was postulated that rapid hydrolysis occurred at the sites of amino substitution, whereas the liberated unsubstituted fragments were slowly attacked by polystyrene sulfonic acid.

IV. ONIUM STARCH DERIVATIVES

1. Preparation

The term, "onium starch," is used to designate starch derivatives bearing fully substituted radicals, such as quaternary ammonium, quaternary phosphonium, and tertiary sulfonium. These radicals, saturated with groups other than hydrogen, carry a formal positive charge over the entire pH range. Starch derivatives bearing these groups become cationic polyelectrolytes when dispersed in water. The hydroxide forms of the derivatives behave as strong bases, a behavior characteristic of monomeric organic quaternary ammonium bases. The discussion to follow deals primarily with quaternary ammonium derivatives, but other onium derivatives are expected to behave similarly.

Quaternary ammonium alkyl ethers of starch may be prepared by treating an alkaline starch slurry or paste with a quaternary ammonium salt containing a 2,3-epoxypropyl (glycidyl) or a 3-chloro-2-hydroxypropyl (chlorohydrin) radical (*34*, *35*). Equations illustrating the reactions of starch with quaternary ammonium salts bearing glycidyl and chlorohydrin radicals are illustrated in equations 6 and 7, respectively:

$$(C_6H_7O_2)_x(OH)_{3x} + a\ \overset{O}{\overset{\diagup\ \diagdown}{CH_2-CH}}-CH_2-\overset{+}{N}(CH_3)_3 + Cl^- \overset{OH^-}{\longrightarrow}$$

$$(C_6H_7O_2)_x(OH)_{3x-a}[-O-CH_2-CHOH-CH_2-\overset{+}{N}(CH_3)_3]_a + Cl^- \quad (6)$$

$$(C_6H_7O_2)_x(OH)_{3x} + a \; Cl\text{-}CH_2\text{-}CHOH\text{-}CH_2\overset{+}{N}(CH_3)_3 + Cl^- + OH^- \rightarrow$$

$$(C_6H_7O_2)_x(OH)_{3x-a}[\text{-}O\text{-}CH_2\text{-}CHOH\text{-}CH_2\text{-}\overset{+}{N}(CH_3)_3]_a + 2 \; Cl^- + H_2O \quad (7)$$

The chlorohydrin form of the reagent shown in equation 7 is equivalent to the glycidyl form, equation 6. However, for reaction with starch, the chlorohydrin reagent must be converted to the epoxide form first, which is the active etherifying species. This conversion occurs rapidly in the presence of a strong base such as sodium hydroxide.

Glycidyl or chlorohydrin salts containing trimethyl-, triethyl-, benzyl-dimethyl-, dodecyldimethyl-, stearyldimethyl-, and morpholinodimethyl-ammonium radicals are reported to be particularly useful for preparing quaternary ammonium alkyl ethers of starch (34). These salts may be prepared by treating epichlorohydrin with a tertiary amine or a tertiary amine hydrochloride in an aqueous solution. To prevent unwanted cross-linking during derivatization, unreacted epichlorohydrin must be completely removed by solvent extraction, by distillation, or by crystallization of the quaternary salt from an anhydrous organic solvent. Glycidyl quaternary ammonium salts have also been prepared by quaternization of glycidyl tertiary amines with methyl tosylate (36). Several of the salts were obtained in crystalline form.

Since their nitrogen is fully alkylated, glycidyl quaternary ammonium salts are not susceptible to the condensations which frequently occur with glycidyl tertiary amines. By proper control of reaction variables, 80% reaction efficiencies can be achieved in starch etherification. The fact that this reaction with starch is more rapid than with other epoxides may be attributed to the strong electron attracting effect of the quaternary ammonium nitrogen (37). This effect increases the positive charge on the terminal carbon of the oxirane group facilitating attack by the nucleophilic starch–sodium hydroxide complex.

Quaternary ammonium alkylstarches may also be prepared by quaternizing tertiary aminoalkylstarches with alkylating agents as shown in equation 8. Caldwell and Wurzburg (20) obtained the methyldiethyl-

$$(C_6H_7O_2)_x(OH)_{3x-a} [\text{-}O\text{-}CH_2\text{-}CH_2\text{-}N(CH_3)_2] + a \; CH_3I \longrightarrow$$

$$(C_6H_7O_2)_x(OH)_{3x-a}[\text{-}O\text{-}CH_2\text{-}CH_2\text{-}N(CH_3)_3]_a + a \; I^- \quad (8)$$

aminoethyl quaternary derivative by treating an alcoholic suspension of the diethylaminoethyl ether of starch with methyl iodide at reflux temperature. The product forms a water-clear sol when gelatinized in water.

Starch derivatives containing quaternary ammonium and tertiary amino radicals have also been prepared by treating dialdehyde starch with betaine hydrazide hydrochloride or N,N-dimethylglycine hydrazide hydrochloride to form hydrazones (38). Derivatives containing 1.5–7.3%

of cationic hydrazone groups were readily prepared by performing the reaction at pH 2.5 and 35°–40° in an aqueous slurry. Cationic activity of these aldehydes is sufficient to obtain good retention on cellulose fibers.

Starches containing the cationic sulfonium group have been prepared from sulfonium compounds containing chloroethyl radicals, such as 2-chloroethylmethylethyl sulfonium iodide (*39*). Vinyl sulfonium as well as 2,3-epoxypropyl sulfonium salts may also be used. Etherification of starch with all three types of reagents is catalyzed with strong bases such as sodium or potassium hydroxide. The sulfonium alkyl ethers of starch are characterized by a positive electrical charge, superior viscosity stability, increased paste clarity, and cohesiveness. They may be prepared from a slurry of granular starch or from gelatinized starch.

Phosphonium alkyl ethers of starch have been prepared from phosphonium salts carrying functional groups similar to those described above for the sulfonium salts (*40*). As an example, tributylphosphonium ethyl ether of starch was prepared from 2-chloroethyltributylphosphonium chloride. The cationic nature of the quaternary phosphonium derivative was demonstrated by its mobility in an electrophoresis cell.

2. Properties

In common with anionically charged starch derivatives, onium ethers of starch are characterized by low gelatinization temperatures, high paste viscosities, reduced paste setback or retrogradation tendency, and high paste clarity. The hydrophilic quaternary ammonium ion very effectively reduces the gelatinization temperature, which decreases with increasing degree of substitution. Cold water swelling of the granules begins at about 0.07 D.S. In contrast, a D.S. of 0.2–0.3 is required to obtain cold water swelling in granular hydroxyethylstarch.

Cold water swelling granular derivatives may be prepared by performing the etherification in an aqueous alkaline slurry to which salts or water miscible organic solvents, such as isopropanol, have been added to suppress starch gelatinization. To obtain cold water swelling in the product, the gelatinization suppressant generally must be removed. If the degree of substitution is less than about 0.1, this can be done by washing the dewatered product with methanol–water mixtures. Methanol evaporates during drying.

Cold water swelling granular products may also be obtained by etherification of alkaline starch in which insufficient moisture is present to initiate swelling of the starch. Usually, such reactions are carried out at moisture levels of 15% to 20%, based on starch dry substance.

Quaternary ammonium derivatives prepared from unmodified starch develop high viscosity at D.S. levels of only about 0.01. Viscosity is increased only slightly at higher D.S. levels. As with most polyelectrolytes, soluble salts reduce paste viscosity. Derivatives of lower viscosity may be obtained by depolymerizing the starch by conventional methods before or after derivatization.

V. PRIMARY AND SECONDARY AMINOALKYL STARCHES

Cationic starch derivatives containing primary and secondary amine groups generally are more difficult to prepare than the tertiary amino and quaternary ammonium ethers. Primary and secondary amines containing 2-haloethyl or 2,3-epoxypropyl radicals react inefficiently with starch, presumably because of inter- and intramolecular condensations of the amines. However, secondary 2,3-epoxypropyl amines containing bulky groups, such as tertiary butyl or cyclohexyl, are sufficiently hindered so that secondary amino starch ethers can be prepared at fair reaction efficiencies (41).

One direct route for preparing a primary amino derivative of starch or polyglucose involves treatment of the polysaccharide with ethylenimine as described by Kerr and Neukom (19). Following Kerr's procedure, Wood and Mora (28) obtained basic polyglucose derivatives of 0.2 D.S. from ethylenimine, but were unable to obtain higher D.S. products under more vigorous reaction conditions, presumably because of polymerization of ethylenimine. It has not been confirmed, by isolation of substituted D-glucose, that the 2-aminoethyl ether is formed from ethylenimine.

As mentioned previously, aryl sulfonate groups of starch have been partially replaced with ammonia or primary amines to give primary and secondary amino starch ethers in which amine D.S. is approximately equal to aryl sulfonate D.S. (18). Derivatives having an amine D.S. of about 0.5 were soluble in dilute acid, but insoluble in dilute alkaline solutions. Other workers (28) have partially replaced tosyl groups on polyglucose with ethylenediamine to obtain a 0.75 and 1.0 D.S. product with respect to aminoethylamino and tosyl, respectively. The product was insoluble in water because of cross-linking through the bifunctional diamine group. Complete displacement of aryl sulfonate groups apparently cannot be achieved with ammonia and amines. However, complete displacement occurs with strong nucleophiles such as azide (42) and hydrazine (43). The resulting azido and hydrazino polysaccharide derivatives may then be reduced to give the amino derivative.

Whistler and Medcalf (42) prepared 6-amino-6-deoxyamyloses ranging from 0.1 to 1.0 D.S. by complete replacement of tosyl on 2,3-di-O-phenylcarbamyl-6-tosylamylose with the azido group, followed by quantitative reduction of azido and complete removal of phenylcarbamyl units with lithium aluminum hydride. The higher-molecular-weight products (about 52,000), with D.S. values above 0.1, are soluble in water and dilute acid, but not in dilute base. Also, viscosity decreases with increasing pH. Insolubility in dilute base and lower viscosity at high pH are expected from the conversion of the extended ionic amine salt to the more coiled free base form. Wolfrom and co-workers (*43*) prepared a 1.4 D.S. aminoamylose by treatment of 1.7 D.S. tosylamylose with hydrazine followed by reduction with Raney nickel. In addition to amine groups present on C-6 and presumably on C-2, the 3,6-anhydro ring was found on about 16% of the D-glucose units. This was attributed to the base catalyzed elimination of the tosyloxy group on C-6.

In their study of methods for preparing basic polyglucose derivatives, Wood and Mora (*28*) prepared an 0.8 D.S. 3-aminopropylpolyglucose by reduction of the 2.0–2.6 D.S. cyanoethyl ether derivative with lithium aluminum hydride. Reduction was effected under a dry atmosphere of nitrogen using tetrahydrofuran or the dimethyl ether of diethylene glycol (diglyme) as the solvent. This method was considered to be less satisfactory than the use of 1-diethylamino-2,3-epoxypropane in aqueous sodium carbonate for preparing the basic polyglucose derivative.

The direct condensation of dry starch with amines and amino acids, such as aniline and aminobenzoic acids, by heating at 115°–120° in the absence of oxygen, has been claimed to give yellow derivatives containing up to 1.3% of nitrogen (*44*). The derivatives were proposed as useful foaming agents.

Primary amino alkyl ethers of starch have also been prepared from β-aminoethylsulfuric acid (*45, 46*). Aminoalkylation was effected by heating a water solution of potato starch for 2 hr. at 130° in the presence of 20% sodium hydroxide, based on starch; the product contained 1% nitrogen.

VI. MISCELLANEOUS CATIONIC STARCHES

Cationic starch derivatives, referred to as "imino starches" (iminoalkylstarches), may be prepared by treatment of starch with disubstituted cyanamides in the presence of a strong base catalyst. Compounds suitable for preparing the imino derivatives include dimethyl-, diallyl-, and dibenzylcyanamides (*47*).

The reaction is believed to occur in the manner analogous to that proposed for the preparation of trialkyl isoureas from alcohols and disubstituted cyanamides (*48*), as shown in equation 9.

$$ROH + R_1R_2NCN \xrightarrow{OH^-} R_1R_2NC(=NH)OR \tag{9}$$

Cationic activity results from the basic imino group, =NH, which forms ionic imine salts when protonated with acids. These derivatives are similar to quaternary ammonium and tertiary aminoalkyl ethers of starch with respect to cationic activity.

The imino group in free base form is readily hydrolyzed to the carbonyl function with liberation of ammonia when the derivative is heated in water. On the other hand, the salt form is relatively stable and shows little hydrolysis of the imino group when similarly treated.

Iminoalkylstarches may be prepared from a slurry of granular starch, from pasted starch or from starch containing 15–20% of moisture. A product in granular form prepared from dimethylcyanamide does not gelatinize completely when boiled in water indicating slight cross-linking or intermolecular hydrogen bonding. Products prepared from pasted starch, however, show no evidence of cross-linking. This observation is expected since pasted starch is less easily cross-linked than granular starch.

Cationic starches related to the above imino derivatives have been prepared from cyanamide salts at an alkaline pH, followed by acidification to form the more stable cationic salt (49–51). Alkali metal or alkaline earth metal cyanamides, and their acid salts, may be used. The mechanism of the reaction is uncertain, but the product appears to be structurally similar to the iminoalkylstarches discussed previously and may be formed by the same mechanism.

Starch cyanamide reaction products are said to vary in ease of gelatinization depending on the type of anion present (49). Derivatives containing chloride, nitrate, and sulfate gelatinize upon cooking, whereas those containing phosphate, sulfite, or acetate anions do not readily gelatinize. The tendency of the pasted products to undergo thickening upon standing has been overcome by the addition of aluminum sulfate or sodium pyrophosphate (51).

Other polymers in aqueous colloidal dispersion, such as cellulose derivatives, pectin, and polyvinyl alcohol, have been treated with cyanamide salts to form cationic derivatives (52). Since these dispersions lose cationic activity on standing, they must be used within a day or two after preparation. Low temperature and low pH improve shelf life.

Reagents such as β-propionolactone (53), isatoic anhydride, and quinolinic anhydride (54) have been proposed for use in the preparation of cationic esters of starch.

VII. Uses for Cationic Starches

1. Paper

Cationic starches are used extensively as internal binders in the manufacture of paper where they are added to the paper furnish before the sheet is formed. They are highly effective for improving such physical properties of paper as bursting and tensile strength, elongation, fold endurance, and pick resistance (55). Usually, a 0.5% addition of cooked cationic starch, based on dry weight of pulp, gives the same improvement in paper strength as does a 1.5–2.0% addition of corn starch. Other benefits claimed for cationic starch are improved drainage on the wire, better sheet formation, and enhancement of the sizing efficiency of an alum–rosin size (56).

Cationic starches also improve the retention of fillers used in the manufacture of paper. Titanium dioxide, clay, and calcium carbonate are frequently incorporated in the furnish to a paper machine to improve the opacity of high grade printing papers, fine writing paper, and light weight papers such as bread wrap, catalog, glassine, and Bible. With increasing filler retention, the sheet loses strength, apparently because the inert filler reduces the number of sites for fiber-to-fiber bonding. Because cationic starch acts both to improve strength properties and filler retention, its use gives high strength properties at high levels of filler retention (57).

The mechanism by which cationic starches improve fiber-to-fiber bonding is not completely understood. High retention of cationic starch by the negatively charged cellulose fibers is known to occur, but this does not necessarily account for improved fiber-to-fiber bonding. For example, Cushing and Schuman (58) have shown that fiber-to-fiber bonding does not always increase with increasing starch retention. A possible explanation for the improved strength obtained with cationic starch is that ionic attraction promotes a more intimate contact between the fiber surface and starch hydroxyls to increase hydrogen bond formation when the sheet is dried. However, anionic starches, such as starch phosphate and carboxyethylstarch, also improve the strength properties of paper, particularly when used with alum. If the alum–anionic starch complex is positively charged, the above explanation would be tenable.

The mechanism of improved filler retention is also open to speculation. Many starches actually reduce filler retention, possibly because of a protective colloid action on the pigment (59). For example, oxidized starches, although excellent fiber bonding agents, cause poor retention of titanium dioxide, even at very low starch concentrations. A low concentration of oxidized starch in the furnish, however, does not impair the efficiency of cationic starch for retaining titanium dioxide (60). Since cationic starch is known to induce pigment flocculation, it is likely that the floc is retained on the wire by both mechanical filtration and ionic attraction of the cationically charged floc to the negatively charged cellulose fibers. This theory has been advanced for the retention of titanium dioxide in the presence of alum (61, 62).

A colorimetric procedure has been developed for measuring cationic activity of pulp–cationic starch complexes (63). The procedure is proposed as a screening test for estimating the value of cationic starches as retention aids. The method consists of the indirect measurement of an anionic pigment absorbed on pulp which has been treated with cationic starch. Cationic activity of the pulp–cationic starch complex varies with the cationic group, degree of substitution, and method of dispersing the cationic starch.

Cationic starches are also used as emulsifying agents and retention aids for various types of water-repellent sizing agents for paper. These sizing agents include aqueous emulsions of high-molecular-weight alkyl ketene dimers (64, 65), waxes and rosin derivatives (66), cyclic dicarboxylic acid anhydrides (67), and vinyl acetate polymers (68). The water-repellent sizing agent is usually emulsified in water with gelatinized cationic starch, and the emulsion is added to the cellulose fibers before the sheet is formed. When added in this manner, the emulsion functions as an internal sizing agent as opposed to external sizes which are applied after the sheet is formed.

Alkyl ketene dimer emulsions containing cationic starch are widely used in the paper industry in the manufacture of a neutral or alkaline sized sheet which resists penetration of water and alkaline inks. Accelerated aging tests indicate that an alkaline sheet would be usable after 400 years, whereas one containing alum would have a useful life of only about 50 years (64). The alkyl ketene dimer emulsions do not adversely affect strength, brightness, or sheet formation as does the alum–rosin size (64). Emulsions of cyclic dicarboxylic acid anhydrides containing cationic starch are purported to show similar advantages (67). Harris and Weisgerber (69) claim that the use of tertiary aminoalkylstarch bearing hydroxyethyl groups improves the sizing efficiency of alkyl ketene dimer emulsions.

Positively charged latices of polyvinyl acetate, prepared by polymerizing vinyl acetate in the presence of pasted tertiary aminoalkyl-starch, have been proposed for internal sizing of paper as well as for sizing synthetic and natural fibers (68). A positive charge on the latex particle was demonstrated electrophoretically.

Cationic starches are also useful for increasing the retention of dialdehyde starch in the manufacture of wet-strength paper. Retention of dialdehyde starch may be improved by the addition of cationic starch, or by rendering the dialydehyde starch cationically active by substitution with amino or quaternary ammonium groups. For detailed information, see "Production and Uses of Dialdehyde Starch" in Chapter XVIII of this volume.

It is claimed that water-resistant surface sizings and coatings for paper or paperboard can be obtained by applying to the paper an aqueous dispersion of a primary aminoalkyl ether of starch and an aldehyde, such as glyoxal or formaldehyde (53). Presumably, the aldehyde condenses with the primary amino group during drying to cause insolubilization. Ethylenimine or β-aminoethyl sulfate may be used for preparing the aminoalkylstarch.

Low D.S., cationic tertiary aminoalkylstarch has been proposed as an adhesive binder in pigmented coatings for paper (54, 70). Use of cationic starch permits reduction in solids content in the coating color while maintaining high coating strength. Cationic starch may be used alone or in combination with conventional coating starches. Flocculation, which normally occurs when pigment slurries are treated with cationic starch, is apparently overcome by maintaining a low degree of substitution in the cationic starch.

Cationic starch mixed with glycerol monostearate and kerosene is claimed to be effective for removal of pitch which sometimes accumulates on paper manufacturing machinery as sticky, dark deposits (71). Addition of the cationic starch composition ahead of the pitch deposit is said to peptize the agglomerates; the peptized pitch is carried onto the wire, but the particles are too small to be harmful.

2. Textiles

Although they are excellent adhesives for both natural and synthetic fibers, cationic starches have not found widespread use for textile sizing. High cost in comparison with conventional starches and problems with soil redeposition in laundry starching are some reasons for the lack of commercial acceptance. Benefits derived from the use of cationic starches for warp sizing or slashing of cotton and various synthetic fibers include resistance to loom abrasion, elimination of static electricity in the dried yarns, reduction in softness requirements, and reduction in starch usage because of better cohesion and adhesion properties (72).

Cationic starches obtained by treatment of starch with cyanamide salts are claimed to be particularly useful for warp sizing of wool or wool–polyester blends, which are usually difficult to size (49, 51, 52).

The use of tertiary aminoalkylstarch for sizing glass filaments has been proposed (73). Cationic starch strongly adheres to the negative surface of the glass filament and minimizes migration of the size from the core of wound filaments during drying. Such size migration is a problem with many sizing agents.

Fukushima (74) claims to have improved the dyeability of regenerated cellulose by adding water-insoluble, basic aminoalkylstarches to the viscose mother liquor. This treatment is claimed to improve dye-ability with acid mordant dyes and acid dyes which have substantially no affinity for ordinary regenerated cellulose. The starch derivatives contain at least 0.2% of basic nitrogen and may be prepared by treating starch with ethylenimine, epoxy compounds containing basic amino groups, or β-aminoethyl sulfuric acid. Dyeability of polyvinyl alcohol is also improved by treatment of the polyvinyl alcohol spinning solution with the above basic aminoalkylstarches (75).

Cationic starches have also been proposed for cold water starching of cotton fabrics (76). The fabric is dipped into a cold water slurry of ungelatinized cationic starch. Nearly complete deposition of the starch to the negatively charged cellulose fabric occurs. The fabric is then ironed while sufficiently wet to promote complete gelatinization of the starch. Much greater fabric stiffening per unit weight of starch is obtained than with ordinary pasted or dried precooked starches. However, most cationic starches impart a permanent cationic charge to the fabrics. When the soiled fabric is washed, negatively charged soil particles are redeposited on the fabric. Soil redeposition is overcome by using a cationic starch in which the cationic group decomposes during ironing. Such a cationic starch, prepared from thin-boiling corn starch and dimethylcyanamide and dehydrated with an organic solvent, eliminates soil redeposition and gives greater sizing efficiency than quaternary ammonium or tertiary aminoalkyl ethers of starch (77).

3. Flocculation

Cationic starches are effective flocculating agents for aqueous suspensions of organic and inorganic particles which carry a negative charge. Their use as retention aids for various fillers in paper manufacture has already been discussed as involving flocculation. They have also been proposed as flocculating agents for waste slimes from various mining operations, for concentration and recovery of valuable minerals in colloidal suspension, for purification of industrial waters, and for removal of silt from river waters (35, 78–80).

Flocculation with cationic starch probably results when the positively charged starch and the negatively charged suspended particles form aggregates of sufficient size to settle from suspensions. However, forces other than those of simple ionic attraction induce flocculation since certain anionic and nonionic polymers are excellent flocculating agents for suspensions of negatively charged particles. Flocculation is influenced by sign and magnitude of the charge on the suspended particle, surface tension between the liquid and solid phases, Van der Waal's forces of attraction between solid particles, particle shape, and size and solids concentration (*81*). La Mer and Smellie (*82*) have given an excellent review of some of the theoretical aspects of flocculation.

It is often impossible to predict the actual merit of a flocculating agent by laboratory testing because of the difficulty of simulating use conditions. For most applications, floc density, rate of settling, and ease of filtration or removal of the solid fraction are important considerations in judging the effectiveness of a flocculating agent.

Cationic starches have also been evaluated in ore refining. In this use, one of the ore components is selectively depressed with a protective colloid, and the other is removed by froth flotation. Aminoethylstarch was found to be an excellent depressant for iron oxide, but it also depressed the quartz impurities resulting in poor separation (*83*). This finding supports the observation of Schulz and Cooke (*84*) that aminoethylstarch is strongly adsorbed by both hematite and quartz.

4. Ion-Exchange

Cationic derivatives of polysaccharides have been employed as anion exchangers for the separation, purification, or concentration of various biologically active materials such as enzymes, bovine plasma, and nucleic acids. Much of the work has been with cellulose derivatives since these can be prepared in water-insoluble forms at the relatively high D.S. levels required for high anion-exchange capacity (*31, 85*). Diethylaminoethylcellulose is most often employed, although primary amino and quaternary ammonium derivatives have also been proposed as anion exchangers (*7*). Recently, the diethylaminoethyl ether of cross-linked dextran has become available in commercial quantities; the product sold under the trade name of DEAE Sephadex, is claimed to be useful for separation of serum proteins and purification of enzymes. When placed in water the product swells to form gel grains which have a high ion-exchange capacity.

Starch in its native granular form possesses many of the requirements of an anion exchanger, such as water insolubility, ability to absorb moisture, high specific gravity, and a sufficiently porous structure in a packed column to permit easy flow of water. However, starch suffers from the disadvantage that cold water solubility occurs at relatively low D.S. levels so that anion-exchange capacity is limited. Bullock and Guthrie (*86*) apparently overcame this deficiency by cross-linking the starch granules with formaldehyde at pH 2 prior to etherification of the starch with 2-chloroethyldiethylamine to obtain the tertiary amino derivative. The cross-linked cationic starch retains its granular structure in cold aqueous solutions of dilute acids or bases as well as in boiling water.

Cationic starch in the form of water-insoluble gel grains has also been proposed as an anion exchanger (*87*). Preparation consists of cross-linking pasted starch with difunctional reagents, such as epichlorohydrin, to obtain a water-insoluble gel. After neutralization and washing, the gel is treated with an epoxyamine or a haloalkylamine to obtain the tertiary amino derivative, which may, if desired, be quaternized. The derivatives are claimed to have relatively high anion-exchange capacities and a sufficiently porous structure to permit easy contact of the amino groups with the liquid to be treated. Gels of similar ion-exchange properties were also prepared from dextran and ethylhydroxyethylcellulose.

The tertiary aminoalkyl ether of granular starch has been employed as a weak base anion exchanger for chromatographic fractionation of nucleic acids which differ in molecular weight and chemical structure (*88*). The nucleic acid fractions are not altered during passage through the column, and the flow rate is faster than is usually observed with other exchangers.

The interaction of water-soluble diethylaminoethyl ethers of dextran with biologically active materials, such as fibrinogen, albumin, and suspensions of cells, has also been studied (*31*). The dextran derivative formed insoluble complexes with fibrinogen and albumin and also agglutinated suspensions of cells. Cationic derivatives of polyglucose, because of their highly branched compact structure, have been suggested as useful tools for studying the interaction of charged macromolecules (*30, 89*).

VIII. REFERENCES

(*1*) M. Hagedorn and A. Ossenbrunner, British Patent 279,801 (1926); *Chem. Abstr.*, **22**, 3044 (1928).
(*2*) P. Karrer and W. Wehrli, *Helv. Chim. Acta*, **9**, 591 (1929); *Chem. Abstr.*, **20**, 3819 (1926).
(*3*) H. Dreyfus, German Patent 550,760 (1929); *Chem. Abstr.*, **26**, 4950 (1932).
(*4*) M. Hartmann, U.S. Patent 1,777,970 (1930); *Chem. Abstr.*, **25**, 204 (1934).
(*5*) C. P. L. Vaughan, U.S. Patent 2,591,748 (1952); *Chem. Abstr.*, **46**, 5842 (1952).
(*6*) C. P. L. Vaughan, U.S. Patent 2,623,042 (1952); *Chem. Abstr.*, **47**, 3564 (1953).
(*7*) C. L. Hoffpauir and J. D. Guthrie, *Textile Res. J.*, **20**, 617 (1950).
(*8*) E. F. Evans, U.S. Patent 2,768,162 (1956); *Chem. Abstr.*, **51**, 8783 (1957).
(*9*) P. Schlack, U.S. Patent 2,131,120 (1938); *Chem. Abstr.*, **32**, 9341 (1938).
(*10*) R. Stahn, U.S. Patent 2,120,513 (1938); *Chem. Abstr.*, **32**, 6076 (1938).
(*11*) H. Fink and R. Stahn, U.S. Patent 2,097,120 (1937); *Chem. Abstr.*, **32**, 353 (1938).
(*12*) J. D. Guthrie, *Textile Res. J.*, **17**, 625 (1947).
(*13*) P. C. Scherer and J. M. Field, *Rayon Textile Monthly*, **22**, 607 (1941).
(*14*) H. Dreyfus, U.S. Patent 2,073,052 (1937); *Chem. Abstr.*, **31**, 3274 (1937).
(*15*) J. W. Mench and B. Fulkerson, U.S. Patent 2,861,068 (1958); *Chem. Abstr.*, **53**, 4737 (1959).
(*16*) H. C. Olpin, S. A. Gibson, and J. E. Jones, U.S. Patent 2,348,305 (1945); *Chem. Abstr.*, **39**, 617 (1945).

(17) F. Pancirolli, *Boll. reparto fibre tessili vegetali staz. sper. ind. carta e fibre tessili vegetali*, **32**, 314 (1937); *Chem. Abstr.*, **31**, 7247 (1937).

(18) A. A. Houghton, British Patent 493,513 (1938); *Chem. Abstr.*, **33**, 2626 (1939).

(19) R. W. Kerr and H. Neukom, *Staerke*, **4**, 253 (1952).

(20) C. G. Caldwell and O. B. Wurzburg, U.S. Patent 2,813,093 (1957); *Chem. Abstr.*, **52**, 2438 (1958).

(21) C. H. Hullinger and N. H. Yui, U.S. Patent 2,970,140 (1961).

(22) Y. Merle, *Compt. Rend.*, **246**, 1425 (1958); *Chem. Abstr.*, **52**, 14533 (1958).

(23) G. C. Harris and R. A. Leonard, U.S. Patent 3,070,594 (1962); *Chem. Abstr.*, **58**, 11460 (1963).

(24) H. Gilman and L. Fullhart, *J. Am. Chem. Soc.*, **71**, 1478 (1949).

(25) J. H. Ross, D. Baker and A. T. Coscia, *J. Org. Chem.* **29**, 824 (1964).

(26) C. G. Caldwell and O. B. Wurzburg, U.S. Patent 2,917,506 (1959); *Chem. Abstr.*, **54**, 10358 (1960).

(27) E. T. Hjermstad and L. C. Martin, U.S. Patent 3,135,739 (1964).

(28) J. W. Wood and P. T. Mora, *J. Org. Chem.*, **27**, 2115 (1962).

(29) E. A. Peterson and H. A. Sober, *J. Am. Chem. Soc.*, **78**, 751 (1956).

(30) W. McKernan and C. R. Ricketts, *Chem. Ind. (London)*, 1490 (1959).

(31) C. E. Brockway, R. E. Estes, and R. D. Smith, U.S. Patent 3,095,391 (1963).

(32) T. J. Painter and W. T. J. Morgan, *Chem. Ind. (London)*, 437 (1961).

(33) T. J. Painter, *J. Chem. Soc.*, 1982 (1964).

(34) E. F. Paschall, U.S. Patent 2,876,217 (1959); *Chem. Abstr.*, **53**, 12720 (1959).

(35) E. F. Paschall and W. H. Minkema, U.S. Patent 2,995,513 (1961); *Chem. Abstr.*, **55**, 26489 (1961).

(36) D. M. Burness and H. O. Bayer, *J. Org. Chem.*, **28**, 2283 (1963).

(37) W. C. Ross, *J. Chem. Soc.*, 2257 (1950).

(38) C. L. Mehltretter, T. E. Yeates, G. E. Hamerstrand, B. T. Hoffreiter, and C. E. Rist, *Tappi*, **44**, 750 (1962).

(39) M. W. Rutenberg and J. L. Volpe, U.S. Patent 2,989,520 (1961); *Chem. Abstr.*, **55**, 22878 (1961).

(40) A. Aszalos, U.S. Patent 3,077,469 (1963); *Chem. Abstr.*, **59**, 3000 (1963).

(41) Corn Products Refining Co., British Patent 854,161 (1960).

(42) R. L. Whistler and D. G. Medcalf, *Arch. Biochem. Biophys.*, **104**, 150 (1964).

(43) M. L. Wolfrom, M. I. Taha, and D. Horton, *J. Org. Chem.*, **28**, 3553 (1963).

(44) V. P. Goguadze and G. M. Yashvile, *J. Appl. Chem. (London)*, **8**, 530(1958); *Zhur. Priklad. Khim.*, **30**, 618 (1957); *Chem. Abstr.*, **51**, 14302 (1957).)

(45) O. Fukushima, U.S. Patent 3,066,032 (1962); *Chem. Abstr.*, **58**, 6967 (1963.

(46) O. Fukushima and K. Matsubayashi, U.S. Patent 3,067,152 (1962); *Chem. Abstr.*, **58**, 5825 (1963).

(47) E. F. Paschall, U.S. Patent 2,894,944 (1959); *Chem. Abstr.*, **54**, 2794 (1960).

(48) R. H. McKee, *Am. Chem. J.*, **42**, 1 (1909); *Chem. Abstr.*, **3**, 2444 (1909).

(49) L. H. Elizer, G. C. Glasscock, and J. M. Seitz, U.S. Patent 3,051,699 (1962); *Chem. Abstr.*, **58**, 14280 (1963).

(50) L. H. Elizer, G. C. Glasscock, and J. M. Seitz, U.S. Patent 3,051,700 (1962); *Chem. Abstr.*, **58**, 11564 (1963).

(51) L. H. Elizer, G. C. Glasscock, and J. M. Seitz, U.S. Patent 3,136,646 (1964).

(52) L. H. Elizer, G. C. Glasscock, and J. M. Seitz, U.S. Patent 3,051,691 (1962); *Chem. Abstr.*, **58**, 1624 (1963).

(53) Nationale Zetmeelindustrie N.V., British Patent 944,804 (1963); *Chem. Abstr.*, **60**, 10920 (1964).

422   E. F. PASCHALL

(54) J. Kronfeld, U.S. Patent 3,052,561 (1962).
(55) C. G. Caldwell and O. B. Wurzburg, U.S. Patent 2,935,436 (1960); *Chem. Abstr.*, **54,** 16831 (1960).
(56) National Starch Products, Technical Bulletin No. 228.
(57) Corn Products Company, Technical Bulletin, QT-27-002.
(58) M. L. Cushing and K. R. Schuman, *Tappi*, **42,** 1006 (1959).
(59) W. R. Willets, *Paper Trade J.*, **102,** No. 3, 36 (1936).
(60) H. C. Brill, *Tappi*, **38,** 522 (1955).
(61) H. C. Brill and F. L. Hecklau, *Tappi*, **43,** 229A (1960).
(62) R. D. Fraik, *Tappi*, **45,** 159A (1962).
(63) C. L. Mehltretter, F. B. Weakley, M. L. Ashby, D. W. Herlocker, and C. E. Rist, *Tappi*, **46,** 506 (1963).
(64) C. A. Weisgerber and C. B. Hanford, *Tappi*, **43,** 178A (1960).
(65) C. H. Chapman, U.S. Patent 3,130,118 (1964).
(66) C. H. Chapman, U.S. Patent 3,096,232 (1963); *Chem. Abstr.*, **59,** 8988 (1963).
(67) National Starch and Chemical Corp., British Patent 957,136 (1964).
(68) R. J. Kray and F. M. Berardinelli, U.S. Patent 3,001,957 (1961); *Chem. Abstr.*, **56,** 2620 (1962).
(69) G. C. Harris and C. A. Weisgerber, U.S. Patent 3,070,452 (1962); *Chem. Abstr.*, **58,** 10398 (1963).
(70) D. S. Greif, *Tappi*, **43,** 254 (1960).
(71) J. F. Thurlow, U.S. Patent 3,102,065 (1963); *Chem. Abstr.*, **59,** 15491 (1963).
(72) H. C. Olsen, *Textile Ind.*, **123,** No. 9, 104 (1959); H. C. Olsen, U.S. Patent 2,946,705 (1960); *Chem. Abstr.*, **54,** 21780 (1960).
(73) Pittsburgh Plate Glass Co., Belgian Patent 618,146 (1962).
(74) O. Fukushima, U.S. Patent 3,066,032 (1963); *Chem. Abstr.*, **58,** 6967 (1963).
(75) O. Fukushima and K. Matsubayashi, U.S. Patent 3,067,152 (1962); *Chem. Abstr.*, **58,** 5825 (1963).
(76) H. Meisel, U.S. Patent 2,965,518 (1960); *Chem. Abstr.*, **55,** 6864 (1961).
(77) E. F. Paschall and W. J. Katzbeck, U.S. Patent 3,068,124 (1962); *Chem. Abstr.*, **58,** 5874 (1963).
(78) V. K. La Mer, R. H. Smellie, Jr., and P.-K. Lee, *J. Colloid. Sci.*, **12,** 230 (1957).
(79) C. G. Caldwell and O. B. Wurzburg, U.S. Patent 2,975,124 (1961); *Chem. Abstr.*, **55,** 16043 (1961).
(80) A. D. Nevers, U.S. Patent 3,157,549 (1964).
(81) D. J. I. Evans, W. Kunda, and P. Chiang, *Can. J. Chem. Eng.*, **35,** 25 (1957).
(82) V. K. La Mer and R. H. Smellie, Jr., *J. Colloid. Sci.*, **11,** 710 (1956).
(83) C. S. Chang, *Mining Eng.*, **6,** 922 (1954).
(84) N. F. Schulz and S. R. B. Cooke, *Ind. Eng. Chem.*, **45,** 2767 (1953).
(85) Glaxo Laboratories Ltd., British Patent 911,223 (1962); *Chem. Abstr.*, **58,** 4730 (1963).
(86) A. L. Bullock and J. D. Guthrie, U.S. Patent 2,992,215 (1961); *Chem. Abstr.*, **55,** 22878 (1961).
(87) Aktiebolaget Pharmacia, British Patent 936,039 (1963); *Chem. Abstr.*, **60,** 733 (1964).
(88) K. C. Smith, S. Rebhun, and H. Kaplan, *Anal. Biochem.*, **1,** 202 (1960).
(89) J. W. Wood and P. T. Mora, *J. Polymer Sci.*, A, **1,** 3511 (1963).

CHAPTER XVII

PRODUCTION AND USES OF HYDROXY-ETHYLSTARCH

By Erling T. Hjermstad

Penick & Ford Ltd., Cedar Rapids, Iowa

I. History

The preparation of hydroxyalkyl ethers of starch has been described in the literature for several decades. Early references to work on hydroxyalkyl ethers of starch are found in German patents issued in 1920 (*1, 2*). These patents describe the reaction of cellulose and starch with ethylene oxide to form plastic, swollen masses. During the 1930's some additional work was done to prepare hydroxyalkyl ethers of starch by reacting alkaline starch with ethylene oxide (*3–12*). These treatments generally resulted in starch ether products in the gelatinized or dispersed state. No particular commercial use was made of these processes. This was probably due to the high cost of preparation and the difficulty in purifying such ether derivatives.

Since about 1950, considerable attention has been given to the preparation of starch ethers having relatively low levels of ether group substitution. In 1964, the production of low-substituted hydroxyethylstarch has exceeded 100 million pounds per year.

II. Low-Substituted Hydroxyalkylstarches

1. Preparation

A number of processes have been developed whereby starch in its native, ungelatinized granule form is etherified to a low level of substitution, generally from 0.05 to 0.10 hydroxyethyl group per D-glucose unit, without significant granule swelling or degradation of the starch polymer chains. Since most of the commercial starch is produced by wet-milling processes, it is convenient and economical to conduct the etherification reaction in high solids starch suspensions in water before final filtration, purification, and drying. By keeping the product in the native ungelatinized granule it is easily dewatered and washed on filters and, thus, can be economically produced in a relatively pure state.

Several processes for the production of low-substituted hydroxyalkyl-starch have been patented. The process most widely used by corn wet-milling companies in the United States is the wet-process reaction (13-21). Starch in a 40–45% solids' suspension is made alkaline with an alkali metal hydroxide or alkaline earth metal hydroxide. Ethylene or propylene oxide is dissolved in the suspension. The reaction is conducted at temperatures well below the swelling temperature of the starch, usually not exceeding 50°. The introduction of hydroxyalkyl groups lowers the swelling temperature of the starch. Swelling of the starch to an unfilterable state can be prevented by the addition of swelling inhibitors such as neutral alkali metal salts. By using these salts, sufficient strong alkali can be added to starch suspensions to promote efficient and relatively rapid reaction with epoxy reagents. Degrees of substitution up to 0.1 hydroxyalkyl group per D-glucose unit are easily obtained in commercial production without loss of filterability. Higher degrees of substitution are possible provided the proportion of salt is increased, though starch having a hydroxyalkyl group substitution higher than 0.1 alkyl group per D-glucose unit is difficult to purify since it tends to swell as the salt is washed out of the filter cake.

Hydroxyalkylstarch can also be produced by contacting commercially dry starch containing alkali or a latent alkaline catalyst with ethylene or propylene oxide gas (22-24). Starch ether products in the native granule form having any desired swelling temperature below that of normal starch can be prepared (see also Volume I, pp. 460–463).

2. Properties

The introduction of 0.05 to 0.1 hydroxyethyl group per D-glucose unit has a considerable effect on the paste and film properties of starch (25, 26). This is especially true for starches which normally form opaque gels and which retrograde on aging. Generally, the introduction of hydroxyethyl or hydroxypropyl groups in starch results in a reduced gelatinization temperature (27), increased rate of granule swelling and dispersion on cooking (28), increased paste clarity and cohesiveness, and a greatly lowered tendency of pastes to gel and retrograde on cooling and aging. Film clarity, flexibility, smoothness (29, 30), and solubility are substantially improved, probably because of the inhibition of reassociation tendencies which ordinarily result in opacity and brittleness.

Ether linkages are not cleaved by acids, alkalis, and mild oxidizing agents. Thus, hydroxyalkylated starch can be subjected to various depolymerizing treatments to obtain a wide range of viscosity grades without altering the substituent groups. Hydroxyalkyl ether groups appear to survive such drastic treatments as conversion by acids and heat to dextrins, hydrolysis to sugars, and hypochlorite oxidation.

Hydroxyalkylated starches are non-ionic and, therefore, their pastes are relatively unaffected by electrolytes or water-hardness. Hydroxyethyl- and hydroxypropylstarches are hydrophilic, and, when thoroughly cooked, they form cohesive or "glutinous" pastes with high water-binding ability. Hydroxyalkylstarches can be used in strongly alkaline media since the ether linkages are not broken by alkali.

3. Uses

a. *In Paper*

Low-substituted hydroxyethylstarches have found wide acceptance in the paper industry (31–36) and are especially useful for coating and sizing. They are widely used at the tub, size press, and calenders to improve sheet strength and stiffness as well as surface characteristics. The improved water-holding properties and cohesiveness of starch hydroxyethyl ethers decrease the tendency of the wet films to penetrate into the paper, which results in a more continuous surface film. Films of hydroxyethylstarch shrink less on drying and, because of minimized retrogradation tendencies, are smoother, more continuous, and more flexible than those of underivatized starch. The film continuity of hydroxyethylstarch is especially important because it increases the resistance of paper surfaces to penetration by hydrophobic materials such as grease, wax, varnish, lacquer, and inks. Large quantities of low-substituted hydroxyethylstarch are used for controlling the wax penetration on bleached kraft milk bottle stock, for reducing the penetration of animal glue in gummed tape, and for improving gloss when board or paper is subsequently printed with high-gloss inks.

Low-substituted hydroxyethylstarches have properties which make them ideal adhesives in paper coating colors (37, 38). Improved flow properties of these derivatives result in colors having good levelling. The greatly reduced gelling tendencies result in good viscosity stability when the colors are aged. Improved water-holding properties of hydroxyethylstarch reduce adhesive penetration into the paper stock thus minimizing coating failures due to adhesive "starved" areas in the coating layer. Adhesive strength of the highly hydrated hydroxyethylstarch is excellent and this results in uniformly high pick values in paper coatings. Ink receptivity (39) and printing properties (40) of coatings containing hydroxyethylstarch are good. Hydroxyethylation of starch results in increased granule dispersion on cooking which is of benefit in preparing coating colors. Hydroxyethylated starch has been found to be superior to ordinary starch for preparing starch–clay–glyoxal paper coatings (41).

Low-substituted hydroxyethylstarch has also been used for beater or furnish addition (31) to increase internal fiber bonding. Here the property of low swelling temperature is useful since such derivatives will cook-out to a greater extent than ordinary starch under the conditions of temperature and moisture present in the dryers.

Low-substituted hydroxyethylstarch is used to some extent in adhesive formulations. Its improved water-holding and filming properties are of value in adhesive applications where adhesive penetration into the sheet is to be minimized. It has also been used in corrugating adhesives because its low gelatinization temperature enables high-speed production of non-alkaline board. Sometimes, it is advantageous to use the pasted product as the carrier portion of a corrugating adhesive; its improved water-holding capacity decreases the tendency for the adhesive to migrate away from the glue line into the sheet.

b. *In Textiles*

Low-substituted hydroxyethylstarch is used in the textile industry chiefly for warp sizing (42). Its greatly reduced gelling tendency minimizes the formation of hard size at the slasher. Improved film smoothness and flexibility contribute to improved abrasion resistance and maximum weaving efficiency. Improved film solubility greatly facilitates desizing; frequently, size removal can be accomplished solely by a conventional soap scour.

Because of the excellent film clarity of low-substituted hydroxyethylstarch, it is used in textile finishing to give a crisp finish on colored fabrics without dulling the fabric's color. The chemical reactivity of hydroxyethylstarch toward both melamine and urea–formaldehyde resins enables the formulation of so-called permanent textile finishes.

c. *Other Uses*

Low-substituted hydroxyalkylstarches are useful as liquid laundry starches in which a fluid paste of stable viscosity is required.

Hydroxyethylstarch may be dextrinized by conventional methods. The resulting dextrins have improved paste stability at higher solids concentrations compared to conventional dextrins. These dextrins are well suited to such applications as bag pastes, case sealing glues, label adhesives, waterproof and non-waterproof veneer glues, and envelope adhesives.

Low-substituted hydroxypropylstarch derivatives are considered to be suitable for use in foods. They have desirable properties for pie-fillings, salad dressings, and food thickeners.

III. HIGHER-SUBSTITUTED HYDROXYALKYLSTARCHES

1. Preparation

Because of granule swelling, it is difficult to prepare ungelatinized, monofunctionally substituted products containing more than 0.1 alkyl group per D-glucose unit when reactions are conducted in water suspensions. In order to obtain higher degrees of substitution in ungelatinized granules, it is necessary to conduct etherification in the presence of a limited amount of moisture or in a liquid such as a lower aliphatic alcohol which has little or no tendency to swell the product. One process (23), which is economical and efficient, involves the reaction of alkylene oxides in the gaseous form with ungelatinized granule starch containing a small proportion of alkali or a latent alkaline catalyst. Neutral alkali metal salts are convenient to use as alkaline catalysts because of their low cost and the ease with which they may be incorporated into ungelatinized starch granules. Salts such as sodium chloride combine with alkylene oxides in the presence of moisture to produce sufficient sodium hydroxide to promote the hydroxyethylation of ungelatinized starch to substitution levels approaching one alkyl group per D-glucose unit. A similar process (43) describes the use of tertiary amines or quaternary ammonium bases as catalysts to promote the reaction of alkylene oxides with dry, ungelatinized starch. Tertiary amines combine with alkylene oxides to form strong quaternary ammonium bases which catalyze etherification reactions. Another process (44) involves the reaction of swollen, but ungelatinized, starch with etherifying agents, including alkylene oxides. In this process, concentrated solutions of alkali are mixed with dry starch without swelling the granules to the gelatinized, gummy state. Several other processes which involve reacting starch or cereal flours with gaseous alkylene oxides have been patented (45–49).

Hydroxyalkylation reactions of ungelatinized starch proceed smoothly and efficiently when moist, alkaline starch is suspended in lower aliphatic alcohols (50–52) or ketones. Ungelatinized starch has the ability to adsorb strongly or to combine with alkali. The etherifying agents, therefore, react preferentially with the strongly alkaline starch rather than with the lower alcohol in which the starch is suspended. Average substitution values of 0.75 to 1.0 hydroxyethyl group per D-glucose unit are readily obtained without swelling the granules to the sticky or unfilterable state. Substitution to higher levels increases the solubility of the hydroxyalkylstarch in lower alcohols, and the very highly substituted products are thermoplastic (53). Other processes have been disclosed wherein starch is hydroxyalkylated in higher alcohols (54) and in mixtures of organic liquids (55).

Hydroxyalkylated starches in the ungelatinized granule form can also be prepared by cross-linking the granules first to suppress gelatinization and then reacting with an alkylene oxide in water suspensions (56). Products of a high degree of substitution, which are filterable and washable, can be prepared.

Cold-water-soluble hydroxyalkyl ethers of starch are produced by reacting alkaline starch with appropriate etherifying agents and then drum-drying the reaction mixture. Several processes have been patented (18, 57, 58). Other processes involve drum-drying hydroxyalkylstarches with additives such as boric acid, borax, gum arabic, and sulfate salts (59–62). Products having improved dispersibility in cold water are obtained.

Sodium starchate prepared in alcohol has been treated with ethylene oxide to form the hydroxyethyl ether (63). Another process combines cross-linking with bifunctional reagents and etherification with monofunctional reagents including alkylene oxides (64). Improved water dispersibility and viscosity stability are obtained. Another process involves precipitating starch ethers from solution with salts and separating the salt from the ether fraction (65).

2. Properties

Hydroxyalkylation of ungelatinized starch with lower alkylene oxides, such as ethylene or propylene oxide, results in progressively lower gelatinization temperatures as the degree of hydroxyalkyl group substitution is increased from 0.1 to 0.4 per D-glucose unit. As the degree of substitution is increased from 0.4 to 1.0 per D-glucose unit, the granular starch ethers become increasingly soluble in cold water. As the substitution is carried above 1.0 hydroxyalkyl group per D-glucose unit, the starch ether becomes increasingly solvated by lower alcohols, such as methanol and ethanol. Hydroxyethylstarches having substitution values approaching 3.0 hydroxyalkyl groups per D-glucose unit are water- and alcohol-soluble and thermoplastic.

Higher-substituted hydroxyethyl- and hydroxypropylstarches form translucent, colorless sols in cold water. These sols have no tendency to retrograde, and they have excellent freeze-thaw stability. Since non-ionic groups are substituted into the starch polymer chains, the sols are relatively unaffected by electrolytes. They also resist biological spoilage.

Films of higher-substituted hydroxyethyl- and hydroxypropylstarch have a high degree of clarity and smoothness and are fairly flexible at normal humidities. These films are relatively non-tacky at normal and high humidities and undergo considerably more elongation under stress at higher humidities than do underivatized starch films. They rehydrate very rapidly to a tacky, adhesive state when wetted.

3. Uses

The commercial applications of the higher-substituted hydroxyalkyl ethers of starch are still in the exploratory stage, and their production has not been appreciable in comparison with the production of low-substituted hydroxyethylstarch ethers. The higher-substituted starches have merit as low-cost, cold-water-soluble thickening agents and film formers. Hydroxyethylstarches having relatively high levels of substitution resist biological spoilage and have been used as low biochemical oxygen demand (low B.O.D.) textile warp sizing agents in order to minimize stream pollution from desizing wastes.

Other uses of cold-water-soluble hydroxyalkyl ethers include textile printing pastes, textile back filling, poster pastes, laundry starches, and special adhesives (66). Hydroxyethylstarch has been investigated as a plasma volume expander (67–70). It was found to be non-toxic to animals and effective in maintaining blood pressure. It has been investigated as a suspending agent in the preparation of dermatological lotions (71). Water soluble hydroxyalkyl ethers with preservatives have been proposed as soil conditioners (72). Polysaccharide ethers, including hydroxyethylstarch, are suitable for forming intermediate, water-soluble layers in photographic multilayer material (73–75).

IV. Other Hydroxyalkylstarch Derivatives

Hydroxyethylamylose ethers are said to be effective in sizing textile fibers (76) and in paper coating (77). Hydroxyethylamylose gelatinizes and disperses readily under normal cooking procedures. Wheat flour has also been hydroxyethylated (78–80) and products having increased dispersibility and paste stability were obtained.

Mixed starch derivatives containing both hydroxyalkyl groups and other groups have been prepared. Starch containing tertiary amino alkyl and hydroxyalkyl groups are reported to be useful in the sizing of paper as emulsifiers and retention aids, particularly for ketene dimers (81, 82).

Ethylene and propylene oxide are available at low cost, and, hence, most developmental work with starch and epoxides has been with these reagents.

However, other epoxides are being examined and some of their reaction products with starch are undergoing commercial development. Epoxide reagents containing tertiary amino groups or quaternary ammonium groups have been reacted with starch and other polymeric carbohydrates to produce tertiary amino and quaternary ammonium alkyl ether derivatives exhibiting cationic properties (83–86). These products are useful for paper sizing and as flocculants. Hydroxystyrylstarch, prepared by reacting starch with styrene oxide, has been proposed for paper and textile sizing (87, 88). Improved pasting properties have been found for starch which is modified by epoxides of fatty acids, fatty acid amides, higher alcohols, and higher aliphatic hydrocarbons (89).

Epoxide reagents have also been used to prepare cross-linked starches. Epichlorohydrin (90, 91) and diepoxides such as limonene dioxide (92) react readily with ungelatinized starch to yield products having increased resistance to gelatinization and granule dispersion on cooking.

V. REFERENCES

(1) E. Hubert, German Patent 363,192 (1920).
(2) O. Leuchs and E. Hubert, German Patent 368,413 (1920).
(3) M. Hagedorn, W. Ziese, B. Reyle, and R. Bauer, U.S. Patent 1,876,920 (1932); Chem. Abstr., 27, 101 (1933).
(4) A. W. Schorger, U.S. Patent 1,863,208 (1932); Chem. Abstr., 26, 4174 (1932).
(5) A. W. Schorger, U.S. Patent 1,941,276 (1933); Chem. Abstr. 28, 1861 (1934).
(6) A. W. Schorger, U.S. Patent 1,941,277 (1933); Chem. Abstr., 28, 1861 (1934).
(7) A. W. Schorger, U.S. Patent 1,941,278 (1933); Chem. Abstr., 28, 1861 (1934).
(8) W. Ziese, Z. Physiol. Chem., 229, 213 (1934).
(9) W. Ziese, Z. Physiol. Chem., 230, 235 (1935).
(10) H. Dreyfus, U.S. Patent 2,055,892 (1936); Chem. Abstr., 30, 8615 (1936).
(11) H. Dreyfus, U. S. Patent 2,055,893 (1936); Chem. Abstr., 30, 8615 (1936).
(12) H. Dreyfus, U.S. Patent 2,094,100 (1937); Chem. Abstr., 31, 7888 (1937).
(13) C. C. Kesler and E. T. Hjermstad, U.S. Patent 2,516,633 (1950); Chem. Abstr., 44, 11142 (1950).
(14) C. C. Kesler and E. T. Hjermstad, Canadian Patent 520,865 (1956).
(15) K. C. Hobbs, U.S. Patent 2,801,241 (1957); Chem. Abstr., 51, 18666 (1957).
(16) K. C. Hobbs, R. W. Kerr, and F. E. Kite, U.S. Patent 2,833,759 (1958); Chem. Abstr., 52, 14205 (1958).
(17) K. C. Hobbs, U.S. Patent 2,999,090 (1961); Chem. Abstr., 56, 1658 (1962).
(18) R. A. Brobst, U.S. Patent 3,049,538 (1962); Chem. Abstr., 58, 651 (1963).
(19) E. E. Fisher and R. R. Estes, U.S. Patent 3,127,392 (1964).
(20) C. C. Kesler and E. T. Hjermstad, in "Methods in Carbohydrate Chemistry," R. L. Whistler, ed., Academic Press Inc., New York, N. Y., Vol. IV, 1964, p. 304.
(21) J. V. Tuschhoff, U.S. Patent 3,176,007 (1965); Chem. Abstr., 62, 14918 (1965).
(22) C. C. Kesler and E. T. Hjermstad, U.S. Patent 2,516,632 (1950); Chem. Abstr., 44, 11141 (1950).
(23) C. C. Kesler and E. T. Hjermstad, U.S. Patent 2,516,634 (1950); Chem. Abstr., 44, 11142 (1950).

(24) C. C. Kesler and E. T. Hjermstad, Canadian Patent 520,866 (1956).
(25) E. T. Hjermstad, in "Industrial Gums," R. L. Whistler, ed., Academic Press Inc., New York, N. Y., 1959, p. 727.
(26) R. L. Whistler and W. W. Spencer, Arch. Biochem. Biophys., 87, 137 (1960).
(27) T. J. Schoch and E. C. Maywald, Anal. Chem., 28, 385 (1956).
(28) A. Harsveldt, Tappi, 45, No. 2, 85 (1962).
(29) G. A. Hull and T. J. Schoch, Tappi, 42, No. 6, 438 (1959).
(30) T. J. Schoch, Tappi, 35, No. 7, 11 (1952).
(31) J. P. Casey, "Pulp and Paper," Interscience Publishers, Inc., New York, N. Y., 2nd Ed., Vol. II, 1960, pp. 956, 1128.
(32) A. Harsveldt, Chem. Ind. (London), 2062 (1961).
(33) A. J. Desmarais, U.S. Patent 3,151,996 (1964); Chem. Abstr., 61, 16292 (1964).
(34) A. H. Nadelman and G. H. Bauldauf, Paper Trade J., 149, No. 40, 46 (1965).
(35) E. J. Barber, R. H. Earle, Jr., and G. C. Harris, U.S. Patent 3,219,519 (1965).
(36) E. J. Barber and C. E. Maag, U.S. Patent 3,219,518 (1965).
(37) W. C. Black, Tappi, 39, No. 12, 199A (1956).
(38) E. D. Klug, U.S. Patent 3,117,021 (1964); Chem. Abstr., 60, 8234 (1964).
(39) C. H. Fletcher, Paper Trade J., 142, No. 42, 32 (1958).
(40) E. J. Sweeney, U.S. Patent 2,885,374 (1959); Chem. Abstr., 53, 17511 (1959).
(41) G. W. Buttrick and N. R. Eldred, Tappi, 45, No. 11, 890 (1962).
(42) H. Rüggeberg, Staerke, 7, 101 (1955).
(43) R. W. Kerr and W. A. Faucette, U.S. Patent 2,733,238 (1956); Chem. Abstr., 50, 6824 (1956).
(44) C. G. Caldwell and I. Martin, U.S. Patent 2,802,000 (1957); Chem. Abstr., 51, 17215 (1957).
(45) M. A. Staerkle and E. Meier, U.S. Patent 2,698,936 (1955); Chem. Abstr., 49, 4314 (1955).
(46) R. W. Kerr and K. C. Hobbs, British Patent 741,742 (1955); Chem. Abstr., 51, 3168 (1957).
(47) Duintjer Wilkens Meihuizen & Co., N.V., British Patent 801,524 (1958); Chem. Abstr., 53, 8674 (1959).
(48) L. T. Monson and W. J. Dickson, U.S. Patent 2,854,449 (1958); Chem. Abstr., 53, 12209 (1959).
(49) A. E. Broderick, German Patent 1,019,288 (1957); Chem. Abstr., 54, 15974 (1960).
(50) C. C. Kesler and E. T. Hjermstad, U.S. Patent 2,845,417 (1958); Chem. Abstr., 53, 2657 (1959).
(51) E. T. Hjermstad and L. C. Martin, U.S. Patent 3,135,739 (1964); Chem. Abstr., 61, 4580 (1964).
(52) H. Zuzuki, Y. Murakami, and N. Taketomi, Kogyo Kagaku Zasshi, 67, No. 6, 932 (1964).
(53) W. Jarowenko, U.S. Patent 2,996,498 (1961); Chem. Abstr., 56, 1658 (1962).
(54) A. E. Broderick, U.S. Patent 2,682,535 (1954); Chem. Abstr., 43, 11100 (1954).
(55) D. B. Benedict and A. E. Broderick, U.S. Patent 2,744,894 (1956); Chem. Abstr., 50, 16865 (1956).
(56) L. O. Gill and J. A. Wagoner, U.S. Patent 3,014,901 (1961); Chem. Abstr., 56, 7564 (1962).
(57) J. Lolkema, U.S. Patent Reissue 23,443 (1951); Chem. Abstr., 46, 2830 (1952).
(58) E. D. Klug, U.S. Patent 3,033,853 (1962); Chem. Abstr., 57, 2484 (1962).
(59) R. W. Kerr, U.S. Patent 2,732,309 (1956); Chem. Abstr., 50, 6824 (1956).
(60) R. W. Kerr, U.S. Patent 2,903,391 (1959); Chem. Abstr., 54, 1850 (1960).

(61) W. A. Scholten's Chemische Fabrieken, British Patent 816,049 (1959); *Chem. Abstr.*, **53**, 20868 (1959).

(62) G. Moes, German Patent 1,117,510 (1960); *Chem. Abstr.*, **56**, 8984 (1962).

(63) K. M. Gaver, U.S. Patent 2,518,135 (1950); *Chem. Abstr.*, **44**, 11142 (1950).

(64) J. Lolkema and G. Moes, U.S. Patent 2,853,484 (1958); *Chem. Abstr.*, **53**, 1797 (1959).

(65) L. Balassa, U.S. Patent 2,588,463 (1952); *Chem. Abstr.*, **46**, 4830 (1952).

(66) J. Lolkema and W. A. Van der Meer, Dutch Patent 81,917 (1956); *Chem. Abstr.*, **51**, 9192 (1957).

(67) M. Wiedersheim, *Arch. Intern. Pharmacodynamie*, **111**, No. 3, 353 (1957).

(68) W. L. Thompson, J. J. Britton, and R. P. Walton, *J. Pharmacol. Exptl. Therap.*, **136**, 125 (1962).

(69) W. L. Thompson and R. P. Walton, *J. Pharmacol. Exptl. Therap.*, **146**, 359 (1964).

(70) G. P. Murphy, D. E. Demaree, and J. A. Gagnon, *J. Urol.*, **93**, No. 5, 534 (1965).

(71) D. H. Cronk and L. C. Zopf, *J. Am. Pharm. Assoc., Pract. Pharm. Ed.*, **14**, 302 (1953).

(72) F. A. Möller and J. Lolkema, German Patent 963,690 (1957); *Chem. Abstr.*, **54**, 10210 (1960).

(73) Gevaert Photo-Producten N.V., Belgian Patent 617,036 (1962); *Chem. Abstr.* **58**, 9789 (1963).

(74) T. A. Scott, U.S. Patent 3,047,392 (1962); *Chem. Abstr.*, **57**, 16044 (1962).

(75) J. D. Overman, German Patent 1,161,478 (1964); *Chem. Abstr.*, **60**, 10100 (1964).

(76) J. Lolkema, G. Moes, and W. F. Vogel, German Patent 1,118,151 (1961); *Chem. Abstr.*, **56**, 14501 (1962).

(77) Coöperatieve Verkoop-En Productiever-eniging van Aardappelmeel en Derivaten "Avebe" G.A., British Patent 869,192 (1961); *Chem. Abstr.*, **55**, 22878 (1961).

(78) J. C. Rankin, C. L. Mehltretter, and F. R. Senti, *Cereal Chem.*, **36**, 215 (1959).

(79) E. B. Lancaster and V. F. Pfeifer, *Cereal Chem.*, **37**, 189 (1960).

(80) J. C. Rankin, J. G. Rall, C. R. Russell, and C. E. Rist, *Cereal Chem.*, **41**, 111 (1964).

(81) G. C. Harris and R. A. Leonard, U.S. Patent 3,070,594 (1963); *Chem. Abstr.*, **53**, 11460 (1963).

(82) G. C. Harris and C. A. Weisgerber, U.S. Patent 3,070,452 (1963); *Chem. Abstr.*, **58**, 10398 (1963).

(83) P. Schlack, U.S. Patent 2,131,120 (1938); *Chem. Abstr.*, **32**, 9341 (1938).

(84) C. G. Caldwell and O. B. Wurzburg, U.S. Patent 2,813,093 (1957); *Chem. Abstr.*, **52**, 2438 (1958).

(85) C. H. Hullinger and N. H. Yui, U.S. Patent 2,970,140 (1961); *Chem. Abstr.*, **57**, 2483 (1962).

(86) E. F. Paschall, U.S. Patent 2,876,217 (1959); *Chem. Abstr.*, **53**, 12720 (1959).

(87) K. P. Satterley, U.S. Patent 3,037,017 (1962); *Chem. Abstr.*, **57**, 7504 (1962).

(88) Y. Merle, *Compt. Rend.*, **249**, 2560 (1959).

(89) H. Wolff, U.S. Patent 2,923,707 (1960); *Chem. Abstr.*, **54**, 11525 (1960).

(90) M. Konigsberg, U.S. Patent 2,500,950 (1950); *Chem. Abstr.*, **44**, 6666 (1950).

(91) G. E. Hamerstrand, B. T. Hofreiter, and C. L. Mehltretter, *Cereal Chem.*, **37**, 519 (1960).

(92) D. Commerford and I. Ehrenthal, U.S. Patent 2,977,356 (1961); *Chem. Abstr.*, **55**, 19289 (1961).

CHAPTER XVIII

PRODUCTION AND USE OF DIALDEHYDE STARCH

By C. L. Mehltretter

Northern Regional Research Laboratory,[1] Peoria, Illinois

I. Introduction

A significant development in polysaccharide technology is the periodic acid oxidation of starch to dialdehyde starch (*1, 2*). The process is based upon a low cost electrolytic procedure for the conversion of iodine and iodic acid to periodic acid (*3, 4*) and employs recycling of spent oxidant to the electrolytic cell for regeneration to periodic acid (*5*). Other factors which enhance the efficiency of the process are the rapidity of oxidation of starch granules in aqueous suspension and the insolubility of dialdehyde starch in the reaction mixture (*6*).

The specificity of periodic acid and periodates for the oxidative cleavage of 1,2-glycol structures in carbohydrates to produce aldehydes has been adequately described (*7–9*) and was first recognized by Malaprade (*10*). In 1937 Jackson and Hudson (*6*) used this technique to oxidize starch to dialdehyde starch. The nearly stoichiometric reaction of periodic acid with a monomer unit of starch under controlled conditions to form the corresponding dialdehyde unit is illustrated by the equation in Figure 1.

Oxidation by periodic acid of the reducing and nonreducing end-groups of starch to formaldehyde and formic acid also occurs and is of some significance in the process. The buildup in the electrolysis liquors of these substances and of the impurities in commercial starch reduces the oxidation

[1] This is a laboratory of the Northern Utilization Research and Development Division, Agricultural Research Service, U.S. Department of Agriculture.

efficiency of the electrolytic cell. However, these materials can readily be removed from solution by adsorption on activated carbon (5, 11).

Periodic acid oxidation of starch is readily controlled so that oxystarches of any level of dialdehyde content may be prepared. However, the product obtained by oxidation to the extent of over 90% of theory is the one that

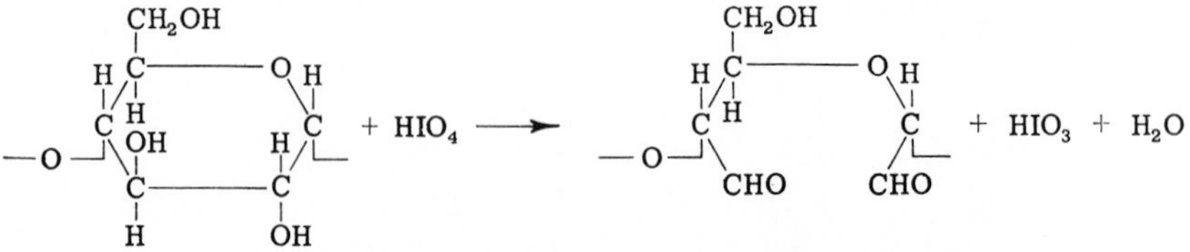

FIG. 1.—Periodic acid oxidation of monomer unit of starch.

shows most industrial promise at present (12). The trivial name dialdehyde starch was given to this product to show its parentage and carbonyl functionality. Dialdehyde starch has few of the physical and chemical properties of starch (6, 12–15) and has a completely different monomeric structural unit from starch as the formulas in Figure 2 illustrate.

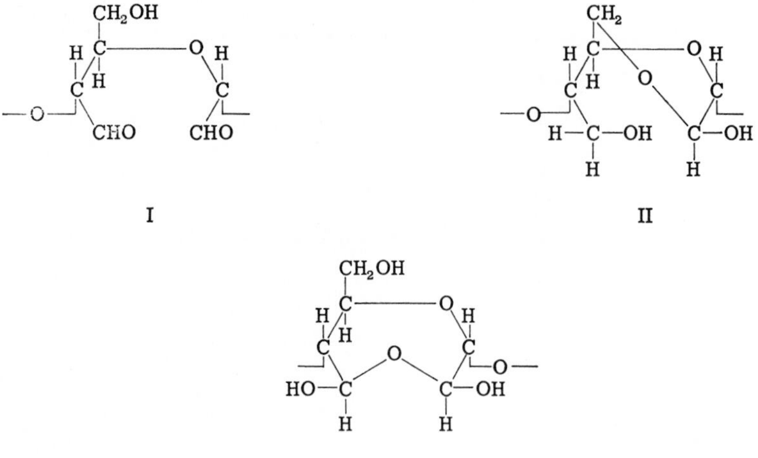

FIG. 2.—Structural units in dialdehyde starch.

Not many of the carbonyl groups of dialdehyde starch are free (I) but appear to be in hemiacetal linkage (II) with primary alcohol groups and in hemialdal linkage (III) by reaction with water.

II. ELECTROLYTIC CELL

The electrolytic cell used to make periodic acid consists of alundum diaphragm catholyte chambers which contain a 5% caustic soda (sodium

hydroxide) solution and an iron cathode. The surrounding anolyte compart-
ment holds an aqueous solution of iodine in caustic soda or iodic acid and a
lead dioxide-coated lead anode (16).

The main anolyte reaction is the oxidation of sodium iodate and sodium
iodide, formed by reaction of iodine with aqueous caustic soda, to periodic
acid or sodium periodate. The periodic acid solution used in the dialdehyde
starch process may consist of a mixture of periodic acid, iodic acid, sodium
periodate, sodium iodate, and sodium sulfate. Adjustment of the acidity

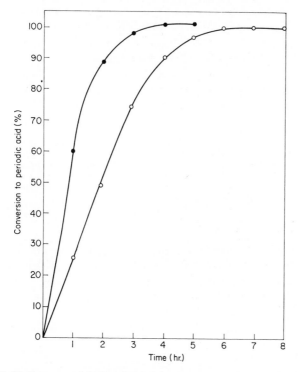

Fig. 3.—Oxidation rate of iodic acid to periodic acid at 25°. (Current density in
amperes per square centimeter: ● = 0.036, ☉ = 0.012.)

of the solution with sulfuric acid to pH 0.7–1.4 allows variation of the salt-
free acid composition of the mixture. The dialdehyde starch process depends
greatly upon the efficient recycling to the electrolytic cell of spent oxidation
liquors containing iodic acid for conversion to periodic acid. A loss of about
1% of iodic acid occurs in the process, which is made up by oxidation of
iodine or by addition of iodic acid. Sodium hydroxide is produced in the
catholyte chamber and is removed periodically by flushing with deionized
water. Hydrogen that is formed is vented from the chamber. These by-

products, if of sufficient purity for industrial use, would decrease the cost of the main product. Deionized or distilled water must be used in the part of the process concerned with electrolysis.

Figure 3 illustrates the pronounced effect of current density on the rate of oxidation of iodic acid to periodic acid (17).

New ideas in cell design have been covered in several publications (11, 18). Mantell's work is of particular interest in regard to the design and operation of a commercial electrolytic cell for periodic acid production. Although alundum diaphragms are quite satisfactory, other meterials were investigated by Mantell, and the possibility exists that an ion-exchange diaphragm may be developed. The most effective anode material was lead containing 1% silver. Preliminary electrolysis in dilute sulfuric acid with this anode produces a coating of lead dioxide on its surface that apparently catalyzes the oxidation of iodate ions to periodate ions (19, 20).

A small percentage of silver in the lead reduces the sloughing off of lead dioxide from the anode during electrolysis. The cathode may be fabricated from iron, steel, or carbon.

An annular cell (18) has been constructed that has high current efficiency for the conversion of iodate ions to periodate ions. This cell has been used in the development of a continuous process for making dialdehyde starch (21).

III. DIALDEHYDE STARCH PROCESS

The present commercial process for the manufacture of dialdehyde starch is a two-stage or out-cell procedure (5, 22). Earlier efforts to make dialdehyde starch by an in-cell process (16, 17) were not entirely satisfactory, chiefly because of mechanical difficulties such as diaphragm failure and excessive lead contamination of the product.

The relative simplicity of the two-stage process is illustrated in the schematic flowsheet of Figure 4.

Factors such as temperature and pH of reaction, mole ratio of periodic acid to starch, and concentration of periodic acid were investigated during the development of the two-stage process. Metal contamination of periodic acid from stainless-steel equipment seriously affected the course of the oxidation and the character of the dialdehyde starch (5). Polyethylene, polyvinyl chloride, or glass-lined equipment should be used throughout.

Because sodium iodate is considerably less soluble in water than iodic acid, the quantity of periodic acid in the reaction mixture is limited by the low concentration of sodium iodate beyond which crystallization from solution and contamination of dialdehyde starch will occur at the pH and temperature of the process. The solutions of lower pH used by Slager (22) convert greater proportions of sodium iodate to more soluble iodic acid;

thus higher concentrations of periodic acid and of starch may be utilized. However, higher acidity is conducive to hydrolysis of the starch and dialdehyde starch with the formation of increased organic solubles and attendant decrease in oxidation efficiency.

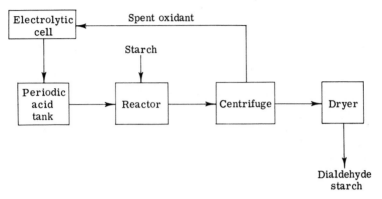

Fig. 4.—Schematic flowsheet of the dialdehyde starch process.

Figure 5 illustrates the rate of oxidation of corn starch to dialdehyde starch observed by Pfeifer and co-workers (5) in eleven consecutive experiments under conditions b in Table I.

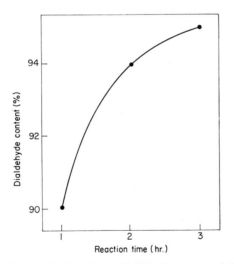

Fig. 5.—Relationship of oxidation time to dialdehyde content of dialdehyde starch.

Starch is rapidly oxidized to dialdehyde starch by periodic acid, and most of the reaction occurs within the first hour. Because periodic acid appears to penetrate the interior of starch granules with difficulty, con-

Table I

Reaction Conditions for Dialdehyde Starch Process

Periodic acid (wt. %)	Pearl corn starch (wt. %) (d.b.)	Periodic acid/ starch (mole ratio)	pH	Reaction temp. (°C)	Reaction time (hr.)	Yield (%)
22.6[a]	13.0	1.25	0.6	30–32	3.5	102
6.0[b]	5	1.1	1.2–1.4	32–38	3	98

[a] Reference *22*.
[b] Reference *5*.

siderably more time is required to achieve oxidations of 95–100% of theory. For practical purposes, however, dialdehyde starch of a minimum of 90% dialdehyde content is quite satisfactory and is representative of the commercial product (*12*).

Much of the investigation on the periodic acid oxidation of starch was conducted with pearl corn starch because of its relatively high purity, cold water insolubility, low cost, and availability in large volume. Other starches may readily be converted to dialdehyde starch. Wheat and sorghum starches have been successfully used (*23*).

Advantages of the two-stage process are good control, simplicity of operation, excellent product quality, low lead contamination, and minimum loss of oxidant. Estimated production cost of dialdehyde starch by this process on the basis of 10 million pounds per year is 15.6 cents a pound (*5*).

IV. ANALYTICAL METHODS

Periodic acid and iodic acid or their sodium salts can be determined in oxidation liquors by the method of Fleury and Lange (*24*).

Dialdehyde content of the dialdehyde starch may be estimated readily by sodium borohydride reduction (*25*) or by the spectrophotometric *p*-nitrophenylhydrazine procedure (*26, 27*).

V. APPLICATIONS OF DIALDEHYDE STARCH

The hemiacetal and hemialdal linkages (Fig. 2, II, III) of dialdehyde starch are relatively weak and are readily cleaved for reaction of the liberated carbonyl groups with bisulfite, hydroxyl groups, amines, hydrazines, hydrazides, and the like. Oxystarches of low-dialdehyde content may be oxidized to dicarboxyl starches, which are water-soluble gums (*28*). Dialdehyde starch may be reduced to polymeric alcohols (*29*), hydrolyzed to D-erythrose and glyoxal (*30*), and reductively hydrolyzed to erythritol and ethylene glycol (*31*). Most of the characteristic reactions of carbonyl groups are exhibited by dialdehyde starch.

Numerous derivatives of dialdehyde starch have been prepared (*1*, *2*) and are being investigated for various purposes. However, at present, the chief uses for dialdehyde starch are concerned with its ability to cross-link various natural and synthetic polymers.

Most of the annual production of dialdehyde starch is utilized in the production of wet strength paper for toweling, sanitary tissue, maps, and the like. Other applications include the insolubilization of casein (*32*) in wood adhesives (*33*) and paper coatings (*34*) and of gelatin (*35*) in photographic films (*36*); the pretanning of hides (*37*); the insolubilization of polyvinyl alcohol films (*38*); the binding of tobacco sheets (*39*); and the preparation of protective coatings, molding resins, and films through the allyl acetal derivative (*40*). Doubtless there are many uses not yet publicized which will be recognized in future patents.

Improvements in the application of dialdehyde starch to cellulosic pulp to achieve better retention at lower cost and to obtain a softer and more water-absorptive tissue with good wet strength should greatly expand its utilization. A less permanent type of wet strength than that obtained with the presently used resins is achieved with dialdehyde starch. This property allows ease of broke recovery in papermaking and rapid biological degradation of the paper tissues in septic tanks and other sewage systems.

Several processes (*12*, *41–45*) have been developed in which dialdehyde starch is used to produce wet-strength paper. All but one (*41*) depend upon the addition of properly dispersed dialdehyde starch to cellulosic pulp in water before sheet formation, which is called wet-end addition and which is the most practical method of application.

Nearly clear aqueous dispersions are prepared by cooking 3% of dialdehyde starch in water containing 0.45% sodium metabisulfite for 30–40 minutes at 95°. Dialdehyde starch is degraded under these conditions to polymeric dialdehydes having molecular weights in the range of 300,000 to 5 million. The hydrocolloid produced is negatively charged because of the sulfonate radical in its structure and is thus not retained well by the negatively charged cellulosic pulp. To achieve better retention of dialdehyde starch, the pulp is given a positive charge by a prior treatment with a small percentage of cationic starch in aqueous dispersion. This step is followed by the addition of 0.25 to 0.75% of the dialdehyde starch hydrocolloid at pH 4.5, and the treated pulp is then processed through a Fourdrinier machine (*42*). High retention of dialdehyde starch in the pulp is achieved at 1.5% level of addition by recycling the white water (*43*).

Figure 6 illustrates the relationship of wet strength to dialdehyde starch content in paper prepared from several types of pulp.

Sulfate pulps, both bleached and unbleached, when treated with dialdehyde starch, yield higher wet-strength paper than bleached sulfite and semibleached groundwood pulps.

Cationic properties may also be built into dialdehyde starch by appropriate derivatization to improve dispersibility and retention. This combination has been achieved by reacting about 2% of the dialdehyde groups in dialdehyde starch with betaine hydrazide hydrochloride [(carboxymethyl)trimethylammonium chloride hydrazide; Girard reagent T] as shown in Figure 7 (44).

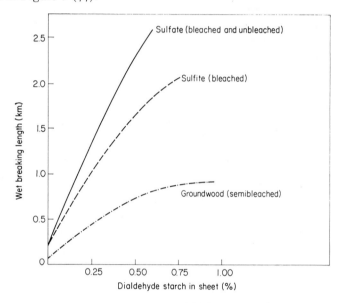

Fig. 6.—Wet strength versus dialdehyde starch in paper.

The cationic-dialdehyde starch hydrazone prepared in granule form is readily dispersed in hot water for addition to pulp at levels of 0.5% or more, and at pH 4.5. The betaine hydrazide hydrochloride, preferably in aqueous solution, is cooked with dialdehyde starch at 95° for about an hour before direct application to pulp at the paper mill (45). Wet-strength results on machine paper prepared by addition of 0.5 to 2.5% of cationic dialdehyde starch to unbleached softwood sulfate pulp are shown in Table II.

The improvement in wet tensile strength by the addition of a small amount of cationic-dialdehyde starch is impressive. The increase in dry tensile strength is also significant. Dialdehyde starch may also be dispersed in slightly alkaline solution prior to treatment with a cationic agent to obtain good retention in pulp for high wet-strength paper (12).

Although the mechanism of wet-strength production by dialdehyde starch has not been accurately determined, presumably cross-linking of cellulose occurs through acetal formation between the carbonyl groups of dialdehyde starch and the free hydroxyl groups of cellulose.

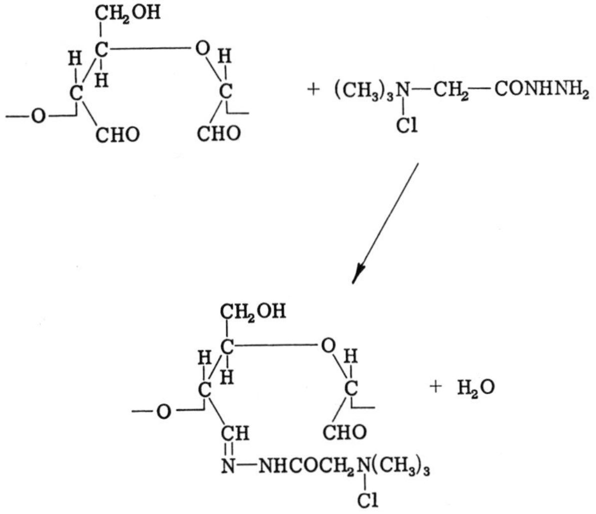

FIG. 7.—Reaction of Girard reagent T with dialdehyde starch.

A comparison of the wet-strength efficiency of dialdehyde starch with that of several commercial wet-strength resins on paper prepared from bleached kraft pulp is illustrated in Figure 8.

Table II

Physical Properties of Machine Paper Containing Cationic Dialdehyde Starch

		Cationic dialdehyde starch added	
Test	*Control[a]*	*0.5%*	*2.5%*
Burst factor (g./cm.^{2}/g.s.m.)	37	56	68
Tear factor (g./g.s.m.)	192	160	117
Breaking length (m.)			
Dry M.D.	7300	9800	13,000
Wet M.D.	270	2200	4400
Schopper fold	1600	2400	2800
Cationic dialdehyde starch in sheet (%)	—	0.45	1.95

[a] Unbleached softwood sulfate, S.R. 700 ml.

Wet-strength resins are presently being used to the extent of over 35 million pounds per year, and it is expected that dialdehyde starch will assume a significant role in this field in the future.

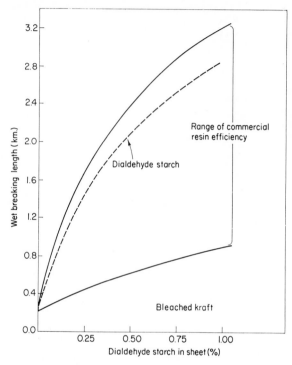

FIG. 8.—Wet-strength efficiency, dialdehyde starch versus resins.

Using dialdehyde starch as a wet-strength agent for paper has the following advantages:

1. High temporary wet strength at low levels of addition.
2. Nearly maximum wet strength obtained without an after-cure.
3. Ease of broke recovery.
4. Good biodegradability of the wet-strength paper.
5. Stability of treated papers on aging.
6. Simple preparation of stable dialdehyde starch dispersions.
7. Production of improved wet- and dry-strength paper from a variety of pulps.

VI. REFERENCES

(1) G. Von Tegge, *Staerke*, **12**, 321 (1960).
(2) P. J. Borchert, *Kunstoffe*, **51**, 137 (1961).

(3) C. L. Mehltretter and C. S. Wise, *Ind. Eng. Chem.*, **51**, 511 (1959).
(4) C. L. Mehltretter, U.S. Patent 2,830,941 (1958); *Chem. Abstr.*, **52**, 15312 (1958).
(5) V. F. Pfeifer, V. E. Sohns, H. F. Conway, E. B. Lancaster, S. Dabic, and E. L. Griffin, Jr., *Ind. Eng. Chem.*, **52**, 201 (1960).
(6) E. L. Jackson and C. S. Hudson, *J. Am. Chem. Soc.*, **59**, 2049 (1937).
(7) E. L. Jackson, *Org. Reactions*, **2**, 341 (1944).
(8) J. M. Bobbitt, *Advan. Carbohydrate Chem.*, **11**, 1 (1956).
(9) R. D. Guthrie, *Advan. Carbohydrate Chem.*, **16**, 105 (1961).
(10) L. Malaprade, *Bull. Soc. Chim.*, **43**, 683 (1928).
(11) C. L. Mantell, *Ind. Eng. Chem., Process Design Develop.*, **1**, 144 (1962).
(12) Miles Chemical Company, Elkhart, Indiana, Technical Bulletins No. 6-129 (1959) and No. 3-073 (1963).
(13) J. W. Sloan, B. T. Hofreiter, R. L. Mellies, and I. A. Wolff, *Ind. Eng. Chem.*, **48**, 1165 (1956).
(14) R. L. Mellies, C. L. Mehltretter, and I. A. Wolff, *Ind. Eng. Chem.*, **50**, 1311 (1958).
(15) S. Levine, H. L. Griffin, and F. R. Senti, *J. Polymer Sci.*, **35**, 31 (1959).
(16) H. F. Conway and V. E. Sohns, *Ind. Eng. Chem.*, **51**, 637 (1959).
(17) C. L. Mehltretter, J. C. Rankin, and P. R. Watson, *Ind. Eng. Chem.*, **49**, 350 (1957).
(18) H. F. Conway and E. B. Lancaster, *Electrochem. Technol.*, **2**, 46 (1964).
(19) A. Hickling and S. H. Richards, *J. Chem. Soc.*, 256 (1940).
(20) E. B. Lancaster and H. F. Conway, *Electrochem. Technol.* **1**, 253 (1963).
(21) H. F. Conway, E. B. Lancaster, and E. L. Griffin, Jr., *Abstr. Papers, Am. Chem. Soc.*, **145**, 39M (1963).
(22) J. E. Slager, U.S. Patent 3,086,969 (1963).
(23) H. F. Conway, E. B. Lancaster, and E. L. Griffin, Jr., unpublished data.
(24) P. P. Fleury and J. Lange, *J. Pharm. Chim.*, **17**, 107 (1933).
(25) J. C. Rankin and C. L. Mehltretter, *Anal. Chem.*, **28**, 1012 (1956).
(26) C. S. Wise and C. L. Mehltretter, *Anal. Chem.*, **30**, 174 (1958).
(27) D. J. Kay, G. E. Hamerstrand, and B. T. Hofreiter, *Tappi*, **45**, 943 (1962).
(28) B. T. Hofreiter, J. Bennie, G. E. Hamerstrand, and C. L. Mehltretter, *J. Chem. Eng. Data*, **5**, 480 (1960).
(29) M. Abdel-Akher, J. K. Hamilton, R. Montgomery, and F. Smith, *J. Am. Chem. Soc.*, **74**, 4970 (1952).
(30) C. A. Wilham, T. A. McGuire, J. W. Van Cleve, F. H. Otey, and C. L. Mehltetter, *Ind. Eng. Chem., Prod. Res. Develop.*, **1**, 62 (1962).
(31) F. H. Otey, J. W. Sloan, C. A. Wilham, and C. L. Mehltretter, *Ind. Eng. Chem.*, **53**, 267 (1961).
(32) F. B. Weakley, C. L. Mehltretter, and C. E. Rist, *Tappi*, **44**, 456 (1961).
(33) F. B. Weakley, M. L. Ashby, and C. L. Mehltretter, *Forest Prod. J.*, **13**, 51 (1963).
(34) A. J. Ernst, M. E. Carr, F. B. Weakley, B. T. Hofreiter, and C. L. Mehltretter, *Tappi*, **45**, 646 (1962).
(35) A. M. Krogh, *Bull. Brit. Gelatine Glue Res. Assoc.*, **9**, No. 3, 15 (1958).
(36) J. L. Graham, U.S. Patent 3,058,827 (1962).
(37) J. F. Wagoner, J. C. Stemoroski, W. Windus, and W. C. Witham, *J. Am. Leather Chemists' Assoc.*, **57**, 302 (1962).
(38) C. L. Wilson, U.S. Patent 3,034,999 (1962).
(39) S. Rosenberg and D. Bandel, U.S. Patent 2,887,414 (1959); *Chem. Abstr.*, **53**, 13520 (1959).
(40) L. A. Gugliemelli, G. L. Mayer, and C. R. Russell, U.S. Patent 3,037,018 (1962).

(41) E. J. Jones, B. Webers, J. W. Swanson, C. L. Mehltretter, and F. R. Senti, *Tappi*, **42**, 862 (1959).

(42) G. E. Hamerstrand, B. T. Hofreiter, C. L. Mehltretter, W. E. Schulze, and D. J. Kay, *Tappi*, **44**, 430 (1961).

(43) B. T. Hofreiter, G. E. Hamerstrand, D. J. Kay, and C. E. Rist, *Tappi*, **45**, 177 (1962).

(44) C. L. Mehltretter, T. E. Yeates, G. E. Hamerstrand, B. T. Hofreiter, and C. E. Rist, *Tappi*, **45**, 750 (1962).

(45) G. E. Hamerstrand, B. T. Hofreiter, D. J. Kay, and C. E. Rist, *Tappi*, **46**, 400 (1963).

CHAPTER XIX

PRODUCTION AND USE OF CROSS-LINKED STARCH

By Clifford H. Hullinger

American Maize-Products Company, Roby, Indiana

I. Introduction

The cross-linking of a polymer into a three dimensional network has been used to vulcanize rubber since the turn of the century (*1*). Flory (*2*) has reviewed the theoretical aspects of polymer cross-linking with particular reference to solution polymerization.

It is generally agreed (*3*) that cross-linking is the mechanism by which a wide variety of polyfunctional agents insolubilize starch. Most carbohydrate-based, water-resistant adhesives, wet rub coatings, permanent textile sizes, water-resistant films, crease-resistant textiles, and wet-strength papers are cross-linked to some extent. The cross-linking may be through primary linkages, or through weak temporary bonds such as those formed between starch and borax (sodium tetraborate). The linkages not only tie adjacent starch molecules together but, in many cases, cross-link to a substrate that is often a cellulose matrix.

No attempt will be made to cover the rather extensive literature on the wide variety of industrial applications listed in the preceding paragraph. This chapter will deal only with one particular aspect of cross-linking in which the intact starch granules are stabilized by primary bonds. These cross-linked or "inhibited" starches first came into prominence after World War II. With tapioca and other root starches in short supply, the food industry did not have a starch that would give the clear, non-congealing paste that is desirable in many formulations. Waxy corn starch had been produced commercially (*4*) by 1942, but unmodified waxy starch pastes are too stringy and cohesive and break down too rapidly under shear to be readily acceptable in many food uses. These defects can be remedied by introducing a small number of cross-links into the intact starch granule. One cross-link per several hundred D-glucose units can eliminate the objectionable cohesiveness and stabilize the viscosity of the hot paste. By varying the degree of cross-linking, one may obtain products that are excellent thickeners under conditions which vary from mild cooking at neutral pH levels to high pressure jet cooking and retorting in low pH pie fillings and salad dressings.

Starch granules that are so highly cross-linked that they will not swell even when autoclaved at elevated temperatures and pressures have found commercial acceptance as dusting powder for surgical rubber gloves (5, 6). These starches prevent the inside of the gloves from sticking during sterilization. Additional packets of the starch, either dry or in a solvent suspension, can be sterilized at the same time and applied to the surgeons hands before they insert them in the gloves (7, 8). It is reported (6) that when 1.7 to 4.5% of the hydroxyl groups are involved in the linkage, the starch is readily absorbed by the body tissues with less danger of adhesions. If the degree of cross-linking is too low, the starch may get sticky during sterilization, and, if too high, it is not readily absorbed by the patient.

II. Preparation

Maxwell (9) may have been the first to apply the cross-linking reaction to starch knowingly, although Classen (10) in 1898 had disclosed that non-swelling starches could be prepared by treatment with formaldehyde. Felton and Schopmeyer (11) disclosed the treatment of intact starch granules with very low levels of phosphorus oxychloride to give products with controlled swelling power and viscosity stability. Epichlorohydrin (12-14) and trimetaphosphate (15) are also used in cross-linking food and industrial starches. Other cross-linking agents include aldehydes (16-19), dialdehydes (20), vinyl sulfone (21), diepoxides (22), 1,3,5-trichloro- and 1,3,5-triacryl-s-triazine (23-25), hexamethylene diisocyanate (26), bis-(hydroxymethyl)ethyleneurea (27), and N,N'-methylenebisacrylamide (28). The various urea–formaldehyde resins are also effective cross-linking agents (29, 30). In general, any molecule capable of reacting with two or more hydroxyl groups can cross-link. This includes such relatively unreactive molecules as the aliphatic dihalides (12), although it is difficult to react such substances without damaging the starch granule.

III. Evaluation

In most cases, the manufacturer of a cross-linked starch does not attempt to determine the extent of cross-linking directly. Instead, he examines the physical properties of the starch paste. Viscosity, swelling power, solubility pattern, and resistance to shear (31, 32) are commonly measured.

Viscometers that continuously record the paste viscosity of the starch throughout a cooking cycle, such as the Corn Industries Viscometer or the Brabender Viscometer (33), are the preferred instruments. Observation of the viscosity at various points on the curve tells the operator if the product is appropriate for the intended use.

The viscosity of an unmodified starch such as waxy corn, white milo, tapioca, or potato rises quickly upon reaching a critical temperature to a relatively high level, and then decreases steadily under continued cooking and agitation. With a small amount of cross-linking, the peak viscosity will not be as high, and the viscosity will remain relatively stable during the cycle. With additional cross-linking, the viscosity may not reach a peak, but may continue to rise throughout a normal cooking period. If the degree of cross-linking is high enough, the apparent viscosity will rise very slowly or not at all. Since products of the latter type are usually designed for the more acid foods such as salad dressings or some pie fillings, it is customary to add a definite amount of an organic acid to the starch slurry before cooking (34). Granules swell more readily in such a medium, and a much better picture is obtained of how the starch will perform in its intended function. It is sometimes advisable to incorporate enough sugar into the mixture to simulate end use conditions even more closely.

Direct analysis of the extent of cross-linking is difficult because of the very low degree of substitution in most cross-linked starches. Radioactive tracer techniques should prove useful, but none has been reported to date.

Hamerstrand and co-workers (35) obtained a quantitative estimate of the amount of epichlorohydrin reacting with starch by deducting the glycerol and epichlorohydrin found in the combined filtrate and washings from the total amount added to the reaction. However, they point out that all the bound epichlorohydrin was not necessarily involved in cross-linking Since each reactive site on this bifunctional reagent can react either with starch or with water, one must assume that at least part of the reagent will be bound to the starch by only one link. It is therefore quite likely that the ratio of cross-links to D-glucose units reported by Hamerstrand and co-workers is on the high side. However, by relating the hot water solubles to the apparent number of D-glucose units per cross-link, they were able to relate quantitatively the degree of cross-linking to some physical property for the first time. It is of interest to note that as little as one cross-link per 1000 D-glucose units had a marked effect on the hot water solubility of the starch granule.

IV. Uses

Cross-linked starches are used when high viscosity or shear resistance are needed in a starch paste. Low levels of cross-linking are adequate when the starch is to be cooked for a short time at atmospheric pressure. Many processers now desire continuous cooking which generally requires more cross-linking. Continuous cooking can be accomplished by some type of heat exchanger in which a thin film of starch is heated by contact with a hot surface. Considerable mechanical shear is encountered with a thick paste, and granule disintegration as well as some primary bond breakage can occur. One test in this laboratory showed a decrease in the intrinsic viscosity of regular corn starch from about 1.40 to 1.20 in one pass through a thin film heat exchanger at about 110°.

Jet cooking by direct steam injection into a stream of starch slurry is a very efficient and effective method of cooking but is even more destructive to starch granules. Because of the relatively low equipment costs as well as rapid and uniform paste production, this type of installation is spreading rapidly. These systems are most effective at relatively high temperatures and pressures. Microscopic studies have shown that starch granules are destroyed at the steam inlet and during the short holding time but that the disruption is most apparent at the exit. The vigorous vaporization of the superheated water in the paste almost seems to explode the remaining granules. Very few granules survive this type of cooking unless they have been reinforced by cross-linking. The starch manufacturer must offer products capable of withstanding these severe processing conditions as well as products that will swell readily under atmospheric cooking conditions. To do so requires different degrees of cross-linking for different uses.

Cross-linked starches are found in most of the fruit pie fillings now on the market, including the fresh, frozen, and canned types. These starches are also more effective in canned soups, gravies, and sauces in which the contents are sterilized by retorting after sealing. Cross-linked waxy starch is particularly desirable as a thickener in Chinese foods because of the clarity, shine, and low gel tendencies of its pastes. Other food applications include baby foods, cream style corn, Harvard beets, Danish desserts, and spaghetti sauces (36).

Salad dressing starches require more cross-linking because their low pH accelerates the viscosity breakdown during preparation and storage of the dressings.

Non-food uses of cross-linked starches are widespread, and the manufacturer has more latitude in his choice of cross-linking agent. Porowski (30) has shown that it is possible to cross-link starch with urea–formaldehyde resins so that the granules are stable under shear, yet swell at a lower temperature than unmodified starch. Senti and co-workers (14) disclose that the properties of a starch can be modified by oxidizing to tenderize the granule while cross-linking to stabilize it. These starches have greatly reduced pasting temperatures; their pastes are stable under shear and are remarkably free of tendency to gel when stored.

Since cross-linked starch granules cooked under atmospheric conditions are swollen but unbroken, one would expect them to be effective internal sizes for paper (*11*) because they would be largely retained in the sheet as it is formed. They would also remain near the surface in sizing textile yarns (*13*) and thus give good abrasion resistance. Cross-linked starches are used in alkaline textile printing pastes in which they contribute the high viscosity needed to suspend the printing color, yet give a short, non-cohesive paste that does not string or throw on the rolls even though the medium is highly alkaline.

Adhesives for high speed applications, including corrugating and paper coating formulations, must withstand high shear at the nip of applicator or doctor rolls and in recirculating systems. The short, stable pastes of cross-linked starches should be of value for such uses.

Cross-linked starches are also found in oil well drilling muds, paints, printing inks, ceramics, core binders and binders for coal and charcoal briquettes. They have been recommended as electrolyte-holding media for dry cells (*37*).

More highly cross-linked starches, such as the surgical dusting starches discussed previously, are useful in dusting rubber goods and as carriers for insecticides or herbicides in dusting applications where pasting of the granules might be a problem. When phosphorus oxychloride is the cross-linking agent, those products may be used as cation exchangers (*38*).

V. REFERENCES

(*1*) K. H. Meyer, "Natural and Synthetic High Polymers," Interscience Publishers, Inc., New York, N. Y., Vol. 4, 1950, p. 200.

(*2*) P. J. Flory, "Principles of Polymer Chemistry," Cornell University Press, Ithaca, N. Y., 1953, p. 356.

(*3*) R. W. Kerr, "Chemistry and Industry of Starch," Academic Press Inc., New York, N. Y., 2nd Ed., 1950, p. 466.

(*4*) H. H. Schopmeyer, G. E. Felton, and C. L. Ford, *Ind. Eng. Chem.*, **35**, 1168 (1943).

(*5*) J. E. Fenn, U.S. Patent 2,469,957 (1949); *Chem. Abstr.*, **43**, 5910 (1949).

(*6*) C. G. Caldwell, T. A. White, W. L. George, and J. J. Eberl, U.S. Patent 2,626,257 (1953); *Chem. Abstr.*, **47**, 3528 (1953).

(*7*) A. A. Stonehill, U.S. Patent 3,072,537 (1963); *Chem. Abstr.*, **58**, 6655 (1963).

(*8*) P. V. Laakso, U.S. Patent 3,113,675 (1963).

(*9*) R. W. Maxwell, U.S. Patent 2,148,951 (1939); *Chem. Abstr.*, **33**, 4453 (1939).

(*10*) A. Classen, U.S. Patent 602,697 (1898).

(*11*) G. E. Felton and H. H. Schopmeyer, U.S. Patent 2,328,537 (1943); *Chem. Abstr.*, **38**, 889 (1944).

(*12*) M. Konigsberg, U.S. Patent 2,500,950 (1950); *Chem. Abstr.*, **44**, 6666 (1950).

(*13*) B. T. Hofreiter, C. L. Mehltretter, J. Bennie, and G. E. Hamerstrand, U.S. Patent 2,929,811 (1960); *Chem. Abstr.*, **54**, 13704 (1960).

(*14*) F. R. Senti, R. L. Mellies, and C. L. Mehltretter, U.S. Patent 2,989,521 (1961); *Chem. Abstr.*, **59**, 3000 (1961).

(*15*) R. W. Kerr and F. C. Cleveland, Jr., U.S. Patent 2,801,242 (1957); *Chem. Abstr.*, **51**, 18666 (1957).

(16) R. W. Kerr and N. F. Schink, U.S. Patent 2,438,855 (1948); *Chem. Abstr.*, **42**, 4380 (1948).

(17) B. W. Rowland and J. V. Bauer, U.S. Patent 2,113,034 (1938); *Chem. Abstr.*, **32**, 3963 (1938).

(18) G. G. Pierson, U.S. Patent 2,417,611 (1947); *Chem. Abstr.*, **41**, 4326 (1947).

(19) C. E. Smith and J. V. Tuschoff, U.S. Patent 3,069,410 (1962); *Chem. Abstr.*, **58**, 5874 (1963).

(20) J. F. Walker and S. E. Kokowicz, U.S. Patent 2,548,455 (1951); *Chem. Abstr.*, **45**, 5927 (1951).

(21) D. L. Schoene and V. S. Chambers, U.S. Patent 2,524,400 (1950); *Chem. Abstr.*, **45**, 4474 (1951).

(22) J. D. Commerford and I. Ehrenthal, U.S. Patent 2,977,356 (1961); *Chem. Abstr.*, **55**, 19289 (1961).

(23) T. S. W. Gerwitz, U.S. Patent 2,805,220 (1957); *Chem. Abstr.*, **52**, 767 (1958).

(24) E. L. Wimmer, U.S. Patent 2,910,467 (1959); *Chem. Abstr.*, **54**, 1906 (1960).

(25) D. Trimnell, C. P. Patel, and J. F. Johnston, U.S. Patent 3,086,971 (1963); *Chem. Abstr.*, **59**, 3000 (1963).

(26) I. A. Wolff, P. R. Watson, and C. E. Rist, *J. Am. Chem. Soc.*, **76**, 757 (1954).

(27) E. A. Sowell, J. E. Voigt, and R. J. Horst, U.S. Patent 3,001,985 (1961); *Chem. Abstr.*, **56**, 3712 (1962).

(28) D. Trimnel, C. P. Patel, and J. F. Johnston, U.S. Patent 3,035,045 (1962); *Chem. Abstr.*, **57**, 6194 (1962).

(29) L. O. Gill and J. W. McDonald, U.S. Patent 2,407,071 (1946); *Chem. Abstr.*, **41**, 612 (1947).

(30) T. Porowski, U.S. Patent 2,838,465 (1958); *Chem. Abstr.*, **52**, 15106 (1958).

(31) T. J. Schoch, *Staerke*, **11**, 156 (1959).

(32) F. E. Kite, T. J. Schoch, and H. W. Leach, *Baker's Dig.*, **31**, No. 4, 42 (1957).

(33) E. G. Mazurs, T. J. Schoch, and F. E. Kite, *Cereal Chem.*, **34**, 141 (1957).

(34) T. J. Otterbacher and F. E. Kite, *Baker's Dig.*, **32**, No. 5, 44 (1958).

(35) G. E. Hamerstrand, B. T. Hofreiter, and C. L. Mehltretter, *Cereal Chem.*, **37**, 519 (1960).

(36) T. J. Schoch and A. L. Elder, "Uses of Sugars and Other Carbohydrates in the Food Industry," Advances in Chemistry Series, No. 12, American Chemical Society, Washington, D.C., 1955, p. 21.

(37) T. Shimizu, *Kogyo Kagaku Zasshi*, **64**, 683, 1241 (1961); *Chem. Abstr.*, **57**, 7502, 10908 (1962).

(38) F. Wettstein, H. Neukom, and H. Deuel, *Helv. Chim. Acta*, **44**, 1949 (1961).

CHAPTER XX

PRODUCTION AND USE OF AMYLOSE

By David P. Langlois and John A. Wagoner

A. E. Staley Mfg. Co., Decatur, Illinois

I. Introduction

1. Definition

Amylose is a linear polymer obtained by the fractionation of starch. Its character is best understood by reference to the starch of its origin and the manner of its separation.

Starch is a homopolymer of D-glucose in which 96% or more of the D-glucose units are linked α-D-$(1 \rightarrow 4)$ and 4% or less are linked α-D-$(1 \rightarrow 6)$. Furthermore, all D-glucose units which are linked α-D-$(1 \rightarrow 6)$ are also linked α-D-$(1 \rightarrow 4)$. This evidence is interpreted to mean that starch is primarily a branched polymer consisting of chains of D-glucose units linked α-D-$(1 \rightarrow 4)$ with branches at the C-6 position on an average of once every 26 or more D-glucose units. This evidence further supports the concept that starch may be either a homogeneous branched polymer or a heterogeneous mixture of branched and linear polymers. One of the most perplexing and disputed problems in the long history of starch chemistry has centered around this matter of the heterogeneity of starch and it is probably not yet resolved. Now, however, the consensus is that some starches are homogeneous and some are heterogeneous. This conclusion follows from the fact that some starches can be separated by many methods into two fractions, one of which appears to be linear, while other starches, for example, the waxy varieties, cannot be separated by these same techniques. The separation methods are not entirely devoid of procedures which might cause splitting of the polymer. Hence, the separation of the starch into fractions is not *ipso facto* evidence that the two polymers exist preformed in the starch.

Regardless of how the linear polymer exists in the native starch, it has been conclusively established that a polymer can be separated from starch by certain techniques which generally attest to its linearity.

Meyer (1) gave the name amylose to the unbranched component of starch and amylopectin to the branched component.

Meyer's definitions of amylose and amylopection are based on the assumption that one of the starch components is entirely unbranched and that there are methods of differentiating between straight chains and branched chains sufficiently precise to establish the absolute absence of branch points.

Even if available methods were precise enough to establish the absolute absence of branching, they are far too involved to be used in ordinary control operations. Therefore, although it is accepted that amylose is the linear fraction of starch, it is well to recognize that it may not be wholly unbranched.

Commercial amylose is almost certain to contain some molecules which are slightly branched, but the chains are sufficiently long and the branches sufficiently infrequent that the polymer exhibits the characteristics of linear polymers.

2. Historical Background (see also Vol. I, Chapt. X)

Somewhat illogically, the structure of the individual starch fractions was established before the authentic fractions were actually isolated in pure state. The concept of starch and its fractions as polymeric chains of α-D-$(1 \rightarrow 4)$-linked glucopyranoside units had its origin in cellulose chemistry. Herzog and Jancke (2) and Sponsler (3) concluded from x-ray studies that starch possessed a crystalline space lattice similar to that of cellulose. Meyer and co-workers (4) suggested that starch was composed of long polymeric "main valence chains" of D-glucose units associated laterally by secondary valence forces. Cellulose was considered an extended chain because of its β-D-glucose linkage and starch a zig-zag chain because of its α-D-glucosidic linkage. The methylation studies of Haworth (5) presented strong evidence for a chainlike structure since hydrolysis of trimethyl starch gave about 4% of 2,3,4,6-tetramethyl-D-glucose. On the consideration that the tetramethyl-D-glucose was derived from the nonaldehydic terminal D-glucose of the starch chain, the chain length was calculated to be 26 D-glucose units. Methylation studies on starch fractions obtained by early investigators showed no difference between the fractions probably because the existing methods of fractionation were too crude.

The Haworth estimates of the chain length of the starch was challenged on both physical and chemical grounds. Carter and Record (6) determined a molecular weight corresponding to 630 D-glucose units from osmotic pressure measurements on methylated starch in chloroform solution. This was in contrast to the 26 units obtained by methylation assay. Other investigators (7) also observed corresponding discrepancies between molecular weight determinations based on osmotic properties and on methylation studies. Staudinger and Husemann (8) reconciled these conflicting viewpoints by suggesting a branched chain structure for starch.

The studies of K. H. Meyer and co-workers (1) are responsible for the present structural concept of the starch fractions. Meyer and co-workers developed the theory that the minor component, amylose, is an unbranched linear chain approximately 300 D-glucose units in length, while the major component, amylopectin, represents a ramified or branched structure of several thousand D-glucose units.

Meyer and co-workers obtained the fractions by leaching amylose from the swollen starch granules at temperatures slightly above the gelatinization point. The soluble amylose was then purified using the characteristic property of retrogradation. Methylation of the original starch and of the amylose and amylopectin fractions obtained from it, followed by hydrolysis and fractional distillation of the methyl D-glucosides, gave yields of tetramethyl-D-glucose from the corn starch, amylose, and amylopection of 3.5%, 0.32%, and 3.7% by weight, respectively (9). Amylose, therefore, appeared to have a linear structure with one nonaldehydic end-group per 300 D-glucose units in agreement with the osmotic molecular weight of 50,000. Amylopectin had one such end-group per every 26 D-glucose units and starch one in every 27 D-glucose units. A molecule of 200,000 molecular weight must therefore be branched about 50 times. By turbidimetric methods, Meyer, Wertheim, and Bernfeld (9) measured the reducing power of amylose toward ammoniacal silver oxide. While the results were at best only an approximation, they indicated that the content of aldehydic terminal groups in amylose was of the same magnitude as the content of nonaldehydic terminals. This was further evidence of the linearity of amylose. Once the branched and linear polymers of starch were clearly identified and recognized, many attempts by numerous investigators were made to separate the fractions into their pure state by various other techniques. It remained for Schoch (10) to point the way toward the possible commercial separation of the starch fractions. He discovered a fundamentally new method of starch fractionation. He showed that 1-butanol or pentasol selectively precipitates one component of starch and leaves the other component in solution. The fraction precipitated by 1-butanol was called the A fraction. The fraction remaining in solution was called the B fraction. The A fraction exhibited a high affinity for iodine. The B fraction, on the other hand, exhibited a low iodine affinity. The A fraction crystallized in minute six-lobed spherules, in hairlike needles, or in beautifully formed six-petaled rosettes. These crystals were moderately birefringent in polarized light and markedly dichroic when lightly stained with iodine. X-ray and optical analyses of the butanol precipitate showed it to be in the form of helical coils, presumably around the alcohol molecules. These cylindrical molecules pack closely to form the characteristic rectangular platelet and hexagonal rosettes.

Frequently, the B fraction co-precipitated with the A fraction; but, after the former was removed by repeated precipitations, the resulting purified A fraction was shown to be identical to the amylose of Meyer and co-workers (1).

Schoch's (10) work was probably the greatest single contribution that led to the conclusive establishment of the existence of two main fractions in starch and to an understanding of the chemical nature of the two fractions. His method of separation made large quantities of the two fractions available. Fractionation and subfractionation of Schoch's original fractions and detailed chemical and physical studies of these fractions and subfractions have led to our present understanding of the polymer composition of starch.

3. Occurrence and Biosynthesis (see also Vol. I, Chapt. VII)

Amylose is widespread throughout the plant kingdom; it is almost as widespread as starch itself. Most starches are a mixture of amylose and amylopectin. Amylose is usually in the smaller proportion. Bourne and Peat and co-workers (11) are the chief exponents of the belief that the formation of amylose is the first step in the plant's manufacture of starch and that branching of the amylose under the influence of branching enzymes accounts for the formation of amylopectin. Evidence for this mechanism came, in the first place, from parallel studies on the synthesis of glycogen in the animal and was mainly the contribution of C. F. Cori and co-workers (12). They found that the intermediate in the breakdown and buildup of glycogen in muscle was neither free D-glucose nor maltose but D-glucose 1-phosphate. Furthermore, the enzyme phosphorylase, which catalyzed this interconversion was isolated from a number of animal tissues, and the phosphorylase isolated from muscle was ultimately obtained in the crystalline state. In 1940, Hanes (13) isolated a phosphorylase system from higher plants and was able to isolate it in quantity from peas and potatoes. This enzyme catalyzed the reversible reaction:

D-Glucose 1-phosphate ⇆ "starch" + inorganic phosphate

This "starch" had the properties of an amylose rather than that of whole starch. Hanes' experiment led to the view that phosphorylase effected the synthesis only of the unbranched component of natural starch.

Since starch synthesized in the plant contains about 75% amylopectin whereas that synthesized in vitro by purified phosphorylase consists mainly of "amylose," the conclusion is inevitable that phosphorylase is at most only a part of the enzyme system concerned with the in vivo synthesis of polysaccharides from D-glucose 1-phosphate. In living tissue, the synthetic action of phosphorylase must be supplemented by some other enzyme which is capable of introducing linkages between the unbranched chains of glucose residues if it is indeed a synthetic enzyme.

The isolation of the branching enzyme of potato starch was reported in 1944 (11). It was shown that the action of a mixture of phosphorylase, called P-enzyme by these investigators, and a newly isolated factor, referred to as Q-enzyme, on D-glucose 1-phosphate resulted in the synthesis of typical amylopectin apparently unaccompanied by amylose. The synthesizing function of Q-enzyme appears to be confined solely to the formation of polymeric bonds, that is $(1 \rightarrow 6)$-D-glucosidic links, between pre-existing chains of $(1 \rightarrow 4)$-D-glucose units. Unless it is acting in conjunction with phosphorylase, Q-enzyme cannot utilize D-glucose 1-phosphate as a substrate and it appears quite doubtful that Q-enzyme participates at all in the phosphate interconversion.

The hydrolytic function of Q-enzyme has been demonstrated to be confined to the fragmentation of long unbranched chains into dextrins (also unbranched), the average length of which is about 20 D-glucose units. Q-enzyme then functions in the formation of branches on linear chains of α-D-$(1 \rightarrow 4)$-linked glucopyranose units.

All tuber starches and most cereal starches, as well as leaf and stem starches contain both amylose and amylopectin. A few starches have been found, however, that show no amylose by the normal methods of detection. The two best known of these are waxy maize starch and waxy sorghum starch. The plants producing the waxy starches are genetically different from the plants producing ordinary starch which is a mixture of amylose and amylopectin. A partial list of starches with their amylose content is given in Table I (14–20).

Table I

Amylose Content of Starches

	Amylose (%)	References
Acorn	24.0	14
Apple	26.5	15
Arrowroot	20.5	16
Banana	16.8	16
Barley	22.0	16
Easter lily	34.0	17
Elm tree, sapwood	21.5	18
Iris tuber	27.0	16
Maize	24.0	16
Hybrid amylomaize	50.0	19
Waxy maize	0.8	16
Oat	26.0	16
Pea, smooth	34.5	20
Wrinkled	66.0	20
Manioc	15.7	16
Potato	20.0	16
Rice	18.5	16
Sago	25.8	16
Sweet potato	17.8	16
Tapioca	16.7	16
Wheat	25.0	16

Most native starches contain only 20–30% of the amylose fraction. However, an occasional starch has been isolated that has a much higher percentage of amylose; a certain variety of wrinkled pea contains a starch having 60% amylose. Certain new varieties of corn produce starch which is even higher in amylose.

The hypothesis has been suggested that the ratio of P- to Q-enzyme is a function of the genetic makeup of the plant. A plant lacking Q-enzyme should produce only amylose as its starch polymer. A plant having a high Q- to P-enzyme ratio should produce only amylopectin and plants having intermediate or low Q- to P-enzyme ratios should produce starches having varying amounts of amylose and amylopectin (21). However, Fuwa (21a) found approximately equal activity in developing seeds of waxy and non-waxy maize (corn) for both phosphorylase and the Q-enzyme, making it unlikely that different proportions of these enzymes could explain the difference.

Other theories such as those involving glucosyltransferase enzymes are discussed in Volume I, Chapter VII. Further information may come from genetic studies aimed at developing strains of corn which produce high-amylose starch. Excellent reviews of this field are given by Augustat (22), Zuber (Vol. I, Chapt. IV), and Senti (This Volume, Chapt. XXI).

High amylose starch as a commercial source of amylose appeared unlikely until Vineyard and Bear (23) reported the discovery of a variety of corn carrying a gene which linked high-amylose starch with high starch yield. Subsequently, they reported the discovery of gene modifiers which had the property of increasing the amylose to amylopectin ratio. A starch containing 70% amylose is currently being marketed. A starch with 85% amylose has recently been reported. Hence, the production of concentrated amylose by the corn plant is now a commercial reality.

In the meantime, by virtue of the discovery and application of commercial separation techniques, amylose is available in quantity from both potato starch and yellow dent corn starch by separation of the amylose component.

II. Analyses

There are many marked differences between amylose and amylopectin that could form the basis for analytical methods to distinguish between them. Some of the characteristic and distinguishing properties of amylose are:

1. High digestibility with beta-amylase (approximately 100%)
2. Relatively low molecular weight (600 to 1600 D.P.)
3. Deep blue color with iodine
4. Absorption of large amounts of iodine isopotentiometrically.
5. Complex formation with 1-butanol and other organic compounds
6. Adsorption on cellulose
7. High intrinsic viscosity and low solution stability
8. Ratio of reducing end-groups to nonreducing end-groups per molecule equal to one.

The corresponding properties of amylopectin are:

1. Lower digestibility with beta-amylase (about 50%)
2. High molecular weight (greater than 10,000 D.P.)
3. Purple or reddish color with iodine
4. Low adsorption of iodine isopotentiometrically
5. Inability to combine with 1-butanol or other organic compounds
6. Low adsorption on cellulose
7. Ratio of nonreducing end-groups to reducing end-groups per molecule greater than one (usually several hundred).

In spite of all the differences between amylose and amylopectin, few of these characteristics are suitable for the quantitative differentiation between the two or for the quantitative determination of either of the fractions. Quantitatively distinguishing between the two fractions is further complicated by the genetic differences in plants which leads to the production of amyloses and amylopectins of various molecular size and degree of branching. It is also complicated by the difficulty of dissolution of the starch or starch fraction for analytical measurement. Many of the methods employed to disperse the amylose will cause considerable degradation in molecular size. The analytical methods which have been most generally employed in distinguishing between amylose and amylopectin are:

1. Iodine absorption
2. Nonreducing end-group analysis
3. Reducing end-group analysis
4. 1-Butanol crystallization
5. Adsorption on cellulose

Methods involving iodine absorption are the only ones that lend themselves readily to rapid analysis with a reasonable degree of accuracy.

The nonreducing end-group analysis, based on the work of Hirst and co-workers (24), involves exhaustive methylation of the starch or the starch fractions, hydrolysis of methylation products, and quantitative separation of the methylation products. This method is satisfactorily accurate in the hands of experts, but is a rather long and tedious process.

Another method of determining nonreducing end-groups is based on periodate oxidation of the starch or starch fraction and determination of the formic acid produced (25). The procedure is described as follows: 100–500 mg. of amylose is dissolved in sodium hydroxide. After the amylose is completely dissolved and just before the next operation, the pH is adjusted to approximately 7 with hydrochloric acid. Fifty ml. of

0.5M sodium metaperiodate is added, and the reaction mixture is adjusted to 250 ml.; the solution is cooled to 5°–6° and stored in the dark. At the end of 3 days, a formic acid determination is made on an aliquot and repeated every 12 hr. until three consecutive determinations are the same. To perform a formic acid determination, 0.5 ml of ethylene glycol is added to a 20-ml. aliquot. After 10 minutes, an excess of potassium iodide and then an excess of 0.01N sodium thiosulfate are added, and the excess sodium thiosulfate is back-titrated with 0.01N iodine using starch indicator. Based on the fact that one nonreducing end-group furnishes one mole, and one reducing end-group furnishes two moles of formic acid, the number of D-glucose units that are associated with one nonreducing end-group can be calculated.

The method is more precise for the determination of the molecular weight of amylopectin than for amylose. Furthermore, this procedure lacks precision since the amount of oxidant required to oxidize a reducing end-group varies depending upon the conditions of oxidation and the size of the molecular group. For example, the amount of oxidant required to oxidize the reducing group on glucose is different from the amount of oxidant required to oxidize the reducing group on maltose. In addition, the alkalinity of the solution, the temperature of oxidation, and the time of oxidation all have a bearing on the amount of oxidant used. As an empirical method for determining the relative molecular sizes of amylose or amylopectin molecules, however, the method has a certain value.

Periodate overoxidation of reducing end-groups has been recommended for determining the degree of polymerization of amylose (*26*).

Analytical methods based on iodine absorption are the ones most generally employed for determining amylose quantitatively. The methods, however, suffer from a certain lack of specificity. Amylose combines with iodine to form a deep blue complex. The intensity of the color formed can therefore be used to measure the amount of amylose that combined with the iodine. It must be borne in mind, however, that short length amylose chains combine with less iodine than long chains and tend to give a lower color intensity, thus producing a low analytical value. Conversely, long chains on branched-chain molecules may form iodine complexes that have colors comparable to those of the amylose molecule, thus giving a deceptively high analytical value for amylose.

Two general methods are in use, and both depend on the iodine binding capacity of the linear or amylose fraction. The amylose content may be determined spectrophotometrically by measuring the intensity of the blue color imparted to a solution containing the amylose and an excess of iodine. On the other hand, the amylose solution may be titrated potentiometrically by using iodine and determining the amount of iodine that is bound by the amylose. Both methods are relative and depend on comparison with a standard. Defatted starch or starch fractions must be used in these determinations. The starch may be defatted by any of the standard methods. One of the simplest is to extract the starch in a Soxhlet extractor for several hours with 80% methanol.

The method of McCready and Hassid (27) is generally used for the spectrophotometric determination of amylose. According to this procedure, 100 mg. of defatted carbohydrate is moistened with 1 ml. of ethanol; then 10 ml. of water and 2 ml. of 10% sodium hydroxide are added in that order. The mixture is heated until a clear solution is obtained, and diluted to 100 ml. Five ml. of this solution is added to a 500-ml. flask which contains about 100 ml. of water, 3 drops of 6N hydrochloric acid and 5 ml. of iodine solution (0.2% I_2 and 2% KI). The solution is adjusted to volume and the absorbance is read at 640 mμ in a 2-cm. cell. The percentage of amylose is determined by reference to a standard curve that has been prepared using an authentic sample of amylose.

For a more rapid and reasonably precise determination of amylose, the spectrophotometric absorption method may be used in a Technicon analyzer (28). The reagents used are acetic acid solution (3.4 ml. of glacial acetic acid diluted to 1 liter), iodine–potassium iodide stock solution (2.0 grams I_2 plus 20 grams KI diluted to 1 liter), and 1N potassium hydroxide. For the actual titration, 40 ml. of the iodine stock solution is diluted to 1 liter. The defatted starch sample is weighed out and dissolved in 5 ml. of 1N potassium hydroxide, the resulting solution is transferred to a 100-ml. volumetric flask and diluted to volume. The basic carbohydrate solution is placed in the sampler of the autoanalyzer. The sample is then fed into the reagent stream where it is diluted, combined with appropriate reagents, held in a 35° constant temperature bath for 3 minutes, and finally pumped through a flow colorimeter in which the absorbance is recorded. A standard amylose solution is run through the system before the first sample and after each sixth sample. A flow diagram of the analyzer is illustrated in Figure 1. To determine amylose, the absorbance of the sample and the absorbance of the closest standard amylose are read from the Technicon chart. The amylose content of the unknown may be calculated by comparison with the standard by the formula:

$$\frac{A_x}{A_s} \times 100 = \%\ \text{amylose}$$

where A_x = absorbance of sample corrected to 100 mg. per 100 ml. and A_s = absorbance of standard corrected to 100 mg. per 100 ml.

Bates, French, and Rundle (*29*) developed the potentiometric method of estimating the iodine affinity of starch fractions. According to their procedure, a starch sample is dissolved in dilute sodium hydroxide solution, neutralized with hydriodic acid, and titrated electrometrically with standard iodine–potassium iodide solution. The plot of the electromotive force (EMF) against the amount of iodine added gives a typical "S" curve, and the amount of iodine that combined with the starch can be calculated from the second inflection point of the curve. Bates and co-workers, using Kerr's crystalline corn amylose (*30*) as a standard, estimated 17% amylose for tapioca and rye starches, 21% to 24% for corn,

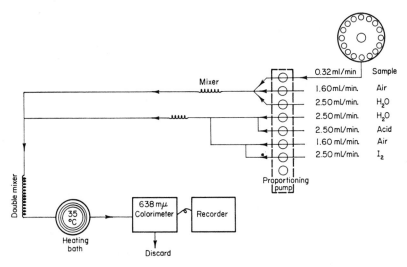

Fig. 1.—Flow diagram of continuous analyzer for amylose determination.

potato and wheat starches, 27% for sago starch, and 34% for starch from Easter lily bulbs. Waxy cereal starches showed very low iodine-binding capacity.

Schoch and co-workers (*31*) have adapted the Bates' (*29*) method for routine evaluation. They find that a more precise estimate of iodine affinity may be made by plotting the free iodine against the bound iodine. A hyperbolic type of curve is obtained; and, by extrapolating the one leg of this curve to an intersection, the iodine absorption may be readily calculated. The defatted starch is dispersed in potassium hydroxide and allowed to stand several hours in order to obtain a perfectly clear solution. Forty mg. of amylose, 200 mg. of amylopectin, or 100 mg. of whole starch are usually adequate and are dispersed in 5 ml. of $1N$ potassium hydroxide. Just before titration, the solution is neutralized to methyl orange with $0.5N$ hydrochloric acid. Ten ml. of $0.5N$ potassium iodide solution is added, and the whole is diluted to 100 ml. The standard iodine reagent is 0.05N with respect to potassium chloride and 0.05N to potassium iodide and contains 0.2 mg. of iodine per ml. For the titration, a bright platinum electrode is used in conjunction with a saturated calomel half cell, and the EMF is measured with any null point potentiometer capable of being read to ±1 millivolt. The starch solution must be stirred during the titration and the potential determined

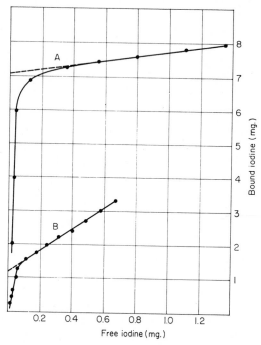

Fɪɢ. 2.—Iodine titrations with Leeds and Northrup Type K potentiometer. Curve A represents titration of 48.7 mg. of high amylose fraction. Extrapolation to the vertical axis gives an iodine affinity of 7.09 mg. or 15.5% on a dry basis. Curve B represents titration of 197.1 mg. of low amylose fraction (7.9% moisture). Iodine affinity 0.64% is on dry basis.

at 8 to 12 points between 220 and 280 millivolts. For calibration, an identical titration is run in the absence of any starch material in order to translate the millivolt readings into mg. of free iodine in solution. The free iodine in solution is calculated from the corresponding EMF of the calibration curve for each point on the starch titration curve. The value is deducted from the total iodine added at this point to give the bound or absorbed iodine. Free iodine can be plotted against bound iodine as shown in Figure 2. The upper linear portion of the curve when extrapolated back to the zero axis gives the amount of bound iodine at zero free iodine concentration or the iodine affinity for the starch sample. From the iodine affinity value, the percentage of amylose may be calculated by referring it to the value obtained from a standard amylose sample.

III. Properties

1. Molecular Structure (see also Vol. I, Chapt. XV)

Amylose is a polymer consisting of chains of D-glucopyranose units linked $(1 \rightarrow 4)$. The linkage is assigned an alpha configuration in contradistinction to the beta configuration that occurs in cellulose. The two different linkages impart strikingly different characteristics to the two polymers. The beta-linked cellulose molecules are relaxed linear chains that crystallize into fibrous materials, which is the way cellulose usually occurs in nature.

Amylose molecules, on the other hand, are coiled or spiral chains and form extended linear chains only under a high orientation force. Even before the amylose molecule was isolated in the pure form, Hanes (32) had suggested that the starch molecule is arranged in the form of a helically coiled spring with approximately 6 glucose units in each turn of the helix. Freudenberg and co-workers (33) also subscribed to this view of the starch structure and constructed space models in which the hydroxyl groups of the glucose unit existed on the exterior of the helix. Rundle and his co-workers (34) have made an extensive study of the x-ray spectra and other optical properties of the amylose complexes with iodine and 1-butanol and have concluded that amylose in the granule and in pasted starches appears to be an extended, somewhat relaxed helix that assumes regular uniform helical configuration in the presence of the complexing agent. Rundle and Baldwin (35) observed that amylose solutions stained with iodine when subjected to high velocity gradients in a flow polarization apparatus showed a marked dichroism of flow. These observations confirm the fact that amylose is a linear molecule and, furthermore, that the iodine must be parallel to the axis of the starch molecule. Foster and Lepow (36), studying the streaming birefringence of amylose from various starches, observed qualitative correlation between intrinsic viscosities and the ease of orientation. They concluded that, in strong solvents, amylose molecules appear to be randomly kinked or coiled, elongating to an extended linear form in a streaming gradient. Rundle and French (37) interpreted the optical birefringence of amylose crystals and the dichroism of flow of the dissolved amylose stained with iodine on the basis of helical configuration, the iodine axis coinciding with that of the helix. They also observed that amylose that was combined with iodine or butanol gave the V-type x-ray patterns described by Katz and co-workers (38). Retrograded amylose or granular starch gave A- and B-type spectra. The unit cell dimensions calculated from the V-spectrum corresponded to a helical structure 12.97 Å in diameter with a distance of 7.91 Å between turns. These values are in agreement with the Hanes–Freudenberg (32, 33) model for amylose which postulates 6 glucose residues per turn.

Bear (39), on the other hand, observed that amylose precipitated by branched-chain alcohols, gives x-ray patterns which suggest larger unit cell dimensions. He concluded that the helix accommodates itself to these precipitants. Everett and Foster (40) found that water is a poor solvent for amylose; and, therefore, many of the measurements of amylose in water solution are not clearly indicative of amylose in true solutions. They find that in solvents such as dimethylsulfoxide, 0.33N potassium chloride, and 0.5N potassium hydroxide the polymer is in a coil conformation.

Further confirmation of the helical structure of starch lies in the studies of the action of an enzyme from *Bacillus macerans* (41). This enzyme appears to attack the nonaldehydic terminals of the starch molecules and splits moieties that cyclize into the crystalline Schardinger dextrins; these are cyclic dextrins containing 6 to 8 D-glucose units per molecule.

There is some evidence that commercial amylose is not completely unbranched. Kerr and Cleveland (42) deduced from the rates of amyloglucosidase hydrolysis that some amyloses are slightly branched. Stepanenko and Afanas'eva (43) found that amyloses from potato starch are not wholly linear but averaged 0.2 to 0.8 points of branching per molecule. Commercial amyloses nevertheless exhibit the properties of linear polymers and may be considered linear polymers wherever their application is reported.

2. Complex Formation

Amylose has the capacity to complex with a very large number of different organic compounds. The literature is replete with examples of amylose complexed with polar organic compounds that have a sufficient solubility in water. Complexes of amylose with nonpolar compounds, such as the paraffin hydrocarbons and cyclic hydrocarbons, have only recently been reported. Among the many reported amylose complexes are those with the aliphatic alcohols, such as isoamyl, n-butyl, and isopropyl (39); lower aliphatic ketones and lower fatty acids, as well as benzenoid derivatives having aldehyde groups (39); long-chain fatty acids, such as stearic and oleic acids (*44*); alkyl halides (*45, 46*); nitroparaffins (*47*); cyclic alcohols and phenols (*48, 49*); aliphatic and aromatic esters (*47*); benzene (*46*); and cyclic and aliphatic hydrocarbons (*46*).

From the extensive study of the iodine complex, the prevailing opinion is that the iodine molecule enters the amylose helix and aligns itself parallel to the axis of the helix (*35*). In solution, amylose combines with more than 20% of its weight of iodine. Dried amylose in the V-configuration has been found to absorb as much as 26% of its weight of iodine which is equivalent to 1 iodine molecule for each turn of the helix of 6 D-glucose units (*50*). Rundle and Edwards (*51*) measured the cell dimensions of the amylose–1-butanol complex and concluded that the alcohol precipitant also occupied a similar lengthwise position within the helix.

From x-ray evidence, Mikus, Hixon, and Rundle (*44*) have found that the complexes between amylose and fatty acids have unit cell dimensions similar to those of the complexes of iodine and of 1-butanol. They presume, therefore, that the higher fatty acids induce the amylose to assume a helical structure with the fatty acids taking a lengthwise position within the helix.

The fatty acid complex has been shown to contain 6–7% of its weight of oleic, palmitic, or lauric acid, which corresponds to the theoretical internal capacity of the helix when calculated from space considerations. We may therefore assume that the orientation of complexing agents is generally lengthwise down the amylose helix and that the core of the helix is filled with the complexing agent.

The amylose complexes with the various complexing agents are relatively insoluble in water and are precipitated or crystallized from the solution on standing. The dried complexes are quite stable, and the absorbed materials cannot be removed with hydrocarbon solvents or anhydrous dioxane. Aqueous solvents such as 80% dioxane or 80% methanol, however, will readily remove the complexing agents. Anhydrous methanol can remove some of the complexing agents but with more difficulty than the aqueous solution.

3. Retrogradation

The term retrogradation was originally used to describe a phenomenon occurring during the aging of starch pastes. Freshly prepared starch solutions are strongly opalescent. On standing under aseptic conditions, the opalescense increases until finally a precipitation of a portion of the starch occurs. The precipitated starch is insoluble in cold water.

Early investigators noted the granular appearance of the precipitated starch fraction. They considered that the pasted starch had reverted to its original insoluble granular state, hence the term retrogradation. With a better understanding of the structure of the starch fractions, it is now recognized that the phenomenon of retrogradation is the result of hydrogen bonding between starch molecules that have both hydroxyl groups and hydrogen acceptor sites. The extended linear molecules of amylose are more free to orient themselves with respect to other amylose molecules in solution than are the larger more compact branched molecules of amylopectin. Hence retrogradation is associated almost exclusively with the amylose fraction. The amylose structure permits the formation of a great many hydrogen bonding sites between adjoining molecules so that a solution of amylose is highly unstable. At amylose concentrations above 2%, hydrogen bonding occurs broadly with numerous adjoining molecules and a gel is formed.. At lower concentrations or under controlled temperature conditions, the molecules orient themselves in a manner that permits the formation of numerous crystallites. When the aggregates of crystallites exceed colloidal dimensions, a granular precipitate separates.

Amylose molecules must therefore be able to assume several configurations in solution. The stable form in solution is probably the helix. A gel results when the helical or partly uncoiled helical molecules form hydrogen bonds between each other. In order to retrograde to the solid state, molecules must uncoil and align themselves to permit the formation of crystallites which ultimately grow into large aggregates. Greenwood (52) proposes an equilibrium solution as follows:

"'aggregated helices" ⇌ helical configuration ⇌ linear configuration

⇌ aggregated linear chains

Intermediate forms must exist because of the large size and flexibility of the amylose molecule. Evidence of stable aggregates of amylose molecules is provided by the observations of Paschall and Foster (53) on the light scattering of amylose in solvents at various pH's.

Few quantitative measurements have been made on the retrogradation phenomenon. Whistler and Johnson (54) related retrogradation to molecular weight and showed that the rate of retrogradation varied in the order potato < corn < wheat, whereas the molecular size varied in the inverse direction. The rate of retrogradation of a series of acid-hydrolyzed amyloses passed through a maximum which suggests that a critical size exists at which retrogradation is a maximum. Larger or smaller molecules retrograde more slowly or not at all. Schoch's observations on the rate of retrogradation of various subfractions of corn starch also confirmed this hypothesis (*31*). The rate of retrogradation was inversely related to the chain length until a certain critical value was reached below which the molecules were too small to crystallize. The extent of retrogradation of amylose was measured by Meyer and co-workers (*55*) who showed that less than 0.4% remains in solution.

Many other factors affect the rate of retrogradation (*56*). The rate increases with decreasing temperature. It is fastest at pH 7, and decreases at higher or lower pH's. Above pH 10, retrogradation does not occur, and below pH 2 the rate is extremely low. Magnesium sulfate speeds up the rate of retrogradation. At a magnesium sulfate concentration of 13% potato amylose is precipitated completely in 5 min. The freshly precipitated amylose is only partially retrograded. It can be redissolved in water at 100°, but it becomes completely retrograded after standing a few hours in the presence of the magnesium sulfate solution.

Considerable practical importance is attached to retrogradation. It is believed to be a factor involved in the staling of bread and in the changes in textures occurring in canned soups, peas, corn, and other foods made with amylose-containing starches (see This volume, Chapt. VIII).

4. Solubility

Amylose, as it is usually obtained commercially, is the retrograded product. This retrograded amylose is inherently insoluble in water. Meyer and Bernfeld (*57*) give the solubilities of retrograded rice, potato, and corn amyloses as 0.11, 0.054, and 0.04%, respectively. Amylose, freshly leached from the starch granule, has a much higher solubility than this, but the solution is unstable and the amylose quickly undergoes retrogradation. Amylose, separated as the butanol complex, may be isolated as a dry, free-flowing powder which is completely soluble in boiling water at concentrations as high as 15%; of course, the amylose must be handled in such a manner as to avoid retrogradation (*30*). It is, therefore, meaningless to discuss the solubility of amylose without qualification. The discussion of this section relates only to retrograded amylose.

Aqueous solutions of amylose can be prepared at elevated temperature and pressure. At 150° the dispersion is rapid and complete. A continuous autoclave that has a holding time of less than 2 minutes is the recommended equipment for dispersing amylose if hydrolytic degradation is to be avoided. Under most conditions, amylose solutions rapidly set to gels, even at elevated temperatures. The rate of gelling is a function of time, temperature, pH, concentration of amylose, and the method used to solubilize the amylose.

Stable solutions of amylose that remain fluid indefinitely can be prepared by the addition of formaldehyde. Three factors influencing the stability of corn amylose are illustrated in Figure 3. Potato amylose, because of its lesser tendency to gel, can be handled at higher concentrations and requires less formaldehyde for stabilization as can be seen from Figure 4 (58). It is probable that the stabilization of amylose takes

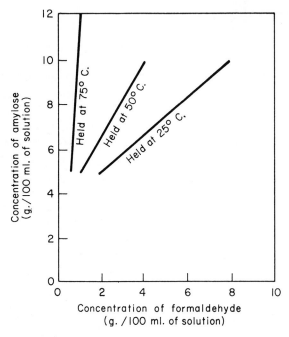

FIG. 3.—Factors that are involved in stabilizing corn amylose solutions with formaldehyde. Stable areas are to the right of the curves.

place through the formation of hemiacetals which make the amylose less stereo-regular. Addition of the formaldehyde to the amylose slurry prior to autoclaving markedly reduces the temperature of dispersion.

Amylose is readily soluble in dilute alkali. Potassium and sodium hydroxides are the most effective agents for this purpose. There is an optimum amount of alkali required for the solution of corn amylose as can be seen by reference to Figures 5 and 6. Concentrations greater or less than the critical amount will promote gelling. Amylose is soluble in the following organic solvents:

Aqueous chloral hydrate	Formamide
Dichloroacetic acid	Pyrrolidine
Dimethylsulfoxide	Acetamide
Ethylenediamine	Piperazine
Formic acid	Urea

Because of the relatively high molecular weight and linearity of amylose, concentrations in most of these solvents are limited by the high viscosities. Dimethylsulfoxide is probably the solvent of most interest. The anhydrous reagent will dissolve up to 50% of its weight of commercial amylose which normally contains 7–10% moisture. The amylose

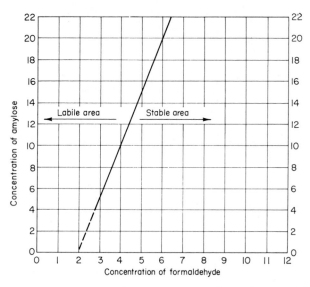

Fig. 4.—Concentration relationship in potato amylose solutions stabilized with formaldehyde.

may then be precipitated by the addition of water as is indicated in Figure 7.

5. Rheology

Amylose molecules are both linear and stereo-regular. In solution they tend to associate with the formation of crystallites. If the association is allowed to proceed at a minimum rate, the amylose will form an insoluble, granular mass of retrograded amylose. If the association is allowed to proceed at a maximum rate, congelation of the solution will occur. Retrograded amylose is essentially insoluble in cold water, but it

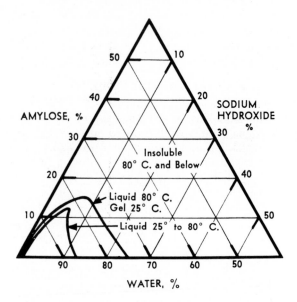

FIG. 5.—Solution properties of corn amylose in sodium hydroxide system.

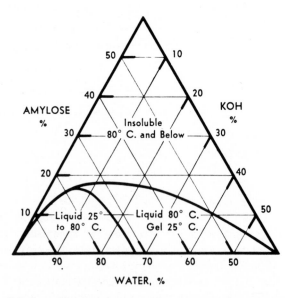

FIG. 6.—Solution properties of corn amylose in potassium hydroxide systems.

does have the property of absorbing large amounts of water. Some amylose preparations will absorb approximately four times their weight of water. Very high viscosity slurries of amylose can thus be prepared. If these amylose preparations are allowed to stand with less than four times their weight of water, all the water will be absorbed and the amylose will form a thixotropic gel. Figure 8 illustrates the viscosity characteristics of amylose slurries in water and in aqueous acetone.

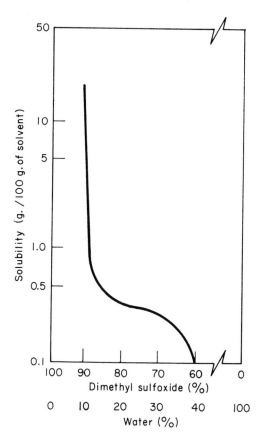

Fig. 7.—Solubility of amylose in dimethyl sulfoxide–water system at 25°.

Amylose gels are opaque white masses that are irreversible at normal temperatures. They do not show any appreciable syneresis. Microscopic examination of the gels shows that they have a distinct granular structure. These data indicate that a crystallization type of insolubilization has occurred (59).

The difference between congelation and retrogradation, therefore, is merely one of degree of orientation. Some factors affecting the gel time of amylose are indicated in Figure 9. The information in this graph was developed using a corn amylose of approximately 700 D.P. It is not valid for amylose of all molecular weights. Muetgeert and Bus (59) found that potato amylose of 1000 D.P. has a much lower congelation

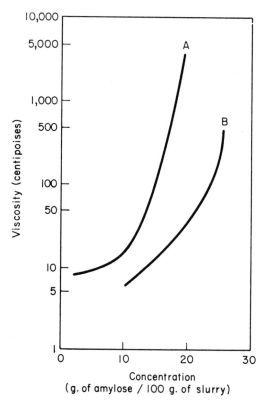

FIG. 8.—Viscosities of amylose slurries in water (A) and in water–acetone (B) systems. Determined at 25° by Brookfield Viscometer, Model RVF, 20 rpm.

temperature and therefore higher concentrations of potato amylose may be handled as is shown in Figure 10.

The gel strength of amylose gels is a function of both concentration and time. A fully hydrated gel will reach its maximum strength in 24 hours or less. For corn amylose, the gel strengths indicated in Figure 11 can be expected. As the gels dry out, they become tough and horny and cannot be restored to their original state by soaking in water.

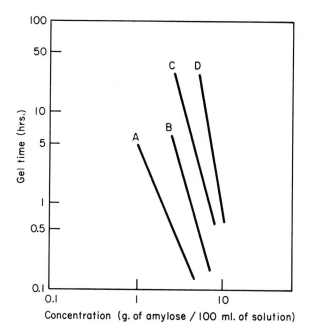

Fig. 9.—Gel time of corn amylose solutions. Solutions prepared in an autoclave at 150° for 1.5–2 minutes. [Held at (A) 25°C; (B) 50°C; (C) 75°C; (D) 90°C.]

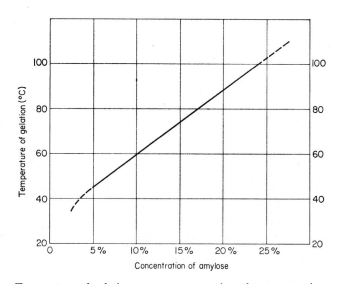

Fig. 10.—Temperature of gelation versus concentration of potato amylose solutions.

It is difficult to measure the viscosities of aqueous amylose solutions because of the instability of the amylose under the normal temperatures used for viscosity determination. Therefore, amylose viscosities are usually measured in potassium or sodium hydroxide solutions. The viscosity of amylose is a function of both the concentration of amylose and the concentration of alkali as indicated in Figure 12 and Figure 13. Note that the viscosity is at a minimum in 1N alkali.

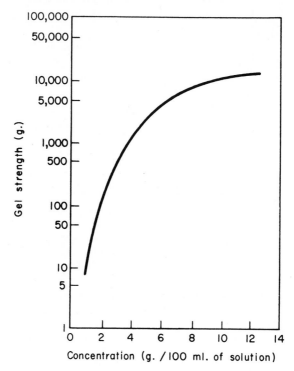

Fig. 11.—Gel strength of corn amylose at 25°.

6. Chemical Properties (see also Vol. I, Chapt. XX and XXI)

Cleavage of the α-D-(1 → 4) glucosidic bonds in amylose occurs in both acidic and alkaline solutions. Amylose should therefore be handled in a way to avoid any inadvertent degradation due to these influences.

Acid hydrolysis of starch and amylose has been exhaustively studied and its more common ramifications need no treatment here. Of interest, however, is the fact that there is evidence that not all linkages in amylose are α-D-(1 → 4), and it is suggested that a kinetic study of the acid hydrolysis of amylose may give valuable information on these anomalous linkages. Swanson and Cori (60) have already used the technique to show that α-D-(1 → 4) linkages are less stable than α-D-(1 → 6) linkages.

The degrading effect of alkali on starch and amylose has been known for some time. Schoch, Wilson, and Hudson (61) proposed that the degradation occurs on the reducing end-group of the molecule, probably through an enolic form. Degradation may also occur randomly. Whistler

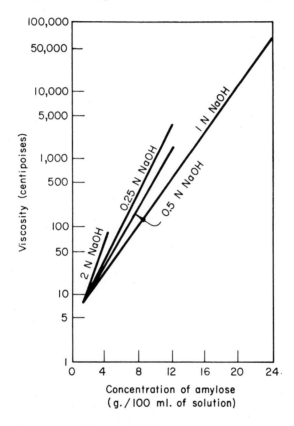

Fig. 12.—Viscosity of amylose in solutions of sodium hydroxide. Determined at 25° by Brookfield Viscometer, Model RVF, 20 rpm.

and Johnson (54) observed that the specific viscosity of a solution of amylose in 0.1N alkali decreased with time. The degradation was reduced to a minimum if the solution was stored at 0° under nitrogen.

Bottle, Gilbert, Greenwood, and Saad (62) measured the limiting viscosities of amylose in neutral, alkaline, and buffered solutions. Potato amylose was found to be stable in 0.2N alkali at 100° if oxygen was excluded. In the presence of oxygen, the neutral solution of amylose showed a slow rate of decrease in viscosity and the alkali solution a very rapid one. Oxidative degradation occurred in neutral buffered solutions and increased as the buffer concentration was increased. These authors suggest that a simple nonoxidative hydrolysis may occur. They also suggest that an intermediate stage may occur in the degradation since amylose, which they had prepared without taking precautions to

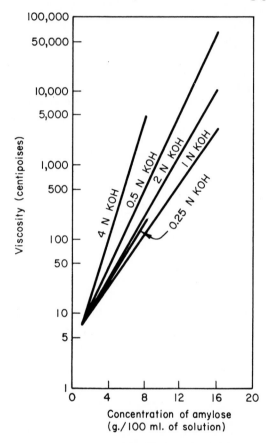

Fig. 13.—Viscosity of amylose in solutions of potassium hydroxide. Determined at 25° by Brookfield Viscometer, Model RVF, 20 rpm.

exclude oxygen, contained on an average one bond per molecule that was selectively broken during acetylation with glacial acetic acid in the presence of trifluoroacetic anhydride. All such bonds were opened in the first acetylation treatment.

Baum and Gilbert (63) suggest that potato amylose has "oxygen sensitive" bonds. Amylose prepared by them in the absence of oxygen showed no decrease in viscosity when heated in aqueous solution in the absence of oxygen, but it showed a rapid decrease in viscosity (followed by a slower oxidative breakdown) when it was heated in the presence of oxygen.

It is not improbable that an anomalous unit, for example D-xylose or D-glucofuranose, or linkage, for example $(1 \rightarrow 2)$ or $(1 \rightarrow 3)$, occurs in amylose. Oxidative degradations and alkaline hydrolyses of certain of these anomalous linkages in carbohydrates are known to occur.

IV. METHODS OF SEPARATION
(see also Vol. I, Chapt. XIV)

Three methods are available for the large scale separation of amylose from starch. A fourth method may have application in large scale separations but its feasibility has not yet been established. The methods differ from each other in significant respects, so that each one must be described individually. The product from each of the processes is called amylose, but the criteria of purity for the amylose differ from process to process. There are no absolute methods agreed upon for determining the purity of amylose so that there can be no assurance that amylose obtained from one process is identical with that obtained from a different process. Moreover, the starches used to provide the amylose differ from one another in certain significant respects. Root starch amyloses have a much higher molecular weight than the amyloses from the cereal starches. Potato amylose, for example, has approximately twice the molecular weight of corn amylose. Phosphorus is associated with potato and tapioca amylose and long-chain fatty acids with corn, wheat, and sorghum amylose. Processing steps are necessary in the different methods to remove these associated substances, and commercial products can be made which are virtually free of them.

Any of the commercial starches that contain amylose may be used for commercial separation. It is probably uneconomical to separate amylose from starches with less than 20% of amylose. Potato starch and yellow dent corn starch are the principal sources of amylose; but wheat, sorghum, rice, and tapioca starches have at times been used and may become a major source in the future. The four methods of separation to be described differ to some extent in their action on different varieties of starch.

1. Complexes with Polar Organic Compounds

Quantitative separation of amylose from starch by means of complexes with polar organic compounds was first described by Schoch (10). Although the process has never been used for the large scale separation of amylose, it is an excellent method for small scale separation. It now appears that it might be possible to use it on a commercial scale if certain modifications suggested by Bus (64) are applied. The method involves cooking the starch in the presence of an aliphatic organic alcohol that contains at least four carbon atoms and crystallizing the amylose as an amylose–alcohol complex. As high as 5% concentrations of starch may be used, but the optimal purity of the amylose fraction is obtained at starch concentrations of about 0.5–1.5%. Optionally, the alcohol may be added to the starch paste after cooking.

A starch slurry containing the desired alcohol is adjusted to between pH 5.9 and 6.3 and is heated in an autoclave at 105° for 1 hour. The cooked starch is discharged from the cooker to a crystallizer and allowed to cool slowly to room temperature. The amylose–alcohol complex crystallizes; at the end of 24 hours it is removed from the slurry by centrifuging at 2000 g in a Sharples supercentrifuge. The crystalline amylose–alcohol complex is slurried with fresh water, heated to boiling to dissolve the complex, and allowed to recrystallize. Additional alcohol may be added before the crystallization step to replenish any loss during re-solution.

Pentasol (a mixture of commercial pentyl alcohols) is recommended for the first crystallization, and 1-butanol is recommended for the second crystallization. The alcohols are often used at saturation concentrations. Muetgeert (65) has proposed that less-than-saturation quantities of the alcohol provide a more satisfactory separation, and he offers the information in Table II as a guide for selecting the amount of alcohol for the crystallization step. The amylopectin is recovered from the supernatant

Table II

Critical Concentrations of Some Complexing Agents and Their Corresponding Saturation Concentrations in Water (65)

Complexing agent	Critical concentration (g./100 ml. of water)	Solubility (g./100 ml. of water at 20°)
1-Butanol	4.2	7.9
Amyl alcohol[a]	1.8	3.1
1-Hexanol	0.3	0.59
2-Octanol	0.04	0.13
Isopropyl ketone	0.6	1.0
Chloral hydrate	5–8	470
Butyric acid	11.0	∞
Cyclohexanol	0.5	5.7
Phenol	2.5	6.7
Quinoline	0.6	6.0

[a] Fermentation amyl alcohol.

liquid from the centrifuge by spray drying, roll drying, or methanol precipitation.

The efficiency of the alcohol fractionation method is somewhat less than 90% for the first crystallization. The iodine affinity of the product is about 16.5%. It is necessary to use a recrystallization step if higher purity amylose is required. A single recrystallization will give an amylose with an iodine affinity of 19%. The alcohol precipitation method may be used on any starch. The Pentasol–butanol combination is optimum for the cereal starches; 2-octanol is preferred for potato and root starches.

2. Fractional Precipitation

The fractional precipitation procedure, which was the first method used commercially for fractionating amylose and amylopectin, was developed by Bus, Muetgeert, and Hiemstra (66) in Holland. The method is based on the principle that the gradual addition of a nonsolvent to a polymer solution causes the polymer to be precipitated in fractions of decreasing molecular weights. This is the method of fractional precipitation which is commonly used for the fractionation of homogeneous polymers. Homogeneous polymers consist of molecular species differing only in molecular weight. They show only minor differences with respect to their solubility in a binary solvent of any given composition. It is obvious, therefore, that much greater differences in solubility will be found to exist between polymers differing in their chemical structure.

The fractionation of heterogeneous polymers by the method of fractional percipitation effects a much sharper and usually a quantitative separation of the individual polymers of this system. Often chemically dissimilar polymers cannot be combined in one solvent system since they will mutually precipitate each other. Starch, on the other hand, affords an example of one of the few exceptions to this rule. Its aqueous solution contains two chemically dissimilar polymers, namely amylose and amylopectin, which do not mutually precipitate each other.

Bus, Muetgeert, and Hiemstra (66) showed that the amylose from potato starch can be precipitated from a solution of 10% magnesium sulfate at room temperature. Amylopectin, on the other hand, requires 13% magnesium sulfate solution to precipitate it. The separation of the amylose and amylopectin may be made, therefore, by dispersing the starch in a 10% magnesium sulfate solution, precipitating the amylose, increasing the concentration of magnesium sulfate to 13%, and precipitating the amylopectin. Temperature has an effect on the precipitation of the polymers. Both may be precipitated from 13% magnesium sulfate;

amylose alone precipitates at a temperature of about 80° and amylopectin at room temperature.

Commercially, the process is operated as follows (65). Potato starch is suspended in an aqueous solution of magnesium sulfate so that the suspension contains 10% by weight of starch and 13% by weight of magnesium sulfate. In order to prevent excessive decomposition of the starch fractions during the pasting and separation process, the pH of the system is adjusted with minor amounts of magnesium oxide. Sulfur dioxide is also added as a buffering agent and to prevent excessive oxidation occurring during the process. A pH 6.5–7.0 is maintained throughout the operation. The slurry is continuously fed into a series of steam heated multipass heat exchangers of the tube and shell type by means of high pressure positive displacement pumps. The operating temperature of the system, 100°, is reached within 3 minutes, and the solution is maintained at this temperature for 15 minutes as it passes through the appropriately designed residence vessel. Connected with this vessel is a closed system of properly dimensioned heat exchangers which cools the solution to the desired temperature within the desired time. Optimum temperature for crystallization of the amylose is 80°, and the time is approximately 25 minutes. At the end of the selected residence time, the precipitated amylose is continuously separated in a series of closed centrifuges operating at a gravitational field of about 2000 g and at a temperature of 80°. The supernatant liquor is then continuously cooled to 20°, at which temperature amylopectin precipitates and is kept in contact with the salt solution for several hours at this temperature. Contact with magnesium sulfate solutions converts the amylopectin into a water-insoluble form that can be separated by filtration and freed from the mother liquor by washing. The resulting mother liquor which contains most of the magnesium sulfate and small amounts of unprecipitated carbohydrate may be recycled and used in subsequent separations. The amylose from the centrifuge, because of its insolubility in cold water, may be washed repeatedly with cold water to remove magnesium sulfate and occluded water-soluble amylopectin.

According to the patents, since the separation of amylose at 80° is often technologically difficult to achieve, an alternative procedure may be employed. Starch is dissolved in 13% magnesium sulfate solution as described in the foregoing procedure. The cooling, however, differs in that when the temperature has reached 90° the calculated amount of water is added to adjust the magnesium sulfate concentration to exactly 10%. Thereafter, the temperature may be lowered to 20°, at which point the amylose separates. Amylose is recovered in centrifuges at 2000 g and washed as described above. In order to precipitate the amylopectin, the salt concentration must be increased to 13% by the addition of saturated magnesium sulfate solution.

The efficiency of the fractional precipitation process is approximately 90% when calculated from the formula:

$$\text{Fractionation efficiency} = \frac{\%\ \text{yield} \times \text{iodine affinity of the product}}{3.75}$$

where 3.75 is the iodine affinity attributed to the amylose portion of native starch.

The purity of the amylose is approximately 90% when calculated from iodine affinity on the basis that pure amylose has an iodine affinity of 19.

The fractional precipitation process is used commercially only on potato starch. The inventors, however, aver that several kinds of starches can be fractionated by the process and that concentrations up to 20% of starch can be handled. Starch-containing raw materials, for example, potatoes, corn, wheat, and other cereals, after being ground to destroy their cell structure but without separation of the starch in pure form, are claimed to give reasonable results. The crude raw materials obviously make the process more involved and cycling becomes increasingly difficult. If the amylose fraction has been degraded or exists in its natural state so that the molecular weight is less than 2×10^4, the process does not give satisfactory results.

In 1960, the Avebe Company which operates the fractional precipitation process in Holland produced 5.4 tons per day of amylose and 15.4 tons per day of amylopectin (*22*).

3. Crystallization without Added Complexing Agents

The crystallization of amylose without added complexing agents depends for its success on two factors which are not inherently significant in other methods of separation. These factors are high temperature dispersion of the starch and controlled temperature of crystallization. It is imperative that the starch be highly dispersed and that adequate crystallization sites be present. Then the kinetic energy in the system must be controlled at such a level that large aggregates of retrograded amylose form which can easily be separated.

A short treatment at a very high temperature appears to produce effective dispersion of the starch. Hydrolytic cleavage of the starch can result when too severe conditions of treatment are used to disassociate the strongly associated starch molecules. The experience of Baum and Gilbert (*62, 63*) indicates that, when such cleavage occurs, it is likely to occur at the anomalous linkages in the amylose rather than at the (1 → 4) linkages.

This method of crystallization of amylose is particularly well adapted to the separation of amylose from yellow dent corn starch. The amylose from yellow dent corn starch has a degree of polymerization of approximately 700. Production of amylose by crystallization without added complexing agents is described by Etheridge and co-workers (67) as follows: A suspension of granular native corn starch in water at a density of 5.6° Bé, a concentration of 10%, and a pH of 6.5 is cooked in a heat exchanger designed to paste and disaggregate the starch almost instantaneously. A jet cooking apparatus is usually employed. In this apparatus, steam at super atmospheric pressure is continuously mixed with the starch suspension in the throat of a steam jet. In this way, the starch suspension is brought to the desired temperature virtually instantaneously. Temperature in the cooker is approximately 150°. The starch is transferred from the cooker directly into a holding tank and held at the same elevated temperature for 10 minutes. The starch is thereby dispersed in what is called a fluid solution.

The starch solution is then transferred to a crystallizer held at atmospheric pressure. During removal from the cooker and during reduction to atmospheric pressure, the temperature of the solution drops to approximately 95°. Control of the temperature during cooling in the crystallizer is critical to obtain a high yield of amylose and a high quality product. The cooling rate is sufficient to change the temperature from 95° to 30° over a period of 40 hours. At the end of the cooling cycle, the amylose is separated in a Sharples Super Centrifuge at 15,000 rpm. The centrifuge cake is washed by slurrying it with 2 pounds of water per pound of wet cake and recentrifuged. The yield is reported as 17% of the raw starch, and amylose from the process is reported to have a blue value of about 1.00. Its purity as calculated from its iodine affinity is approximately 90%. The amylopectin is recovered either by spray drying the supernatant liquid from the centrifuge or by drying it on hot rolls.

The amylose prepared from corn starch by this method contains approximately 1.5% fatty acids. The natural fats of starch are apparently concentrated in the amylose fraction, probably as the fatty acid complex. The fats can be removed by extraction with solvents of the type used on starch.

4. Hydrodynamic Separation

The hydrodynamic separation of amylose depends for its success on making a gelled system with amylose as the solid phase and amylopectin solution as the fluid phase. Hydrodynamic forces are applied to the gelled system by means of a centrifugal disperser. Under these forces the gelled structure is destroyed and two distinct phases appear. The amylose occurs as insoluble globules in the amylopectin solution. The two phases can be separated by filtration or centrifugation. Cooling the system prior to filtration greatly improves the ease of separation of the components.

The proponents of this separation method claim very low production costs and a high degree of purity for the components. Untreated starch, chemically treated starches, and compounds of starch with metals are all satisfactory raw materials for the separation process.

The operation of the hydrodynamic separation process is described in a patent (68) as follows: 800–1000 ml. of water at a temperature of 100° is added to a thin starch paste consisting of 100 g. of potato starch in 100 ml. of water. The mixture is subjected to hydrodynamic forces in a high speed centrifugal disperser with heating until the temperature is about 85°. The time from the point at which the paste clogs (60°–80°) until the end of the reaction is about 5 minutes. The heating step is completed as soon as the structure of the swollen starch grains can no longer be recognized under the microscope and the starch solution becomes thinly fluid. The disperser is then stopped. After cooling of the mixture without agitation, the globules of amylose are centrifuged off, washed with water, and dried. The amylopectin is advantageously recovered as a dry powder by evaporating the remaining solution to dryness.

The "centrifugal dispersion devices" according to the patent are those devices that have rotating perforated or cam discs in which the material is continually or intermittently subjected to high frequency hydrodynamic pressure waves or pressure pulses (sound waves) which are produced in the continuous liquid phase.

While no criteria of purity have been established for the amylose and amylopectin produced by this method, the inventors imply that the products are different from the products obtained by other methods of separation. They have included a patent claim to the amylose and amylopectin obtained by their process.

V. Industrial Applications

The similarity of amylose and cellulose immediately suggests certain uses for amylose. A review of the section on the properties of amylose will also suggest other uses of it. Some of the well-defined areas will be discussed here individually.

1. Films

Films of amylose can be produced by a variety of methods. To some extent, the technology of the manufacture of cellophane films can be translated to the manufacture of amylose films. Methods of preparing amylose films by casting from water solution with and without the aid of complexing agents or from water solutions stabilized with formalde-hyde or glyoxal have been described or referred to in numerous patents (*69–75*).

Other methods of making flat films or tubes of amylose are based on the regeneration of an alkaline solution of amylose (*76–79*). The pro-duction of water-soluble films is the subject of another series of patent disclosures (*80–82*). The Midwest Research Institute reported the pro-

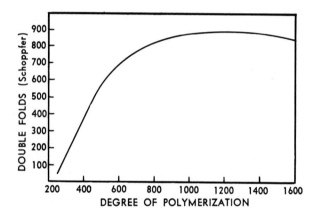

Fig. 14.—Relation of molecular weight of amylose to film-fold properties. Deter-mined at 50% relative humidity and 72° F. (23°).

duction of films by the direct extrusion of amylose (*83*). Films prepared from amylose are quite similar to those prepared from cellulose. Their properties are greatly influenced by the molecular weight of the polymer as well as by the kind and amount of plasticizer used. The effect of molecular weight on the capacity of amylose films to endure folding is illustrated in Figure 14. According to these data, films from corn starch amylose with an average D.P. (degree of polymerization) of 800 will endure about 800 Schoppfer double folds. Films from potato starch amylose with a D.P. of 1600 will withstand the same amount of folding. Films made from amylose in the wide range of 800 to 1600 D.P. show little difference in the film-fold properties. As Figure 14 illustrates, the ability of amylose to endure folding declines as the degree of polymeriza-tion is reduced below 800.

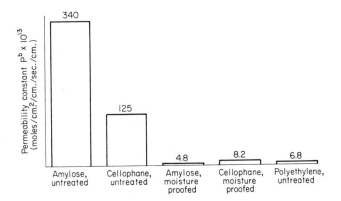

FIG. 15.—Permeability of films to water vapor at 25°. Relative humidity difference: 1% to 53%. (From data in reference *83*.)

In the data reported by Rankin and co-workers (*84*), amylose films were essentially equivalent to cellulose films with respect to their permeability to water vapors as can be seen by reference to Figures 15 and 16. The permeability was greater at the higher relative humidity differential. Moisture-proofed amylose film seemed to be no more permeable than polyethylene film.

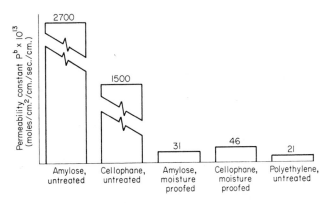

FIG. 16.—Permeability of films to water vapor at 25°. Relative humidity difference: 1% to 100%. (From data in reference *83*.)

Permeability of amylose film to organic vapors was similar to cellophane as shown in Figure 17. Methanol appears as a single exception; it permeates amylose at a much slower rate than cellophane.

The permeability of amylose and cellophane to various gases is illustrated in Figure 18. There appears to be a marked difference between the permeabilities of the two films. Under dry test conditions, amylose is

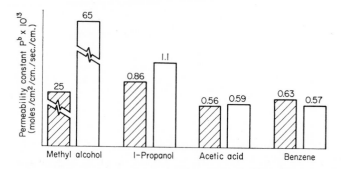

FIG. 17.—Permeability of films to organic vapors at 35°. Dry test condition. (From data in reference *83*.) (Striped columns, untreated amylose; hollow columns, untreated cellophane.)

practically impermeable to air or its constituents, whereas cellophane shows an appreciable permeability. On the other hand, amylose is more permeable to the polar substances ammonia and sulfur dioxide.

Amylose films have approximately the same tensile strength and elastic modulus as cellophane films (*84*). The effect of plasticizer on the tensile strength and elastic modulus of amylose films is illustrated in Figure 19. Both properties decrease in value as the plasticizer content

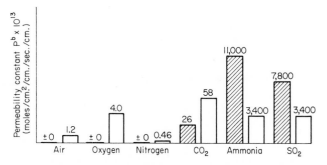

FIG. 18.—Permeability of films to various gases at 25°. Dry test conditions. (From data in reference *83*.) (Striped columns, untreated amylose; hollow columns, untreated cellophane.)

is increased. The effect of a plasticizer on the elongation of amylose films is shown in Figure 20.

O'Brian and O'Brian (*71*) describe an amylose meat casing and a process for using it. According to another patent (*85*), skinless frankfurters are prepared by stuffing a hydrolabile plastic tube made from amylose acid succinate with a sausage mix which sets to a firm gel on cooking and then contacting the casing with an aqueous liquid for a time sufficient to disintegrate and remove the casing. Hydroxyethyl-

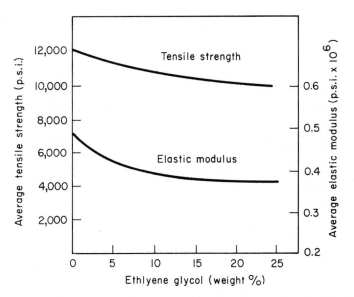

Fig. 19.—Tensile strength of plasticized and unplasticized amylose films equilibrated at 50% relative humidity and 25°.

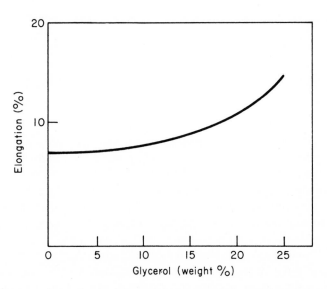

Fig. 20.—The effect of glycerol plasticizer on elongation of amylose films equilibrated at 50% relative humidity and 25°.

amylose and cyanoethylamylose are suggested as cold-water-soluble films for use in the packaging of dry detergents and the like (80–81). Amylose is said to form firmly adherent films on capacitor electrode members and is therefore proposed for use in electrical assemblies (86).

Heat-sealable, water-activatable films are obtained from a 50-50 mixture of sorbitol and starch (87).

Amylose films carried on a paper support, when treated with 35% of propylene oxide, are reported to make heat-sealable separator films for use in cathodic envelope cells (88). Amylose linked to carbamoylmethyl-trimethylammonium chloride by an ether bond is said to give a film suitable for use in permselective electrodialysis (89).

Because of their biological absorbability, amylose films should have extensive use in pharmaceutical applications. Wagner and co-workers (90) report the development of a series of amylose ester derivatives. These derivatives were intended for use as enteric coatings, and according to the report can be designed to have varying degrees of resistance to gastric and other digestive juices.

2. Coatings

Amylose and its derivatives can readily be deposited as films, and the films have many desirable properties such as low oxygen permeability and grease resistance. Yet, there are surprisingly few references in the literature to coatings in which amylose or a derivative is used as the principal film-forming material. Several specific applications of amylose are referred to under the headings "Films," "Textile Finishes and Sizes," and "Miscellaneous." Films of amylose or its derivatives evidently adhere as coatings to such diverse materials as capacitor electrodes, cathodic envelopes, pharmaceuticals, fibers, textiles, and oil well tubing.

3. Fibers

Amylose triacetate and deacetylated amylose triacetate can be spun into fibers by techniques used in the spinning of synthetic fibers (91, 92). These fibers at their highest tensile strength are inferior to regenerated cellulose triacetate fibers.

A direct method for making amylose fibers is to dissolve the amylose in a dilute solution of sodium hydroxide and then extrude the solution into a concentrated aqueous ammonium sulfate solution (76) or into other acidifying solutions. Because the operation can be carried out at low temperatures, little degradation of the amylose is said to occur and high quality, high tensile strength fibers are obtained. Controlling the rate of amylose coagulation and the tension applied to the newly generated fibers is suggested to produce fibers of uniform diameter and to impart high tensile strength. The use of protective colloids and complete de-aeration of the solution also is said to improve the tensile strength of amylose fibers.

Another method for making amylose fibers that is claimed to have advantages over previously used methods is described by Kudera (74). Amylose is dissolved in 10% aqueous formaldehyde at 120° and at pH 3. After ripening to adjust the viscosity to between 20 and 300 poises, the solution is extruded into a coagulant bath containing ammonia or hydrazine hydrate and a mineral salt, preferably trisodium phosphate, to combine with the formaldehyde.

Amylose ester fibers, and particularly amylose triacetate fibers, have been prepared and their properties described (91, 92). The characteristics of the amylose acetate fiber resemble those of cellulose triacetate fibers. The lower molecular weight of the amylose over that of cellulose gives the expected lower tensile strength to the undrawn amylose acetate fibers, but the prediction is made that proper orientation of the amylose acetate should bring the strength up to that of cellulose triacetate fibers.

Spinning characteristics, weaving characteristics, and dyeing characteristics are indicated to be similar to those of cellulose acetate fibers.

4. Complexes

Amylose combines with a large number of organic and inorganic substances. Commercial utilization of this characteristic of amylose has not been revealed in technical or trade publications. Most of the published information on the amylose complexes relates to the iodine complex. The amylose iodine complex is a source of readily available reactive iodine. Amylose absorbs from water solution up to 20% of its weight of free iodine (93). The iodine complex can then be filtered and dried and stored as a stable reactive iodine source. Stable iodine complexes of amylose can also be obtained by subjecting crystalline amylose to iodine vapor (94). One mole of amylose combines with three moles of iodine at 65°. This complex is the richest of the active iodine sources.

I.B.C. Research Laboratories (95) reports that good yield, good growing rate, and increased protein, mineral, and sugar content of plants may be obtained when a water-soluble iodine compound is added to the growing medium, the saturated solution of which provides triiodide ions in a concentration which is normally nontoxic to plant life. They report that the most suitable compound for providing this available iodine is the amylose triiodide complex.

Amylose forms complexes with vitamin A and other autooxidizable fatty materials. The complexed vitamin A is much less susceptible to oxidation. Thus amylose complexing of these substances is suggested as a replacement for the more costly methods of encapsulation (96). The slow rate of loss of activity in the complexes is said to be of value for protecting vitamin A in fortified feeds.

Hollo and co-workers (97) have shown that the presence of alcohols retards the rate of acid hydrolysis of amylose but not of amylopectin. This phenomenon is explained on the basis that amylose is complexed to give a heterogeneous phase.

5. Textile Finishes and Sizes

Amylose is preferentially adsorbed by cellulose fibers from a solution of starch (98). It is thus more efficiently adsorbed and utilized than starch. Because it forms films so readily, amylose should make an effective yarn size for cotton weaving. It should also be effective, for the same reason, as a cotton-textile finishing agent. To overcome the rapid gelling characteristics of unmodified amylose in aqueous solution, it can be applied from solutions stabilized with alkali or formaldehyde, for example, followed by treatment to neutralize the effect of the stabilizing agent.

Synthetic fibers, as well as natural fibers, can be sized with water-soluble esters, ethers, or acetals of amylose (99). Derivatives suitable for both hydrophobic and hydrophilic yarns are the methyl, ethyl, propyl, hydroxypropyl, ethylhydroxypropyl, and ethylbenzyl ethers, and the acetals of acetaldehyde and formaldehyde. For hydrophobic yarns, C_2–C_4 fatty acid esters are recommended. Derivatives containing carboxylic, sulfonic, amino, and substituted amino groups are recommended for hydrophilic yarns.

Amylose esters of fatty acids containing at least eight carbon atoms are reported to be effective waterproofing agents for textiles (100). These esters are said to be tightly adsorbed on the fabric surface and to resist removal by most washing techniques.

Hydroxyethylamylose with amylopectin is suggested as a size for glass fibers. The glass fiber adsorbs amylose from solution so tightly it is said that during the subsequent drying of the glass fibers the migration of the size is suppressed almost completely (101). Many carbohydrate substances are unsatisfactory for this purpose because they migrate to the surface of spun cones of glass fibers making the subsequent removal of the size difficult and giving a nonuniform glass fiber product.

6. Adhesives and Binders

The property of amylose of tightly adsorbing to a surface that contains polar groups makes it useful in adhesives and binders. It is said to be an effective binder for acoustical tile, which is composed of a fibrous base and contains any of the following fibers singly or in combination: glass wool, wood pulp, and mineral wool (102). As little as 1% of the amylose is reported to be sufficient to give high strength to acoustical tiles. Amylose, as well as the phosphate derivative of amylose containing approximately 1% of phosphate, is suggested for use as a foundry core binder (103, 104).

Amylose added to dry cement compositions (105) is reported to improve the strength of products made with this special binder.

Fragmented and ground tobacco powders can be converted into a form suitable for smoking by the use of hydroxyethylamylose binders (106). The dry ground tobacco and individually divided fragments thereof are mixed with approximately 5% by weight of amylose as a binding material. The tobacco is then formed into sheets of the thickness of natural leaf tobacco and subsequently cut into the desired shapes for use either as a cigar, cigarette, or pipe tobacco. The tensile strength of the synthetic leaves is reported to be approximately equal to that of the natural leaf.

7. Pharmaceutical

Amylose and its derivatives have properties that are useful in pharmaceuticals. Its film-forming propensity and the properties of its films suggest its use in coating tablets when its "quick-set" characteristic should prove useful. Amylose, like unfractionated starch, is compatible with many water-soluble dyes and with flavoring agents and sweeteners. It is a food product and has a bland flavor.

Spray-dried amylose is useful as an excipient in the manufacture of tablets by direct compression, a method designed to replace wet granulation. The objective of direct compression is to produce pharmaceutically elegant tablets with a minimum of processing time and cost. Since many drugs cannot be compressed directly, one or more additives must be added in order to impart suitable compression properties.

Amylose is unusual in that it can be tableted directly into pharmaceutically acceptable tablets. It is free flowing, self lubricating, and self disintegrating so that by itself it functions as the filler, lubricant, and disintegrant, as well as the binder. Pharmaceutical tablets fabricated to any degree of hardness with amylose as the sole nondrug component will disintegrate readily in contact with gastric liquids.

Since amylose is composed of large-molecular-weight linear polymers of glucose, it has a minimum of reducing groups and thus should have very little, if any, reactivity with drug ingredients. The 10–12% moisture of amylose may make it unsuitable for use with drugs subject to hydrolytic decomposition. Kwan and Milosovich (107) have been able to effect compression of problem drugs at relatively low concentration to yield tablets possessing the characteristics desired for pharmaceutical use. They recommend amylose as probably the most universal of the available dry compression binders.

Besides its use as a pharmaceutical aid, amylose has also been proposed for use as a physiologically active substance. According to one patent, amylose has been sulfated by treatment with chlorosulfonic acid in dry pyridine (108). The resulting ester containing 17% of sulfur is said to be physiologically active. It is reported to preserve the mucosity of the stomach by inhibiting pepsin activity.

When antibiotics, some alkaloids, local anesthetics, basic cytostatics, antihistamins, and some other drugs, are used in the form of their salts with carboxymethylamylose or sulfonated amylose, their ability to enter the lymphatic system is reported to increase (109).

Amylose–iodine complexes form stable colloidal dispersions that are reported to be effective bactericides (110).

8. Miscellaneous

Amylose sponges are produced by making a dispersion of amylose, foaming the dispersion, for example, by aerating in the presence of a foam stabilizer and inflating agent, and then gelling the foamed dispersion (111). The sponges are said to have high strength, high water absorption, are nontoxic, and are absorbable by the human body. They are, therefore, adapted to use as absorptive stanching sponges in surgical operations. By processing the foamed amylose in thin layers, a gauze-like material can be made which is said to be highly absorbent and useful wherever gauze is traditionally used. The indicated advantage is that active drugs may be dispersed in the amylose solution and thus incorporated in the gauze material (111). Absorptive stanching sponges may also be made from mixtures of amylose and gelatin by foaming the solutions to 2–7 times their volume and drying the foam (112).

Amylose acetate or partially hydrolyzed amylose acetates have been proposed for use as modifiers in acrylonitrile polymers (113).

Amylose was utilized to prevent the deposition of solid hydrocarbonaceous materials from oil onto surfaces that are normally susceptible to the accumulation of these deposits (114). For example, untreated oil well tubing collects paraffin until it is blocked. Production is halted until it can be cleaned. Amylose coated tubes showed no paraffin buildup in 60 days. This apparently depends on the ability of amylose coatings to resist adhesion of nonpolar substances.

Amylose film is permeable to electrolytes and its use as a dividing agent in dry cell batteries has been suggested (115). The electrodes are coated with an amylose film to prevent direct contact between the electrodes and the film material of the dry cell battery.

Amylose nitrate has a stability equal to that of cellulose nitrate and is considerably more stable than its counterpart, starch nitrate.

Amylose as a tobacco flavorant encapsulating agent for coating cigarette paper has been reported (116). The flavored cigarette paper is said to impart flavor to the cigarette.

Improved baking qualities of doughs may be obtained by adding small quantities of amylose fatty acid esters to flour (117). Amylose stearate is said to produce the best results.

Amylose fatty acid esters, particularly amylose stearate, has utility in the manufacture of margarine (117). Two per cent by weight of the amylose ester in margarine increases the viscosity and stabilizes the viscosity so that the product is less sensitive to changes of temperature.

Many of the uses already established for amylose, and many uses not yet technically established, originate from the similarity of amylose to unfractionated starch. The ultimate success of amylose as a new industrial polymer will come when its unique properties are fully recognized and when these properties are incorporated into new products, new processes, and new technical operations.

VI. REFERENCES

(1) K. H. Meyer, W. Brentano, and P. Bernfeld, *Helv. Chim. Acta.*, **23**, 845 (1940); K. H. Meyer, "Natural and Synthetic High Polymers," 2nd Ed., Interscience Publishers Inc., New York, N. Y., 1950, p. 456; K. H. Meyer, *Advan. Colloid Sci.*, **1**, 143 (1942).

(2) R. O. Herzog and W. Jancke, *Z. Physik.*, **3**, 196 (1920); *Ber.*, **53**, 2162 (1920).

(3) O. L. Sponsler, *Am. J. Botany*, **9**, 471 (1922).

(4) K. H. Meyer, *Biochem. Z.*, **208**, 1 (1929); K. H. Meyer, H. Hopff, and H. Mark, *Ber.*, **62**, 1103 (1929).

(5) D. K. Baird, W. N. Haworth, and E. L. Hirst, *J. Chem. Soc.*, 1201 (1935); W. N. Haworth, E. L. Hirst, and M. M. T. Plant, *ibid.*, 1214 (1935); W. N. Haworth, E. L. Hirst, and A. C. Waine, *ibid.*, 1299 (1935).

(6) S. R. Carter and B. R. Record, *Chem. Ind.* (*London*), 218 (1936).

(7) W. A. Richardson, R. S. Higginbotham, and F. D. Farrow, *J. Textile Inst., Trans.*, **27**, 131 (1936).

(8) H. Staudinger and E. Husemann, *Ber.*, **71**, 1057 (1938); *Ann.*, **527**, 195 (1937).

(9) K. H. Meyer, M. Wertheim, and P. Bernfeld, *Helv. Chim. Acta.*, **23**, 865 (1940).

(10) T. J. Schoch, *Cereal Chem.*, **18**, 121 (1941); *J. Am. Chem. Soc.*, **64**, 2957 (1942).

(11) W. N. Haworth, S. Peat, and E. J. Bourne, *Nature*, **154**, 236 (1944); E. J. Bourne and S. Peat, *J. Chem. Soc.*, 877 (1945); E. J. Bourne, A. Macey, and S. Peat, *ibid.*, 882 (1945); S. Peat, E. J. Bourne, and S. A. Baker, *Nature*, **161**, 127 (1948).

(12) G. T. Cori, C. F. Cori, and G. Schmidt, *J. Biol. Chem.*, **129**, 629 (1939); G. T. Cori and C. F. Cori, *ibid.*, **135**, 733 (1940); R. S. Bear and C. F. Cori, *ibid.*, **140**, 111 (1941).

(13) C. S. Hanes, *Nature*, **145**, 348 (1940); W. P. Astbury, F. O. Bell, and C. S. Hanes, *ibid.*, **146**, 558 (1940); C. S. Hanes, *Proc. Roy. Soc. (London), Ser. B*, **128**, 421 (1940); **129**, 174 (1940).

(14) E. L. Hirst, J. K. L. Jones, and A. J. Roudier, *J. Chem. Soc.*, 1779 (1948).

(15) A. L. Potter, W. Z. Hassid, and M. A. Joslyn, *J. Am. Chem. Soc.*, **71**, 4075 (1949).

(16) D. M. W. Anderson, C. T. Greenwood, and E. L. Hirst, *J. Chem. Soc.*, 225 (1955).

(17) F. L. Bates, D. French, and R. E. Rundle, *J. Am. Chem. Soc.*, **65**, 142 (1943).

(18) W. G. Campbell, J. L. Frahn, E. L. Hirst, D. F. Packman, and E. G. V. Percival, *J. Chem. Soc.*, 3489 (1951).

(19) I. A. Wolff, B. T. Hofreiter, P. R. Watson, W. L. Deatherage, and M. M. MacMasters, *J. Am. Chem. Soc.*, **77**, 1654 (1955).

(20) A. L. Potter, V. Silveira, R. M. McCready, and H. S. Owens, *J. Am. Chem. Soc.*, **75**, 1335 (1953).

(21) S. A. Barker, E. J. Bourne, S. Peat, and I. A. Wilkinson, *J. Chem. Soc.*, 3022 (1950).

(21a) H. Fuwa, *Arch. Biochem. Biophys.*, **70**, 157 (1957).

(22) S. Augustat, *Staerke*, **12**, 145 (1960).

(23) M. L. Vineyard and R. P. Bear, *Maize Genetics Coop. Newsletter*, **26**, 5 (1952); W. L. Deatherage, M. M. MacMasters, M. L. Vineyard, and R. P. Bear, *Cereal Chem.*, **31**, 50 (1954).

(24) E. L. Hirst, M. M. T. Plant, and M. D. Wilkinson, *J. Chem. Soc.*, 2375 (1932).

(25) M. Abdel-Akher and F. Smith, *J. Am. Chem. Soc.*, **73**, 994 (1951).

(26) W. J. Whelan, in "Methods in Carbohydrate Chemistry," R. L. Whistler, ed., Academic Press, Inc., New York, N. Y., Vol. 4, 1964, p. 72.

(27) R. M. McCready and W. Z. Hassid, *J. Am. Chem. Soc.*, **65**, 1154 (1943).

(28) R. M. Powers, A. E. Staley Mfg. Co., personal communication.

(29) F. L. Bates, D. French, and R. E. Rundle, *J. Am. Chem. Soc.*, **65**, 142 (1943).

(30) R. W. Kerr and G. M. Severson, *J. Am. Chem. Soc.*, **65**, 193 (1943).

(31) S. Lansky, M. Kooi, and T. J. Schoch, *J. Am. Chem. Soc.*, **71**, 4066 (1949).

(32) C. S. Hanes, *New Phytologist*, **36**, 101, 189 (1937).

(33) K. Freudenberg, E. Schaaf, G. Dumbert, and T. Ploetz, *Naturwissenschaften*, **27**, 850 (1939).

(34) R. E. Rundle and D. French, *J. Am. Chem. Soc.*, **65**, 1707 (1943); R. E. Rundle and F. C. Edwards, *ibid.*, **65**, 2200 (1943); R. E. Rundle and L. W. Daasch, *ibid.*, **65**, 2261 (1943); R. E. Rundle, L. W. Daasch, and D. French, *ibid.*, **66**, 130 (1944); R. E. Rundle, *ibid.*, **69**, 1769 (1947).

(35) R. E. Rundle and R. R. Baldwin, *J. Am. Chem. Soc.*, **65**, 554 (1943).

(36) J. F. Foster and I. H. Lepow, *J. Am. Chem. Soc.*, **70**, 4169 (1948).

(37) R. E. Rundle and D. French, *J. Am. Chem. Soc.*, **65**, 558 (1943).

(38) J. R. Katz and T. Z. van Jtallie, *Z. Physik. Chem. (Leipzig), A*, **150**, 90 (1930); J. R. Katz and J. C. Derkson, *ibid.*, **165**, 228 (1933); **167**, 129 (1933).

(39) R. S. Bear, *J. Am. Chem. Soc.*, **66**, 2122 (1944).

(40) W. W. Everett and J. M. Foster, *J. Am. Chem. Soc.*, **81**, 3464 (1959).

(41) E. B. Tilden and C. S. Hudson, *J. Am. Chem. Soc.*, **61**, 2900 (1939).

(42) R. W. Kerr and F. C. Cleveland, *J. Am. Chem. Soc.*, **74,** 4036 (1952).

(43) B. N. Stepanenko and E. M. Afanas'eva, *Doklady Akad. Nauk S.S.S.R.*, **86,** 789 (1952); *Chem. Abstracts*, **47,** 2282 (1953).

(44) F. F. Mikus, R. M. Hixon, and R. E. Rundle, *J. Am. Chem. Soc.*, **68,** 1115 (1946).

(45) F. F. Mikus, *Iowa State Coll. J. Science*, **22,** 58 (1947); E. Wiegel, *Kolloid Z.*, **102,** 145 (1943).

(46) D. French, A. O. Pulley, and W. J. Whelan, *Staerke*, **15,** 349 (1963).

(47) R. L. Whistler and G. E. Hilbert, *J. Am. Chem. Soc.*, **67,** 1161 (1945).

(48) W. N. Haworth, S. Peat, and P. E. Sagrott, *Nature*, **157,** 19 (1946).

(49) E. J. Bourne, G. H. Donnison, W. N. Haworth, and S. Peat, *J. Chem. Soc.*, 1687 (1948).

(50) R. E. Rundle and D. French, *J. Am. Chem. Soc.*, **65,** 1707 (1943).

(51) R. E. Rundle and F. C. Edwards, *J. Am. Chem. Soc.*, **65,** 2200 (1943).

(52) C. T. Greenwood, *Advan. Carbohydrate Chem.*, **11,** 359 (1956).

(53) E. F. Paschall and J. F. Foster, *J. Polymer Sci.*, **9,** 73, 85 (1952).

(54) R. L. Whistler and C. Johnson, *Cereal Chem.*, **25,** 418 (1948).

(55) K. H. Meyer, P. Bernfeld, and E. Wolff, *Helv. Chim. Acta*, **23,** 854 (1940).

(56) J. Holló, J. Szejtli, and G. S. Gantner, *Staerke*, **12,** 73 (1960).

(57) K. H. Meyer and P. Bernfeld, *Helv. Chim. Acta*, **23,** 875 (1940).

(58) P. Hiemstra, J. M. Muetgeert, and W. C. Bus, *Staerke*, **10,** 213 (1958).

(59) J. Muetgeert and W. C. Bus, *J. Chem. Eng. Data*, **7,** 272 (1962).

(60) M. A. Swanson and C. F. Cori, *J. Biol. Chem.*, **172,** 797 (1948).

(61) T. J. Schoch, E. J. Wilson, Jr., and C. S. Hudson, *J. Am. Chem. Soc.*, **64,** 2871 (1942).

(62) R. T. Bottle, G. A. Gilbert, C. T. Greenwood, and K. N. Saad, *Chem. Ind. (London)*, 541 (1953).

(63) H. Baum and G. A. Gilbert, *Chem. Ind. (London)*, 489 (1954).

(64) W. C. Bus, U.S. Patent 2,803,568 (1957); *Chem. Abstr.*, **52,** 768 (1958).

(65) J. Muetgeert, *Advan. Carbohydrate Chem.*, **16,** 299 (1961).

(66) W. C. Bus, J. Muetgeert, and P. Hiemstra, U.S. Patents 2,829,987; 2,829,988; 2,829,989; 2,829,990 (1958); *Chem. Abstr.*, **52,** 13295, 14204, 13296, 17768 (1958).

(67) O. R. Etheridge, J. A. Wagoner, J. W. McDonald, and D. A. Lippincott, U.S. Patent 3,067,067 (1962); *Chem. Abstr.*, **58,** 4723 (1963).

(68) Hoffmann's Stärkefabriken A. G., British Patent 1,014,105 (1965).

(69) I. A. Wolff, H. A. Davis, J. E. Cluskey, and L. J. Gundrum, U.S. Patent 2,608,723 (1952); *Chem. Abstr.*, **47,** 2523 (1952).

(70) H. A. Davis, I. A. Wolff, and J. E. Cluskey, U.S. Patent 2,656,571 (1953); *Chem. Abstr.*, **48,** 1040 (1954).

(71) R. E. O'Brian and E. D. O'Brian, U.S. Patent 2,729,565 (1956); *Chem. Abstr.*, **50,** 5945 (1956).

(72) J. Muetgeert and P. Hiemstra, U.S. Patent 2,822,581 (1958); *Chem. Abstr.*, **52,** 8602 (1958).

(73) Avebe G. A., British Patent 822,587 (1959); *Chem. Abstr.*, **54,** 6148 (1960).

(74) D. Kudera, U.S. Patent 2,973,243 (1961); *Chem. Abstr.*, **55,** 17030 (1961).

(75) A. Dekker, U.S. Patent 2,999,032 (1961); *Chem. Abstr.*, **56,** 2626 (1962).

(76) P. Hiemstra and J. Muetgeert, U.S. Patent 2,902,336 (1959); *Chem. Abstr.*, **54,** 915 (1960).

(77) Etzkorn and Co., (West) German Patent 1,063,325 (1959); *Chem. Abstr.*, **55,** 15951 (1961).

(78) Kalle A. G., British Patent 847,431 (1960); *Chem. Abstr.*, **55**, 6896 (1961); see also (West) German Patent 1,097,793 (1961) and French Patent 1,205,436 (1960).

(79) W. B. Kunz, U.S. Patent 3,030,667 (1962); *Chem. Abstr.*, **57**, 3684 (1962).

(80) A. E. Staley Mfg. Co., Belg. Patent 609,702 (1961); *Chem. Abstr.*, **57**, 10086 (1962).

(81) A. E. Staley Mfg. Co., Belg. Patent 611,052 (1961); *Chem. Abstr.*, **57**, 14042 (1962).

(82) M. W. Rutenberg and W. Jarowenko, U.S. Patent 3,038,895 (1962); *Chem. Abstr.*, **57**, 10086 (1962).

(83) Midwest Research Institute, 16th Annual Report, May 1961.

(84) J. C. Rankin, I. A. Wolff, H. A. Davis, and C. E. Rist, *Chem. Eng. Data Ser.*, **3**, 120 (1958).

(85) J. L. Louis, U.S. Patent 2,627,466 (1953); *Chem. Abstr.*, **47**, 4520 (1953).

(86) H. A. Davis, U.S. Patent 2,798,990 (1957).

(87) O. B. Wurzburg and W. Herbst, U.S. Patent 3,071,485 (1963); *Chem. Abstr.*, **58**, 7022 (1963).

(88) D. G. Soltis, U.S. Patent 3,081,372 (1963).

(89) H. G. Roebersen and C. van Bochove, U.S. Patent 2,805,196 (1957); *Chem. Abstr.*, **52**, 10462 (1958).

(90) J. G. Wagner, T. W. Brignall, and S. Long, *J. Am. Pharm. Assoc.*, **48**, 244 (1959).

(91) R. L. Whistler and G. N. Richards, *Ing. Eng. Chem.*, **50**, 1551 (1958).

(92) I. A. Wolff, *Ind. Eng. Chem.*, **50**, 1552 (1958).

(93) W. L. Minto, U.S. Patent 2,383,334 (1945); *Chem. Abstr.*, **39**, 4725 (1945).

(94) W. L. Minto, U.S. Patent 2,540,486 (1951); *Chem. Abstr.*, **45**, 5721 (1951).

(95) I.B.C. Research Laboratories, New Zealand Patent 119,879 (1959).

(96) H. Schlenk, D. M. Sand, and J. A. Tillotson, U.S. Patent 2,827,452 (1958); *Chem. Abstr.*, **52**, 12901 (1958).

(97) J. Holló, J. Szejtli, E. Laszlo, G. S. Gantner, and M. Toth, *Staerke* **12**, 287 (1960).

(98) E. Pacsu and J. W. Mullen, *J. Am. Chem. Soc.*, **63**, 1168 (1941).

(99) W. A. Scholten's Chemische Fabrieken N. V., (West) German Patent 1,118,151 (1961); *Chem. Abstr.*, **56**, 14501 (1962).

(100) Rootry Exploitatie Maatschappij N. V., Netherlands Patent 93,356 (1960); *Chem. Abstr.*, **55**, 6736 (1961).

(101) C. W. Charon and L. C. Renaud, U.S. Patent 3,108,891 (1963).

(102) National Starch and Chemical Co., Brit. Patent 916,710 (1962); Canadian Patent 648,053 (1962).

(103) J. W. Frieders, U.S. Patent 2,974,049 (1961); *Chem. Abstr.*, **55**, 14267 (1961).

(104) T. A. Hoglan and J. W. Sietsema, U.S. Patent 2,988,453 (1961); *Chem. Abstr.*, **55**, 19726 (1961).

(105) M. P. Ptasienski and J. W. Gill, U.S. Patent 3,003,979 (1961); *Chem. Abstr.*, **56**, 1160 (1962).

(106) M. M. Samfield and M. G. Christy, U.S. Patents, 3,009,835, 3,009,836 (1961); *Chem. Abstr.*, **56**, 7566 (1962).

(107) K. C. Kwan and G. Milosovich, *J. Pharm. Sci.*, **55**, 340 (1966).

(108) Spofa, British Patent 859,278 (1961); *Chem. Abstr.*, **55**, 11771 (1961); Belgian Patent 565,820 (1958).

(109) J. Hoffman, P. Nalet, M. Herold, J. Capkova, M. Hermansky, M. Vondracek, and J. Kolc, Czech. Patent, 90,970, 90,981 (1959); *Chem. Abstr.*, **54**, 14594 (1960).

(110) W. M. Malisoff, U.S. Patent 2,022,729 (1935); *Chem. Abstr.*, **30**, 819 (1936).

(111) M. W. Rutenberg and W. Jarowenko, U.S. Patent 3,081,181 (1963).

(*112*) American Cyanamid Co., Japan. Patent 16496 (1960).

(*113*) H. J. Hagemeyer, Jr., U.S. Patent 2,763,627 (1956); *Chem. Abstr.*, **51,** 1657 (1957).

(*114*) O. F. Parks, J. E. Strassner, and F. W. Burtch, U.S. Patent 3,096,777 (1963).

(*115*) Matsushita Denki Sangyo K. K., Japan. Patent 2966 (1960); *Chem. Abstr.*,
     55, 9119 (1961).

(*116*) R. J. Reynolds Tobacco Co., Can. Patent 658,442 (1961).

(*117*) Rootry Exploitatiemij. N. V., Brit. Patent 826,226 (1959); *Chem. Abstr.*, **54,**
     11328 (1960); 826,940 (1960).

HIGH-AMYLOSE CORN STARCH: ITS PRODUCTION, PROPERTIES, AND USES

By F. R. Senti

Northern Regional Research Laboratory,[1] Peoria, Illinois

I. Introduction

Except for the waxy starches that consist only of the branched component, amylopectin, nearly all starches also contain 20% to 30% of the linear component, amylose. No starches are known that contain amylose as the sole constituent, and only one plant source has been found which, without genetic improvement, produces starch that contains more than 50% of amylose. This is the wrinkled-seeded pea whose starch analyzes 60–70% amylose (*1–3*). No attention has been given this starch for possible industrial use because its total content in peas is low and separating it from the protein matrix of the seed is difficult.

Hybrid corn varieties are now available which produce starches that contain more than 50% "apparent"[2] amylose. Such high-amylose corn

---

[1] This is a laboratory of the Northern Utilization Research and Development Division, Agricultural Research Service, U.S. Department of Agriculture.

[2] Throughout this chapter the term "apparent" is used or understood in reference to the amylose content of high-amylose starches because the branched fraction in such starches, unlike that in ordinary starch, accounts for a substantial part of the iodine binding on which the analyses for amylose are based. Apparent amylose contents therefore are higher than true values; fractionation studies indicate that about 80% of the apparent amylose content can be isolated by 1-butanol precipitation.

F. R. SENTI

varieties that are agronomically adapted to commercial production are designated by the generic term "amylomaize" (4). In contrast to wrinkled-seeded peas, which have been grown as a garden vegetable for a long time, these new corn hybrids have been systematically developed by corn breeders with the aid of chemists to achieve a unique starch composition. Development of the new amylomaize hybrids stemmed from the discovery of a mutation in an inbred line of corn that doubled the amylose in ordinary corn from 27% to 55% without appreciable increase in water-soluble polysaccharides.

Amylose level varies not only with background dent lines containing different modifying factors but also within the population of individual

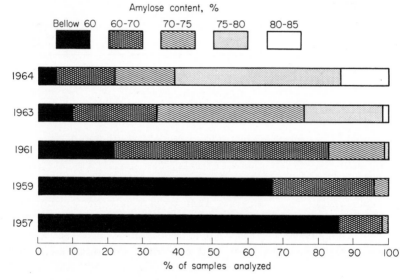

FIG. 1.—Progressive increase in apparent amylose content in samples of high-amylose corn lines.

inbred lines carrying the amylose-enhancing genes. The development of high-amylose hybrids involves thousands of amylose analyses each year in the selection and reselection for high amylose from the large population within gene source stocks, from backcrossed inbred lines, and from the lines bearing combinations of desired genes which are made up from the inbred lines. Good progress has been made toward the development of true-breeding progeny containing over 80% amylose, as illustrated in Figure 1. These analytical results obtained by the Northern Laboratory and cooperating breeders show a steady rise over the past 7 years in the percentage of samples analyzed that fall in the higher amylose ranges. Many samples now exceed the 80% apparent amylose level, and it appears that substantial increases in amylose content will continue to be achieved in the next few years by application of present breeding methods.

The continuous range of amylose contents, resulting from the interaction of specific genes for amylose with the gene modifiers present in various background lines, makes possible the development of amylomaize hybrids containing from 50% upward of amylose. The first double-cross hybrids to be developed had 57% apparent amylose in their starch; these hybrids were grown in 1958 on a scale sufficient for experimental processing in a commercial wet-milling plant. Increasing quantities were grown and processed in subsequent years, and this starch, often designated as a Class 5 amylomaize starch because its amylose content lies in the 50% to 60% range, is now an established commercial product. As the agronomic properties of the Class 5 hybrid were improved, the amylose content of the starch also increased slightly until the 1963 crop was analyzed at 62.1% apparent amylose. Sufficient acreage of a Class 6 single-cross hybrid was grown in 1959 for experimental processing studies and investigation of starch properties in the 60% to 70% amylose range. Amylose content of the starch produced was 67%. The first sizable planting of Class 7 amylomaize (70–80% amylose) was made in 1963, and starch from this corn became available on a limited commercial basis. The amylose content of this starch was about 73%. A Class 8 amylomaize (80% plus amylose) is currently available for experimental purposes.

II. KERNEL PROPERTIES OF AMYLOMAIZE

In the development of amylomaize as a source of industrial starch, a major goal has been to increase the amylose level without undue sacrifice of starch yield. The first high-amylose endosperm genotypes that were studied were characterized by large decreases in starch as the amylose level was increased. Discovery of the *ae* gene provided the basis for the development of amylomaize varieties with starch contents near those of ordinary dent corn lines. In Table I the composition of grain from Classes 5, 6, 7, and 8 amylomaize hybrids is compared with that of ordinary dent corn (5–9). Starch content of the amylomaize hybrids ranges from 57.9% to 66.4%, compared to 73.8% for the ordinary dent hybrid. Note that both Class 5 and Class 7 amylomaize increased in starch content after their first introduction reflecting selection for agronomic improvement and starch yield.

Protein content of amylomaize hybrids (Table I) is substantially higher than that of ordinary dent corn; some hybrids have over 14% of protein compared with 10% in ordinary dent corn listed in the table.

Table I

Composition[a] *of Ordinary Dent Corn and Amylomaize*[b] *by Amylose Content and Crop Year*

Constituent	Ordinary dent corn 1956 (%)	Amylomaize (class and year)						
		Class 5			Class 6	Class 7		Class 8
		1958 (%)	1960 (%)	1963 (%)	1959 (%)	1960 (%)	1963 (%)	1964 (%)
Apparent amylose	24	57	57.8	62.1	66.7	74.6	73.3	80.0
Starch	73.8	62.7	60.6	63.5	66.4	58.1	61.1	57.9
Protein	10.1	13.9	12.5	12.0	11.3	14.5	11.9	13.7
Crude fat	4.5	7.1	6.6	7.1	5.2	7.3	7.0	5.9
Solubles	5.6	8.6	—	9.1	7.1	—	10.0	—
Total sugars	2.3	2.6	—	1.8	3.4	—	1.8	—

[a] Moisture-free basis.

[b] All amylomaize varieties were hybrids grown in commercial plantings except Class 6 and 1960 Class 7 which were experimental hybrids.

As in ordinary dent corn (*10*), the data of Table I suggest an inverse relationship between starch and protein content for amylomaize. Zuber and co-workers (*11*) found a highly significant negative correlation ($r = -0.80$) between endosperm protein and starch content for their high-amylose inbred lines. It may be expected, therefore, that, as starch is increased in amylomaize hybrids by genetic improvement, protein will approach the levels found in ordinary dent corn.

Fat content in the whole grain from amylomaize hybrids (Table I) ranges from 5.2% to 7.1% as compared to 4.5% in the ordinary dent hybrid listed in the table. Hubbard and co-workers (*12*) reported the same value for the average of all grades of dent corn received at principal markets in 1952–1954; it is evident that present amylomaize varieties contain substantially more oil and that a greater recovery of this by-product may be expected in commercial processing.

The relative proportions and composition of the endosperm, germ, and bran fractions in the amylomaize kernel (*13, 14*) provide a basis for estimating the possible yield of various kernel constituents in a wet-milling operation. Relative proportions of kernel fractions for Classes 5, 6, and 7 amylomaize hybrids are presented in Table II; starch, fat, protein, and ash content of these fractions are given in Table III for Class 5 and Class 6 hybrids. Composition of ordinary dent corn is given in each table for comparison. These amylomaize hybrids contain somewhat less endosperm, more germ, and considerably more bran than ordinary dent corn (Table II). The lower starch content of the amylomaize kernel (Table I) results not only from the lower proportion of endosperm but also from the presence of less starch in the endosperm than that of ordinary corn

Table II

Proportion of Kernel Fractions in Ordinary Dent Corn and
Amylomaize of Different Amylose Contents

| | | Amylomaize (class and year) | | | |
| | | Class 5 | | Class 6 | Class 7 |
Fraction	Ordinary dent corn[a]	1958[b] (%)	1963[c] (%)	1959[b] (%)	1963[c] (%)
Amylose content	27.0[d]	57.0	62.1	66.7	73.3
Endosperm	82.0	76.5	78.3	78.9	77.6
Germ	11.7	14.2	13.7	13.1	13.8
Bran	5.6	9.2	8.0	8.0	9.1

[a] Average of five different yellow dent hybrids (10).
[b] Data from reference 13.
[c] Data from reference 14.
[d] Data from reference 27.

Table III

Composition of Kernel Fractions of Amylomaize[a] and Ordinary Dent Corn[b]

| | Endosperm | | | Germ | | | Bran | | |
Constituent	Ordinary dent (%)	Class 5 1958 (%)	Class 6 1959 (%)	Ordinary dent (%)	Class 5 1958 (%)	Class 6 1959 (%)	Ordinary dent (%)	Class 5 1958 (%)	Class 6 1959 (%)
Ash	0.36	0.42	0.42	10.33	8.98	9.08	0.73	1.11	1.31
Protein	7.8	12.2	10.4	18.5	17.2	19.0	3.5	6.2	7.3
Crude fat	0.8	1.7	0.93	33.9	36.1	28.9	1.0	3.92	4.36
Starch	87.3	80.0	82.3	8.1	9.52	12.5	7.3	4.02	4.03

[a] Data from reference 13.
[b] Average of five different yellow dent hybrids (10).

(Table III). The relatively higher fat content of the endosperm and bran as compared to ordinary corn (Table III) indicates that the oil recovery from amylomaize cannot be expected to be as high as the total fat content of the kernel (Table I) would suggest. A greater yield of oil in a wet-milling operation is possible, however, because of the larger germ fraction in amylomaize.

III. PRODUCTION OF STARCH BY WET MILLING AMYLOMAIZE

The recovery of starch and oil to be expected from amylomaize in commercial processing can be judged from laboratory and small-scale pilot-plant wet-milling experiments. Anderson and co-workers (5–7) have evaluated the wet-milling properties of amylomaize as the new hybrids have become available. Some of their results are presented in Table IV along with later data of Anderson (8) on the 1963 crops of

Table IV

Comparison of Processing Characteristics of Amylomaize and Ordinary Dent Corn

	Ordinary dent corn	Amylomaize						Class 8
		Class 5			Class 6	Class 7		
Characteristic	1956 (%)	1958 (%)	1960 (%)	1963 (%)	1959 (%)	1960 (%)	1963 (%)	1964 (%)
Kernel swelling	63	128	110	96	105	125	110	105
Steep water								
Solids	4.2	3.6	4.6	4.7	4.2	3.7	5.4	4.2
Protein	31.2	31.0	25.4	29.0	29.0	29.0	29.1	26.3
Starch								
Yield	64.4	43.5	43.8	46.6	50.8	42.0	43.8	41.0
Recovery	87.3	71.4	71.8	73.0	82.7	71.6	71.4	70.3
Protein	0.51	0.7	0.46	0.52	0.48	0.59	0.52	0.8
Squeegee starch								
Yield	—	4.9	2.9	2.7	4.1	2.5	4.5	—
Protein	—	5.0	9.4	5.0	9.2	4.5	3.7	—
Starch	—	94.4	81.8	92.5	81.9	85.7	—	—
Germ								
Yield	4.7	6.5	—	—	7.6	—	—	—
Oil	53.0	56.0	—	—	41.2	—	—	—
Gluten								
Yield	7.8	15.5	19.4	16.0	11.2	17.7	14.9	17.7
Protein	44.2	33.1	26.2	28.6	34.6	32.3	26.7	27.2
Starch	45.0	52.3	48.1	50.5	44.2	40.7	54.7	—

Class 5 and Class 7 amylomaize, and on the 1964 crop of Class 8 amylomaize (9).

An unexpected property of amylomaize is its greater swelling as measured by over-all volume occupied by the grain in the tank on steeping 48 hr. in 0.25% sulfur dioxide at 52°. Under these conditions ordinary corn (Table IV) swells 63% in volume, amylomaize, 96 to 128%. In swelling, amylomaize absorbs a correspondingly greater amount of water than does ordinary corn (5, 6). The greater imbibition of water by amylomaize kernels during steeping is consistent with the greater percentage of solubles (Table I) in the amylomaize samples (7.1–10.0%) as compared to ordinary dent corn (5.6%). The lack of increased yield of solids in the steep water (Table IV) shows that the additional solubles in the amylomaize are not extracted during steeping of the whole grain but are retained inside the kernel where they can exert an osmotic effect.

Starch yield in percentage of grain weight (Table IV) is lower for the amylomaize samples than for ordinary dent corn. This difference would be expected from the lower starch content of the amylomaize. A better index of milling quality, however, is the percentage of starch recovered. Starch recovery in laboratory milling ranges from 70.3% to 82.7% for the amylomaize hybrids as compared to 87.3% for ordinary dent corn. Class 6 amylomaize is outstanding for its starch recovery, and compares favorably with ordinary dent corn in this respect. The generally lower starch recovery from amylomaize has been attributed to difficulties in separation of small and irregularly shaped granules present in these grains (5–7). In Table V the distribution of granule sizes shown

Table V

Average Granule Diameters of Amylomaize and Ordinary Dent Corn Starches

	Ordinary dent corn	Amylomaize		
		Class 5	Class 6	Class 7
	US 13 hybrid	1963	1959	1962
Diameter	(microns)	(microns)	(microns)	(microns)
Number-average	10.6	6.6	8.9	7.5
Weight-average	15.5	10.9	12.7	11.4

for Class 6 amylomaize starch is closest to that of ordinary dent corn. The poorer separation of amylomaize starch from the protein matrix is evident from the higher starch and lower protein content of the amylomaize gluten fractions and their greater yield, as compared to ordinary dent corn. Further loss in prime starch yield occurs in the additional tabling operation required to reduce the protein content of the amylomaize starch to a level comparable to that in ordinary dent starch. The squeegee starch fraction recovered in this operation represents 2.1–4.6% of starch yield.

IV. Properties of Amylomaize Starch Granules

Granules of the amylomaize starches differ considerably from ordinary corn starch in morphology, birefringence, size, x-ray pattern, gelatinization, swelling, and solubility properties. A comparison of size and shape of Classes 5, 6, and 7 amylomaize starches with ordinary dent corn starch can be made from the photomicrographs in Figure 2. An

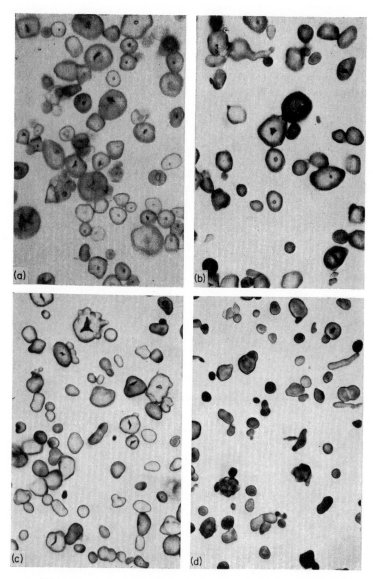

Fig. 2.—Photomicrographs of ordinary dent corn starch and three classes of amylomaize starches stained lightly with iodine: a, ordinary dent corn starch from a Holmes hybrid; b, amylomaize starch, Class 5, 61.8% amylose; c, amylomaize starch, Class 6, 66.7% amylose; d, amylomaize starch, Class 7, 72.1% amylose; 500 × magnification.

obvious difference in the amylomaize starch granules is their smooth surface as compared to the faceted surface of ordinary corn starch. Another characteristic of the amylomaize starches is the presence of granules of unusual shape. Compound granules are fairly numerous and are generally in the size range of the other granules. The elongated or filamentous granules, which may be simple or branched, are most interesting. These are most evident in the photomicrograph of Class 7 starch (Fig. 2d). The elongated granules are frequently thin, but others are short and stubby with thickening at one end or along the filament. A small number of granules have been observed to be a knotted mass of outgrowths. An example of this type of granule appears in the upper center portion of Figure 2c. This type is the one referred to by Badenhuizen (15) as "grape" structures. Such granules were more numerous in some of the earlier Class 5 selections but apparently have been bred out of the latest crosses.

1. Granule Birefringence and Iodine Staining

A large proportion of the granules of amylomaize starches are approximately spherical in shape and differ from ordinary corn starch only by lack of a faceted surface. However, when examined between crossed Nicols, many of these granules do not show the polarization cross characteristic of starch (16). This type of granule occurs most frequently in Class 7 starch. The optically isotropic character is not due to granule damage but appears to result from lack of selective orientation of the starch chains during granule formation. Badenhuizen (17) observed such granules in immature starches from the ae su endosperm genotype. On the basis of the discrete x-ray line pattern of the starches, he concluded that the optically isotropic granules were crystalline, not amorphous. Crystallinity has not yet been demonstrated, however, by x-ray patterns of isolated nonbirefringent granules of the Class 5, 6, and 7 starches.

Some spherical granules of the amylomaize starches stain with iodine much more readily than others. This difference in staining can be seen in Figures 2b and 2d of the Class 5 and 7 starches. There appears to be no relation, however, between iodine staining and birefringence; granules stained to the same depth with iodine may or may not show birefringence. The variability in staining indicates differences in surface layers of the granules which affects binding and penetration of iodine; it may possibly result from a variation in amylose distribution among the granules.

When the iodine-staining characteristics of starch granules from ordinary corn are compared with those of starches from amylomaize, the coloration appears similar if the microscopic examination is made in bright field illumination. However, when iodine-stained granules are examined between crossed polarizers, amylomaize starches with an amylose content above about 65% appear red as against blue for ordinary starch granules (*18*). At relatively low and at intermediate amylose levels, amylomaize starches show a variegated red and blue coloration pattern.

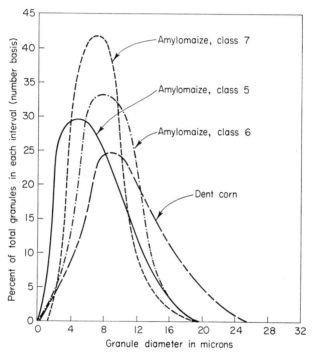

Fig. 3.—Granule size-frequency distribution, number per 2.8 μ interval, for amylomaize starches and ordinary dent corn starch. Identification of starches is as follows: Amylomaize, Class 5, 1963 crop, 62.1% amylose; amylomaize, Class 6, 1959 crop, 66.7% amylose; amylomaize, Class 7, 1962 crop, 72.1% amylose; ordinary dent corn, U.S. 13 hybrid.

The elongated or filamentous granules generally are optically isotropic and show no polarization cross between crossed Nicols. In many cases, however, a low birefringence is evident along the margins of these granules, which indicates molecular orientation in their outermost layers (*16*). The filamentous granules stain less readily with iodine than do the majority of the spherical forms. Frequently the knobs or thickened portions of the filaments are heavily stained while the filamentous portions of the same granule are unstained or only lightly stained. The thickened portions often show the typical polarization cross, indicating normal molecular orientation, whereas the rest of the granule remains isotropic.

2. Starch Granule Size Distributions

Size-frequency distributions for amylomaize starches and a dent corn starch are presented in Figures 3 and 4. The distributions are based on microscopic measurements of a large number of granules (*16*). In preparing the mounts for examination, care was taken to avoid orien-

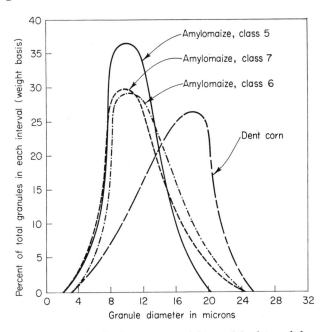

Fig. 4.—Granule size distribution curves, weight per 2.8 μ interval, for amylomaize starches and ordinary dent corn starch. Identification of starches is the same as Figure 3.

tation of the elongated granules; measurements were made as the field was traversed in a single direction, and the diameter of a granule was taken as the width it presented in the direction of traverse. Distribution curves can be expected to depend on the degree of recovery of starch in processing the grain. Usually a part of the small granule fraction is lost in processing, so that size measurements on the recovered starches are generally higher than the true value. The starches described in Figures 3 and 4 were samples either processed commercially or by methods expected to give recoveries similar to commercial practice. Figure 3 shows that the amylomaize starches contain more small granules than does ordinary corn starch, a difference which is also evident from the displacement of the amylomaize starch curves to the left relative to dent corn. The size distributions are narrower for the amylomaize starches than for ordinary starch; the narrower distribution is most evident for the Class 7 starch. Number-average diameters calculated from the curves in Figure 3 are given in Table V. The greater number of large starch granules in ordinary corn starch results in a higher average diameter for this starch.

For some purposes the distribution of weight of starch, rather than the number of granules, according to granule diameter is most important. Weight distribution curves are presented in Figure 4 for the starches given in Figure 3. These curves emphasize the difference between amylomaize starches, as a class, and ordinary corn starch in terms of granule size. As expected, the peaks of the weight distributions are shifted to higher diameters, and since the distributions in Figure 3 have different shapes, the magnitude of the shifts are not the same. Weight-average diameters calculated from the curves in Figure 4 are given in Table V; average diameters are larger, but rank according to diameter is the same as on the number-average basis. For ordinary dent corn starch, Schoch and Maywald (*19*) report a slightly different size distribution for a commercial sample. The respective number- and weight-average diameters for this sample were 9.2 and 14.1 microns.

3. X-Ray Diffraction Patterns

In contrast to ordinary corn starch, which gives an A-type x-ray pattern, amylomaize starches (*20*) give the B-type pattern characteristic of potato starch. Dvonch and co-workers (*21*) first reported the B-pattern for high-amylose starches from su_2, su_2du, and $su^{am}du$ genotypes. Badenhuizen (*17*) later reported that the *ae* and *ae su* endosperms deposited starch with the B-structure. Zobel and co-workers (*20*) concluded from the examination of many different genotypes that the B-structure was obtained only when the *ae* gene was present, regardless of whether the amylose level was above or below that of ordinary starch. The difference from the observations by Dvonch and co-workers (*21*) probably reflects a difference in treatment of the starch samples. In connection with the controlling effect of the *ae* gene on the B-pattern, Sandstedt and co-workers (*22*) found that high-amylose starches with the *ae* gene in their genetic composition were resistant to digestion by pancreatic amylase, as is potato starch, whereas high-amylose starches from other genotypes were more readily digestible. However, differences other than crystal structure are likely involved since sago and arrowroot starches, which give a C-type pattern, are also resistant to pancreatic digestion.

Zobel and co-workers (20) also found that the strongest diffraction lines of the V-, or helical, structure appear on x-ray patterns of starches that contained more than about 40% amylose. Their report presents the first x-ray evidence for the helical structure in a native starch; the avid iodine binding and blue staining of starches of normal amylose content suggests, however, that helical or near-helical chain segments are present in ordinary starches. The V-structure in the high-amylose starches appears to be stabilized by the presence of lipid material; the V-pattern is retained after fat extraction but disappears on subsequent slurrying with water. Analyses (20) of the amylomaize starches, either by solvent extraction or by hydrolysis, show no significant difference in fat content from that reported for ordinary corn starch.

4. Gelatinization of Amylomaize Starches

Starches with amylose contents in the 20 to 30% range lose their birefringence within a fairly narrow temperature range when heated in water (19). A similar phenomenon occurs with high-amylose starches; they differ, however, from starches of ordinary amylose content in that loss of birefringence is not associated with marked granule swelling and development of viscosity at relativity low starch concentrations. Consequently, the temperature at which loss of birefringence occurs for amylomaize starch does not have the same practical significance that it has for ordinary starches; nevertheless, it helps to characterize an amylomaize starch and has been used to aid in distinguishing high-amylose starches from different endosperm genotypes (23, 24). Although Classes 5, 6, and 7 amylomaize starches differ from ordinary corn starch in the temperature at which they lose birefringence, they do not differ significantly among themselves. In the tabulation below, the temperature range over which birefringence loss occurs is defined by three temperatures which correspond to loss of birefringence in the following percentages of granules: first detectable, 50%, and 90%.

Amylomaize starches	66°–68°,	74°–76°,	88°–92°
Ordinary corn starch	61°–62°,	67°–68°,	72°–74°
Maine potato starch	62°–63°,	65°–67°,	72°–73°

In amylomaize starches the crystalline structure responsible for birefringence is more resistant to destruction in hot water than is the crystallinity of ordinary starch. Moreover, the amylomaize starch granules vary more widely in their resistance to destruction; the first 50% of the granules lose birefringence over approximately the same temperature interval as ordinary starch, but destruction of birefringence of the next 49% of the amylomaize granules requires a 15° temperature interval as compared to a 6° interval for ordinary starch.

Since amylomaize starches have the B-crystal structure, their birefringence-loss range might more properly be compared with that for potato starch, which also has the B-structure. The range for the latter is, however, no higher than that for ordinary corn starch; therefore, crystal structure in itself does not account for the higher temperatures required for the amylomaize starches. Neither does percentage crystallinity since x-ray measurements show that the amylomaize starches are less crystalline than ordinary corn starch (25). The high gelatinization temperatures of amylomaize starches cannot be attributed to association through substantially stronger hydrogen bonds; no difference in accessibility of hydroxyl groups to water was found by Taylor and co-workers (26) in studies of deuterium exchange. Association of amylose with lipid material also does not account for the high gelatinization temperatures; defatted and nondefatted amylomaize starches show the same gelatinization temperature range.

A possible explanation for the higher temperatures required to initiate gelatinization in amylomaize starches is that more amylose molecules are involved in the crystalline regions of the high-amylose starches than in ordinary starches. The resulting crystallites would have less irregularity of structure due to branch points; such irregularities probably contribute to instability of the crystallites in waxy (100% amylopectin) and ordinary starches. Following this reasoning, an upper limit to the gelatinization temperature range should be observed when a significant fraction of the crystallites are formed only from amylose. Apparently such a limit may have been reached at 88°–92° by the amylomaize starches; this limit needs to be confirmed, however, by observations on crystalline amylose.

Although amylomaize starches do not swell sufficiently in water to give a measurable viscosity in the conventional heating cycle employed in measuring starch pasting properties either in a CIRF viscometer or a Brabender amylograph, the amylomaize starches will gelatinize below 95° by addition of swelling agents such as calcium chloride. Amylograph curves for amylomaize starches in concentrated calcium chloride (sp. gr. 1.30 at 20°) are given in Figure 5.

The amylograph curves of Classes 5, 6, and 7 amylomaize starches are similar except for the maximum viscosity attained. The peak viscosity is greatest for the Class 5 starch and progressively less for Class 6 and Class 7 starches. Marked granule swelling in Class 5 starch, as evidenced by the sharp rise in viscosity, begins at a temperature (41.5°) slightly lower than for the other two classes (about 44°). All starches reached their peak viscosity at about the same temperature (53.5°–55°); apparently the principal difference between the starches is the capacity of the granules to swell before disintegration and solubilization. Since the capacity for expansion before rupture and distintegration decreases with decreasing amylopectin content, this component appears to contribute importantly to the extensibility of the coherent structure of the swollen granule.

Evidence that amylopectin provides the structural network in gelatinized starch is provided by the observation that most of the amylose

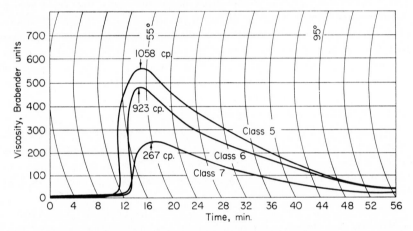

FIG. 5.—Brabender amylograph curves for amylomaize starches in concentrated CaCl₂ solution (sp. gr., 1.30 at 20°). Starch concentration, 5 g. (m.f.b.)/100 ml.; heating rate, 1.5°/min.; spindle speed, 75 rpm. Amylomaize, Class 5, 61.8% amylose; amylomaize, Class 6, 66.7% amylose; amylomaize, Class 7, 73.3% amylose.

can be selectively leached from swollen high-amylose starches leaving a gelatinous, coherent residue mainly of amylopectin (27). The swelling limit for a starch would be expected, therefore, to depend to a considerable extent on the amount, molecular size, and structure of its amylopectin and the manner in which these molecules are associated into a three-dimensional network.

5. Dispersion of Amylomaize Starches

The term dispersion, as applied here to starch, covers a rather wide range of types of solution. In general, the dissolution of starches involves the successive and overlapping stages of granule swelling, disintegration of the swollen granule, possibly preceded by some leaching out of molecular material, and disaggregation of particles or fragments to a molecular state. When a starch dispersion is prepared by cooking in water, for example, various proportions of the granules may be at each stage, depending on the conditions and the characteritsics of the starch. For many industrial uses, dispersion largely to the disintegrated granule stage apparently is sufficient. Thus ordinary corn starch finds many applications as a paste prepared by cooking for 30 min. at 90°–95° with moderate stirring. From such a paste, 60–70% may be removed by a 15-min. centrifugation at 2500 rpm. For research on the molecular properties of starch, of course, solution at the molecular level is necessary.

A discussion of the dispersibility of amylomaize starches is complicated by the fact that, in many cases, no critical tests have been applied to determine quantitatively the state of the starch in the dispersion. However, indications of conditions required for dispersion of amylomaize starches are provided by data which have been reported. Some of the apparent inconsistencies probably arise from differences in criteria of dispersions; others may result from differences in the starches.

Amylomaize starches disperse with greater difficulty than does ordinary corn starch, and dispersibility appears to be affected by amylose content and, possibly, by genetic background. Autoclaving at temperatures of 150°–160° generally is required to disperse amylomaize starches sufficiently to withstand centrifugation at $2000 \times G$ for 15 min. with removal of no more than 1 to 2% of starch. Sloan and co-workers (28), however, reported that an early Class 5 amylomaize starch, having an amylose content of 50%, was incompletely dispersed at 160°–170° as judged by the presence of intact swollen granules in films prepared from the mixture. These workers found that a mild alkali prewash of the starch with sodium bicarbonate facilitated dispersion, which was then complete at 160°–165° in 1 to 5 min.

By contrast, Anderson and co-workers (29–31) dispersed Class 5, 6, and 7 amylomaize starches for fractionation studies in a continuous tube cooker operating at 135°–150° with a retention time of 10 min. Their dispersion was probably aided by subsequent heating at 90° after addition of complexing agent. In still other fractionation studies, a liquid ammonia pretreatment of amylomaize starch was used to loosen the granule structure and permit dispersion at 120° in water or 1-butanol-saturated water (32, 33).

Wurzburg and co-workers (34) dispersed amylomaize starches by heating in water at 60°–100° after the dry starches were subjected to attrition grinding. The dispersed amylomaize produced firmer gels, and films cast from the dispersed starch were clearer and more continuous than when untreated amylomaize starch was used.

Amylomaize starches can be dispersed in 5–10% concentration at room temperature in $0.5N$ sodium hydroxide solution. However, in $0.25N$

sodium hydroxide, the starches do not disperse but swell to form viscous solutions at 5% concentration. Interestingly, Class 6 starch gives the greatest viscosity rather than one intermediate between the values for Classes 5 and 7, as might be expected on basis of amylose content, and probably demonstrates the effect of genetic background on granule properties (*35*). For potassium hydroxide solutions, Wolff and co-workers (*32*) reported that amylomaize starch, 50% amylose content, was incompletely dissolved at an alkali normality of 0.1–0.2 but was dispersed at normalities of 0.3–1.0.

Amylomaize starches can be dissolved at 10 to 15% concentration in formamide or monoethanolamine by heating at 150° (*28*). Dimethylsulfoxide dissolves high-amylose starch at room temperature (*35–37*). Dispersion is slow, however; and even after 3–4 days of shaking, 2–4% of the amylomaize starches may be removed by centrifugation at $2000 \times G$ (*35*). Aqueous dimethylsulfoxide (80–95%) dissolves starch more rapidly than the anhydrous solvent; centrifugation at $2000 \times G$ after 24-hr. shaking removes only a trace of undissolved material (*36*).

Amylomaize starch (Class 7) pretreated by dispersion in dimethylsulfoxide and quantitatively precipitated with alcohol has increased water solubility. The pretreated starch showed a V x-ray diffraction pattern (*38*).

In terms of molecular dispersion, the best solvent for amylomaize starch at room temperature, according to Erlander and co-workers (*39*), is a concentrated aqueous solution containing lithium thiocyanate ($5M$) and guanidinium thiocyanate ($2M$). After 24 hr. in this solvent, only a trace of residue was removed by centrifugation at $39,000 \times G$. In 90% aqueous dimethylsulfoxide, however, molecular dispersion was not reached after 24 hr. shaking for a Class 7 amylomaize starch (*39*); centrifugation at 18,000 rpm. ($39,000 \times G$) for 15 min. removed 11% of the starch. These workers also found that aggregates sufficiently large to be removed by 15-min. centrifugation at $39,000 \times G$ were present in N potassium hydroxide dispersions. Even after 24-hr. shaking, 12% of the starch was precipitated from the dispersion by centrifugation.

6. Molecular Components of Amylomaize Starches

Iodine affinities, intrinsic viscosities, and β-amylase conversion data are given in Table VI for amylose fractions from several high-amylose starches (*40*) and from ordinary corn starch. These data were obtained from fractions isolated from starches subjected to a neutral chemical steep (*41*). In comparison with the intrinsic viscosity in N potassium hydroxide of 1.7 in Table VI, amylose fractions isolated by conventional laboratory wet-milling procedures showed intrinsic viscosities of 1.4 in the same solvent (*27*), which indicates a somewhat lower molecular size for the amylose. Molecular weight of two amylose samples with the lower viscosity were 283,000 and 334,000 in comparison with 312,000 for ordinary corn amylose as determined by light scattering (*27*). The data from these investigations, together with the periodate oxidation and β-amylase conversion data of Wolff and co-workers (*32*), show that

Table VI
Amylose Fractions from High-Amylose Corn Starches

Starch			Amylose				
Source	Apparent amylose (%)	[η] N KOH	Iodine affinity (mg. I₂/g.)	β-Amylose conversion (% maltose)	Average length of unit chain	Length of inner branch	Length of outer branch
Hybrid	59	1.68–1.73	206	96	502	16	486
Hybrid	67	1.68–1.72	205	96	502	16	486
Inbred	68	1.63–1.67	206	98	509	17	496
Hybrid	71	1.63–1.68	206	—	—	—	—
Hybrid[a]	27	1.78	204	96	503	16	497

[a] Ordinary corn.

the amylose component of the high-amylose starches is like that of ordinary corn starch in molecular structure and size.

The amylopectin component of high-amylose starches differs both in structure and molecular size from the branched component of ordinary

Table VII
Properties of Amylopectins of High-Amylose Corn Starch

Starch			Amylopectin					
Source	Apparent amylose (%)	[η] N KOH	Iodine affinity (mg. I₂/g.)	Amylose equivalent (%)	β-Amylase conversion (% maltose)	Average length of unit chain	Length of inner branch	Length of outer branch
Hybrid	50	1.2	51	—	58	—	—	—
Inbred	50	1.2	53	26	62	36	11.7	24.3
Hybrid	57	1.2	79	40	66	40	11.3	28.7
Hybrid	67	1.2	83	41	73	42	10	32
Inbred	68	1.2	85	43	74	43	10	33
Hybrid	71	1.2	89	45	77	45	10	35
Hybrid[a]	27	1.8	12	5	56	27	10	17

[a] Isolated from ordinary corn; steeped in water at 37°C.

corn starch. Periodate oxidation data (*32*) show that the average chain length of the first amylopectin listed in Table VII is 36 D-glucose units as compared with 27 units for ordinary starch amylopectin, but these data do not differentiate between lengths of inner and outer chains of the branched molecule. Evidence that increased length of outer branches accounts for part, if not all, of the increase in average chain length is provided by both the greater iodine affinity, as measured by potentiometric titration, and the higher β-amylase conversion limit for the amylopectins of the high-amylose starches listed in Table VII (*40*). Moreover, the differences between amylopectins are magnified as the amylose content of the starch is increased (*40*).

The tendency of high-amylose starch amylopectins to retrograde from solution at 25° (*27*), resembling amylose in this respect, is further evidence for an increased chain length of outer branches and a more linear structure. The retrograded amylopectins differ from retrograded amylose, however, in that they can be at least partially dissolved on heating at 98°; retrograded amylose requires autoclaving for dissolution. The possibility that retention of amylose in the amylopectin might account for observed differences has been eliminated by ultracentrifugation studies (*27*). No fraction having a sedimentation rate comparable to amylose or smaller molecules was observed in alkaline solutions of these amylopectin preparations.

On the basis of intrinsic viscosities (Table VII), the molecular weight of high-amylose starch amylopectin is less than that of ordinary corn starch amylopectin. This difference is confirmed by molecular weight determinations by light scattering (*39*), which gives values of 9.6 million for amylopectin from a high-amylose starch containing 71% apparent amylose as compared to 1.5 billion for amylopectin isolated from ordinary starch by the same procedure and examined in the same solvent system.

7. Chemically Modified Amylomaize Starch

Swelling and dispersibility of amylomaize starches in hot water, as well as stability of their solutions toward gel formation or retrogradation, are greatly increased by relatively low degrees of chemical derivatization. Rankin and co-workers (*42*) prepared hydroxyethyl ether derivatives of amylomaize starch (50% apparent amylose content) containing from 1% to 27% by weight combined ethylene oxide. At ethylene oxide contents of 5% to 7%, corresponding to 0.17 to 0.24 of hydroxyethyl groups per D-glucose unit, the modified starches on heating at 90° form viscous pastes that remain fluid on cooling to room temperature, even after standing several days. The relatively low light transmittancy (29% at 650 mμ for 1% concentration) of the pastes indicates incomplete dispersion; this was confirmed by microscopic examination which showed that about 20% of the granules at degree of substitution (D.S.) 0.24 remained in suspension, swollen but undisintegrated. Despite the greater clarity of its paste (69%), ordinary corn starch at the same D.S. and temperature does not completely disperse but 15% of the granules remain in suspension. These granules, swollen much more than the amylomaize granules, are responsible for the greater viscosity and clarity of the ordinary starch pastes.

Rankin and co-workers (42) also found that hydroxyethylated amylomaize starches dispersed at 90° form films superior to those of ordinary or waxy corn starch of the same D.S. The relatively low strength properties they report very likely reflect incomplete dispersion in the solutions from which the films were cast and the consequent inhomogeneities in the films. Roth and Mehltretter (43) report that films from hydroxypropylated amylomaize starch of 71% apparent amylose has reduced tensile strength but increased elongation and burst strength when compared to film from the original starch.

Hypochlorite oxidation of amylomaize starch increases dispersibility on the introduction of fewer new functional groups than are required in hydroxyethylation (44). A 6% level of oxidation, or 6 moles of carboxyl and carbonyl groups per 100 D-glucose units (essentially comparable to D.S. = 0.06), is required to obtain a product from amylomaize starch (50% apparent amylose) that yields a relatively stable paste. At 9.8% oxidation level, this high-amylose starch gives very clear, nonsettling pastes that exhibit no setback. Oxidized amylomaize starch granules swell less on heating to 90° than ordinary corn starch granules do at comparable levels of oxidation; 8% to 14% starch concentrations are required to give viscosities comparable to 5% concentrations of oxidized ordinary corn starch.

Sloan and co-workers (45) prepared the carboxymethyl derivative of amylomaize starch, 57% amylose content, by a method that avoids dissolving the granule (46). At D.S. 0.05, the carboxymethylstarch is not soluble in boiling water; products of D.S. 0.1 disperse at 50°–60°, whereas above D.S. 0.2 the products are cold water soluble. Viscosity properties are typical of a polyelectrolyte and the addition of salt markedly reduces viscosity. Compared to similar derivatives of ordinary starch and cellulose, the carboxymethyl amylomaize starches give less viscous solutions, but the viscosity is stable over the heating and cooling range of the pasting procedure in both neutral and alkaline solutions. Soil-suspending activity of carboxymethyl amylomaize starch (45) is superior to that of ordinary starch derivatives. At D.S. 0.7, maximum activity is reached and is about two-thirds that of a commercial carboxymethylcellulose.

Other derivatives of amylomaize starches are reported to impart solubility at low degrees of substitution (37). These include the maleate, sulfate, formate, benzoate, and acetate esters, and the methyl, ethyl, allyl, hydroxyethyl, benzyl, and cyanoethyl ethers.

V. Uses for Amylomaize Starches

At the outset of the high-amylose starch program, it was thought that an amylose content of 80–85% would need to be attained before the new starch could find industrial use. This prediction was based largely on the assumption that high-amylose starch would be used as a film-forming material, and it had been demonstrated earlier by Wolff and co-workers (47) that 80–85% of corn amylose in mixture with corn amylopectin was required to give mechanical properties approaching those for pure amylose in unsupported films. Class 5 amylomaize starches, however, found application soon after the development of agronomically suitable hybrids. An early use was as a sizing material for glass fibers (48); this is applied at the spinnerets to protect the fibers from breakage resulting from fiber-to-fiber abrasion and also to improve fiber handling on the bobbins. A particular advantage of the amylomaize starches is the rapid development of strength in the coating; this is sufficient to resist the centrifugal forces (about $3000 \times G$) encountered during high-speed winding of the fiber tow on spools and to retard migration of the size under the internal pressure to which the fibers are subjected on the spools.

Other applications of amylomaize starches will also depend on the properties of their films as deposited on various substrates where they may serve either as a coating to improve surface properties or as an adhesive to bind particles together. Experimentation with these starches is underway in many industries, but information on usage is not available. The properties of the new starches suggest that applications may be found in the manufacture of paper and paper products.

Pearl (49) has shown that amylose is adsorbed from aqueous solution by wood pulp at a greater rate and in greater amount than amylopectin at comparable concentration. Others had earlier reported that amylose is selectively adsorbed from starch solutions by cellulose fibers (50, 51). The binding of amylose by cellulose appears to be largely irreversible (49, 50) whereas amylopectin can be completely eluted with hot water. This stronger binding of amylose to cellulosic fibers should give superior properties to amylomaize starches as beater additives or surface sizes. Indeed, laboratory experiments with unmodified Class 5 amylomaize starch have shown it to be an effective beater adhesive if it is well dispersed before addition to the pulp furnish (52). The unmodified starch also gave favorable results when evaluated as a surface size. Sizes prepared by solution in alkali provide excellent strength properties; however, strongly alkaline sizes are not recommended since the alkali tends to increase the rate of water absorption by the paper. Other means of stabilization of the amylomaize starch at the concentrations required in sizing must be used; either the bath needs to be maintained above 60°–70° to prevent retrogradation of the amylose, or the starch should be chemically modified as discussed in the preceding section.

The possible utility of amylomaize starches as self-supporting films has received attention. The mechanical properties of films cast from unfractionated Class 5 and Class 7 amylomaize starches (53) were comparable to those reported for films of similar composition made from synthetic mixtures of amylose and amylopectin (47). The very low permeability of amylose films to oxygen (54, 55) is also a characteristic of amylomaize starch films. This property suggests their use as an oxygen barrier, either as a wrapping or a coating.

A pilot plant capable of producing over 800,000 pounds of film annually from amylomaize starch, dedicated in 1965 by a commercial corn wet miller, has brought closer to reality the dream of corn breeders and starch chemists that amylomaize would become an industrial commodity (56, 57).

Amylomaize is a new crop now beyond the early stages of its development. New hybrids will continue to be bred with improved agronomic characteristics and yielding starches with even higher amylose contents. Changes in composition of the kernel, including increase of starch content, also may prove possible. Attainment of the original goal of 80–85% amylose content in the starch appears certain, and ultimately higher levels may be realized at least as "apparent" amylose. Undoubtedly, many uses that require the properties of linear starch molecules, in varying degree, will be served by one or another of the amylomaize starches now avialable or under development.

VI. REFERENCES

(1) G. E. Hilbert and M. M. MacMasters, J. Biol. Chem., **162**, 229 (1946).

(2) W. L. Deatherage, M. M. MacMasters, and C. E. Rist, Trans. Am. Assoc. Cereal Chemists, **13**, 31 (1955).

(3) C. T. Greenwood and J. Thomson, J. Chem. Soc., 222 (1962).

(4) M. L. Vineyard, R. P. Bear, M. M. MacMasters, and W. L. Deatherage, Agron. J., **50**, 595 (1958).

(5) R. A. Anderson, C. Vojnovich, and E. L. Griffin, Jr., *Cereal Chem.*, **37**, 334 (1960).
(6) R. A. Anderson, C. Vojnovich, and E. L. Griffin, Jr., *Cereal Chem.*, **38**, 85 (1961).
(7) R. A. Anderson, *Cereal Chem.*, **39**, 407 (1962).
(8) R. A. Anderson, personal communication, 1964.
(9) R. A. Anderson, *Cereal Chem.*, **42**, 580 (1962).
(10) F. R. Earle, J. J. Curtis, and J. E. Hubbard, *Cereal Chem.*, **23**, 504 (1946).
(11) M. S. Zuber, W. L. Deatherage, C. O. Grogan, and M. M. MacMasters, *Argon, J.*, **52**, 572 (1960).
(12) J. E. Hubbard, F. R. Earle, and J. J. Curtis, "Composition of Commercial Grades of Corn, Oats, and Grain Sorghums," *U. S. Dept. Agr.*, **ARS-71-32**, April 1964.
(13) R. A. Anderson, D. E. Uhl, W. L. Deatherage, and E. L. Griffin, Jr., *Cereal Chem.*, **39**, 282 (1962).
(14) W. L. Deatherage, personal communication, 1964.
(15) N. P. Badenhuizen, "Chemistry and Biology of the Starch Granule," Springer Verlag, Wien, Austria, 1959.
(16) M. J. Wolf, H. L. Seckinger, and R. J. Dimler, *Staerke*, **16**, 375 (1964).
(17) N. P. Badenhuizen, S. *African J. Med. Sci.*, **23**, 276 (1958).
(18) H. L. Seckinger and M. J. Wolf, *Staerke*, **18**, 1 (1966).
(19) T. J. Schoch and E. C. Maywald, *Anal. Chem.*, **28**, 382 (1956).
(20) H. F. Zobel, T. M. Cotton, and F. R. Senti, *Abstr. Papers, Am. Assoc. Cereal Chemists, 49th*, Toronto, Canada, April 1964.
(21) W. Dvonch, H. H. Kramer, and R. L. Whistler, *Cereal Chem.*, **28**, 270 (1951).
(22) R. M. Sandstedt, D. Strahara, S. Ueda, and R. C. Abbott, *Cereal Chem.*, **39**, 123 (1962).
(23) H. H. Kramer, P. L. Pfahler, and R. L. Whistler, *Agron. J.*, **50**, 207 (1958).
(24) P. L. Pfahler, H. H. Kramer, and R. L. Whistler, *Science*, **125**, 441 (1957).
(25) H. F. Zobel and F. R. Senti, unpublished data, 1960.
(26) N. W. Taylor, H. F. Zobel, M. White, and F. R. Senti, *J. Phys. Chem.*, **65**, 1816 (1961).
(27) E. M. Montgomery, K. R. Sexson, and F. R. Senti, *Staerke*, **13**, 215 (1961).
(28) J. W. Sloan, M. M. MacMasters, and F. R. Senti, *Cereal Chem.*, **36**, 196 (1959).
(29) R. A. Anderson, C. Vojnovich, and G. Soedomo, *Staerke*, **15**, 355 (1963).
(30) R. A. Anderson and V. F. Pfeifer, *Staerke*, **16**, 209 (1964).
(31) R. A. Anderson, V. F. Pfeifer, and V. E. Sohns, *Cereal Sci. Today*, **9**, 398 (1964).
(32) I. A. Wolff, B. T. Hofreiter, P. R. Watson, W. L. Deatherage, and M. M. Mac-Masters, *J. Am. Chem. Soc.*, **77**, 1654 (1955).
(33) C. T. Greenwood and J. Thomson, *Chem. Ind. (London)*, 1110 (1960).
(34) O. B. Wurzburg and W. Herbst, U.S. Patent 3,222,220 (1965); *Chem Abstr.*, **64**, 6877 (1966).
(35) E. M. Montgomery and K. R. Sexson, personal communication, 1964.
(36) H. W. Leach and T. J. Schoch, *Cereal Chem.*, **39**, 318 (1962).
(37) M. W. Rutenberg, W. Jarowenko, and L. J. Ross, U.S. Patent 3,038,895 (1962); *Chem. Abstr.*, **57**, 10086 (1962).
(38) A. M. Mark, W. B. Roth, H. F. Zobel, and C. L. Mehltretter, *Cereal Chem.*, **42**, 209 (1965).
(39) S. R. Erlander, R. Tobin, and R. J. Dimler, *Abstr. Papers, Am. Chem. Soc.*, **114**, 15C (1963).
(40) E. M. Montgomery, K. R. Sexson, R. J. Dimler, and F. R. Senti, *Staerke*, **16**, 345 (1964).

(41) E. M. Montgomery, K. R. Sexson, and R. J. Dimler, *Staerke*, **16**, 314 (1964).

(42) J. C. Rankin, J. G. Rall, C. R. Russell, and F. R. Senti, *Cereal Chem.*, **37**, 657 (1960).

(43) W. B. Roth and C. L. Mehltretter, *Food Technol.*, submitted for publication January 1966.

(44) R. L. Mellies, C. L. Mehltretter, and F. R. Senti, *J. Chem. Eng. Data*, **5**, 169 (1960).

(45) J. W. Sloan, C. L. Mehltretter, and F. R. Senti, *J. Chem. Eng. Data*, **7**, 156 (1962).

(46) W. F. Filbert, U.S. Patent 2,599,620 (1952); *Chem. Abstr.*, **46**, 11732 (1952).

(47) I. A. Wolff, H. A. Davis, J. E. Cluskey, L. J. Gundrum, and C. E. Rist, *Ind. Eng. Chem.*, **43**, 915 (1951).

(48) R. H. Karpik and D. H. Griffiths, Canadian Patent 669,984 (1963).

(49) W. L. Pearl, *Tappi*, **35**, 41 (1952).

(50) E. Pacsu and J. W. Mullen, *J. Am. Chem. Soc.*, **63**, 1168 (1941).

(51) M. Samec, *Ber*, **73**, 85 (1940).

(52) Unpublished data, Northern Regional Research Laboratory, 1961.

(53) A. M. Mark, W. B. Roth, C. L. Mehltretter, and C. E. Rist, *Cereal Chem.*, **41**, 197 (1964).

(54) J. C. Rankin, I. A. Wolff, and C. E. Rist, *Chem. Eng. Data Ser.*, **3**, 130 (1958).

(55) A. M. Mark, W. B. Roth, C. L. Mehltretter, and C. E. Rist, *Food Technol.*, **20**, 75 (1966).

(56) R. A. Langenheim, *Chemurgic Dig.*, **22**, 2 (1964).

(57) Anon., *Amaizo Corn Ear*, **4** (July 1965), American Maize-Products Co., Roby, Indiana.

CHAPTER XXII

PRODUCTION AND USE OF PREGELATI-NIZED STARCH

By Eugene L. Powell

American Maize-Products Company, Roby, Indiana

I. Introduction

Kerr (*1*) gives a good introduction to cold water pasting starches in his discussion of the manufacture of modified corn starches. Also, commercially important uses for pregelatinized starches are described in his discussions of dextrins (adhesives), paper making, bakery products, oil well drilling muds, and foundry core binders. More recently, the great increase in easily prepared foods, such as frozen and canned formulated foods and complete meals, prepared dry mixes for baked items, and "instant" foods and beverages in great variety, has materially expanded the market for pregelatinized starches. The advent of genetically controlled starch products, such as waxy maize and waxy sorghum and the high-amylose maizes, coupled with the many chemical modifications of these has greatly increased the variety of precooked thickeners and stabilizers. In the last 15 years evolutionary changes in the development of processing machines and techniques have taken place which have led to a wide variety of high quality products.

II. Production Methods

The literature, particularly the European patent literature, is replete with examples of starchy products that swell to some degree as soon as they are mixed in cold water. Kerr (*1*) describes a number of these so-called soluble starches and gives a lengthy bibliography. These formulated products are still of value in adhesives and similar non-food uses. However, most of these starches contain additives which make them unacceptable in food products. The balance of the present discussion will be directed toward those products that are gelatinized with excess water present and then dried.

The drum dryer or "hot-roll," in spite of all its faults and limitations, is still the most commonly used equipment for production of pregelatinized starches. Spray dryers have been used commercially, but they are generally uneconomical because the high viscosity of starch pastes requires drying at low starch solids. The foam mat drying process (2) may be worthy of consideration since it converts the paste to thin films which are friable when dry. However, there is a serious question as to whether or not an economically high solids starch paste can be foamed effectively. Puffing has long been known as another means for preparing pregelatinized starch products, as Kerr (1) has described. A recent improvement in the technique of puffing that shows promise of practicality is continuous cooking–extrusion-puffing. One example uses the equipment developed by the Wenger Mixer Manufacturing Company (3). To avoid an intractable, horny product, the extruder conditions must be adjusted so that the rope of cooked starch paste will automatically puff as it leaves the extruder die. Advantages claimed are high throughput, lower steam and power costs, and lower mechanical maintenance expense as compared to drum dryers. However, the mechanical shear factor (see IV below) in this machine can be quite high. Van Nieuwenhuyzen (4) describes the use of a fluidized bed, operated either continuously or discontinuously, in which the starch product is both cooked and dried. Two or more such beds may be used in series. Sand or tiny metal balls may be used to help maintain the bed. If this process were reduced to commercial practice, it would be of interest to compare the degree of gelatinization and the extent of granule destruction by shearing shown in these products with those of conventional pregelatinized starches and the extrusion-puffed materials.

Nissan and Hansen (5) developed a mathematical equation to describe the heat transfer and water evaporation rate for a film of material in contact with a heated cylinder and checked the equation by numerical solutions on a digital computer. This work was directed primarily towards the "Yankee" dryer used for paper but is considered applicable to starch drying.

The commercial operation of a drum dryer can be an exasperating and frustrating experience. The process is simple and straightforward in theory, but becomes unpredictable and elusive to control in actual practice. Minor drifts in operating conditions seem to produce magnified changes in the finished product. Operating and maintenance costs are generally considered high in relation to output of finished product. Illustrations (6) of some of the possible arrangements of the basic unit are depicted in Figure 1. Un-

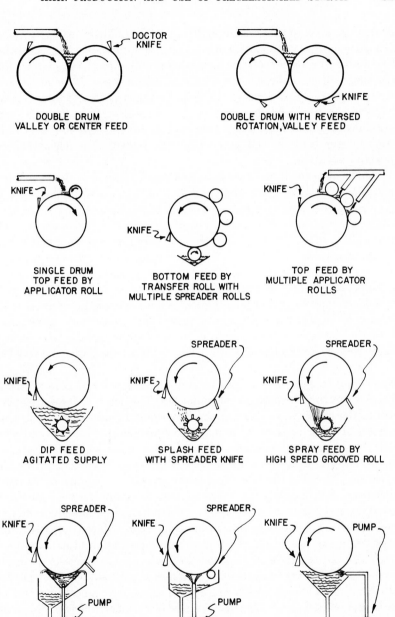

DOUBLE DRUM
VALLEY OR CENTER FEED

DOUBLE DRUM WITH REVERSED
ROTATION, VALLEY FEED

SINGLE DRUM
TOP FEED BY
APPLICATOR ROLL

BOTTOM FEED BY
TRANSFER ROLL WITH
MULTIPLE SPREADER ROLLS

TOP FEED BY
MULTIPLE APPLICATOR
ROLLS

DIP FEED
AGITATED SUPPLY

SPLASH FEED
WITH SPREADER KNIFE

SPRAY FEED BY
HIGH SPEED GROOVED ROLL

ADJUSTABLE PAN FEED
WITH ADJUSTABLE
SPREADER KNIFE

SPRAY NOZZLE FEED
WITH SPREADER ROLL

DIP FEED PLUS
SPRAY NOZZLE

FIG. 1.—Drum dryer arrangements.

fortunately, it is impossible to select any one of these as the optimum arrangement for the production of pregelatinized starches. The arrangement depends on the nature of the feed stream and the desired end-product. The double drum dryer, with feed into the center valley, is the most versatile and commonly used unit. It can handle a greater variety of feed materials and can be operated to give less mechanical shear to the paste than do applicator roll arrangements. It has the disadvantage of low rpm. which limits output per roll, and some inherent mechanical problems demand constant attention.

The feed to the drum dryer may be a moist starch cake from a filter or centrifuge, a slurry of raw starch, or a thoroughly cooked starch paste from a jet cooker or scraped wall heat exchanger. Solids content may be as high as 44% in the raw slurry or 42% in the cooked paste. The supply starch can be chemically modified, enzyme converted, or dextrinized ahead of the drum drying process in accordance with the intended end use. Gelatinization aids (such as salts and alkalies), surface active agents to control rehydration or minimize sticking to the roll, sweetners, flavor improvers, and other ingredients may be included in the feed stream. Actual application of the wet supply to the heated drum can vary widely as is shown in Figure 1. With the double drum dryer, an even distribution of the filter cake or high-viscosity paste along the valley between the rolls presents a problem. Various manifolds and spreader devices have been utilized, including an overflowing trough (7), swinging pendulum feed pipe (8), and a stirring device for mixing the paste in the valley (9). The depth of the starch paste pool in the valley is another variable that must be controlled to obtain a uniform product. The end dams, used to confine the paste at each end of the valley, are a constant source of difficulty caused by leaks, mechanical wear, and formation of hard, horny dried starch deposits. Changing from the valley feed to one of the other indicated methods avoids some of the above difficulties, but may introduce others. Applicator or transfer rolls permit much faster rotation of the main drum, but this does not necessarily increase production if the wet film thickness has to be reduced proportionately to obtain a dry product at the doctor knife. Also, applicators may fail to place a useful thickness of paste on the main roll; or worse, some pastes may stick excessively to the cold roll, rather than the hot one, with possible damage to machinery. These applicators effect mechanical shear of the paste and often degrade the starch so severely that it is unsuitable for the intended use. Splash or spray application reduces the mechanical shear, but many pastes will not adhere and thus not provide a film of the desired uniformity and thickness. Thin cooking pastes, such as enzyme converted starches, dextrins, and shear sensitive waxy maizes, are perhaps best handled on the double drum with valley feed.

Control of the gap at the nip of the two rolls is one of the more critical factors in drum dryer operation. Too thin a wet film results in lost production and a low bulk density in the dried product. If the film is too thick, or too thick in spots, wet material clogs the knife. If the large rolls are ground and aligned cold, they tend to bulge or warp under high steam pressure and heat from differential heating or cooling at the ends so that clearance is no longer uniform along the length of the nip. In large drums, the walls must be thick to contain the high pressure steam safely so they may flex under their own weight. Various designs for internal bracing and end-plate construction have been proposed to attain mechanically stable rolls (10–13). Equipment has been designed to grind the rolls in place under full steam load, but it is difficult to measure the gap with both rolls hot and spinning. One method is to drop a soft metal such as electrical fuse wire between the rolls and then measure the degree of flattening with a caliper. Or, it may be possible simply to estimate or measure dry film thickness along the length of the knife. However, a variation of ±0.003 inch in gap width is enough to give less than optimum performance. While this applies particularly to the valley feed double drum dryer, roll alignment and tension are critical for applicator or spreader rolls as well. In one instance it was impossible to produce the desired product with an applicator roll machine until the applicator was positioned 0.5 inch or more away from the main roll. With this unusually wide gap, and with the two rolls driven at the same linear speed, mechanical shear on the paste was minimized and the desired product came off properly.

Conditioning of the roll surface is another problem that requires attention. Too high a polish, or a non-corrosive metal plating on the surface, may make it difficult to pick up the proper thickness of wet starch. It may also cause the partially dried film to fall from the roll ahead of the knife. Too tight a bond between the dried film and the roll makes it impossible for the doctor knife to remove the film properly. Hence, release agents are frequently applied to the roll surface or mixed with the applied starch slurry.

Sharp, well-adjusted doctor knives add to the mechanical maintenance expense of drum dryers. Knife adjustment that will provide proper product removal without excessive wear presents problems similar to those of roll gap adjustment. Knives may be mechanically oscillated (14), adjusted hydraulically (15), or alternately raised and lowered (16) to permit several layers of dried product to build up before the thickened sheet is removed. Multiple doctor knives with intricate adjusting devices have also been tried (17).

Mechanical or air-stream pick-up systems, or some combination of these, may be used to remove product from the roll. Milling and sorting of the product by screens or air classifiers normally are necessary since particle size and particle size distribution are major factors in the over-all performance of the products.

To add to its other disadvantages, the drum dryer is still an inefficient heat exchanger. The thick walls of cast iron or steel do not conduct heat rapidly to the starch film, which limits the speed of rotation. If any portion of the inside drum surface is covered with a film of condensate or non-condensable gases, efficiency falls off rapidly. Water standing in the drum results in areas of rust and scale so that portions of the roll will allow wet starch to arrive at the knife.

Structural changes that permit higher steam pressures have been tried, but these soon become self-limiting (*18*). Grooving the inside roll surface to increase the area exposed to steam is another possibility (*19*). Building the drum so that it consists of two concentric cylinders with the steam confined to the narrow space between is a further improvement (*20–23*). A variety of internal arrangements are used to assure that high velocity steam is directed continuously to free the inside surface of the outer drum from condensate or air film. One such scheme divides the annular space into compartments which are periodically relieved of condensate. This results in a pulsating action to aid scouring (*22*). Day (*24*) proposed a multitude of corrugations or parallel channels welded to the inside of a single shell drum to confine and direct high velocity steam. Hornbostel (*25, 26*) used the jacketed drum but confined high pressure steam to a system of pipes arranged in the annular space between the two cylinders. A heat exchange oil at essentially atmospheric pressure filling this annular space would uniformly conduct heat to the outer shell. This design permits the use of a thin walled outer cylinder to improve heat transfer. In another rather unusual design, the outer shell rotates with a highly turbulent liquid heat exchange oil between it and the stationary inner cylinder (*27*).

Since a pool or even a film of condensate inside the drum reduces efficiency, it is not surprising that a number of devices have been tried in an effort to improve removal of condensate (*28–32*). Some of these devices utilize continuous suction on the condensate pipe, or bleed through a portion of the gaseous steam to aid in sweeping out the condensate. Provision is sometimes made for removing non-condensable gases continuously.

III. Testing and Evaluation

Since the theory of starch behavior has not advanced to the point at which performance can be predicted with any certitude, one is inevitably forced to the awkward stratagem of the use test. Oil well drilling mud formulations containing starches are made using a specified amount of mechanical shear and heat treatment in order to obtain maximum water holding capacity. The rate of water loss is determined by a standardized pressure filter. For foundry core binders, test pieces are made and green strength determined; duplicate pieces are then baked and hardness and tensile strength are measured. For adhesives and binders also, the usual procedure is to formulate the glue, or make samples of briquettes, and measure final properties.

In food products, pregelatinized starch usually reacts with other ingredients present. Hence, some simplified version of the intended food is formulated and judged or tested. In some tests, it may be possible to omit such minor ingredients as flavors and food colors. Ingredients such as sugars, lipids, salts, acidulants, proteins, gums, and other starches can have profound effects on the rehydration of a pregelatinized starch.

One test for evaluating pregelatinized starch in foods is to rehydrate the starch at room temperature, measure its hot and cold viscosity, and determine the setback or congelation of aged paste as described by Wollermann and Makstell (33). An electric mixer designed for household use is convenient for the rehydration. The starch is sprinkled on top of the water with slow agitation, and then moderate agitation is applied. Entrapped air can cause erratic viscosity readings. Premixing the starch with sugar, salt, fat, or any other dry ingredient improves rehydration without formation of lumps or "fisheyes." The Brookfield viscometer is often used to check the resulting paste viscosities at various temperatures. A preferred procedure is to pour the paste into a recording viscometer, such as the Brabender or Corn Industries' Viscometer, and to record the viscosity as the paste is heated to near 100°. The relationship between cold and hot viscosity and the time and temperature at which peak viscosity is attained provides a clear picture of the probable behavior of the starch in a food. Hot and cold pastes can also be stored at 25° for 24 hours with imbedded disks. The gel strength is then determined. At 10° a fairly valid gel test can be obtained after 2 hours.

Screening starch through a deck of standard sieves with controlled shaking gives important data on average particle size and particle size distribution. Mechanical shakers should be grounded to eliminate electrostatic effects. Bulk density of the dry powder is measured by pouring a weighed sample into a graduated cylinder and recording the volume of the loosely packed powder. Tapping the cylinder until the surface level ceases to sink affords a measurement of the bulk density after packing. When two samples show wide differences in bulk density even though particle size is essentially the same, examination under a moderate power 3D microscope can be informative. Particles that are roughly cubical in shape give high bulk densities and slow rehydration rates on the recording viscometer, which indicates that the dried sheet from the drum must have been thick and dense. Flat particles, on the other hand, give low bulk densities and rapid rehydration in cold water (often with lumping), indicating that a very thin, lacy dried sheet, or snowflake-like particle, came from the roll.

For unknown samples, microscopic examination at 450× is used to determine the type of the parent starch and the degree of gelatinization. Here polarized light is used to locate the raw granules. Iodine staining distinguishes normal starches from the waxy (amylopectin) types, while dyes of opposite charge distinguish between anionic and cationic modifications of starch (This volume, Chapt. XXVI). A determination of pH and an acid-base titration can be helpful if ionic modifications or added buffers are present.

Moisture, protein, lipids, and ash may be determined by standard methods. Color may be compared with a standard or may be measured as "whiteness" with the Agtron instrument or a spectrophotometer with reflectance attachments. Odor and flavor determinations are sometimes done on the dry powder itself; for organoleptic evaluations, it is usually better to make up a thin paste using a Waring Blendor for reconstitution. Obviously the quality of the water used is important. Microbiological contamination is normally not a problem since the product is sterilized on the roll. However, subsequent milling and packing may introduce some contamination, and subsequent microbial counts may be necessary for certain product uses.

IV. PROPERTIES AND BEHAVIOR

Each pregelatinized starch, upon reconstitution with cold water, shows less thickening power and less tendency to set to a gel than pastes of the parent starch. Wollermann and Makstell (33) demonstrated this graphically in a variety of simulated food formulations. Kerr (1) attributes this loss of thickening and gelling power to retrogradation in the wet film during dry, ing. Some retrogradation must occur in the drying of the starch. However-the major change that takes place during the processing of pregelatinized starches is the destruction of the hydrated starch granules. Microscopic examination of reconstituted pastes show that granule destruction is usually extensive. For want of a better name, the term "mechanical shear factor" has been used to designate those forces which act on the granules during processing and bring about disorganization. Parallel changes in properties occur in freshly cooked starch paste that has been homogenized to different degrees. Likewise, similar changes occur in a continuous jet cooker or a heat exchanger in which mechanical shear factors become appreciable. If applicator or spreader rolls are operated so that their linear speeds differ from that of the main roll, or if excessive tension is applied, the homogenizing effect becomes pronounced. When a drum dryer is adjusted to produce a very thick, dense, horny type of starch film, the finished product will have a roughly cubical shape. These particles exhibit slow rehydration rate and possess relatively low cold-paste viscosities and relatively high hot-paste viscosities. The viscosity peak on a Brabender or Corn Industries' Viscometer curve will be displaced well toward the hot end of the cycle. Molecular reassociation must be extensive since the particles behave somewhat like raw starch granules. The particles tend to give a rough, grainy paste which may be unacceptable in food uses. In contrast, drying a thin film at a high rpm. allows less time for reassociation. There is obtained a two-dimensional-type flake with a low bulk density. It rapidly rehydrates (with danger of lumping) and gives a high cold-paste viscosity and a low hot-paste viscosity. This starch properly reconstituted gives a smooth glossy paste, but the low hot-paste viscosity can lead to "boil-out" in those foods that are to be heated before serving.

Another phenomenon related to reassociation is the slow change with age that all pregelatinized starches undergo even under dry storage conditions at moderate temperatures. These changes can be progressive over several months although the magnitude of change gradually tapers off. The changes are toward slower rehydration, lower cold-paste viscosity, and higher hot-paste viscosity. Heat treatment of the dry powder can quicken these changes and reduce the aging time to a few hours. Starch chains must have some mobility, even in the semi-dry state, so that hydrogen bonding can gradually increase during storage. Fortunately, these changes can be anticipated and compensated for in the design of the product. It is of interest that pure amylopectin or waxy starches show much the same loss of function and change with age in their pregelatinized forms as do the more common amylose containing starches. Thus, although granule destruction is the major factor to be considered in drum dryer operation, molecular reassociation also must be considered.

With many puddings and sauces, it is necessary to have rapid rehydration in order to obtain a smooth, glossy or non-grainy type of paste. Fine milling and screening give this characteristic, particularly if the particles are "two dimensional," but such particles wet too rapidly and lumps result. Möller proposed lecithin as an anti-lumping agent (34). Hinz, Schemerhorn, and Dorn (35) recommend the addition of hydrophobic agents such as vegetable oils. Winner (36) controls the rehydration rate by selecting surface-active agents with the proper hydrophilic–hydrophobic balance, and he prefers compounds that do not develop rancidity in the dry powder.

Many starches contain small quantities of unsaturated fatty acids which are naturally protected against oxidation in the raw granule. Destruction of the starch granule during drum drying permits rancidity to develop within a week or two when the dry powder is stored. Evans (*37*) demonstrated that the presence of orthophosphate salts during drum drying overcomes this fault. Extraction of the fatty acids with methanol and ammonia has also been proposed as a means of improving flavor (*38*). Korth (*39*) proposed that polyphosphates, if present during rolling, would sequester heavy metals and thus prevent the development of oxidative rancidity. Development of another off-flavor seems to depend on the completeness of rehydration and may be a result of molecular reassociation during drying and ageing. These rehydrated pastes often have more of a "starchy," "pasty," or "adhesive" flavor than do freshly cooked pastes of the corresponding starch. The presence of sugars during drying tends to overcome this effect (*40*). Sowell and co-workers (*41*) claim that a blend of potato starch, wheat starch, and corn syrup can be drum dried to give a bland flavor in the reconstituted paste. Use of surface-active agents and adjustment of roll-drying conditions can do much to overcome some of these physically produced off-flavors.

V. USES

Industrial non-food uses of the pregelatinized starches are numerous and varied in nature. Pregelatinized starches are added to oil well drilling muds to control water loss. Here, in contrast to most food uses, a high mechanical shear factor is desirable. This helps to explain why acid-modified or waxy maize starches perform better than unmodified cornstarch. Bravos and Evans (*42, 43*) have demonstrated that gelatinization aids such as calcium chloride facilitate disruption of the starch granule. Urea (*44*) probably functions in the same manner. Also, precooked starches are used to bind sand particles in foundry cores (*45*). Cold water wallpaper pastes and other dry adhesive bases are likely to contain a large proportion of precooked starch or dextrin (*46–48*). Cold water laundry starches are based on enzyme converted or chemically or physically modified starch which is cooked and roll dried (*49–53*). Permanent textile finishes for application at the finishing mills are obtained by combining reactive monomers or polymers with pregelatinized starches (*54–56*). Precooked starches are added at the wet end of papermaking machines as internal adhesives to bond fibers within the sheet. Here too, bonding can be improved, or water resistance built in, by modifying the starch or by using reactive additives (*57–59*). Pregelatinized starches are used as the binder in the briquetting of charcoal and powdered coal. They are used in the gypsum wallboard (*60*) and in cement joint formulations (*61*). A pregelatinized waxy maize starch has been used as a protective colloid in water base paints (*62*). Rickert proposes a temporary protective coating for metal objects composed of these starches plus coal acids (*63, 64*). Precooked starches and flours have been tested extensively in the pelletizing of low-grade iron ore and other ores. Here the starches supply green strength to the pellets until sintering can bind the fine particles, firmly together. Pregelatinized starches are considered rather expensive for this use, however. The starches are also used in pelletizing animal feeds.

In food, the pregelatinized starches can be applied in almost any instance in which water thickening or water holding is desired, but cooking is to be avoided. The precooked or instant-type puddings that are ready to serve after whipping in cold milk are good examples of this. In cake mixes, the addition of pregelatinized starch increases water absorption of the batter and aids in the entrapment of air and produces a moist cake of good volume, with only a moderate amount of mixing. If the starch is made from a modified waxy maize base, it also adds a "freshness retention" factor to the baked cake (*65*). In cake frosting mixes and fudge mixes, a pregelatinized starch confers tolerance to varying additions of water. The starch also effectively controls sugar crystal growth (*66, 67*). Some whipped chiffon-type desserts contain a pregelatinized starch, usually in conjunction with gelatin (*68, 69*). In doughnut mixes, and in many other prepared bakery mixes, a precooked starch may be used to control batter properties and hold desired levels of water and gases. A mix for making cream puff shells, in which precooked cornstarch is a major component, has recently appeared on the market (*70*).

When raw frozen pies were developed, it proved advantageous to thicken the fillings with pregelatinized starch. To attain good gloss and smoothness as well as viscosity stability in the pie filling, a waxy (amylopectin)-type of starch is preferred. By using pregelatinized starches, volatile flavor loss, attendant on cooking and cooling pie fillings, is avoided. By the use of these starches, small bakeries and institutional kitchens are able to make a variety of pie fillings with a minimum investment in equipment and labor.

The use of pregelatinized starches and flours as a binder and moisture stabilizer in table-ready meats is well known (*71*). Evans (*72*) has demonstrated that flakes of pregelatinized starch will entrap fat and protect it against oxidative rancidity in dry soup formulations. Carman (*73*) proposed a glaze for candied sweet potatoes and other foods which included a pregelatinized starch. The use of precooked starches for suspending cocoa, raw starch, or similar insoluble solid particles is illustrated by a number of patents (*74–76*). It has been suggested (*77*) that starch esters and ethers in pregelatinized form can serve as effective ice cream stabilizers.

A recent patent describes a process in which amylose, or the high-amylose starches of over 60% amylose, is dispersed in water at superatmospheric steam pressures then drum dried rapidly to prevent serious retrogradation (78). It is claimed that the product serves as a rapidly gelling thickener for puddings and gravies. The inventors substantiate the lack of retrogradation by noting the solubility of the product and its amorphous x-ray diffraction pattern. However, a considerable body of experience with high-amylose starches shows that drum drying always allows considerable reassociation which increases in time in storage.

VI. REFERENCES

(1) R. W. Kerr, in "Chemistry and Industry of Starch," R. W. Kerr, ed., Academic Press Inc., New York, N. Y., 2nd Ed., 1950.
(2) A. I. Morgan, Jr., L. F. Ginnette, J. A. Randall, and R. P. Graham, *Food Eng.*, **31,** 86 (1959).
(3) Anon., *Food Process.*, **24,** No. 9, 134 (1963).
(4) L. J. van Nieuwenhuyzen, U.S. Patent 2,974,069 (1961); Duintjer Wilkens Meihuizen and Co., N.V., Brit. Patent 813,500; *Chem. Abstr.*, **53,** 18523 (1959).
(5) A. H. Nissan and D. Hansen, *A.I.Ch.E. J.*, **6,** 606 (1960).
(6) The majority of these drawings from: Catalog 384, Buflovak Equipment Division, Blaw-Knox Company, Buffalo, New York. See also H. F. Reichard, *Chem. Met. Eng.*, **52,** 118 (1945).
(7) A. M. Fischer, U.S. Patent 2,903,054 (1959).
(8) G. N. Harcourt and D. B. Montgomery, U.S. Patent 2,392,382 (1946); *Chem. Abstr.*, **40,** 5965 (1946).
(9) J. G. Moore and E. B. Pinkel, U.S. Patent 3,082,541 (1963).
(10) H. E. Neubauer, U.S. Patent 2,542,287 (1951).
(11) H. M. Ostertag, U.S. Patent 2,628,433 (1953).
(12) E. J. Charlton and L. Pompa, U.S. Patent 2,697,284 (1954).
(13) L. Hornbostel, U.S. Patent 2,651,114 (1953).
(14) A. M. Fischer, U.S. Patent 2,857,612 (1958).
(15) L. Hornbostel, U.S. Patent 2,470,400 (1949).
(16) G. Stevenson, U.S. Patent 2,566,811 (1951).
(17) C. O. Lavett, U.S. Patent 2,592,914 (1952).
(18) M. L. Schädler, U.S. Patent 2,685,139 (1954).
(19) L. Hornbostel and J. E. Goodwillie, U.S. Patent 2,521,371 (1950).
(20) W. Messinger, U.S. Patent 2,661,545 (1953).
(21) L. W. Petry and J. Baxter, Jr., U.S. Patent 2,661,546 (1953).
(22) P. E. Ohlson and E. A. Hodge, U.S. Patent 2,677,898 (1954).
(23) P. E. Ohlson and E. A. Hodge, U.S. Patent 2,677,899 (1954); Reissued as Re. 24,024 (1955).
(24) G. D. Day, U.S. Patent 2,932,091 (1960).
(25) L. Hornbostel, U.S. Patent 2,844,887 (1958).
(26) L. Hornbostel, U.S. Patent 2,909,849 (1959).
(27) E. J. Justus and R. A. Daane, U.S. Patent 2,915,293 (1959).
(28) W. Westphal, U.S. Patent 2,582,365 (1952).
(29) H. G. Cram, U.S. Patent 2,617,205 (1952).
(30) G. Engstrom, U.S. Patent 2,648,914 (1953).
(31) F. A. Garrett, U.S. Patent 2,707,836 (1955).
(32) R. E. White and A. J. Cirrito, U.S. Patent 2,724,909 (1955).
(33) L. A. Wollermann and E. W. Makstell, *Cereal Sci. Today*, **3,** 244 (1958).
(34) F. A. Möller, U.S. Patent 2,147,104 (1939); *Chem. Abstr.*, **33,** 4074 (1939).

(35) H. C. Hinz, Jr., G. R. Schemerhorn, Sr., and F. L. Dorn, U.S. Patent 2,554,143 (1951); *Chem. Abstr.*, **45**, 6319 (1951).

(36) B. M. Winner, U.S. Patent 2,749,244 (1956); *Chem. Abstr.*, **50**, 14144 (1956).

(37) J. W. Evans, U.S. Patent 2,806,026 (1957); *Chem. Abstr.*, **52**, 612 (1958).

(38) G. C. Harris, U.S. Patent 3,102,054 (1963).

(39) J. A. Korth, U.S. Patent 2,884,346 (1959); *Chem. Abstr.*, **53**, 12719 (1959).

(40) A. A. Halden, U.S. Patent 2,613,150 (1952); *Chem. Abstr.*, **47**, 1307 (1953).

(41) E. A. Sowell, R. L. Curtin, B. A. Hall, and B. L. Scallet, U.S. Patent 2,897,086 (1959).

(42) G. T. Bravos and J. W. Evans, U.S. Patent 2,900,335 (1959); *Chem. Abstr.*, **53**, 22872 (1959).

(43) G. T. Bravos and J. W. Evans, U.S. Patent 3,078,187 (1963).

(44) K. Lunstroth, U.S. Patent 2,773,783 (1956); *Chem. Abstr.*, **51**, 6134 (1957).

(45) H. K. Salzberg, U.S. Patent 2,813,840 (1957); *Chem. Abstr.*, **52**, 2723 (1958).

(46) G. J. Leuck, U.S. Patent 2,222,872 (1940); *Chem. Abstr.*, **35**, 1902 (1941).

(47) J. Lolkema and W. A. van der Meer, U.S. Patent 2,583,268 (1952); *Chem. Abstr.*, **46**, 3784 (1952).

(48) J. V. Bauer and L. H. Elizer, U.S. Patent 3,019,120 (1962).

(49) W. W. Pigman, R. W. Kerr, and N. F. Schink, U.S. Patent 2,609,326 (1952); *Chem. Abstr.*, **47**, 2524 (1953).

(50) R. W. Kerr and W. J. Katzbeck, U.S. Patent 2,669,523 (1954); *Chem. Abstr.*, **48**, 8570 (1954).

(51) J. W. Todd, U.S. Patent 2,865,775 (1958); *Chem. Abstr.*, **53**, 5715 (1959).

(52) J. R. Harrison, U.S. Patent 3,049,434 (1962); *Chem. Abstr.*, **58**, 652 (1963).

(53) G. Moes, U.S. Patent 3,097,102 (1963).

(54) J. Lolkema and W. A. van der Meer, U.S. Patent 2,542,932 (1951); *Chem. Abstr.*, **45**, 4954 (1951).

(55) J. Lolkema and W. A. van der Meer, U.S. Patent 2,542,933 (1951); *Chem. Abstr.*, **45**, 4954 (1951).

(56) J. Lolkema and W. A. van der Meer, U.S. Patent 2,575,423 (1951); *Chem. Abstr.*, **46**, 2324 (1952).

(57) C. J. Yarber, U.S. Patent 2,692,824 (1954); *Chem. Abstr.*, **49**, 2734 (1955).

(58) R. W. Kerr, U.S. Patent 2,903,391 (1959); *Chem. Abstr.*, **54**, 1850 (1959).

(59) C. G. Caldwell and O. B. Wurzburg, U.S. Patent 2,917,506 (1959); *Chem. Abstr.*, **54**, 10358 (1960).

(60) E. L. Wimmer and F. Meindl, U.S. Patent 2,894,859 (1959); *Chem. Abstr.*, **53**, 20868 (1959).

(61) M. P. Ptasienski and J. W. Gill, U.S. Patent 3,003,979 (1961); *Chem. Abstr.*, **56**, 1160 (1962).

(62) P. L. Gordon and A. E. Cohen, U.S. Patent 2,914,495 (1959); *Chem. Abstr.*, **54**, 3992 (1960).

(63) H. B. Rickert, U.S. Patent 2,883,300 (1959); *Chem. Abstr.*, **53**, 14544 (1959).

(64) H. B. Rickert, U.S. Patent 2,887,399 (1959); *Chem. Abstr.*, **53**, 20838 (1959).

(65) R. M. Boettger, *Cereal Sci. Today*, **8**, 106 (1963).

(66) D. J. Young, U.S. Patent 2,221,563 (1940).

(67) R. W. Butler, U.S. Patent 2,914,410 (1959).

(68) A. S. Clausi, J. L. Common, and H. M. Horti, U.S. Patent 2,954,299 (1960).

(69) W. A. Mitchell and W. C. Seidel, U.S. Patent 2,968,565 (1961).

(70) E. W. Johnson, U.S. Patent 2,919,986 (1960).

(71) E. F. Glabe, U.S. Patent 2,635,963 (1953); *Chem. Abstr.*, **47**, 6575 (1953).

(*72*) J. W. Evans, U.S. Patent 2,641,547 (1953); *Chem. Abstr.*, **47,** 8288 (1953).

(*73*) W. E. Carman, U.S. Patent 2,861,889 (1958).

(*74*) D. E. Linn, U.S. Patent 1,989,758 (1935); *Chem. Abstr.*, **29,** 1899 (1935).

(*75*) R. L. Lloyd, U.S. Patent 2,442,658 (1948); *Chem. Abstr.*, **42,** 6021 (1958).

(*76*) J. W. Evans and G. E. Nelson, U.S. Patent 2,749,259 (1956).

(*77*) J. Lolkema, U.S. Patent 2,590,077 (1952); *Chem. Abstr.*, **46,** 5223 (1952).

(*78*) A. Sarko, B. R. Zeitlin, and F. J. Germino, U.S. Patent 3,086,890 (1963); *Chem. Abstr.*, **59,** 1829 (1963).

CHAPTER XXIII

PRODUCTION AND USES OF STARCH ADHESIVES

By Eric F. W. Dux[1]

Sichel Adhesives Ltd.,
The Adhesives Division of
Corn Products (Sales) Ltd., London, England

[1] Present address: J. Lyons and Co., Ltd., London, England.

I. INTRODUCTION

The development of modern starch adhesives for industry has differed greatly between continents and has been affected mainly by the availability of various native starches. Historically, the oldest pastes were made from wheat, and this starch still plays a dominant role in Australia where it is also converted into excellent dextrins. In Europe, potato starch is most easily available and is the basis of an old established industry. In North America, the dominant starch for adhesives is corn starch while in Latin America, tapioca is principally used. Although sago starch is not widely used for adhesives, its dextrins are important for special applications. The recently developed waxy starches are becoming of importance and are the basis for a range of newly developed adhesives. In general, root and waxy starches yield glues with good flow characteristics, whereas unmodified cereal starches show generally poor flow properties and are used for applications in which short pastes are required.

It is the art of the adhesives manufacturer to adapt available starches to meet the demands of modern industry. The trend is toward starch adhesives with good flow properties and minimal set-back. These adhesives can be pumped through narrow pipe lines and can be applied by transfer rollers. To meet these requirements, it is usual to use root or waxy starches that have undergone little or no degradation or cereal starches that have been chemically modified.

Thus, it is fairly simple to make both fluid and pasty adhesives from root and waxy starches, whereas it is much more difficult to produce fluid glues from cereal starches. However, it is common practice for North American adhesive manufacturers to modify readily available corn starch either by limited hydrolysis or by oxidation.

II. GENERAL CHARACTERISTICS

Starch adhesives are used throughout the world in such diverse applications as carton sealing, cylindrical and angular tubes, laminated board, metal foil-to-paper laminations, billposting, corrugated board, container labeling, bag seams, distemper paper, and wallpaper printing.

To meet these demands, numerous different starch adhesives are manufactured. Vegetable adhesives can range from thick pastes with no mobility to almost watery fluids; and solid contents can range from 2–45%. The pH of these adhesives can vary widely, but it is critical for certain applications, particularly when discoloration or corrosion problems are encountered, or when the adhesive contains synthetic resins. Adhesive manufacturers often incorporate other chemicals such as plasticizers, mineral fillers, de-foamers, and preservatives.

Corn starch is characterized by a strong setback. The principal outlet for unmodified corn starch in the adhesives industry is the manufacture of corrugated board, where very large tonnages are consumed. When modified to thin boiling or oxidized varieties, corn starch is of general application.

Wheat starch varies in quality and is commonly used as a thick paste. It is often used as an adhesive base for bill posting and for paper bag making.

Potato starch lends itself to a variety of modifications. Large quantities of short pastes and fluid, stable glues are made from it. Potato starch adhesives form films of good clarity and reasonable water resistance and find extensive use in Europe.

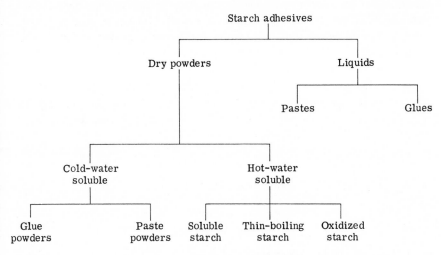

FIG. 1.—Classification of starch adhesives.

Tapioca starch, when of good quality, is superior to most other starches as an adhesive raw material. Fluid, stable glues of neutral pH are easily made, and these are miscible with a wide range of synthetic resin emulsions. Tapioca starch glues range in solids content from 10–28%.

Waxy starches are in many respects similar to tapioca starch. Waxy starch films have excellent color and redisperse in water more readily than those from tapioca.

III. CLASSIFICATION OF STARCH ADHESIVES

Adhesives may be classified as glues or pastes which are supplied either as ready-for-use liquids or as dry powders. Glues are those adhesives which have good mobility and stability and which can be pumped through pipe lines. Pastes are adhesives with little or no mobility (Fig. 1).

"Soluble Starch" is usually made from a mixture of starch and white dextrin or from starch that has had slight hydrolytic treatment. Thin boiling starch has had more vigorous acid treatment. Oxidized starches are usually made by oxidizing starch under alkaline conditions with sodium hypochlorite. Since root and waxy starches show sufficient flow stability without oxidation, the hypochlorite reaction is usually reserved for cereal starches. Oxidized starch adhesives are akin to thin boiling starch pastes, but can be prepared at higher solids and have improved keeping qualities and a whiter and brighter color. They are without the gelatinous sticky nature of unmodified cereal starch pastes. Adhesives made from oxidized starches set back less than those made from thin boiling starches. Oxidized starch pastes are used in paper bags which are made by highspeed, automatic machines. Some oxidized starches are used in wrapping surgical goods because the films do not crack nor stain and will withstand steam sterilization.

1. Liquid Adhesives

The advantage of liquid adhesives is that they can be used directly by the consumer. The available range of these adhesives is wider than that of dry adhesives, because the manufacturer can incorporate a large number of chemicals and make other modifications which are more difficult with dry adhesives. The disadvantages of liquid adhesives are their relatively limited shelf life, susceptibility to attack by microorganisms, and high freight costs.

2. Dry Adhesives

a. *Cold-Water-Soluble Adhesives*

These adhesives require approximately 20 minutes for complete dispersion. During the dissolution, some care is required to insure that correct weights and measures are used. The shelf life of the dry adhesive is almost unlimited if it is properly packed. Dispersions are usually stable for at least a week.

b. *Hot-Water-Soluble Adhesives*

The price advantage of these low-cost adhesive powders is often offset by the costs involved in their dispersion. The adhesives not only require cooking time but often cooling time as well. Their tendency to set back often creates difficulties, particularly when the user wishes to cook his adhesive powders in a central location and pump the product to several points of application. Hot-water-soluble powders, like other dry adhesives, can be stored for a long time without attack by microorganisms.

IV. MANUFACTURE OF LIQUID STARCH ADHESIVES

Machinery required to manufacture starch pastes is often very simple, and may consist merely of a tank fitted with an agitator. Materials of construction vary, but the use of iron is undesirable when alkaline glues are to be manufactured. Wooden vats are satisfactory, and their rough surface improves the shearing action of the agitator arms. Although some vats of wood or metal have plain interiors, others have either horizontal or vertical baffles. The fluid flow between moving and stationary members produces a beneficial shearing action on the paste. Heating may be by direct steam injection or through a heated jacket. The tank outlet must be large enough to permit rapid flow of the viscous dispersion.

The simplest liquid starch pastes are made by cooking starch in water with only preservatives added. These pastes can be used for bill posting and bag making and in tobacco products. Pastes are improved by incorporating inorganic salts, such as calcium chloride or magnesium chloride. A mixture consisting of equal parts of starch and calcium chloride gelatinizes in water at room temperature. Addition of borax increases the viscosity greatly and improves tack. These simple pastes are used widely for making cigarette seams. Wheat and corn starches are commonly modified for this application.

Alkaline modification of starch is widely practiced. Several reviews have been published, the most recent by Leach (1).

The initiation and extent of alkaline gelatinization depends on the relative amounts of each of the three components present; water, sodium hydroxide, and starch. Neither the pH of the system nor the concentration of alkali is a controlling factor by itself. When granular starch is suspended in dilute sodium hydroxide solution, the granules adsorb a portion of the alkali from the surrounding solution, thereby lowering the alkali concentration in the water phase. The stronger the sodium hydroxide solution, the more alkali will be adsorbed by the starch. When the starch has adsorbed a certain critical amount of alkali, the granules begin to swell. Potato starch gelatinizes at a lower level of adsorbed sodium hydroxide than does corn starch. Salts, such as sodium chloride or sodium sulfate, inhibit the gelatinization so that much higher alkali concentrations can be tolerated. The properties of an alkali-gelatinized starch depend upon the starch used and the method of conversion. Tapioca, potato, or waxy starches are easily transformed to transparent and fluid adhesives. Corn and wheat starch produce thick pastes. These adhesives are simple to make and are widely used in such diverse fields as aluminium foil-to-paper laminations and wallpaper printing.

A further modification is obtained by neutralization of the adhesive. A variety of mineral acids can be used, but sulfuric acid tends to destroy the fluid properties of glues made from tuberous starches. Neutralized starch pastes range in solids content from 18 to 26% and retain their flow characteristics for a long period of time. They also find their largest use in foil-to-paper laminations and in wallpaper printing, but are of wider application since corrosion and discoloration problems are minimized. Neutral starch glues are made at high concentrations for use in water resistant formulations for pasting bottle labels.

V. Manufacture of Cold-Water-Soluble Starch Adhesives

These products, first introduced shortly after the first World War, have acquired an important position in the adhesives' market. Their principal advantages are their long storage life and their low shipping costs. In the formation of cold-water dispersible adhesives by alkaline conversion at elevated temperatures, a limited number of D-glucuronic acid groups are formed (2).

These products could be termed cold-water-swelling, dispersing, or soluble starches. Since the final dispersion is usually transparent, the adhesive can be regarded as a colloidal solution; hence, the term "cold-water-soluble starch" is applicable. Some starches, such as wheat or corn starch, form opaque solutions even when "cold-water soluble."

Formulations are adjusted to give adhesives with solids content ranging from 2–40%, with the pH between 6 and 14. For applications involving porous papers or board, it is common to add mineral fillers to prevent the adhesive from soaking away from the glue surface. The adhesive may be made with different degrees of fluidity. Fluid types are required in operations in which the powders are dissolved in a central tank and then pumped to the individual application points. These adhesives must have little or no setback, as the glue is usually left in the pipe line over the weekend, and any material dissolved on Friday must be in good condition on the following Monday.

The manufacturing process has remained almost unaltered since the early 1920's. It consists essentially of preparing a liquid starch paste which is dried on steam-heated rolls. The dried flakes are ground to the required particle size for final packing. Drying rolls may either be single or double nip or doctor type, and the knife arrangement may be varied according to the design of the drums. The final particle size has to be kept within controlled limits. For many applications, it is essential to produce a coarse particle and to remove dust before packaging. Failure to do this results in lump formation when the consumer dissolves the product (see also this Volume, Chapt. XXII).

Consumers often demand cold-water-soluble starch adhesives which produce a water-resistant glue line. The necessary water-resistance is either "built-in" by the adhesive manufacturer, or resins, such as urea–formaldehyde, are added by the consumer. In the latter case, the starch formulation must have an accurately controlled pH, so that the resin can be properly cured in place. Cold-water-soluble starch adhesives are used for multi-wall paper sacks, laminated board, ice-proof bottle labeling, metal-to-foil laminations, dry distempers, and wallpaper printing. When redissolved, the modified starches are also good diluents for polyvinyl acetate emulsions and may be used to make convolute tubes and drinking cups.

VI. Degraded Starches

In the last 20 years, a unique method (NOREDUX process) has been widely used for making dextrins which comply with the high technical demands of the adhesive user (3). This process is characterized by the following sequential steps: commercial starch is dried under vacuum either with or without chemical reagents and catalysts while the temperature is raised continuously. The temperature may reach 200°, and conditions of high temperature and vacuum are maintained until the desired degree of conversion is reached. The material is then cooled with exclusion of oxygen. The absence of oxygen during the process excludes the risk of explosion. The products are of light color and homogeneous composition. All varieties of starch can be subjected to this process, and every desired degree of degradation or conversion can be obtained.

The following are typical examples: high-molecular-weight starches of slight degradation; soluble starches of medium or low viscosity, that is, products that have low cold-water solubility, but exhibit near-Newtonian properties in hot water; white dextrins of every desired viscosity and cold-water solubility; yellow dextrins of every desired viscosity and high cold-water solubility (greater than 95%); and all British gums.

The light color of concentrated dextrin solutions having low viscosities gives them wide utility. On the other hand, high viscosity solutions of high-molecular-weight dextrins are strongly adhesive and form very flexible films suitable for paper gumming, pasting, laminating, and labeling.

VII. Water-Resistant Starch Adhesives

Although starch films, particularly those from cold-water-soluble starches, swell readily in water, in actual use starch adhesives are found to be surprisingly water resistant. Bottle-labeling glues will withstand immersion in iced water for several days, and bill-posting pastes are subjected to all kinds of weather without failure.

For more rigorous demands, starch adhesives can be made more water resistant by addition of thermoplastic or thermosetting adhesives. If correctly made, root starch adhesives can be mixed in all proportions with many synthetic resin emulsions, particularly polyvinyl acetates or the acrylic types. The blends are stable and generally have properties that are intermediate between those of either component. The water resistance is, however, only moderate. For greater water resistance, it is essential to add thermosetting resins, such as urea–formaldehyde or resorcinol–formaldehyde. The basic starch adhesive must have an accurately controlled pH, to effect catalytic hardening of the resin. Proportions of starch to resin vary greatly, and no general indications can be given. A laboratory trial usually establishes the optimum ratio. Water resistance can be built in during the manufacture of cold-water-soluble starches by blending a suitable starch glue with urea and formaldehyde so that the dimethylol–urea precursor is formed during the drying operation.

Water-resistant adhesives for the manufacture of paper sacks and laminated board are often made by heating a mixture of starch, polyvinyl alcohol, and china clay. This operation is usually performed by the consumer.

A short review of the patent literature and the industrial practice in North America is given by Clark (4).

VIII. Additional Aspects of Starch Adhesives

1. Preservatives

All starch and dextrin adhesives must contain preservatives to prevent spoilage. Formaldehyde is most frequently used, but chlorinated hydrocarbons and phenyl mercurials are also often used. The end-use governs the choice of preservative, which is especially important in the manufacture of food containers.

2. De-foamers

Adhesives should not foam during use. Many de-foamers are available, such as silicone compounds, sulfonated castor oil, and a variety of proprietary compounds. Usually, the proper de-foamer is found by trial and error. Certain de-foamers may slowly hydrolyze in the adhesive, thus losing their efficiency.

3. Wetting Agents

While wetting agents are added to many starch and dextrin adhesives, their value is not fully established. They may also induce undesirable foaming.

4. Plasticizers

Plasticizers are added either to prevent films from becoming brittle or to retard the rate of drying. Many plasticizers therefore are humectants;

D-glucose, glycerol, and sorbitol are common examples. Miscible polyvinyl acetate acts as a plasticizer for starch and dextrin adhesives without being a humectant.

5. Mineral Fillers

Fillers may reduce the cost of adhesives, but they are more commonly used to overcome the problems associated with porous substrates. The filler forms a barrier across the substrate surface, so that the adhesive remains at the place of seal. Common fillers are china clay (Kaolin), lithopone, and titanium oxide. The last, although expensive, is sometimes added when no discoloration of the glue line can be tolerated. Amounts of fillers added may vary from 5 to 50% of the weight of starch or dextrin.

6. Starch Adhesives and the Law

Legal requirements for adhesives that are to be used in food packages vary widely from country to country. The United States Federal Register of July 27, 1962, expresses the most comprehensive regulations to date (5). The regulations concern "Components of adhesives" and "Food additives resulting from contact with containers or equipment and food additives otherwise affecting food." The regulations list approximately 680 adhesive components and includes an entry for starch and starch modified by one or more of certain treatments.

A summary of labeling requirements for food packaging adhesives in the United States has been published by the Adhesives Manufacturers' Association of America.

7. Packaging

Liquid adhesives are shipped either in bulk or in individual containers. Alkaline adhesive must not come into contact with sheet steel, but the containers should be coated or lined with resistant plastic materials such as polyethylene.

Adhesives in powder form may be shipped in paper or jute sacks. Many cold-water-soluble adhesive powders contain inorganic salts, hence their packages should possess a moisture-vapor barrier. Multi-wall paper sacks are adequate for most adhesives, but bitumen or polyethylene liners are advantageous for shipments in tropical climates.

IX. Physical and Chemical Tests

1. Physical Methods

a. *Viscosity*

Although a number of well-established methods and instruments are in constant use, there is little correlation among them. Older methods include outflow instruments such as Scott, Ford, and Stern viscometers, which are in wide use. The disadvantage of outflow cups is that the adhesive must be greatly diluted for measurement, and the viscosity at low solids content may have little relation to this property at its working consistency. Ferranti and Brookfield viscometers can measure viscosities up to very high values, but care has to be taken that thixotropy does not give false values. There is also the added difficulty with these electric instruments, that any one combination of cylinders and driving speed embraces only a narrow range, and that a change to the next combination often gives significantly different readings. Care must also be taken to measure the viscosity of an adhesive at the same stage in the life of an adhesive, since retrogradation may give completely erroneous readings. This point is not always appreciated by consumers, who do not always know the problems connected with setback. Many discussions between manufacturer and consumer could be avoided if the consumer were made aware of the nature of retrogradation and thixotropy.

b. *Solids Content*

This adhesive property may be measured with a refractometer. Many instruments are available, and most are sufficiently accurate to be of use to the manufacturer and consumer. Refractometers can be used for a starch or dextrin adhesive which does not contain other water-soluble substances, such as borax or salts. The presence of synthetic resin emulsions or mineral fillers renders refractometers useless for determination of the starch content. In such cases, oven drying must be used.

c. *pH*

Although for accurate measurement an electric pH meter would be used, there are many excellent indicator papers available, which give pH values of sufficient accuracy for everyday adhesive practice.

d. *Tack*

Oddly enough, the most important property of an adhesive, namely its ability to stick, cannot yet be measured scientifically. Many attempts have been made to evaluate "tack," but even the definition of this term has not been settled satisfactorily. Many adhesives' laboratories have developed their own methods, which usually cannot be repeated elsewhere and often bear little relation to experience on the factory floor. A number of instruments have been described; Green's tackmeter (6) measures the force required to lift a vertical "finger" out of a predetermined depth of adhesive. Banks and Mill (7) have used two smooth-ended brass cylinders separated by a thin film of adhesive. The uppermost cylinder is suspended from a spring and the lower one loaded with weights. The extension of the spring measures the force acting across the adhesive film.

2. Chemical Methods

Classic methods of organic and inorganic chemistry are commonly used for the analysis of vegetable adhesives. The committee ISO TC/93 of the International Standards Organisation examined in 1963 all known methods of starch analysis. The committee was particularly interested in a new method for determining starch in the presence of other carbohydrates which may be present. Starch is extracted from the adhesive with calcium chloride and precipitated with iodine. The starch obtained can be estimated by polarimetry or by hydrolysis and titration. Paper chromatography is of use for the determination of polyhydric alcohols, which are often present in adhesives as humectants.

X. TYPICAL APPLICATIONS

1. Manufacture of Multiwall Paper Sacks

The manufacture of paper sacks generally involves two operations. An open sack is produced first on a tubing and cross-pasting machine, and then one or both ends are sealed on the bottoming machine. The cross-pasting unit applies an intermittent line of glue to each ply of paper across the width of the reel; the paper then passes through another glue box supplying a continuous glue line to each ply to form the longitudinal seam.

The adhesive used for cross-pasting should be reasonably tacky and quick setting. Its water content should not exceed 80% at the time of use and should, preferably, be well below this amount to prevent weakening of the paper which results in breakages during subsequent maching operations. In normal practice, either a starch- or dextrin-based adhesive is used for the cross-pasting operation. In order to produce a quicker set, a mineral filler is often added. It is usual for these glues to have solids contents ranging from 25% to 33%. When formulating adhesives for cross-pasting, particular attention is given to the rate of penetration of the adhesive through the outer ply. If the glue tends to bleed through this ply, the sack tubes may stick to one another when stacked after leaving the machine.

The side seam adhesive may be a slow drying, highly diluted starch glue, provided that it possesses the necessary final bond strength. It is usual here to apply glues with solids contents of not more than 5%. The glue used on the seam should not splash in the glue box. Paper runs through the cross-pasting and side-seam machine at speeds of about 200 meters per minute, producing 200 sack tubes per minute. At such speeds, the glue is subject to heavy mechanical agitation and may easily be thrown about the machine.

There are two types of bottoming units. On the old type, a heavy paste is fed to the paper through a glue box with an aperture at the bottom, which allows sufficient paste to be coated on the paper passing underneath. On the modern rotary machines, glue rollers, working from a glue box, transfer a line of fluid glue to the paper. These glues have a starch base with a solid content of about 20%. For the older type machines, a wheat starch, which forms a thick paste that will flow readily from the glue box, is recommended. Potato, tapioca or thin-boiling corn starches are required for the modern, fluid adhesives.

On some machines, a strip of paper is glued over the formed bottom to produce a capped sack. On these machines, both bottoming and capping glues should have a fairly high initial tack and dry reasonably quickly.

In many cases, the paper is treated with a thermosetting synthetic resin to increase the wet strength. Here, the final glue line of the formed sack should also have good resistance to water. For the seam and bottom station, it is common to use starch glues which have a pH of 6–8 and to which a synthetic resin, such as urea–formaldehyde, is added. It is advisable to add a catalyst to promote hardening of the resin, in which case the entire glue mix will have to be used within a limited period. Sacks made in this way are very resistant to weather. The pH of the starch is important even if no resin is added. In many cases, the paper is printed or coated with dyes that are sensitive to changes of pH. Since Kraft sack paper is usually slightly acidic, starch glues should not be strongly alkaline if discoloration is to be avoided.

In North America, corn starch is used as a specially modified thin-boiling type, partially hydrolyzed to lower its viscosity and to obtain the fast initial tack required for seam paste. For high speed machines, white, low-soluble dextrins are necessary. To obtain water resistance, urea–formaldehyde is added during the preparation of the adhesive. Again, the pH of the adhesives is extremely critical. It must be slightly acidic, but not to the extent that pot life is shortened (8).

In Europe, all requirements of fast, modern machines are met by starch adhesive powders which are based on potato, tapioca, or waxy starches, and which dissolve very rapidly in cold water, giving fluid, stable glues. Some of these products have water resistance "built-in" by the addition of dry urea–formaldehyde resin. Resins are also added to the mix in the consumer's plant, and, as the solution is not heated again, the pH is not as critical as for hot-water-soluble powders.

Cold-water-soluble starch adhesives are sufficiently tacky for bag seam application. In fact, one product will serve all three paste applications.

The covering capacities of various typical glues are given in the following tabulation:

Tubing operation	350 g. (on dry basis) per 1000 4-ply sacks
Bottoming operation	40 g. (on dry basis) per 1000 4-ply sacks
Cross-pasting operation	1000 g. (on dry basis) per 1000 4-ply sacks

2. Manufacture of Corrugated Board

Although in the United States approximately 80% of the corrugated board is made with starch adhesives, sodium silicate has been the adhesive of choice in Europe. In the last few years, however, most European converters have realized the advantages of starch adhesives. The principal adhesive consists of raw ungelatinized corn starch suspended in a diluted corn starch paste. Borax and sodium hydroxide are usually added to increase the adhesive strength and tack and to lower the gelatinization temperature. By varying the ratio of gelatinized to raw starch, one can obtain a desired viscosity. Viscosity must be adjusted to supply an adequate amount of adhesive at all machine speeds. This is of particular importance with the older types of corrugating equipment.

Corrugating adhesives do not develop their adhesive properties until they come into contact with the heated fluting rolls, whereupon the starch gelatinizes instantaneously and a strong bond is obtained between the layers of paper. The water content of the adhesive is adjusted so that an extremely tacky adhesive is obtained immediately after gelatinization. This implies that sufficient water is present for complete gelatinization. The adhesive must be so designed that immediate tack is obtained at 60°–70°, and best results are achieved at a starch concentration of 21–22%. Although corn starch is considered to be the best raw material for the manufacture of corrugated board, milo or wheat starches may also be used.

The demand for waterproof board has grown since World War II. Urea–formaldehyde–starch adhesives cannot be used under alkaline conditions, and, at acid pH, the operating efficiency is reduced. The board must be "aged" to attain maximum water resistance, and the use of an acid-curing urea-formaldehyde resin frequently causes a pungent odor. Resorcinol-based, alkaline-curing, waterproof starch adhesives are preferred because they give an excellent water-resistant bond and permit machine speeds of up to 500 feet per minute. The adhesive consists of resorcinol and a specially modified corn starch. It is designed to be used as the carrier portion of the corrugating adhesive, with an unmodified starch and formaldehyde in the uncooked portion. The method of preparation is thus basically the same as that for non-waterproof adhesives. The resorcinol–formaldehyde starch combination gives the board sufficient waterproofness to withstand immersion in water up to 24 hours without delamination (9).

3. Manufacture of Laminated Fiberboard

Many boxes and shipping cartons today are made of solid fiberboard. Two or more plies of heavy Kraft or jute paper board may be laminated into a solid board of suitable thickness. Modern machines will combine up to seven plies into a single board in one operation. For some types of boxes, a lightweight sheet such as aluminum foil, coated paper, or glassine is laminated to one or both surfaces of the paperboard. Different types of starch and dextrin are used to meet the various adhesive requirements. Highly effective adhesives for water-resistant board are made from cold-water-soluble starches to which urea–formaldehyde may be added. From 5 to 25% resin, based on the weight of starch, may be used according to the water-resistance required and economic factors involved. Some starch adhesives are so designed that no additional hardener is required. Using such adhesives, it is possible to obtain laminated fiberboard which will withstand immersion in water for several days without delamination. In the United States, it is common to use acid-treated starches and high-viscosity dextrins in conjunction with resins for water-resistant fiberboard. In cases in which there are no requirements for water resistance, dextrins modified to an intermediate degree are often used. Pastes are prepared having from 25 to 40% solids, depending upon the viscosity required for the particular board or method of application. Solids should be at a minimum since too much moisture in the board may cause curling or shrinking.

4. Metal Foil Lining

Aluminum foil is laminated to paper by means of lining machines which are operated similarly to ordinary board lining machines. In a number of cases, the glues employed are based on potato or tapioca starch and are of a fluid consistency at room temperature. Solids content is usually about 20%, and the pH varies from 7.5 to 12. Glues of high alkalinity are often required if the foil is improperly annealed and is, therefore, coated with a thin film of grease from the rolling process. In spite of the fact that aluminum is strongly attacked by alkalies, glues of high pH may be employed if the subsequent drying is rapid. These glues produce good foil-to-paper bonds. Heat resistance is excellent, but delamination in cold water is fairly rapid. The water resistance of the glue line may be enhanced by the addition of resins, such as polyvinyl acetate.

Dextrins are rarely used because of their relatively poor adhesion to metallic surfaces and high chloride content.

For cigarette packaging, a foil lined with tissue paper is often used. This laminate is usually made by applying thin parallel lines of a plasticized starch glue to the foil.

A full discussion of the prevention of corrosion likely to be caused by foil-lining adhesives has been published by Angel (*10*).

5. Starch Adhesives—Wallpaper Making

Wallpapers are made by printing a single or duplexed paper with a pigment which contains starch adhesive as binder. The duplexing operation produces a two-ply laminate, the purpose of which is not only to produce a stronger paper, but also to act as a moisture barrier during the hanging procedure. Adhesives for duplexing are commonly neutral starch adhesives to which a small proportion of urea–formaldehyde is added. The next process, "grounding," is a coating process using a single color pigment bound with a starch glue. The actual wallpaper pattern is printed on top of this "ground." Pigments are thoroughly mixed with starch adhesives for printing. Washable wallpapers can be made either by coating a printed paper with a synthetic resin or by printing with a casein binder. Wallpapers are hung by means of thick pastes, often made from wheat starch, although cellulose derivatives may be used. Paste consistency must allow the paper to be slipped into place but yet hold it against the wall surface. Flock papers are made by printing the desired pattern with an "ink" that contains a starch adhesive, applying flock material, and erecting the tiny strands electrostatically.

Slightly alkaline starch adhesives are frequently used for mica and bronze printing on wallpapers. Starch adhesives are good for bonding mica because they do not impair its natural sheen. "Plastic" wallpapers are those in which small mounds of material are deposited in discrete spots on top of the paper. This effect is achieved by mixing china clay with a starch adhesive, which gives rigidity to the mounds.

6. Bottle Labeling

Although normal bottle labeling adhesives are usually based on dextrin, starch adhesives may be used when temporary resistance to water is required but subsequent easy removal of the label is desired in the bottle cleaning operation. Here starch adhesives at 40–50% solids content are common. To avoid staining of the label and corrosion of machine parts, the pH should be between 6 and 9 and the salt content should be minimum. These adhesives are extremely tacky and are useful in most modern machines with a horizontal glue box. Starch adhesives for bottle labeling permit high machine speeds, are easy to handle, and clean in use. Liquid starch adhesives find some application here, but cold-water-soluble powders are more common.

7. Billposting Adhesives

Billposting adhesives must be carefully formulated so as not to damage the poster or the poster mounting. They must be able to bind paper to hardboard, galvanized zinc, or aluminum. They must allow the poster to slip into place and then form a hard, weather-resistant bond. Good poster adhesives are usually fluid potato starch–salt conversions, of syrupy consistency, which are diluted 6–7 times before use. Corn starch based adhesives are also used, but these tend to be more pasty and less fluid than glues from tuber starches and do not allow the poster to "slip" as freely.

XI. STARCH ADHESIVES: PAST, PRESENT, AND FUTURE

Before the advent of synthetic resins, adhesives for industry were based on vegetable or animal sources or sodium silicate. In the last 15 years, resin emulsions, particularly polyvinyl acetate, have largely displaced animal glues and to some extent starch and dextrin adhesives. Although in the United States this displacement has made more rapid progress than elsewhere, starch and dextrin adhesives still have 60% of the total adhesive market. In Europe, where manufacturers of starch adhesives produce a much greater range of products, the proportion of vegetable adhesives is probably higher. Synthetic resin emulsions are not perfect and their residual odor and tendency for plasticizer migration make them unsuitable for some applications. In some instances, polyvinyl acetates are blended with a suitable starch glue. This practice has increased the tonnage of starch adhesives in many places, and it is probable that a large proportion of synthetic resin adhesive formulations sold today contain starch.

XII. REFERENCES

(1) H. W. Leach, *Adhesives Age*, **5**, No. 9, 20 (1962).
(2) E. F. W. Dux, *Staerke*, **6**, 90 (1954).
(3) M. A. Staerkle and E. Meier, *U.S. Patent* 2,698,818 (1955); *Chem. Abstr.*, **49**, 4314 (1955); M. A. Staerkle, E. Meier, and C. Christoffel, *U.S. Patent* 2,698,937 (1955); *Chem. Abstr.*, **49**, 4315 (1955); Blattmann & Co., *Swiss Patent* 259,428 (1949); *Chem. Abstr.*, **51**, 4036 (1957); Blattmann & Co., *Swiss Patent* 289,057 (1953); *Chem. Abstr.*, **48**, 10366 (1954).
(4) R. G. Clark, *Can. Pulp Paper Ind.*, **14**, No. 4, 88 (1961).
(5) Anon., *Federal Register*, **27**, No. 145, 7375 (July 27, 1962).
(6) H. Green, *Ind. Eng. Chem., Anal. Ed.*, **13**, 632 (1941).
(7) W. H. Banks and C. C. Mill, *J. Colloid Sci.*, **8**, 137 (1953).
(8) W. J. Macey and E. H. Hill, *Adhesives Age*, **3**, No. 10, 28 (1960).
(9) J. R. Easterly and R. J. Meador, *Adhesives Age*, **5**, No. 10, 26 (1962).
(10) T. H. Angel, *Paper Box Bag Maker (London)*, 214 (1956).

CHAPTER XXIV

PRODUCTION AND USE OF DEXTROSE

By E. R. Kooi and F. C. Armbruster

George M. Moffett Technical Center, Corn Products Co., Argo, Illinois

I. Introduction

Dextrose is the trivial name applied to α-D-glucopyranose. The trivial name is used almost exclusively in the industry to distinguish the compound from "glucose," the name often applied to starch derived syrups. Since starch is composed of D-glucose units, dextrose is the ultimate product of nondestructive starch hydrolysis. The history of the dextrose industry is closely associated with that of the starch industry. These relations have been described by Bode in Volume I, Chapter II.

Dextrose occurs in the unpolymerized state in honey, fruits, and berries. The first partially successful attempt at a commercial process for recovery of crystalline dextrose was carried out by J. L. Proust and involved its recovery from grapes (*1*). However, the present starch hydrolyzate industry undoubtedly had its beginning from the work of Kirchoff in 1811 (*2*). The three types of product obtained by Kirchoff by subjecting potato starch to hydrolysis with sulfuric acid, syrup, solidified hydrolyzate, and dextrose crystals separated from the syrup, are still commerical products in the form of starch syrup, crude corn sugars, and crystalline dextrose.

Until 1920, little success was achieved in the commercial production of crystalline dextrose. Many attempts were made, but these attempts involved crystallization of the anhydrous form of the sugar, and repeated crystallization or crystallization from nonaqueous solvents was required to achieve sufficient purification. The only crystalline material produced in substantial quantity was a solidified product containing both crystals and mother liquor.

It was not until 1920 to 1922 that a process was devised by which successive crops of crystalline dextrose were obtained by crystallization of the monohydrate form. This process, developed by W. B. Newkirk (3), introduced the concept of conducting the crystallization at a controlled rate in the presence of substantial amounts of seed crystals, and the production of crystalline dextrose became an industrial reality. Today, crystalline dextrose production is approximately one billion pounds annually.

II. PHYSICAL PROPERTIES

D-Glucose occurs in three crystalline forms, α-D-glucopyranose, α-D-glucopyranose monohydrate, and β-D-glucopyranose. Selected properties of the three forms are shown in Table I.

Table I

Physical Properties of D-Glucose

	α-D-*Glucose*	α-D-*Glucose* hydrate	β-D-*Glucose*
Formula	$C_6H_{12}O_6$	$C_6H_{12}O_6 \cdot H_2O$	$C_6H_{12}O_6$
Melting point	146°	83°	150°
Solubility (25°), % by wt.	62	30.2[a]	72
$[\alpha]^{20}$D	112.2° → 52.7°	112.2° → 52.7°	18.7° → 52.7°
Heat of solution (25°), cal./g.	−14.2	−25.2	−6.2

[a] Anhydrous basis.

D-Glucose in solutions, glasses, and melts exhibits mutarotation to the equilibrium mixture containing about 62% of the β-D-form. The solubility of the equilibrium mixture at 25° is 51.2% by weight. Solubility behavior of the crystalline forms is thus influenced by initial solubility as well as by the rate of mutarotation and the stability of the specific crystalline phase.

At 25°, anhydrous α-D-glucose dissolves rapidly to a concentration approaching 62%. However, because the monohydrate is the stable crystalline phase at this temperature, crystallization of the monohydrate immediately occurs and the concentration of the solution phase drops to about 30%. As mutarotation occurs, the concentration of the solution raises slowly to 51%, the solubility of the equilibrium mixture. The monohydrate dissolves at 25° to a concentration of 30%, then increases slowly to 51% as mutarotation occurs. Thus, the rate of attainment of saturated equilibrium solutions of the α-D forms of crystalline dextrose is influenced by temperature not only because of the increase in solubility with temperature, but also because of the increase in the rate of mutarotation with temperature.

β-D-Glucose, on the other hand, dissolves immediately to form a permanently clear 50% solution at 25°, but crystallization of the α-D hydrate will occur if the amount of β-D-glucose added exceeds 51.2%. Data on the solubility of the three crystalline forms before mutarotation and in the metastable regions have been given by Jackson and Silsbee (4) and Young (5).

The different crystalline forms of glucose differ in hygroscopic properties. The β-D form, in particular, is sensitive to exposure to humid atmosphere, and the presence of as little as a few tenths per cent moisture results in conversion to the α-D form. At 25°, anhydrous α-D-glucose will remain in the anhydrous state up to about 80% relative humidity (R.H.), but will shift to the monohydrate at 85–89% R.H., and will absorb more than the monohydrate moisture above 90% R.H. (6).

III. Production by Acid Hydrolysis

All commerical dextrose produced today is obtained by the hydrolysis of starch. In the United States, corn starch is the major source of dextrose, although a substantial amount is also produced from grain sorghum starch. Corn starch and potato starch are used in Europe, and white sweet potato starch in Japan. Prior to 1960, all commercial dextrose was produced by acid hydrolysis of starch. The process of acid hydrolysis has been amply described by Newkirk (7), Rogge (8), Kerr (9), and Dean and Gottfried (10).

In the period since 1960, following the discovery that high yields of dextrose could be obtained at practical starch concentrations by enzymic hydrolysis provided that transglucosylase activity was removed from the enzyme preparation (11), substantially all dextrose plants have been converted to enzymic hydrolysis as a means of converting starch to dextrose. Since the only primary difference between the acid process for dextrose production and an enzymic process lies in the use of an enzyme preparation in the place of acid to hydrolyze the starch, processing steps common to both are described in the next section.

IV. Production by Enzymic Hydrolysis[1]

The process of converting starch to dextrose may be divided into the steps of hydrolysis, refining, concentration, and crystallization. Only the

[1] For a discussion of enzyme nomenclature and mode of action, see Volume I, Chapter VII.

hydrolysis step has changed appreciably since previous descriptions of the process (7–10). Therefore, the nature of the enzymes, sources and methods of production of the enzymes, and the conversion processes are described in the greatest detail.

1. Mode of Action of Glucogenic Enzymes

As early as 1881 (12), it was recognized that dextrose could be produced in substantial quantities as the result of fungal amylase action on starch. Early investigators, equating fungal enzymes with diastatic enzymes of cereal grains, assumed that dextrose was produced as a result of maltose hydrolysis, and that the amount of dextrose formed was a function of the maltase activity. Kita, in 1913 (13), is generally credited as being the first to recognize that maltose was not an essential intermediate product in the hydrolysis of starch to dextrose, but that certain fungal amylase preparations could hydrolyze starch directly to dextrose. Besides being referred to as maltase in the literature, the enzyme responsible for the direct conversion of starch to dextrose has been called glucogenic activity (14), γ-amylase (15), glucoamylase (16), and amyloglucosidase (17); the preferred trivial name is glucoamylase (EC 3.2.1.3) (18). The recent progress that has been made in glucoamylase technology is aptly reflected in the fact that today practically all commercial dextrose is produced by the enzymic hydrolysis of starch, whereas prior to about 1960, acid hydrolysis was used exclusively.

Glucoamylase effects the hydrolysis of starch by progressively splitting off single dextrose units from the nonreducing ends of starch molecules (6, 17, 19). Since glucoamylase is capable of hydrolyzing α-D-(1→6)-linked branchpoints in addition to the predominating α-D-(1→4) linkages, essentially complete hydrolysis of starch and starch hydrolyzates is effected, and dextrose may be obtained in nearly quantitative yields. Pertinent studies concerning the purification of glucoamylase and its mode of action and substrate specificities include those of Pazur's group (19–22) and others (23–25).

Dextrose may also be produced in starch hydrolyzates by the combined action of maltase and α-amylase or β-amylase. In hydrolyses of this type, maltose is an essential intermediate product, produced by the action of α- or β-amylase, and is subsequently hydrolyzed to dextrose by the maltase activity present. Although hydrolyzates containing substantial quantities of dextrose may be produced in this manner, the enzyme systems employed in the commercial production of dextrose are usually those containing primarily glucoamylase activity.

The fact that glucoamylase can hydrolyze maltose, although less rapidly than higher saccharides (25), often makes it difficult to distinguish in the literature between glucoamylase, which is capable of effecting the hydrolysis of starch and higher saccharides, and maltase, which is not. One reason for this is that glucoamylase activity is commonly measured by maltose hydrolysis. Therefore, the terms glucoamylase and maltase often refer in the literature to the same enzyme (14).

2. Commercial Sources of Glucoamylase

Several microorganisms produce glucoamylase activity when grown under suitable conditions on appropriate media. Microorganisms which are reported to produce glucoamylase, or a glucoamylase-like enzyme, include many species of *Rhizopus*, such as *R. delemar*, *R. javanicus*, and *R. niveus*, several strains of the *Aspergillus niger* group, *Aspergillus oryzae*, *Mucor sp.*, *Endomyces sp.* (26), *Endomycopsis fibuliger* (27), *Saccharomyces diastaticus* (28), and *Clostridium acetobutylicum* (29). Le Mense and co-workers (30) screened more than 350 fungi grown under submerged culture conditions for starch hydrolyzing enzyme activity.

Table II
Characteristics of Commercial Glucoamylase Preparations

| | Optimum use conditions | | Contaminating carbohydrases[a] | |
| | | | | |
Microbial source	Temperature	pH	α-Amylase	Trans-glucosylase
Aspergillus niger group	55°–60°	3.5–5.0	+	+
Rhizopus sp. (31)	50°–55°	4.5–5.5	+	0
Endomyces sp. (32)	50°	4.8–5.0	0 (33)	0
Aspergillus oryzae	50°–55°	4.5–5.5	++	+

[a] Present in readily detectable amount; ++ present as major contributing activity; 0 not readily detectable.

Selected strains of *A. niger*, *Rhizopus*, *Endomyces*, and *A. oryzae* are employed in the commercial production of glucoamylase. *Rhizopus* and *A. oryzae* strains are commonly cultivated on semi-solid media by the mold bran process, whereas the glucoamylases of *A. niger* and *Endomyces* are generally produced under conditions of submerged culture fermentation. These enzymes accumulate extracellularly in the culture medium during and immediately following growth of the organisms. Besides being similar in mode of action, the glucoamylases of commerce also possess similar temperature and pH optima (Table II); however, the glucoamylase of *A. niger* is slightly more thermostable and aciduric, and that of *Endomyces* is slightly less thermostable than the others. While slight differences in pH optima are of minor importance in the production of dextrose enzymically, the temperature at which the conversion is performed is fairly critical. Microbial growth and contamination of the conversion liquors represent a potential problem when conversions are conducted at temperatures below about 55°; therefore, it is a distinct advantage to operate above 55° if practicable. Glucoamylase preparations derived from *A. niger* strains are most commonly used in this country for enzymic dextrose production, while those derived from *Rhizopus* are most commonly used in Japan (*34*). The *Endomyces* enzyme was developed only recently by Hattori in Japan (*26, 33*). *Aspergillus oryzae* enzymes are not used primarily for dextrose production, but are widely used in production of syrups of high maltose and dextrose content.

Commercially available glucoamylase preparations are usually comprised of several enzymes in addition to the predominating glucoamylase. Besides such enzymes as proteinases, cellulases, and the like, which are not of recognized significance in the hydrolysis of starch, other enzymes such as α-amylase and transglucosylase are frequently present in sufficient quantities to exert a pronounced effect on starch hydrolysis. Transglucosylase (*35, 36*), which is also referred to as transglycosidase or transglucosidase in the literature, catalyzes the synthesis, particularly from maltose, of unfermentable oligosaccharides containing α-D-(1$\rightarrow$6)- linkages. These unfermentable sugars are not readily hydrolyzed to dextrose by glucoamylase, a factor which leads to substantially reduced dextrose yields if glucoamylase preparations containing significant amounts of transglucosylase are used for starch hydrolysis. Therefore, for maximum yields of dextrose, it is essential to employ glucoamylase preparations that are devoid of transglucosylase. The α-amylase present in glucoamylase preparations is considered to assist in the conversion of starch to dextrose (*37*) by randomly hydrolyzing the large dextrose polymers to smaller molecules, thereby furnishing glucoamylase with readily available substrate. Although the culture strain used for enzyme production is an important determining factor, transglucosylase is normally present in glucoamylase preparations derived from *Aspergillus* but not those derived from *Rhizopus* or *Endomyces* (Table I). Alpha-amylase is generally present except apparently in the case of *Endomyces* preparations.

To complicate the enzyme composition picture further, the glucoamylase enzyme in at least some preparations has been found to be heterogeneous in nature. Pazur and Ando (*19*) have shown that the glucoamylase of *A. niger* is comprised of two distinct isozymes which possess different mobilities upon paper electrophoresis and different temperature stabilities at elevated temperatures. Pazur and co-workers

(*38*) have shown that *A. niger* glucoamylase is a glycoprotein and that the carbohydrate portion of each of the isozymes differs in composition. They offer this as a possible explanation for the observed differences between the two isozymes. Presumably the action of the isozymes is indistinguishable in the conversion of starch to dextrose.

3. Production of Glucoamylase

Glucoamylase is produced by submerged culture fermentation in a manner similar to that described in 1948 by Le Mense and Van Lanen (*39*). By this procedure a fermentor containing sterile culture medium is aseptically inoculated with an actively growing liquid culture of the desired strain of enzyme producing organism. The inoculated medium is vigorously aerated and agitated and maintained at the desired temperature as microbial growth and enzyme production proceed. Incubation continues until the maximum yield of enzyme is attained, at which time the microorganisms and other insolubles present in the medium are removed by filtration or centrifugation and the glucogenic enzymes are recovered in the filtrate. The enzymes may be used in the form of culture filtrate for the conversion of starch to dextrose, or they may be further concentrated or purified if desired. Culture liquors containing substantial amounts of transglucosylase are frequently refined at this time to reduce the level of transglucosylase present.

The fermentation medium of Le Mense and Van Lanen (*39*) for the cultivation of *Aspergillus* strains contained thin stillage, ground corn, and calcium carbonate. Eliminating the calcium carbonate and increasing the level of ground corn resulted in improved yields of saccharifying enzyme (*40*). Production media containing 14% to 20% ground corn are among those presently used with *Aspergillus* strains for glucoamylase production (*11, 41, 42*). The development of media and fermentation conditions for the production of glucoamylase by *Aspergillus* strains has been examined (*43–45*). The results of similar investigations pertaining to *Endomyces sp.* are reported by Yamamoto, Hattori and Takatsu (*46*).

The particular strain of microorganism used for production determines, to a large extent, the enzyme yield obtainable. In their early screening program, Le Mense and co-workers (*30*) found that of over 350 fungi including 278 *Aspergilli*, *A. niger* NRRL 330 was the most active saccharifying enzyme producer. Now available are selected strains of the *A. niger* group which, when grown under identical culturing conditions, produce two to four times the amount of glucoamylase produced by *A. niger* NRRL 330 or NRRL 337 (*41, 42*). These potent enzyme producing cultures, of which at least one is an ultraviolet-induced mutant, possess the additional advantage of producing substantially less transglucosylase per unit of glucoamylase than the previously available *Aspergillus* cultures.

A process similar to that described by Underkofler and co-workers (47) is employed to produce mold amylases on semi-solid media by the mold bran process. The medium of choice, which usually consists of moistened, cooked, sterilized wheat or rice bran, is aseptically inoculated with a spore culture of the enzyme-producing strain of *Rhizopus* or *A. oryzae*, and the inoculated medium is incubated in shallow trays in a ventilated chamber under carefully controlled conditions of temperature and humidity. After completion of growth and enzyme production, the moist bran is dried and ground and is ready for use. Enzyme concentrates are prepared by extracting the bran cultures with water and then evaporating the extracts or precipitating the enzymes contained therein.

The importance of using glucoamylase preparations that are devoid of transglucosylase is reflected in the fact that a failure to do so can result in a 5% to 10% reduction in the yield of dextrose obtainable upon starch enzymolysis. This loss in yield is compounded when pure crystallized dextrose is the desired product, for the amount of non-dextrose carbohydate present in the conversion hydrolyzate reduces by a like amount the quantity of dextrose that can be economically recovered by crystallization techniques. Thus, the 5% to 10% loss in dextrose yield in the hydrolyzate amounts to a 10% to 20% loss upon crystallization. As a result, efficient and economical procedures for removing transglucosylase from glucoamylase preparations have proven to be of great value to dextrose producers. By the procedure of Kooi and co-workers (11), the transglucosylase present in culture liquor is effectively and selectively adsorbed onto a suitable clay mineral, such as bentonite, and simply removed by filtration. Processes have also been patented for transglucosylase removal by the employment of synthetic magnesium silicates (48), lignin or tannic acid (49), surface active agents (50), and magnesium oxide (51).

4. Enzymic Starch Conversion Processes

The problem of producing dextrose by acid hydrolysis is that considerable quantities of by-products are formed during conversion because of the lack of specificity of the hydrolyzing agent. These by-products, which detract from the yield of dextrose and increase the amount of refining required to produce good quality dextrose from the hydrolyzate, are formed to a much lesser extent during enzymic hydrolysis. Although the cost of suitable enzymes remained prohibitive until recently, the advantages of the enzymic route were recognized by

Langlois (52), who disclosed a process for producing solidified enzyme hydrolyzates containing up to 90% dextrose (dry basis) and by Wallerstein (53), who described a process for the manufacture of crystalline dextrose. Additional patents (54–56) have been issued since the production of dextrose by enzymolysis became economically feasible. From these patents and other accounts (31, 34, 57–59), a clear picture of current commercial enzymic processes for dextrose production may be obtained.

Before starch can be effectively converted by glucoamylase, it must first be gelatinized and thinned. This is accomplished by heating the starch in a water slurry above the gelatinization temperature of the starch and then partially hydrolyzing the solubilized starch with either acid or α-amylase. The object of this pretreatment is to reduce the starch to a manageable, essentially completely soluble and non-retrogradable form. Whether acid or α-amylase is employed in the thinning step distinguishes between acid–enzyme and enzyme–enzyme, or dual enzyme, dextrose processes.

Factors which affect the efficiency of the enzymic conversion of starch include starch concentration, type and extent of thinning, temperature, pH and time of saccharification, and the amount of saccharifying enzyme employed. In general, low substrate concentrations are converted more efficiently than high substrate concentrations, particularly those above about 40% dry substance. The more extensively starch is thinned prior to glucoamylase conversion, at least if acid-thinning is employed, the less efficiently it is converted to dextrose. For efficient enzyme utilization, it is necessary to conduct the conversions within the optimum temperature and pH ranges of the enzyme employed; and within limits, the more enzyme used, the less time is required to reach maximum dextrose yields. In practice, conversions are usually conducted at 55°–60° at starch concentrations of 30–40% by weight with sufficient glucoamylase to give a maximum dextrose yield within 24 to 96 hours.

In the acid–enzyme process, starch is thinned under conditions of heat and pressure to a dextrose equivalent (D.E.) value (reducing sugar content, calculated as dextrose on a dry substance basis) of 15 to 20. The thinned starch is cooled and neutralized to pH 4.0–5.5 depending upon the glucoamylase preparation to be employed, and transferred to the enzyme convertor, which consists of a large, agitated, thermo-regulated tank. The desired amount of glucoamylase is added and saccharification proceeds until conversion is completed, at which time the saccharified hydrolyzate is filtered and processed further. The maximum conversion attainable in the acid–enzyme process is usually about 95–96 D.E., which amounts to a 92–94% yield of dextrose. As shown in Table

III, this represents a substantial improvement over the conversion efficiency of the classic acid process, both from the standpoint of dextrose yield and lack of formation of color and carbohydrate breakdown products, such as 5-hydroxymethylfurfural (HMF).

Table III
Analysis of Dextrose Process Samples[a]

	Filtered hydrolyzate		
	Acid process	Acid–enzyme process	Enzyme–enzyme process
D.E.	91	95	98
Dextrose, % dry basis	86	93	97
Ash, % dry basis	1.6	0.4	0.1
Protein, % dry basis	0.08	0.08	0.10
HMF, % dry basis	0.30	0.008	0.003
Color at 2°Baumé	10.0	0.3	0.2

	Sugar		
	Acid process	Acid–enzyme process	Enzyme–enzyme process
D.E.	99.7	99.9	99.9
Dextrose, % dry basis	99.4	99.7	99.8
Color at 17.5°Baumé	1.1	0.6	0.3
Ash, % dry basis	0.07	0.02	0.01

[a] As obtained in laboratory equipment.

Various procedures have been described for enzymically thinning starch for the enzyme–enzyme process (*31, 58–62*). By the usual procedure, thinning is accomplished using bacterial α-amylase preparations derived from selected strains of *Bacillus subtilis*. The thinning is usually effected at pH 5.5–7.0 at 80°–90°, although higher temperatures may be used (*60*) if sufficient enzyme is employed or if a lesser degree of hydrolysis is wanted. The time required is usually an hour or less, since the enzyme, despite its remarkable heat stability, is nevertheless inactivated upon prolonged holding at the high temperature used. Therefore, the amount of enzyme used is determined by the temperature and time cycles of the thinning procedure as well as by the degree of hydrolysis desired, which is usually in the range of 10 to 20 D.E.

A major difficulty experienced with enzyme-thinned hydrolyzates is that they frequently fail to filter at appreciable rates because of the presence of relatively small quantities of retrograded starch (often only

1% to 2% of the starch solids present). This filtration problem is reported to be minimized by the use of an efficient thinning procedure and by the addition of small amounts of calcium and sodium salts which promote enzyme thermostability during thinning (*61*) as well as by boiling or autoclaving the thinned starch prior to saccharification to resolubilize the insoluble portion (*31, 62*).

After thinning, the starch is cooled and the pH is readjusted if necessary. The thinned starch is then saccharified and processed as in the acid–enzyme process. In the enzyme–enzyme process, D.E. values of 98–99 and dextrose yields of about 97% are regularly attained (Table III).

It has been shown, since the advent of commercial enzyme dextrose processes, that glucoamylase is able to polymerize dextrose (*61, 63, 64*). The result of this synthesis is the formation from dextrose of predominantly α-D-($1\rightarrow6$)-linked oligosaccharides, particularly isomaltose and isomaltotriose. This polymerizing reaction, the rate and extent of which is affected by both dextrose and glucoamylase concentrations, possibly explains why starch is not converted quantitatively to dextrose in the enzyme–enzyme process. On the other hand, the formation of acid reversion products during acid-thinning is probably the major cause for the lower dextrose yields in the acid–enzyme process.

5. Refining and Crystallization

After completion of the hydrolysis, the dextrose-containing liquor is filtered and treated with powdered carbon, granular carbon, or ion-exchange resins to remove color, ash, and other minor impurities. The decolorized liquor is then evaporated to 50–55% solids in triple effect evaporators. The liquor may be given a second carbon treatment at this point to remove color formed during evaporation.

In the production of α-D-glucose monohydrate, the solution is evaporated under vacuum to 70–78% solids, cooled to about 46°, and fed to 10,000-gallon crystallizers. The most common form of crystallizer is a horizontal cylindrical tank fitted with a cooling jacket and slowly rotating cooling coils. About 20–25% of a previous batch is retained in the crystallizer to provide a seed bed. After mixing, the temperature is about 43°. The mass is then cooled slowly according to a preset schedule to about 20–30° over a period of 3 to 5 days, at the end of which about 60% of the solids are crystallized as α-D-glucose monohydrate. The actual temperatures, times, and solids concentrations are carefully adjusted according to the dextrose content of the hydrolyzate and the amount of crystallization equipment available.

The magma is then fed to large centrifuge baskets lined with perforated screens. Spinning separates most of the mother liquor, which passes through the screen. While still spinning, the cake is washed with a spray of water to displace the residual mother liquor.

The wet sugar will contain about 14% moisture, including hydrate moisture. After removal from the centrifuge basket, it is dried in large rotary dryers in a stream of warm air until it reaches a moisture content of about 8.5%. Drying to a moisture content slightly less than the theoretical 9.1% for dextrose monohydrate reduces the tendency of the material to cake under adverse storage conditions.

The mother liquor is refined and decolorized as described above, and it is either evaporated and crystallized to recover a second crop of crystals, or it may be partially recycled to the initial crystallization step to recover the total product as a single crop of crystals. Generally, the recovery of good quality dextrose requires that the dextrose content of the massecuite be above about 85%, dry basis.

The yield of crystalline dextrose of adequate quality is dependent on the dextrose content of the hydrolyzate and the extent of refining employed. Under commercial conditions, it is usually practical to crystallize to a mother liquor dextrose content of about 60%, dry basis. Thus, the yield of dextrose obtainable from a hydrolyzate of given dextrose content is:

$$Y = 2.5D - 150$$

where Y is the yield of dextrose (anhydrous basis) as percentage of total hydrolyzate solids and D is the dextrose content of the hydrolyzate, per cent dry basis.

For hydrolyzates with very high dextrose content, that is, above 97%, minor impurities such as inorganic constituents, protein, and color become highly concentrated in the mother liquor, necessitating their removal by special techniques such as ion exchange in order to maintain the quality of the last crops of dextrose. In addition to dextrose, the final mother liquor from an enzyme process contains primarily α-D-$(1{\rightarrow}6)$-linked glucose polymers. These may originate from transglucosylase action, from polymerization of dextrose by glucoamylase, or from original α-D-$(1{\rightarrow}6)$ linkages in the starch itself. The major nondextrose constituent is isomaltose, with maltose, panose, and higher saccharides being present in varying quantities.

Recrystallized dextrose hydrate, marketed as a USP grade for therapeutic purposes, such as intravenous injection, is produced by redissolving the wet centrifuge cake and recrystallizing in the manner described above.

Anhydrous α-dextrose is generally produced by evaporative crystallization of redissolved dextrose hydrate in a vacuum pan. The temperature of crystallization is regulated at 60°–65°. Evaporative crystallization is required to maintain proper supersaturation, to avoid color formation at high temperatures, and to prevent hydrate formation at low temperatures. Batch pan crystallization is usually completed in 5–6 hours, and yields are on the order of 50%. The mother liquor is recycled to the hydrate crystallization system.

Anhydrous β-dextrose is obtained by crystallization from concentrated solutions (above 90%) or melts at high temperatures. Because of the difficulties with color formation at high temperatures and the tendency of β-dextrose to revert to α-dextrose under only slightly humid conditions, crystalline β-dextrose has never been a major article of commerce. If a solution of dextrose is rapidly converted to the solid form, the β-dextrose content of the equilibrium mixture can be "frozen," for example by spraying a hot concentrated solution onto a bed of dry material. If the solution contains an appreciable amount of D-glucose polymers and the moisture content is low, the product will be stable with respect to retention of the β-dextrose content (65). β-Dextrose can be crystallized from water solution at elevated temperatures (66).

V. Uses

Current United States production of pure crystalline dextrose is on the order of a billion pounds annually. The monohydrate is by far the most common product, but a substantial amount of anhydrous α-dextrose is marketed as a very pure grade of sugar for special applications. The monohydrate is shipped in bags and bulk hopper cars. Dextrose is also shipped as a concentrated solution in tank trucks and tank cars and kept at a temperature sufficient to prevent crystallization.

Dextrose is also manufactured in a number of other countries, including Argentina, Belgium, Brazil, Canada, France, Germany, Great Britain, Italy, Japan, The Netherlands, and the U.S.S.R.

The major uses of dextrose are in the food processing industry. Dextrose contributes sweetness, body, osmotic pressure, flavor retention and enhancement, moisture control, and nutritive value to food products. Dextrose is the lowest cost pure crystalline carbohydrate available.

The largest consumer of dextrose is the baking industry in which dextrose serves primarily as a fermentable sugar, but also aids in formation of flavor and aroma and contributes to crust color. Substantial quantities are used in the beverage industry to supply sweetness, body, and osmotic pressure. These same properties apply to its application in the canning industry in which dextrose has been found to contribute to better natural color retention in certain products. Dextrose is used to advantage in confectionery applications to supply sweetness and softness control and to regulate crystallization. In the dairy industry it is used in frozen desserts to prevent oversweetness and to improve flavor. In many instances, dextrose is used in combination with sucrose. While dextrose is somewhat less sweet than sucrose, combinations of the two sugars may be as sweet as sucrose alone (67). The approximate distribution of dextrose consumption in the food application areas is as follows:

Baking	33%
Confectionery	18%
Beverage	11%
Canning	11%
Dry Mixes	6%
Dairy	3%
Miscellaneous	18%

Dextrose is used in making tableted products in both the food and pharmaceutical industries. The cooling effect obtained when dextrose hydrate dissolves in the mouth enhances certain flavors. Dextrose is a raw material for biochemical synthesis and a source of energy for micro-organisms in the fermentation industry. In the chemical industry, it serves as a raw material for production of sorbitol, mannitol, and methyl glucoside. In addition to its use in tableting, dextrose is used in the pharmaceutical industry for intravenous feeding and formulations. In the foundry industry, dextrose is used as a binder in foundry cores based on its ability to polymerize under heat in the presence of a catalyst.

VI. REFERENCES

(1) H. Wichelhaus, "Der Stärkezucker," Akademische Verlagsgesellschaft, Leipzig, 1913.

(2) G. S. C. Kirchoff, Acad. Imp. Sci. St. Petersbourg, Mem., 4, 27 (1811).

(3) W. B. Newkirk, U.S. Patent 1,508,569 (1924); Chem. Abstr., 18, 3736 (1924).

(4) R. F. Jackson and C. G. Silsbee, Natl. Bur. Standards Sci. Paper, No. 437, U.S. Govt. Printing Office, Washington, D.C., 1922.

(5) F. E. Young, J. Phys. Chem., 61, 616 (1957).

(6) J. H. Dittmar, Ind. Eng. Chem., 27, 333 (1935).

(7) W. B. Newkirk, Ind. Eng. Chem., 31, 18 (1939).

(8) R. H. Rogge, Ind. Eng. Chem., 41, 2070 (1949).

(9) R. W. Kerr, in "Chemistry and Industry of Starch," R. W. Kerr, ed., Academic Press Inc., New York, N. Y., 2nd Ed., 1950, Chapt. 14.

(10) G. R. Dean and J. B. Gottfried, Advan. Carbohydrate Chem., 5, 127 (1951).

(11) E. R. Kooi, C. F. Harjes, and J. S. Gilkison, U.S. Patent 3,042,584 (1962); Chem. Abstr., 57, 8790 (1962).

(12) R. W. Atkinson, Proc. Roy Soc. (London), 32, 299 (1881).

(13) G. Kita, Ind. Eng. Chem., 5, 220 (1913).

(14) J. Corman and A. F. Langlykke, Cereal Chem., 25, 190 (1948).

(15) K. Kitahara and M. Kurushima, Mem. Res. Inst. Food Sci., Kyoto Univ., 1, 28 (1951); Chem. Abstr., 46, 4589 (1952).

(16) L. L. Phillips and M. L. Caldwell, *J. Am. Chem. Soc.*, **73**, 3559 (1951).
(17) R. W. Kerr, F. C. Cleveland, and W. J. Katzbeck, *J. Am. Chem. Soc.*, **73**, 3916 (1951).
(18) "Report of the Commission on Enzymes," I.U.B. Symposium Series, Pergamon Press, Ltd., London, 1961, Volume 20, p. 109.
(19) J. H. Pazur and T. Ando, *J. Biol. Chem.*, **234**, 1966 (1959).
(20) J. H. Pazur and T. Ando, *J. Biol. Chem.*, **235**, 297 (1960).
(21) J. H. Pazur and K. Kleppe, *J. Biol. Chem.*, **237**, 1002 (1962).
(22) J. H. Pazur, K. Kleppe, and J. S. Anderson, *Biochim. Biophys. Acta*, **65**, 369 (1962).
(23) S. A. Barker and J. G. Fleetwood, *J. Chem. Soc.*, 4857 (1957).
(24) J. G. Fleetwood and H. Weigel, *Nature*, **196**, 984 (1962).
(25) M. Abdullah, I. D. Fleming, P. M. Taylor, and W. J. Whelan, *Biochem. J.*, **89**, 35P (1963).
(26) Y. Hattori, *Staerke*, **17**, 82 (1965).
(27) Y. Hattori and I. Takeuchi, *Rika Gaku Kenkyusho Hokoku*, **37**, 37 (1961); *Chem. Abstr.*, **55**, 26132 (1961).
(28) R. H. Hopkins, *European Brewery Conv. 5th Congr., Baden-Baden, 1955*, 52 (1955).
(29) D. French and D. Knapp, *J. Biol. Chem.*, **187**, 463 (1950).
(30) E. H. Le Mense, J. Corman, J. M. Van Lanen, and A. F. Langlykke, *J. Bacteriol.*, **54**, 149 (1947).
(31) "DIASTASE 73," Tech. Bull. SP-254 (11/63), Rohm and Haas Co., Philadelphia, Pa.
(32) "MATULASE Amyloglucosidase," Tech. Bull., Matsutani Kagaku Kogyo Co. Ltd., Japan.
(33) Y. Hattori, *Agr. Biol. Chem.*, **25**, 737 (1961).
(34) S. Suzuki, *Staerke*, **16**, 285 (1964):
(35) S. C. Pan, A. A. Andreasen, and P. Kolachov, *Science*, **112**, 115 (1950).
(36) J. H. Pazur and D. French, *J. Biol. Chem.*, **196**, 265 (1952).
(37) H. Okazaki, *Arch. Biochem. Biophys.*, **63**, 322 (1956).
(38) J. H. Pazur, K. Kleppe, and E. M. Ball, *Arch. Biochem. Biophys.*, **103**, 515 (1963).
(39) E. H. Le Mense and J. M. Van Lanen, U.S. Patent 2,451,567 (1948); *Chem. Abstr.*, **43**, 1526 (1949).
(40) J. Corman, H. M. Tsuchiya, and H. J. Koepsell, U.S. Patent 2,676,905 (1954); *Chem. Abstr.*, **48**, 9618 (1954).
(41) F. C. Armbruster, U.S. Patent 3,012,944 (1961); *Chem. Abstr.*, **56**, 5224 (1962).
(42) K. L. Smiley, M. C. Cadmus, D. E. Hensley, and A. A. Lagoda, *Appl. Microbiol.*, **12**, 455 (1964).
(43) H. M. Tsuchiya, J. Corman, and H. J. Koepsell, *Cereal Chem.*, **27**, 322 (1950).
(44) R. W. Liggett, W. C. Mussulman, D. F. Rentshler, and J. Ziffer, U.S. Patent 2,881,115 (1959); *Chem. Abstr.*, **53**, 16479 (1959).
(45) D. P. Langlois and W. Turner, U.S. Patent 2,893,921 (1959); *Chem. Abstr.*, **53**, 19294 (1959).
(46) T. Yamamoto, F. Hattori, and M. Takatsu, *Bull. Inst. Chem. Res., Kyoto Univ.*, **42**, 252 (1964).
(47) L. A. Underkofler, G. M. Severson, K. J. Goering, and L. M. Christensen, *Cereal Chem.*, **24**, 1 (1947).
(48) R. W. Kerr, U.S. Patent 2,970,086 (1961); Brit. Patent 849,509 (1960); *Chem. Abstr.*, **55**, 5864 (1961).
(49) T. L. Hurst and A. W. Turner, U.S. Patent 3,047,471 (1962); *Chem. Abstr.*, **57**, 12898 (1962).
(50) T. L. Hurst and A. W. Turner, U.S. Patent 3,067,108 (1962).

(51) H. R. Kathrein, U.S. Patent 3,108,928 (1963); Chem. Abstr., 60, 5834 (1964).

(52) D. P. Langlois, U.S. Patent 2,305,168 (1942); French Patent 851,470 (1940); Chem. Abstr., 36, 2176 (1942).

(53) L. Wallerstein, U.S. Patent 2,531,999 (1950); Chem. Abstr., 45, 2698 (1951).

(54) D. F. Rentshler, D. P. Langlois, R. F. Larson, L. H. Alverson, and R. W. Liggett, U.S. Patent 3,039,935 (1962); Chem. Abstr., 57, 10085 (1962).

(55) J. F. Lenney and L. R. Shively, U.S. Patent 3,039,936 (1962); Chem. Abstr., 57, 7748 (1962).

(56) T. L. Hurst, A. W. Turner, and R. T. Gaudlitz, U.S. Patent 3,197,338 (1965).

(57) T. Komaki, Denpun Kogyo Gakkaishi, 7, 161 (1960).

(58) "DIAZYME," Tech. Bull. No. 2-122 (1/62), Miles Chemical Co., Elkhart, Ind.

(59) L. J. Denault and L. A. Underkofler, Cereal Chem., 40, 618 (1963).

(60) T. Komaki, Denpun Kogyo Gakkaishi, 6, 91 (1959).

(61) L. A. Underkofler, L. J. Denault, and E. F. Hou, Staerke, 17, 179 (1965).

(62) T. Iwazawa, K. Yamashita, and M. Takahashi, Japan. Patent 15219 (1964).

(63) S. Kuroiwa and M. Nakamura, Kogyo Kagaku Zasshi, 64, 942 (1961).

(64) M. Nakamura and S. Kuroiwa, Kogyo Kagaku Zasshi, 66, 1466 (1963); Internat. Chem. Eng., 4, 530 (1964).

(65) A. L. Wilson and I. Frankel, U.S. Patent 2,854,359 (1958); Chem. Abstr., 53, 1798 (1959).

(66) R. L. Whistler and B. F. Buchanan, J. Biol. Chem., 125, 557 (1938).

(67) C. Nieman, Mfg. Confectioner, 40, No. 8, 19 (1960).

CHAPTER XXV

CHARACTERIZATION AND ANALYSIS
OF STARCHES

By Robert J. Smith

Moffett Technical Center, Corn Products Co., Argo, Illinois

I. Introduction

Starches used by food and nonfood industries are obtained from several cereal grain and tuber crops, corn being the most important source in the United States. Molecular composition and inherent properties of the native starches are related to their origin; however, physical as well as chemical properties may be altered by the recovery process

569

and by modification and derivatization reactions or both applied to the isolated starch. Manifold starch modification procedures are practiced by producing and consuming industries to provide products having a broad range of chemical and physical properties.

Analytical methods detailed in the following sections are divided into three categories: general methods, physical property methods, and methods for starch derivatives. With but few exceptions, the general and physical property methods can be applied to all starch products, although careful judgment is sometimes required in the interpretation of results. For example, the alkali number method for detecting reducing end-groups in substantially unmodified starches would not be applied to highly modified or derivatized products. In similar manner, the inherent viscosity procedure, which utilizes an alkaline sample solution, would not be applied to starch esters without prior validation. Methods for starch derivatives, that is, for the determination of substituent groups or degree of substitution, are intended primarily for characterization of the pertinent derivative, but they may be applied to other starches without interference in most cases. A notable exception would be interference by methoxy or ethoxy groups in the determination of hydroxyethyl or hydroxypropyl groups, or vice versa.

In most instances, a single method is recommended for a particular component or property, and pertinent background information is cited. In some instances, however, alternative methods are described because use of the preferred procedure may entail acquisition of equipment which cannot be justified for infrequent use.

II. GENERAL METHODS

1. Moisture

Under average ambient temperature and humidity conditions, the equilibrium moisture content of most unmodified cereal starches is about 12%, whereas that of some of the root starches, notably potato starch, is considerably higher—up to 18%. The values for modified and derivatized starches often vary from those of the parent starches, and most manufacturers dry their products so that final moisture contents are near the equilibrium values, thus preventing significant weight change during storage and transit.

Moisture or volatile contents of unmodified and modified starches are most commonly determined by drying to constant weight in a vacuum oven at 100°–120° (1–3); air oven techniques (4) are sometimes employed, but results are usually low. The azeotropic distillation method (5) is the referee procedure of the corn wet-milling industry, but it is rarely used except for referee or calibration work because of its time-consuming nature.

The chemical method of Karl Fischer (6, 7) is frequently applied to starch products containing other volatiles which would be included in the weight loss obtained by oven drying, and it is similarly applied to those products showing evidence of decomposition at customary drying temperatures. Karl Fischer moisture values on starch products containing no other volatiles are in good agreement with oven results (8). Recent improvements in reagent stability and automatic titration equipment provide for rapid and accurate moisture determination.

a. *Oven-drying Method*

The vacuum oven should provide uniform heat distribution throughout the working chamber, and it should be capable of retaining a vacuum after the vacuum supply has been shut off. The vacuum supply should maintain an oven pressure below 100 mm. (Hg) during operation. A drying tower filled with an indicating desiccant and a gas scrubber containing concentrated sulfuric acid are connected serially to the air inlet of the oven.

Samples containing hard pellets or large lumps should be ground prior to analysis, taking precautions to prevent significant change in moisture content if the original value is of interest.

About 5 g. of sample is weighed accurately in a predried, cooled, and tared moisture dish (with cover). Aluminum dishes, about 5-cm. diameter by 2.5-cm. tall, are commonly used, but dishes constructed of glass or other metal serve equally well. The dish and cover (cover removed) are placed in a vacuum oven operating at 120°, and the oven is maintained 4 hr. at a pressure below 100 mm. (Hg). While the sample is drying, a small stream of air is bled through the drying train and oven.

The vacuum supply is then shut off, and the oven is slowly filled with air drawn through the drying train. The dish with the sample is removed, quickly covered, cooled in a desiccator, and weighed. Moisture or volatile content is calculated as follows:

$$\text{Percent Volatile} = \frac{\text{Weight loss in grams} \times 100}{\text{Sample weight in grams}}$$

b. *Karl Fischer Method*

Several titration and end-point detection techniques are available, but an instrument such as the Beckman Aquameter (9) Model KF-2 (Fig. 1) permitting fully automatic titration, is preferred because it provides the best precision and accuracy. If this unit is employed, it should be equipped with a 25-ml. automatic leveling buret with a Teflon stopcock plug for Karl Fischer reagent delivery; the second automatic buret for delivery of standard "water-in-methanol" reagent is removed because it is not used in the preferred procedure.

FIG. 1.—Beckman Aquameter, Model KF-2.

A single-solution, stabilized Karl Fischer reagent is recommended. Commercial reagents are available having exceptional stability and a high water equivalent, for example, 6 mg. of water per milliliter. The exact water equivalent of the reagent may be determined with distilled water, but sodium tartrate dihydrate is usually preferred (10) because of ease of handling, and because it can be obtained as a certified primary standard containing about 15.7% water. Methanol required in the procedure may be commercial reagent containing less than 0.1%

water; higher water content results in excessive reagent consumption.

Instrument preparation.—The instrument and accessories should be assembled and operated as directed in the manufacturer's instruction manual. Specific instrument features mentioned hereinafter refer to the Beckman Model KF-2 Aquameter, and equivalent operations should be practiced with alternative equipment. Karl Fischer reagent supply is attached, and the automatic buret is filled. The instrument is set for direct titration, the preferred technique for practically all starch products which are insoluble in the Karl Fischer solvent system. The delay circuit timer is set at 60, and the power switch is turned on.

A clean and dry beaker is positioned on the instrument platform, and the titration head is lowered so as to produce an air-tight seal between the beaker and rubber diaphragm. The glass stopper is removed from the diaphragm; 20 ml. of methanol is pipetted into the beaker, and the stopper is replaced. More methanol may be required if this quantity is not sufficient to cover the platinum buttons on the end of the electrode probe after the probe height has been adjusted to avoid interference with rotation of the stirring bar.

The stirring rate is adjusted to obtain effective agitation without splashing. The buret stopcock is closed, and the "titrate" switch is actuated. The stopcock is then carefully opened until the desired titration rate is obtained, for example, rapid dropwise addition. As the end-point is approached, the automatic valve will close occasionally, which activates the timer. If the presence of water is sensed before the end of the 60-sec. delay period, the valve will be reopened, and the timer will be reset. When no additional water is sensed during the delay period, the valve will remain closed; the timer will be reset, and the neon light will indicate the end of the titration.

The solvent system in the beaker, treated as indicated, contains neither water nor reactive Karl Fischer reagent, and it is ready for standardization or sample analysis.

Standardization.—Although daily standardization is usually adequate, ambient conditions and reagent stability will determine standardization frequency. About 800 mg. of standard sodium tartrate dihydrate is weighed accurately in a dried, cooled, and tared weighing tube. (The weighing tube is constructed of a short length of 20-mm. diameter glass tubing. One end, about 35 mm., is drawn down to a diameter of 5 mm.) The reagent buret is refilled; the glass stopper is removed from the beaker diaphragm, and the small end of the weighing tube is inserted in the opening. The tartrate is allowed to flow into the prepared solvent, and the transfer is completed by rinsing the weighing tube with

10.0 ml. of methanol delivered from a pipet. The glass stopper is re-placed; the "titrate" switch is actuated, and the titration is allowed to proceed to completion.

In like manner, a blank is run on 10.0 ml. of methanol pipetted into prepared solvent through a dry weighing tube.

Sample analysis.—Samples containing hard pellets or large lumps should be ground prior to analysis, taking precautions to prevent significant change in moisture if the original value is of interest.

A clean beaker may be mounted on the instrument platform, and the assembly can be prepared for analysis as directed under *"Instrument preparation."* Or, if the beaker contains sample residues and considerable spent reagent, a quantity can be removed by siphoning, leaving sufficient reagent to cover the platinum electrodes. Actuation of the "titrate" switch will cause titration of residual water, if any, leaving the solvent mixture free of water and reactive reagent and ready for sample analysis.

A quantity of sample containing 80–100 mg. of water is weighed accurately in a dried, cooled, and tared weighing tube, and the reagent buret is refilled. The glass stopper is removed from the beaker dia-phragm, and the small end of the weighing tube is inserted in the opening. The sample is allowed to flow into the prepared solvent, and the transfer is completed by rinsing the weighing tube with 10.0 ml. of methanol delivered from a pipet. As before, the glass stopper is replaced; the "titrate" switch is actuated, and the titration is allowed to proceed to completion. Another blank is run on 10.0 ml. of methanol pipetted into prepared solvent through a dried weighing tube.

Calculations.

$$K = \text{Water equivalent of Karl Fischer reagent (milligrams of water per milliliter of reagent)}$$
$$= \frac{\text{Tartrate wt., mg.} \times \text{Tartrate Moisture, \%}}{(\text{Tartrate titer} - \text{Blank titer}) \text{ in milliliters} \times 100}$$

$$\text{Percent water (sample)} = \frac{(\text{Sample titer} - \text{Blank titer}) \text{ in milliliters} \times K \times 100}{\text{Sample weight in milligrams}}$$

2. Ash

All commercial starches from cereal and tuber sources contain minor or trace quantities of uncombined inorganic materials. The bulk of these originate in the crop from which the starch is isolated, but a small fraction may be contributed by water used in processing. The approxi-mate concentration of these salts is customarily determined as the residue after ignition at a specified temperature (*2, 11–13*).

In contrast with most native starches, potato starch contains phosphate ester groups, and ordinary processing at near neutral pH levels yields products in the salt form, the cation being that contained in the raw material or in the processing water. In this case, ashing by the usual procedure produces an orthophosphate or pyrophosphate residue depending on the temperature. In similar manner, neutral salts of oxidized starches and carboxymethylstarches yield sodium carbonate residues upon ignition, while neutral starch sulfates give residues of metal sulfates or hyposulfites depending on ignition temperature.

Ash determination is frequently practiced to control the concentration of inorganic salts, such as calcium salts added to some commercial starches, and to measure the concentration of salts remaining after derivatization reactions.

About 5 g. of the preground and well-blended starch product is weighed in a preheated, cooled, and tared platinum or silica dish. Platinum ware is preferred when the product contains only trace amounts of ash because silica dishes tend to lose weight during ignition. The dish and contents are heated carefully over an open flame or on a hot plate until the sample is thoroughly carbonized. Excessive foaming during this step can usually be controlled by igniting the sample with an open flame or by heating the surface of the sample with an infrared heat lamp during the charring process.

The partially decomposed sample is then heated in a muffle furnace at 525° until the residue is free from carbon; 2 hr. is usually sufficient. If complete ignition of carbon is slow or difficult, as is sometimes the case with high-ash samples, the process may be hastened by cooling the dish, moistening the residue with a few drops of water, and then reheating.

When the residue is carbon free, the dish is cooled to room temperature in a desiccator and weighed.

$$\text{Percent ash} = \frac{\text{Residue weight in grams} \times 100}{\text{Sample weight in grams}}$$

3. Calcium

It has already been mentioned in this section that commercial starches isolated from cereal and tuber crops contain minor or trace amounts of inorganic materials, and calcium salts are usually a minor fraction thereof. The bulk of this calcium probably pre-exists in the crop from which the starch is isolated, although some may arise from the processing waters. On the other hand, some commercial starches contain added calcium salts, particularly those which may be converted subsequently by enzymes.

Most commercial starches contain less than 50 p.p.m. calcium; the exceptions are enzyme converting starches which contain added calcium salts, and starches which contain anionic functional groups such as carboxyl, sulfate, or phosphate, resulting from oxidation or derivatization reactions, or occurring naturally as in the case of potato starch. Products having anionic functional groups often contain more calcium than nonionic starches because their natural ion-exchange properties cause them to remove calcium from processing waters.

The classic method for calcium determination, based on precipitation and isolation of calcium oxalate, followed by titration with permanganate or another oxidizing agent, is rarely applied to starches except those containing added calcium because prohibitive quantities of sample must be ignited. To avoid this cumbersome operation, high-calcium samples are sometimes analyzed by extracting the calcium salts with $1.2N$ hydrochloric acid at room temperature, followed by precipitation and titration of the oxalate salt (14).

The preferred calcium method comprises ignition of the sample to destroy organic matter and dissolution of the ash residue in dilute hydrochloric acid. This solution or an aliquot thereof is then titrated with a standard solution of disodium (ethylenedinitrilo)tetraacetate (ethylenediamine tetraacetic acid disodium salt, EDTA) after addition of potassium hydroxide and other complexing agents as recommended by Patton and Reeder (15, also 16) to prevent interference by magnesium, iron, copper, and other cations. The end-point is detected with the aid of hydroxynaphthol blue indicator (marketed as Calcium Indicator, No. 5630, by Mallinckrodt Chemical Works, St. Louis, Mo.); the end-point color change is sharpened by the addition of magnesium ion, particularly when the sample contains a negligible magnesium content.

A $0.002M$ solution of disodium (ethylenedinitrilo)tetraacetate is recommended for titration because calcium contents of most samples are quite low. Because such a reagent is relatively unstable, it is prepared fresh daily by diluting a $0.01M$, or stronger, stock solution. The reagent should be standardized by titrating an aliquot of a calcium solution, about $0.001M$, prepared by dissolving a weighed amount of reagent-grade anhydrous calcium carbonate in a small quantity of hydrochloric acid prior to dilution to volume. Titration and end-point detection are accomplished by the procedure described in subsequent paragraphs.

To analyze the starch sample, not more than 10 g. is weighed in a platinum or Vycor dish of 100–150 ml. capacity (larger samples are difficult to ignite). The dish and contents are heated carefully over an open flame or on a hot plate until the sample is thoroughly carbonized.

Excessive foaming during this step can be controlled by igniting the sample with an open flame or by heating the surface of the sample with an infrared heat lamp during the charring process. The partially decomposed sample is then heated in a muffle furnace at 525°–600° until the residue is free from carbon; 2 hr. is usually sufficient, and trace amounts of carbon have not been observed to interfere in the subsequent titration.

The dish and ash residue are cooled, and 10 ml. of 0.1N hydrochloric acid is added; more acid may be required if the ash residue is large and highly alkaline, for example, if it contains sodium or calcium carbonate. The dish is covered with a watch glass and heated 15 min. on a steam bath to dissolve all calcium. The solution and any residue are quantitatively transferred to a beaker or flask for titration and diluted to about 50 ml. with distilled water. If the calcium content is known to be high, the solution is diluted to a known volume and an aliquot containing not more than 1 to 2 mg. of calcium is selected for titration.

To the sample solution or aliquot, 10 ml. of 0.002M magnesium chloride is added for end-point improvement. Then, 4 ml. of 8N potassium hydroxide is added, and the solution is allowed to stand about 5 min. Next, about 25 mg. each of potassium cyanide and hydroxylamine hydrochloride are added and dissolved by mixing. About 0.2–0.3 g. of hydroxynaphthol blue indicator is added and the solution is titrated with standard EDTA solution until the pink indicator color disappears and a blue color persists.

Knowing that the equivalent weights of EDTA and calcium are equal to the molecular weight and gram atomic weight, respectively, the calcium content of the sample is calculated from the titer as follows:

$$\text{Calcium in p.p.m.} = \frac{\text{EDTA titer} \times \text{EDTA Molarity} \times 0.040 \times 10^6}{\text{Sample weight in grams}}$$

4. Sulfur Dioxide

Starches are frequently recovered from grain or tuber sources in a processing system which incorporates small amounts of sulfurous acid as a preservative. The latter is commonly determined by the well-known "Monier–Williams" procedure (17), which determines free as well as combined sulfur dioxide or sulfites frequently present in complex food products, particularly those containing reducing sugars. Sulfur dioxide is released from the sample by heating in dilute acid, and it is removed by sweeping with an inert gas such as carbon dioxide (17) or nitrogen (18). Free sulfur dioxide can be recovered from some products by sweeping an acidified solution of the sample with air under reduced pressure at room temperature *(19)*. The liberated sulfur dioxide is usually absorbed in a dilute, neutral hydrogen peroxide solution in which it is oxidized to sulfur trioxide forming sulfuric acid; the latter is determined by titration or by gravimetric analysis.

Sulfur dioxide in foods is sometimes determined by titrating the product extract with iodine *(20–23)* and colorimetrically *(24, 25)*. Although these procedures provide the speed desired for control analysis, food extracts often contain substances which complex sulfur dioxide or react with iodine, and it is recommended that the "Monier–Williams" method be used directly or to validate the abbreviated technique.

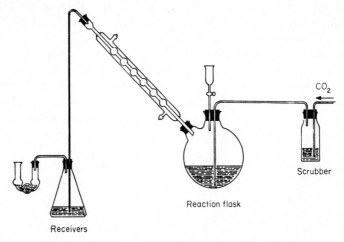

FIG. 2.—Apparatus for determination of sulfur dioxide.

Apparatus for the determination is constructed of standard laboratory glassware with rubber stopper connections as shown in Figure 2, or with standard taper joints. The assembly consists of a 200- to 300-ml. gas scrubber, followed by a 1-liter, two-necked, round-bottomed boiling flask to which a gas inlet tube, a 60-ml. dropping funnel having a 2-mm. bore stopcock, and a sloping Allihn condenser are attached. A delivery tube connected to the upper end of the condenser leads to the bottom of a 250-ml. Erlenmeyer receiving flask, followed by a small Peligot tube. Inlet tubes in each component must deliver the gas stream below the liquid surface.

About 100 ml. of 15% sodium carbonate solution is added to the gas scrubber (see Fig. 2) to remove any residual chlorine in the carbon dioxide supply. Neutral 3% hydrogen peroxide, 15 ml. and 5 ml., is pipetted into the receiving flask and Peligot tube, respectively. The apparatus is connected as indicated in Figure 2, and carbon dioxide is passed through the assembly at a moderate rate; all connections must be tight to insure complete recovery of sulfur dioxide. Three hundred milliliters of distilled water and 20 ml. of concentrated hydrochloric acid are added to the reaction flask by means of the dropping funnel. The solution is heated to the boiling temperature and boiled 10 min. in a stream of carbon dioxide to expel all air from the apparatus.

The starch sample, up to 100 g. depending on the sulfur dioxide content, is dispersed in about 200 ml. of freshly boiled and cooled water. The slurry is transferred immediately to the reaction flask by means of the dropping funnel, while regulating sample addition rate and gas flow rate through the apparatus so as to prevent drawback of hydrogen peroxide solution, inclusion of air, or burning the sample. The mixture is brought to a boil and boiled gently for 1 hr. while continuing the flow of carbon dioxide through the apparatus at a moderate rate.

Water flow through the condenser is discontinued just before the end of the boiling period. When the delivery tube directly above the receiving flask becomes hot, the tube joining the upper end of the condenser is disconnected. The delivery tube and contents of the Peligot tube are washed into the receiving flask, and the solution is titrated with standard $0.1N$ sodium hydroxide solution to a bromophenol blue indicator end-point. A blank determination is made on all reagents, substituting freshly boiled water for the sample.

A gravimetric determination may be made following the titration if the neutral peroxide reagent is free of sulfate and other materials precipitated with barium in acid solution. The solution is acidified with hydrochloric acid, and sulfate is precipitated by adding excess barium chloride solution. The precipitate is settled, recovered by filtration, dried, ignited, cooled, and weighed as barium sulfate.

Percent sulfur dioxide =

$$\frac{(\text{Sample titer} - \text{Blank titer}) \text{ milliliters} \times \text{NaOH normality} \times 0.032 \times 100}{\text{Sample weight in grams}}$$

5. Acidity

Some modified starches and starch derivatives are processed in the presence of acid or acidic reagents. Since these affect physical properties of resultant starch pastes, they are neutralized in process and removed by washing. Nevertheless, residues sometimes remain and these are determined by titration of a pasted sample or the filtrate from a sample slurry.

Samples containing hard pellets or large lumps should be ground before analysis. When the sample contains a high concentration of solubles which would make recovery of a filtrate difficult, it is pasted and the paste is titrated. A 10.0-g. sample is mixed thoroughly in 300 ml. of distilled water at room temperature. The water used for sample preparation should be of such quality that 200 ml. will require not more than 0.05 ml. of 0.1N acid or base to obtain the methyl red or phenolphthalein end-points, respectively. The slurry is placed on a hot plate, heated to boiling in about 15 min. while stirring occasionally to prevent settling, and boiled for 10 min. The pasted sample is removed from the heat source; about 1 ml. of phenolphthalein indicator is added and the sample is titrated immediately with standard 0.1N sodium hydroxide.

Since different acids may contribute to the acidity of the sample, the value usually reported is the milliequivalents of acid per unit sample weight.

Acidity (milliequivalents/gram) =
$$\frac{\text{Sample titer in milliliters} \times \text{NaOH normality}}{\text{Sample weight in grams}}$$

If the sample contains a negligible amount of soluble material, a slurry technique is sometimes used alternatively. A 10.0-g. sample is mixed with 100.0 ml. of good quality distilled water, and the mixture is agitated continuously at a moderate rate for 30 min. in a closed container. The mixture is gravity filtered through a good quality filter paper; the filtrate is collected in a clean and dry receiver, and the first few milliliters of filtrate are discarded. Then, 50.0 ml. of filtrate is pipetted into a clean Erlenmeyer flask, followed by dilution with 50 ml. of good quality distilled water and addition of phenolphthalein indicator. The diluted filtrate is titrated with standard 0.1N sodium hydroxide to a permanent pink end-point, and the acidity value is calculated as follows:

Acidity (milliequivalents/gram) =
$$\frac{\text{Sample titer in milliliters} \times \text{NaOH normality} \times 100 \text{ ml.}}{\text{Sample weight in grams} \times 50 \text{ ml.}}$$

6. pH

Since the pH of a starch product affects the physical properties of pastes, most unmodified starches are adjusted to a pH level of about 5.0 during the final stages of processing. Some modified and derivatized starches, on the other hand, may be adjusted to a somewhat higher pH value.

pH, which is a measure of hydrogen ion concentration rather than titratable acidity or alkalinity, is measured with a hydrogen ion meter (pH meter) equipped with suitable glass and calomel electrodes; several good instruments are commercially available. Immediately before use, the instrument and electrode assembly are standardized with a buffer of known pH value near that of the sample; for example, a buffer having a pH value of 4.0 is used if the pH of the sample is in the range between 3 to 6. Then, the assembly is checked with a second buffer having a pH value of about 7. If the observed pH reading on the second buffer is within 0.1 unit of the known value, reliable values can be obtained.

Samples containing hard pellets or large lumps should be ground prior to analysis. A starch sample weighing 10.0 g. is placed in a 400-ml., tall-form beaker, and to this is added 200 ml. of distilled water. The water used for sample preparation should be of such quality that 200 ml. will require not more than 0.05 ml. of $0.1N$ acid or base to obtain the methyl red or phenolphthalein end-points, respectively. The starch is dispersed by stirring, and the beaker is placed in a boiling water bath so that the bath liquid level is slightly above the sample level in the beaker. The sample is stirred until gelatinization is complete (about 5 min.), after which the beaker is covered with a watch glass and the sample is cooked 10 min. longer (total time in bath is 15 min.). The cooked sample is cooled immediately to room temperature (25°) and stirred to destroy any gel which might have formed, and the pH is measured with the calibrated pH meter.

Alternatively, a 20-g. sample is dispersed in 100 ml. of good quality distilled water, and the mixture is stirred at a moderate rate until an equilibrium pH has been attained. A stirring time of 5 min. is sufficient for most products, but some containing additives must be stirred as long as 30 min. to assure pH equilibrium. The agitation is stopped, and the pH is measured immediately at room temperature with a calibrated instrument.

7. Nitrogen (Protein)

Commercial starches are recovered from cereal grains and tubers containing various concentrations of protein, fiber, and fat, in addition to starch, together with other minor components. Principal operations in the separation of starch are steeping, milling, filtration, and centrifugation and tabling or both. Separations are rarely quantitative, however, and recovered starch contains minor to trace amounts of protein, together with trace quantities of the other components in the starting material.

Protein contents of starches are estimated from the determined nitrogen contents, using conversion factors appropriate for the particular crop. Direct colorimetric techniques for protein determination (26) have been successfully applied to some cereal products, but modifications (*27*) of the Kjeldahl procedure (*28*) are most commonly practiced. Starch derivatives containing substituent groups with nitrogen, for example, quaternary ammonium, amine, carbanilate or others, are analyzed also by the Kjeldahl procedure. In the examination of these derivatives, the original starch is analyzed simultaneously, and the increase in nitrogen content is the basis for calculating the degree of substitution. The Dumas technique (*29*) utilizing automated analyzers (*30*) can be applied conveniently to those products containing appreciable amounts of nitrogen.

Standard Kjeldahl digestion and distillation equipment is recommended. A starch sample weighing about 10 g. is placed in an 800-ml. Kjeldahl flask. Most commercial unmodified starches contain less than 0.1% nitrogen; if the sample is known to contain significantly more nitrogen, for example, a nitrogen-containing derivative, a smaller sample may be more appropriate.

Ten grams of reagent-grade, nitrogen-free potassium sulfate, 0.3 g. of reagent-grade copper selenite, and 60 ml. of concentrated reagent-grade sulfuric acid are added to the sample. Mercury and other copper salts are frequently used catalysts. The flask is placed in an inclined position on the Kjeldahl digestion unit and heated carefully until foaming has stopped. Heating is then increased until the acid boils briskly, and digestion is continued for 1 hr. after the reaction mixture clears.

An excess of 0.1N sulfuric acid (10 ml. or more depending on sample size and nitrogen content) is measured accurately into a 500-ml. Erlenmeyer flask serving as a receiver. Distilled water is added, and the flask is connected to the Kjeldahl distillation assembly so that the condenser delivery tube is immersed in the absorbing acid.

After the digest has cooled, it is diluted carefully with about 300 ml. of distilled water and *mixed thoroughly*. The reaction mixture should be discarded if crystallization occurs because nitrogen recovery will probably be low. Crystallization can be avoided by using more acid for sample digestion. A pinch of granular zinc (20 mesh, C.P. grade) is added to prevent bumping during distillation. Sufficient concentrated sodium hydroxide solution (prepared so as to contain about 610 g. of technical-grade, nitrogen-free sodium hydroxide per liter of solution) is added to make the solution strongly alkaline (75 ml. is usually sufficient); it is poured down the inner wall of the flask to avoid immediate mixing with the acid solution. It is essential that the digest be made strongly alkaline prior to digestion. This can be checked by adding phenolphthalein indicator to the diluted digest prior to alkali addition; if sufficient alkali has been added, the indicator color change will be noted when the flask is shaken.

The flask is connected to the distilling unit condenser through a suitable Kjeldahl connecting bulb to prevent sodium hydroxide containing spray from entering the condenser; the heater is turned on, and the contents of the flask are mixed by gentle swirling. After the reaction mixture reaches the boiling point, distillation is continued at a moderate rate until all ammonia has passed into the absorbing solution (250 ml. of distillate is collected normally).

The receiving flask is removed and the excess acid is titrated with 0.1N sodium hydroxide solution, using methyl red–bromcresol green mixed indicator, or equivalent, for end-point detection.

A blank determination should be run on all reagents substituting pure sucrose or D-glucose for the sample, using the same amount of 0.1N sulfuric acid in the receiver as for sample analysis. Nitrogen and protein contents of the sample are calculated in the following manner.

$$\text{Percent nitrogen} = \frac{(B - A) \times \text{NaOH normality} \times 0.014 \times 100}{\text{Sample weight in grams}}$$

in which,

A = Sample titer (milliliters of standard sodium hydroxide solution)
B = Blank titer (milliliters of standard sodium hydroxide solution)
Percent Protein = Percent Nitrogen × 6.25[1]

8. Fatty Materials

Cereal starches contain trace amounts of fatty acid glycerides, usually less than 0.1%, which can be removed by extraction with hydrophobic solvents such as ether, hexane, or carbon tetrachloride, using conventional Soxhlet or Butt-type extraction equipment. Most starches also contain about 0.5 to 0.6% of free fatty acids which appear to be complexed with the linear fraction (amylose) of the native starch (31). Since these complexed fatty acids alter the physical and chemical properties of the starch, it is often of interest to know their concentration, and sometimes their removal is a prerequisite for accurate analysis, such as, for example, the determination of iodine affinity. The complexed fatty acids can usually be removed by extended extraction with hot, hydrophilic solvents such as methanol, ethanol, 80% dioxane, and 2-methoxyethanol (methyl Cellosolve), so as to provide essentially fat-free starches for analysis. Total concentration of fatty substances (fats and fatty acids) is usually determined by a procedure involving partial hydrolysis of the starch, precipitation of the freed fatty substances, and recovery by solvent extraction.

The starch sample is ground prior to analysis if it contains hard pellets or large lumps. About 25 g. of sample is weighed accurately and

[1] A factor of 5.70 is used for wheat products.

transferred to a 600-ml. beaker, and this is suspended in 100 ml. of distilled water. When the mixture is homogeneous, 300 ml. of boiling 4N hydrochloric acid is added; the mixture is heated to boiling on a hot plate and boiled for about 5 min. or until a negative starch test is obtained when a drop of the hydrolysis mixture is tested with a dilute iodine solution (absence of the characteristic blue starch–iodine complex). The beaker with sample is placed in a cold water or iced water bath, cooled to a temperature below 25°, and maintained at that temperature for 30 min. or longer to allow complete precipitation of fatty acids.

All precipitate is recovered by gravity filtration through Whatman No. 1 filter paper. The hydrolysis beaker is washed with distilled water to make the precipitate transfer as nearly quantitative as possible; precipitate adhering to the inside of the beaker is recovered by wiping with small pieces of dry, clean filter paper, and these are added to the main residue in the gravity funnel. The combined residues are then washed with distilled water at room temperature until the washings are neutral to methyl orange indicator. The filter paper on which the residue has been recovered is folded around the residue to avoid loss, and the total is placed on a watch glass and dried 3 hr. in an air oven or over-night in a warm place.

The folded filter paper containing the dried residue is placed in a paper extraction shell (22 mm. diameter by 80 mm. height), and the top of the shell is closed with a cotton ball extracted previously with carbon tetrachloride or petroleum ether so as to be fat free. Glass extraction shells with fritted glass bottoms or Alundum thimbles may be used alternatively. The sample-containing shell is placed in a Butt-type extractor and attached to a standard extraction assembly consisting of a flat-bottom flask, an extractor, and a water-cooled condenser. A Soxhlet extractor may be used alternatively, and complete assemblies with standard-taper glass joints are preferred.

After attaching a previously dried, cooled, and tared extraction flask containing about 50 ml. of carbon tetrachloride (petroleum ether may be substituted), the assembly is placed on a heater. Heating is adjusted to produce 150 to 200 drops of condensed solvent per minute, and the residue is extracted 3 hr. under these conditions. The extraction flask is disconnected from the assembly, and carbon tetrachloride is evaporated on a steam bath until no odor of solvent remains. The flask and residue are dried 1 hr. in a vacuum oven at 100°; prolonged drying at higher temperatures is avoided to prevent fat oxidation. After cooling the flask and residue in a desiccator, the residue and flask are weighed, and the total fat content is calculated.

$$\text{Percent total fat} = \frac{\text{Residue weight in grams} \times 100}{\text{Sample weight in grams}}$$

9. Solubles

Native starches in granular form are insoluble in water at room temperature. When an aqueous starch slurry is heated, the granules swell, lose their birefringence, and eventually rupture. The effects of these changes during gelatinization on physical properties of the system are described in Chapter XII of Volume I.

Physical properties, including solubility of starches, are altered by the method of drying, by heat treatment especially in the presence of acid or other modifying agents, and by chemical derivatization. The last two treatments may decrease solubility at elevated temperatures as well as increase solubility at room temperature, depending on the type of derivative produced.

To measure the solubles content of an unmodified or slightly modified starch, an accurately weighed sample, about 20 g., is placed in a 250-ml. bottle and slurried in 198 ml. of distilled water at room temperature. The container is closed and the slurry is agitated continuously at a moderate rate for 30 min. The suspension is gravity-filtered through a Whatman No. 12 or equivalent filter paper; filtrate is collected in a dry receiver, and the first 25 ml. of filtrate is returned to the suspension.

In the event that the product is a pregelatinized starch or a highly soluble modified or derivatized starch, a sample weighing about 2 g. is dispersed in 199 ml. of distilled water at $25° \pm 1°$, and the suspension is agitated 30 min. before filtration.

An aliquot of the filtrate, not more than 100 ml. and containing not more than 0.2 g. of dry residue, is pipetted into a predried and tared evaporating dish, and the solution is evaporated to apparent dryness in a steam bath. The residue is then dried to constant weight in a vacuum oven at 100° (2 hr. is usually sufficient), cooled in a desiccator, and weighed.

$$\text{Percent solubles} = \frac{\text{Residue weight in grams} \times 200 \text{ ml.}[2] \times 100}{\text{Aliquot volume in milliliters} \times \text{Sample weight in grams}}$$

10. Waxy and Nonwaxy

Most of the common starches from tuber and cereal sources are mixtures of linear and branched polymers, usually identified as amylose and amylopectin, respectively. Control of genetic factors resulted in successful development of the so-called waxy cereal grains, such as corn,

[2] Solution phase volume is assumed to be 200 ml. in all cases.

grain sorghum, and rice, which contain granular starches consisting entirely of branched polymers—amylopectin; starches from these sources are often referred to as waxy types because of the waxlike material which sometimes occurs on the seed coat, whereas granular starches containing both amylose and amylopectin are usually referred to as non-waxy or common types.

Because the properties of waxy and common starches are quite different, and because waxy starches usually bring premium prices, the parent grains are processed separately. Nevertheless, commingling of the different species occurs, and this can be detected and quantitated by utilizing the iodine staining characteristics described by Schoch in Chapter XXVI of this volume. Ungelatinized as well as gelatinized waxy starch granules stain red with iodine while the nonwaxy or common types, containing amylose, stain an intense blue.

To determine whether a granular starch is waxy or nonwaxy, or to determine their respective concentrations in mixtures, about 0.3 g. of sample is dispersed in 15 ml. of distilled water, and, if the suspension is neutral or alkaline, it is acidified with dilute hydrochloric or acetic acid. A solution containing 3 ml. of $0.1N$ iodine in 85 ml. of distilled water is added to the starch dispersion while stirring vigorously with a glass rod. After mixing is complete, the rod is withdrawn rapidly and the adhering drop is transferred to the counting chamber of a haemocytometer; the drop is quickly covered with a cover glass. The Levy improved Neubauer, bright line, double ruling haemocytometer is recommended because its use facilitates counting.

The haemocytometer is placed on the stage of a microscope with substage illumination and about 250-power magnification, and, after focusing, the counting chamber is alligned so that the finely ruled center section of 25 squares is in the microscope field. The red and blue stained granules in the 25-square center section are counted separately, proceeding over the ruled section in an orderly fashion to avoid duplication. Counting is simplified by the use of a hand tally counter. Many of the blue stained granules will appear almost black under the microscope, and slight changes in focus will serve to show the blue color at the edges of the granule.

The sample size and dispersion volume are chosen to give a total count of 350–600 granules in the cross-ruled center section of the haemocytometer. Differences from this total count are largely a matter of technique because starch granules settle rapidly in the dispersion. If the total number of granules in the ruled field varies significantly from this range, the dispersion should be stirred vigorously again and a fresh drop should be applied to a clean haemocytometer. Alternatively, the sample concentration may be increased or decreased to suit individual requirements.

If more accurate results are desired, a duplicate sample dispersion should be prepared and counted. The percentage of waxy or nonwaxy granules is expressed in terms of the total granule count without regard to any differences in average granule size which might exist. Therefore, the result is a number rather than weight percentage.

11. Alkali Number (Reducing Value)

Reducing values of native starches are extremely small because of the low incidence of reducing end groups in amylose and amylopectin. These polymers theoretically contain only one reducing end group per molecule, and a relative measure of the number of terminal reducing groups, or an estimate of molecular size, can be obtained by determining the alkali number (*32, 33*). This method involves degradation of the starch sample under controlled alkaline conditions, wherein the terminal aldehydic groups are presumed to undergo enediol rearrangement, followed by decomposition to form simple organic acids. The concentration of such acids produced under rigorously controlled conditions is an indication of the concentration of reducing end groups.

The method can be applied to unmodified and to many modified starches such as those obtained by acid or enzyme conversion, but it is not applicable to starch esters which undergo saponification during the alkaline digestion, to starch ethers wherein the substituent group blocks the progressive alkali degradation, nor to oxidized starches which undergo internal cleavage in addition to degradation from the reducing end.

When the product to be analyzed is an ungelatinized granular starch, a portion of the powdered or finely ground (60-mesh) sample containing 500 mg. of dry starch is weighed accurately and transferred quantitatively to a clean and dry, 8-ounce Pyrex bottle with a narrow mouth. The actual sample weight is calculated from prior knowledge of the moisture content measured by one of the recommended procedures. Distilled water (10 ml.) is added and the mixture is swirled gently to obtain a uniform suspension. Then, 25.00 ml. of $0.4 \pm 0.02N$ sodium hydroxide solution (carbonate free) is added while swirling the contents of the bottle to insure uniform gelatinization and dispersion of the sample. If lumping occurs at this point, the sample should be discarded and the determination repeated. Finally, 65 ml. of distilled water at 95°–100° is added; the contents are mixed, and the bottle is closed with a 1-hole rubber stopper containing a short length of capillary tubing serving as a vent, and then placed immediately in a *vigorously boiling* water bath, in a position so that the bottle is immersed to the neck in boiling water. The sample is digested in the bath for exactly 60 min., and during this period the contents are swirled frequently to insure rapid and uniform heat transfer.

At the end of the heating period, the bottle is immediately placed in an ice-and-water bath. As an additional aid in halting the alkaline degradation, 50–75 ml. of distilled water at 0° is added. The solution is transferred quantitatively to a 400-ml. beaker by rinsing the bottle with several small portions of distilled water. The excess alkali, that is, that which has not been neutralized by organic acids formed during the alkali degradation, is titrated electrometrically to pH 8.0 with 0.2N standard sulfuric acid. A thymol blue indicator end point may be used alternatively, but electrometric titration is preferred.

A 25.00-ml. aliquot of the 0.4N sodium hydroxide solution used for sample degradation is titrated with the 0.2N standard sulfuric acid solution after dilution with about 100 ml. of water. The difference between this titer and that obtained on the sample is the net sample titer.

Starch products sometimes contain significant amounts of acidic or basic materials which would decrease or increase the net sample titer, respectively. When the sample history is unknown, analysis of a sample blank is highly desirable. A sample containing 0.500 g. of dry starch is dispersed in 10 ml. of distilled water and gelatinized by adding 100 ml. of water at 95°–100°. The solution is titrated electrometrically to pH 8.0 with either the 0.2N standard sulfuric acid or sodium hydroxide solution of equal normality, whichever is required. The blank titer is added to the net sample titer if acid is required, and subtracted if base is needed to bring the blank sample paste to pH 8.0. The alkali number is calculated as the milliliters of 0.10N alkali required to neutralize acids formed by alkaline degradation of 1.0 g. of dry starch under the specified conditions.

Alkali number =
$$\frac{(\text{Net sample titer} \pm \text{Blank titer}) \text{ milliliters} \times \text{Acid normality} \times 10}{\text{Dry sample weight in grams}}$$

Pregelatinized starches and those exhibiting pronounced swelling tendencies in cold water require a different dispersion technique to avoid lump formation. The weighed sample is transferred to the 8-ounce bottle and wetted completely with 1–2 ml. of benzene; then, 25 ml. of 0.4N sodium hydroxide solution is added with continuous agitation to gelatinize the starch, followed by 75 ml. of distilled water at 95°–100°. In other respects, the analysis is the same as that for ungelatinized granular starches.

12. Ferricyanide Number (Reducing Value)

Starch is modified by treatment with acid and other reagents in numerous ways causing molecular degradation. When the degree of modification is small, the properties of the product or the course of the reaction may be followed by means of physical properties such as hot paste viscosity, inherent viscosity, or alkali fluidity. While such procedures are frequently the most practical from an industrial point of view because the modification reaction is performed to alter physical properties, the extent of molecular degradation may also be obtained by measuring the increase in the number of reducing end groups.

Reducing value methods employing alkaline copper reagents (34) are rarely used for the analysis of modified starches. Such products are analyzed by alkaline reagents employing dintirosalicylate (35, 36) or, more frequently, by alkaline ferricyanide reagents (37, 38). The ferricyanide reducing method is preferred because it is the least influenced by sample size, amount of reagent, or minor variation in other reaction parameters. The method described here is that recommended by Schoch (39).

The ferricyanide reagent is prepared by dissolving 16.5 g. of potassium ferricyanide and 22 g. of anhydrous sodium carbonate in distilled water and diluting to a volume of 1 liter. The solution should be allowed to stand 3 or 4 days and any precipitate which forms should be removed by filtration. The filtered reagent should be kept in a dark brown glass bottle and stored in a dark cabinet when not in use since it deteriorates when exposed to the light. Reagent prepared and stored in this manner is stable for several months.

The starch sample of known moisture or volatiles content is powdered or finely ground (60 mesh) prior to analysis. A sample weighing 200–250 mg., or less if the reducing value is high, is transferred to a clean and dry, 8-ounce Pyrex bottle with a narrow mouth. If the material is pregelatinized or displays significant swelling tendencies in cold water, it is wetted completely by the addition of 2–3 ml. of benzene. The sample is suspended in 25 ml. of distilled water; the bottle is placed in a boiling water bath and heated several minutes while mixing the contents continuously so as to disperse and gelatinize the sample uniformly. If lumps appear in the sample dispersion at this point, the test should be repeated.

Next, 25 ml. of alkaline ferricyanide reagent is added to the hot sample dispersion, and the contents of the bottle are mixed. The bottle is closed with a 1-hole rubber stopper containing a short length of capillary tubing which serves as a vent, and then placed immediately in a *vigorously boiling* water bath, in a position so that the bottle is immersed to the neck in boiling water. The bottle is kept in the bath for exactly 15 min., and the contents are swirled frequently to insure rapid and uniform heat transfer.

After removal from the bath, the bottle and contents are cooled immediately in a stream of cold water or an ice-and-water bath; 60 ml. of zinc sulfate–acetic acid solution (200 ml. of glacial acetic acid, 70 g. of potassium chloride, and 20 g. of zinc sulfate heptahydrate dissolved in water and diluted to 1 liter) is added carefully to avoid loss of sample through excessive foaming, and the contents are mixed. Twenty milliliters of 20% potassium iodide solution is added, and the iodine liberated by reaction of iodide ion with excess ferricyanide ion is titrated with standard $0.05N$ sodium thiosulfate solution. The starch sample usually serves as the indicator for end point detection, but if the product does not provide the characteristic intense blue or purple color, starch indicator solution should be added. Near the end of the titration, the presence of insoluble, blue-black starch–iodine complex may obscure the end point. In this case, the bottle should be stoppered and the contents shaken vigorously; the titration is then completed by dropwise addition of standard thiosulfate solution, and shaken after each addition.

A blank determination is performed on 25 ml. of the ferricyanide reagent; 25 ml. of water is added, and, without heating, 60 ml. of zinc sulfate–acetic acid reagent and 20 ml. of 20% potassium iodide solution are added as described previously. The reaction mixture is titrated with standard $0.05N$ sodium thiosulfate solution; starch indicator solution is added as the end point is approached, which can be judged by perceptible fading of the yellow ferricyanide color. The ferricyanide number or reducing value, expressed as the number of milliliters of $0.1000N$ ferricyanide solution reacting with 1 g. of dry sample, is calculated as follows:

Ferricyanide number =
$$\frac{(\text{Blank titer} - \text{Sample titer}) \text{ in milliliters} \times \text{Thiosulfate normality} \times 10}{\text{Dry sample weight in grams}}$$

Prior knowledge of the sample history is useful in determining the preferred sample size which will consume 50% or more of the reagent to provide optimum precision. In the case of modified soluble starches and dextrins having low reducing values, sample sizes may be increased to 1 g., if desired, without any change in the observed reducing value. On the other hand, sample weights should not exceed 250 mg. in the case of unmodified granular starches because observed ferricyanide values are concentration dependent at higher concentrations of these difficultly dispersible products.

III. Physical Property Methods

1. Color

Starches produced in commercial channels are isolated from cereal and root crops which contain significant amounts of protein, fiber, fat, and other minor components. The color of corn starch, the major starch supply in the United States, is related primarily to nonstarch residues, particularly pigments associated with protein (gluten). Color is minimized by processing methods that give products having the lowest possible concentrations of nonstarch components, or by bleaching. Starches recovered from white corn or other pigment-free crops are the lowest in color.

Starch color is often assessed by visual comparison with a standard product, or by matching against certified color standards such as the Munsel color disks (40, 41). However, instability of standards and the subjective nature of visual methods, except in the hands of color experts, has led to the introduction of spectrophotometric procedures employing diffuse reflectance measurements. The color method recommended here is similar to that employed for starch hydrolysis products (42–44) except for the use of reflectance rather than transmittance values. When applied to corn starch and other products exhibiting similar color characteristics, the method gives color and brightness values which correlate with visual appearance through use of the Commission Internationale de l'Eclairage (C.I.E.) color specification system (45). Color values so obtained are related to excitation purity or color saturation, and brightness is related to luminous reflectance or lightness, when the sample hue is equivalent to that of corn starch, or, more specifically, when the dominant wavelength is approximately 575 mμ.

The spectrophotometer used should possess high photometric accuracy and permit operation at a spectral band width of no more than 10 mμ at the three wavelengths: 450, 550, and 600 mμ. These characteristics are provided in the Beckman Model B spectrophotometer (Beckman Instruments, Inc., Fullerton, California), and operating details in succeeding paragraphs pertain to this instrument although equivalent equipment can be employed. The spectrophotometer should be equipped with the integrating sphere accessory for diffuse reflectance measurements, the beam expanding lens, and the blue-sensitive phototube. The instrument and accessories should be calibrated and operated as directed in the manufacturer's instruction manual.

Starch samples are sometimes examined without grinding because a change in particle size usually affects the brightness significantly. On the other hand, powdered or finely ground (60-mesh or finer) samples yield much more reproducible color values and "intrinsic" brightness values. The sample cup is filled with a well-blended portion of the sample, and the cup is tapped on a hard surface to pack the material; the sample is not compressed by force. The sample cup may be prepared by cutting a 12-mm. length from the bottom of a 10-ml. beaker, and grinding the cut edge so that it is smooth and free of irregularities; alternatively, a black plastic bottle cap of comparable size may be used. The sample surface is smoothed by the rotary motion of a flat article such as a microscope slide, and the loaded cup is inserted in the sample carrier of the reflectance attachment; care should be taken so as not to disturb the sample surface. A second sample cup is filled with a block of magnesium carbonate, cut to size, and the exposed surface is leveled and smoothed by rubbing against an abrasive paper (fine sandpaper) on a flat surface. Three or four thin layers of magnesium oxide are freshly deposited thereon as recommended by the National Bureau of Standards (46), and this reflectance standard is carefully inserted in the sample carrier.

The sample carrier is moved to place the magnesium oxide standard in the light path; the wavelength scale is set at 450 mμ, and the sensitivity switch is turned to the maximum sensitivity position. With the shutter closed, the dark current control is adjusted to give a zero reading on the reflectance (transmittance) scale. The shutter is opened, and the slit control is adjusted to give a reflectance reading of 100% on the reflectance (transmittance) scale. The sample carrier is moved to place the sample in the light path, and the reflectance (% R) at 450 mμ is observed on the reflectance (transmittance) scale.

Sample reflectance values at 550 and 600 mμ are determined in like manner, and color and brightness values are obtained as indicated below.

Color   = Log % R at 600 mμ − Log % R at 450 mμ
Brightness = % R at 550 mμ

Magnesium oxide coatings used as reflectance standards are fragile and unstable; consequently, Vitrolite structural glass is recommended as a working standard (47). The glass is cut to fit the sample carrier of the reflectance attachment and calibrated against a freshly prepared magnesium coating (46) at the three wavelengths employed. When the Vitrolite working standard is used for instrument standardization, the slit control is adjusted to produce a reflectance reading on the transmittance (reflectance) scale equal to the calibration value (against magnesium oxide) at the particular wavelength.

2. Density

Commercial starches are obtained in powder, crystal, flake, and lump forms by several commercial methods resulting in a variety of particle sizes and shapes. These physical differences together with differences in origin and type and/or degree of modification or derivatization affect absolute density of starch products to a minor degree, but they affect bulk density to a large degree. Bulk density is important particularly to starch producers because of its relation to package design.

a. Bulk Density

A 250-ml. graduated cylinder, having a graduated section (0- to 250-ml. mark) not less than 24 cm. and not more than 26 cm. in length, is tared and carefully filled to the 250-ml. graduation mark with loose sample. Filling is accomplished with the aid of a 7-cm., 60-degree powder funnel with a 0.5-inch I.D. stem, 1 inch in length. The funnel is mounted with the stem inside the graduated cylinder so that the end of the square-cut stem is 6 cm. above the 250-ml. graduation mark. The sample is carefully added to the funnel with a spoon or spatula until the cylinder is loosely filled to the 250-ml. graduation ʼmark, and the cylinder and contents are weighed.

The loose sample is then packed by vibration until the sample volume reaches a minimum value. This is usually accomplished by placing the cylinder, loosely supported, on the wooden deck of a paper jogger (for example, Syntron Paper Jogger, type PJ 4, style 1783; available from Syntron Company, Homer City, Pa.) and vibrating for about 5 min. at a frequency and amplitude which cause the cylinder to vibrate rhythmically with the wooden deck.

The packed sample volume is measured and the loose and packed bulk densities are calculated as follows:

Bulk density, grams/milliliter (Loose) =
$$\frac{\text{Loose-filled sample weight in grams}}{250 \text{ ml.}}$$

Bulk density, grams/milliliter (Packed) =
$$\frac{\text{Loose-filled sample weight in grams}}{\text{Packed sample volume in milliliters}}$$

b. Absolute Density

Absolute densities of starches can be determined by the liquid displacement technique of Schoch and Leach (48) using either water or xylene depending on sample characteristics. The method is rather time-consuming, and, because skill is required to insure solvent penetration of all sample voids and to eliminate all entrapped air, the air or inert gas displacement technique introduced by Remington and Pariser (*49*) is recommended. The determination can be performed very rapidly and accurately with the acid of the Beckman Air Comparison Pycnometer (*50, 51*) marketed by Beckman Instruments, Inc.

The instrument (Fig. 3) has two chambers or cylinders of equal volume with a piston in each, and these are connected through a coupling

FIG. 3.—Beckman Air Comparison Pycnometer.

valve which can be opened to equalize pressure in the two chambers. They are connected also through a differential pressure indicator which indicates any pressure difference between the chambers when the coupling valve is closed. When a solid such as starch is sealed in the sample chamber and the piston is advanced to reduce chamber volume and increase pressure, the piston in the alternate chamber must be advanced a greater distance to maintain equal pressures in the two chambers when the coupling valve is closed. The difference is distances traveled by the two pistons is a direct function of the absolute sample volume, assuming that the air or inert gas does not react with the sample.

In practice, the user should follow the procedure given in the operating manual supplied with the instrument. After allowing the instrument to equilibrate with the environment in which it is to be used, the coupling valve is opened, and the handwheels controlling the piston positions in both the reference and sample chambers are rotated counterclockwise until the pistons in both chambers seat firmly against the stops. The position of the measuring piston in the sample chamber is then adjusted by rotation of the balance handwheel until the attached counter indicates the reference chamber volume as specified by the manufacturer.

Sufficient starch sample is weighed into the sample cup to fill it within 5 or 6 mm. of the top of the cup, and the lip of the cup is wiped clean. The cup is placed on the sample platform, and the platform is raised, sealing and making the sample cup an integral part of the sample chamber. After waiting about 15 sec. to insure equalization of pressure in the two chambers, the coupling valve is closed.

Handwheels controlling positions of pistons in both chambers are rotated clockwise simultaneously, and the pressures in the two chambers are kept about equal. The piston in the reference chamber is advanced until it seats firmly (do not force) against the stop, and the pressure is increased to about two atmospheres. The balance handwheel on the measuring piston is adjusted to give an equal pressure in the sample chamber, as shown on the differential pressure indicator. Equality of pressures in the two chambers can be verified by carefully opening the coupling valve while observing the differential pressure indicator closely; the pointer should not move.

The difference in distances traveled by the two pistons corresponds exactly to the sample volume in cubic centimeters, which is read directly on the digital counter connected to the measuring piston. Dividing the sample weight in grams by the observed volume· gives the absolute density in grams per cubic centimeter.

3. Inherent Viscosity

Treatment with hydrochloric or sulfuric acid and oxidation with hypochlorite are two of the oldest and most commonly practiced methods for starch modification. These treatments bring about significant changes in both chemical and physical properties, and changes in the latter are attributed in large measure to reductions in molecular size. Although such changes are often detected by means of intrinsic or limiting viscosity measurements, the method is not suitable for control work, nor can it be recommended for accurate appraisal of molecular size of most starches containing mixtures of amylose and amylopectin which differ in both molecular size and structure.

Even though limiting viscosity may be deficient for the fundamental characterization of heterogeneous polymer mixtures, it does have value in the determination of the extent of degradation occurring during starch modifications involving hydrolysis. However, since the method is time-consuming and not suited for control analysis, simplified procedures have been employed. One of the earliest one-point procedures was the alkali fluidity method introduced by Buel (52) in 1912; fluidity is the reciprocal of viscosity. Modifications of the Buel procedure continue in use, one of the most significant being that of Fetzer and Kirst (*53*), who selected sample concentrations related to the extent of molecular degradation. While these methods have much practical value for control purposes, the starch and alkali concentrations employed do not provide molecular dispersions or solutions, and geometrics of the measuring units do not permit a rational viscosity determination. Consequently, the results correlate poorly with limiting viscosity.

To overcome these deficiencies, the Corn Industries Research Foundation, Inc., sponsored at Lehigh University the development of an acceptable standard procedure in cooperation with the Foundation's Analytical Procedures Sub-Committee. The resulting inherent viscosity (*54*) method has been adopted as a standard procedure in the corn wet-milling industry.

Because inherent viscosities as well as limiting viscosities of un-modified and slightly modified starches are shear-rate dependent, and because samples must be properly dispersed to obtain inter- and intra-laboratory agreement, the standard method (*54*) has been carefully detailed. A size 75, Catalog No. CUBU Cannon–Ubbelohde capillary viscometer (*55*; Cannon Instrument Co., P.O. Box 812, State College, Pa.), or equivalent, should be used. It should be scrupulously cleaned and dried before using. The viscometer is filled with chromic acid cleaning solution and allowed to stand 2 hr. at room temperature. It is then drained and rinsed with a large volume of distilled water to insure complete removal of acid. The viscometer is next attached to a vacuum source by means of rubber tubing and clean air is drawn through the unit until it is dry (about 10 min.). The viscometer is cleaned periodically in this fashion or whenever doubt exists concerning the condition of the unit.

The sample must be adequately dispersed to obtain precision and interlaboratory agreement. A constant-speed (shaft speed 750 rpm.) stirring motor equipped with a self-centering chuck is recommended, but a resistance- or governor-controlled motor operating at a shaft speed of 750 rpm. may be used alternatively. A 2-in. (5-cm.) diameter hoop-type propeller (Arthur H. Thomas Co., Catalog No. 9240-U) is attached to a $\frac{5}{16}$-in. (8-mm.) shaft held by the chuck.

The moisture content of the ground (if necessary) and well-blended sample is determined by one of the procedures described in Section II,1, and a portion containing 1.000 g. of dry substance is weighed accurately and transferred quantitatively to a 400-ml., tall-form beaker. Exactly 100.0 ml. of distilled water at 25° is added to the sample, and the beaker is positioned in a constant temperature water bath, operating at

25.0° ± 0.1°, so that the bath liquid will be above the starch solution level after the addition of sodium hydroxide solution. The stirring assembly is lowered into the beaker and fixed in position with the hoop-type propeller centrally located about ⅛ in. (3 mm.) above the bottom of the beaker. The stirring motor is started, and stirring is continued at 750 rpm. until the sample is dispersed (about 2 min.). The sample dispersion is stirred while 100.0 ml. of 2.00 ± 0.02M sodium hydroxide solution is added by pipet, holding the pipet tip against the inside wall of the beaker so that the solution is delivered at a relatively slow rate. The dispersion is stirred for 30 min. at 750 rpm. after the addition of sodium hydroxide solution is complete. At this point, the starch solution should appear uniform and free of lumps; the presence of any incompletely dispersed starch lumps is sufficient reason for rejecting the dispersion. The stirring assembly is then removed, and the beaker is covered with a watch glass or other suitable closure to prevent evaporation. The starch solution is then gravity-filtered through a 6.0-cm. coarse porosity, fritted glass funnel, after which it is ready for viscosity determination.

A short length of rubber tubing is attached to the upper capillary of the clean and dry Cannon–Ubbelohde viscometer. With the aid of a standard Neoprene rubber holder, the viscometer is fixed in the constant temperature (25.0° ± 0.1°) water bath in a vertical position so that the bath liquid level is above the meniscus bulb. Ten milliliters of filtered starch solution is pipetted into the charge bulb. The viscometer vent is covered with a finger; suction is applied to the rubber tubing attached to the upper capillary, and starch solution is drawn into the meniscus bulb. Suction is released; the vent is opened, and the solution is allowed to drain from the meniscus and efflux bulbs. These bulbs are flushed a second time in the same manner with the starch solution.

The starch solution is again drawn into the meniscus bulb as described in the preceding paragraph. After releasing the suction and opening the vent, the time required for the solution meniscus to flow from the upper timing mark to the lower timing mark (sample solution efflux time) is determined accurately (within 0.1 sec.) while the solution flows from the meniscus and efflux bulbs. This operation should be repeated to obtain a series of three readings from which the mean value is calculated. The viscosity of the starch solution decreases slightly during this period, but the rate of decrease is small and uniform, and the mean of three successive readings is a reproducible result.

The sample solution is drained from the viscometer which is then rinsed with distilled water; it is then rinsed with 1M sodium hydroxide solution followed by a large volume of distilled water to insure complete removal of sodium hydroxide, and aspirated with clean air until dry.

The *clean* viscometer is positioned in the constant temperature bath as before, and 10 ml. of 1.00M sodium hydroxide solution is pipetted into the charge bulb. The 1.00M sodium hydroxide solution should be prepared by adding 100.0 ml. of the 2.00 $\pm$ 0.02M sodium hydroxide solution used for sample preparation to 100.0 ml. of distilled water, followed by mixing. The meniscus and efflux bulbs are rinsed with the solution, and the flow time (solvent efflux time) is determined accurately by the procedure described in the preceding paragraphs. Relative (η_r) and inherent (η_i) viscosities are calculated from the solvent (t_o) and sample (t_s) efflux times as described in the following equations:

Relative viscosity. $\eta_r = t_s/t_o$

Inherent viscosity, η_i, in deciliters per gram $= \dfrac{2.303 \times \log \eta_r}{0.5 \text{ g.}}$

4. Hot Paste Viscosity

Substantially all starch applications involve the use of cooked pastes. In some instances, the user receives the product in granular form and prepares cooked pastes to suit his particular needs, while in other instances the starch supplier precooks and dries the material so as to supply the market with pregelatinized products. Heating or cooking aqueous suspensions of granular starches cause the granules to become highly hydrated and swell to many times their original volume (*56*). Continued cooking, particularly in the presence of shear, produces cooked pastes which are mixtures of swollen granules, granule fragments, and molecularly dispersed starch leached from the granules (*57*).

Changes in granule dimensions and structure during the cooking process are accompanied by significant changes in the viscosity and other rheological properties (*58*; see also Volume I, Chapter XVI) of the paste. These are important to starch processors and users alike because they reflect processing and equipment requirements during the preparation of usable products and because they indicate utility of products in specific applications.

Methods for the determination of starch paste viscosities have been the subject of considerable research and much controversy. Reviews by Fetzer (*59*) and by Mason and Fetzer (*60*) reveal a variety of procedures based on rotational devices and flow-through orifices. Most methods in common use measure consistency of which viscosity is the principal component. The dynamic method developed by Myers and Knauss (Chapter XVI, Volume I) gives both viscosity and coefficient of rigidity of the cooked paste, the latter being a function of elasticity.

Methods described here are representative of those used by manufacturers of corn and grain sorghum starches and their modifications and derivatives.

a. *Procedure with the Brabender Amylograph*

The Brabender Amylograph shown in Figure 4 (Brabender Corporation, Rochelle Park, New Jersey) is a rotational instrument which permits continuous determination of viscosity or consistency while cooking and cooling the starch paste. Similar information can be obtained with the VISCO-amylo-GRAPH (C. W. Brabender Instruments, Inc., South Hackensack, New Jersey). The rotating sample cup or bowl contains a number of fixed vertical pins and is driven at constant speed

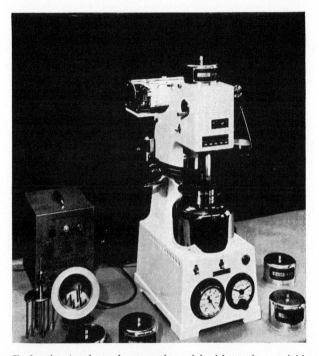

FIG. 4.—Brabender Amylograph, research model with stepless variable speed control, interchangeable sensitivity cartridges, and zero suppression attachment.

by a synchronous motor. A circular metal disk with several metal pins projecting vertically downward into the sample serves as the sensing element. Rotation of the viscous sample exerts a force on the sensing element which is dynamically balanced by a calibrated torsion spring. Application of this restoring force is accompanied by an angular deflection of the sensing element shaft, and this is recorded continuously on a strip chart recorder.

The sample cup is positioned in an electrically heated air bath, and a cooling coil projects into the cup. Heating and cooling are controlled by a mechanically operated thermoregulator which maintains a constant temperature, or which increases or decreases the temperature at a constant rate of 1.5° per minute. Meanwhile, the viscosity or consistency is recorded continuously. In some laboratories, the instrument is calibrated with standard oils so that results can be presented optionally in absolute viscosity units.

The method of Schoch and co-workers (61) is recommended, but alternative procedures, such as that of Anker and Geddes (62), will be obvious to those familiar with the instrument and with starch paste characteristics.

A weighed sample containing an appropriate amount of starch dry substance is placed in a 500-ml. beaker; the sample weight depends on the sample source and history and may range from as little as 2 g. for an unmodified potato starch to as much as 150 g. for a highly modified product such as a dextrin. It is desirable to select a sample weight or concentration that will produce a scale deflection of 50% or more at the important points in the viscosity recording during the cooking and cooling cycle. About 250 ml. of distilled water is added to the sample and the mixture is shaken or stirred to form a lump-free suspension. At this point, additives may be incorporated if their effects are being investigated, or, a buffer may be added or the pH adjusted so as to control pH of the paste during the analysis. The slurry is transferred quantitatively to a 500-ml. volumetric flask, diluted to volume with water at 25°, and mixed. The sample slurry is then trasferred to the sample cup in the instrument; the sensing element is placed in position, and the instrument head is lowered into the operating position, the thermoregulator having previously been adjusted to 25°. A short-stem thermometer can be mounted adjacent to the thermoregulator so that it dips into the sample, permitting temperature determination independent of the thermoregulator.

The instrument is started, and temperature of the sample is increased at a rate of 1.5° per minute. Heating is continued until the sample temperature reaches 95°, and the sample is maintained at this temperature for 1 hr. while stirring and recording the viscosity continuously. The paste is then cooled to 50° at a rate of 1.5° per minute and held 1 hr. at this temperature while stirring. Heating and cooling at the specified rate and holding at the specified temperatures are accomplished automatically by the instrument controls.

When the Brabender curves for several concentrations of a given sample are replotted and superimposed on rectangular coordinates, a family of curves similar to that shown in Figure 5 is obtained. These contain five successive points of significant interest (61):

A. The peak viscosity, irrespective of the temperature, indicates the highest viscosity that the user might encounter during the preparation of a usable paste.

B. The viscosity of the paste when it reaches a temperature of 95°, in relation to the peak viscosity, reflects the ease of cooking the starch.

C. The viscosity after cooking 1 hr. at 95° indicates the stability or breakdown of the paste.

D. The viscosity of the cooked paste after cooling to 50° is a measure of the setback produced by cooling.

E. The final viscosity after stirring 1 hr. at 50° indicates the stability of the cooked paste as it might be used.

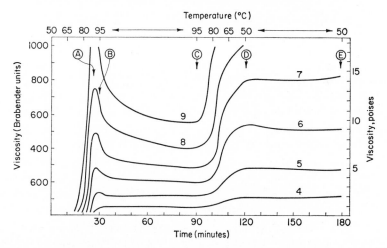

FIG. 5.—Brabender curves of a thick-boiling corn starch. Letter keys indicate significant viscosity reference points (see text). Numerals indicate concentration in g. per 100 ml.

When evaluating starches from different sources or with different histories of chemical and physical treatments or both, complete cooking and cooling curves are determined for each sample at 5 to 8 concentrations chosen to cover the range of the Brabender instrument. Viscosities corresponding to each significant point, outlined above, may be taken from the resulting family of curves and plotted on linear coordinates against logarithm of sample concentration (Fig. 6). This plotting technique facilitates direct comparison of samples as different as thick-boiling and thin-boiling starches because a 100% change in concentration on the logarithmic concentration ordinate is represented by the same linear distance at all concentrations.

b. *Procedure with the Corn Industries Viscometer*

The Corn Industries Viscometer (Fig. 7), marketed by the Gaertner Scientific Corporation, Chicago, Illinois, is another rotational instrument designed especially for continuous measurement of viscosity or consistency during the preparation of a starch paste under standard conditions. The removable sample cup is fixed in a stationary position in a constant

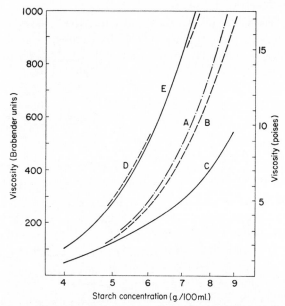

Fig. 6.—Viscosities at significant reference points in Figure 5 plotted as a function of logarithm of starch concentration in g. per 100 ml. Letter keys indicate significant reference points described in text.

temperature water bath which can be maintained at any desired temperature. The sample is stirred by an assembly composed of a scrapper and propeller attached to concentric shafts driven in opposite directions at constant speed by a synchronous motor. The propeller is driven through a differential gear arrangement which detects and transmits propeller torque to a dynamometer. The restoring force supplied by the dynamometer to balance the propeller torque is recorded continuously on a strip chart recorder.

The recommended operating procedure is that of Kesler and Bechtel (*63*), who developed the instrument under the auspices of the Corn Industries Research Foundation, Inc. Other operating techniques, such as the suggested TAPPI method (*64*), will be apparent to those familiar with the instrument and with starch paste characteristics.

A weighed sample containing an appropriate amount of starch dry substance is placed in a 1500-ml. beaker, and distilled water at room temperature is added to bring the total dispersion weight to 1000 g. The actual sample weight is a function of starch origin and history; concentrations in the range of 4% (w/w) are most suitable for unmodified starches while concentrations in the range of 25%, or higher, are suitable for highly oxidized or thin-boiling starches. The mixture is stirred to form a lump-free suspension, and this is transferred to the sample cup of the operating viscometer with the constant temperature water bath

FIG. 7.—Corn Industries Viscometer.

regulated at 92°. Other temperatures may be selected if the investigator is interested in the effect of cooking temperature on paste characteristics. The cup is covered with the condenser on which is mounted a thermometer that dips into the sample.

The remainder of the test is accomplished automatically as the sample viscosity, in gram-centimeters torque, is recorded continuously during the cooking cycle. Torque values are sometimes converted to more basic viscosity units, that is, poises, if the instrument is calibrated with viscosity standards.

Ordinarily, the test is discontinued at the end of 20 min. This provides the sample viscosity at any time during the cooking cycle, and if desired, the corresponding sample temperature can be noted during the operation. The duration of the test can be extended if stability or breakdown of the paste during cooking is important. On the other hand, if the setback produced by cooling or if low temperature stability of the cooked paste are important, the sample viscosity can be recorded continuously after turning off the bath heater and circulating cold water through the water bath.

Fig. 8.—Modified Scott Viscometer developed by Corn Products Company.

The latter method provides information similar to that obtained by the recommended procedure of Schoch and co-workers (61), particularly when the logarithm of viscosity at significant points on the curve is plotted as a function of the logarithm of sample concentration as suggested by Bechtel (65).

c. Scott Hot Paste Procedure

Although designed originally for the evaluation of petroleum products, the Scott viscometer, a flow-through orifice device, has been modified and adapted to the determination of viscosities of hot starch pastes. The modification developed by Corn Products Company (Fig. 8) is used extensively for the evaluation of unmodified, acid-modified, oxidized, and derivatized corn and grain sorghum starches as well as other starches. The principal unit is a specially constructed water bath maintained at the boiling point by introducing live steam. Samples are cooked in metal beakers, designed to permit reproducible placement in the bath, while stirring at constant speed with a special paddle driven by a synchronous motor. Flow characteristics of the cooked paste are determined with the Scott cup which is maintained in a chamber of the bath. The cup contains an accurately machined and polished orifice through which the sample paste flows and an overflow to assure a reproducible sample head.

In practice, an appropriate weight of sample, often calculated on a 12% moisture basis, is placed in a Scott beaker, and 280 ml. of distilled water at room temperature is added; the mixture is stirred to insure a lump-free suspension. It is customary to select a sample weight which will give a cooked paste delivering 100-ml. paste volume through the standard orifice in 40 to 80 seconds. The beaker is then placed in the bath; the stirring assembly is lowered into position, and the sample is cooked for exactly 5 min. while stirring at 200 rpm. The stirring motor is stopped; the paddle is removed, and the beaker is covered with a watch glass.

At the end of 10 min. elapsed time, the sample is stirred manually at a similar rate for 10 sec. At the end of 13 min. elapsed time, the watch glass is removed and adhering condensate is allowed to drain into the sample beaker. The sample is again stirred manually for 10 sec., and then transferred to the Scott cup, filling to a level above the overflow. At the end of 15 min. elapsed time, the plunger closing the orifice is raised, and the time, in seconds, required to deliver 100 ml. of paste into a graduated cylinder is observed.

This procedure provides a viscosity value at only one time point in the cooking cycle. Information indicating the high-temperature stability of a cooked paste can be obtained by repeating the test using an extended cooking time. Simplicity, speed, and precision of the Scott hot-paste procedure render it an effective tool in the starch manufacturing industry for process control and finished product analysis. It should be remembered, however, that the Scott value is a viscosity-dominated consistency value rather than a true viscosity because the standard orifice has a small length-to-diameter ratio which precludes laminar flow, a prerequisite for rational measurement of viscosity.

d. *Procedure with the Brookfield Viscometer*

Instrument portability and procedure simplicity have promoted increasing use of the Brookfield Synchro-Lectric Viscometer (Fig. 9;

Brookfield Engineering Laboratories, Inc., Stoughton, Massachusetts) by starch users as well as manufacturers. The instrument employs a rotating cylinder or disk, referred to as a spindle, driven by a constant speed synchronous motor. The drive shaft is connected to the spindle shaft through a torsion spring which provides the restoring force to balance the viscous resistance to rotation of the spindle. Application of

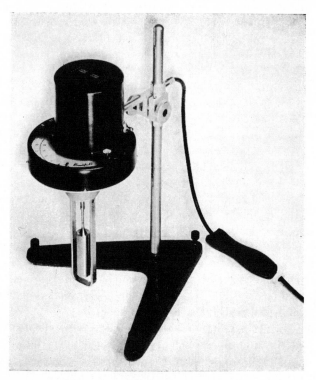

FIG. 9.—Brookfield Synchro-Lectric Viscometer.

the restoring force is accompanied by an angular deflection of the spindle shaft relative to the drive shaft. This deflection is proportional to sample viscosity and spindle size and speed, and it is indicated on the viscometer scale.

The Brookfield Viscometer is equipped with several spindles of different size, and the instrument contains a gear transmission permitting spindle rotation at several speeds. These features permit determination of viscosities over a broad range even though the instrument is limited to a single torque range defined by the torsion spring because viscosity is related also to size and speed of the spindle. Thus, low viscosity samples might best be evaluated with large spindles at high speeds, and high-viscosity samples with small spindles at slow speeds.

To evaluate a starch sample, an aqueous suspension containing an appropriate percentage of dry substance is stirred in a metal beaker or other suitable container until free of lumps. Actual concentration may be as low as 2–3% for an unmodified starch or lower for a cross-bonded product, and as high as 50–60% for a highly modified starch product, such as a dextrin. The beaker is then placed in a boiling water or steam bath, and the starch suspension is cooked while stirring in a prescribed manner. The time of heating will usually be about 30 min., but will depend on the volume of suspension and type of sample, and it should be sufficiently long to bring the paste temperature to about 95°. In routine sample evaluation, the type and vigor of stirring, the rate of temperature rise, and the cooking time should be reproduced from sample to sample.

The viscosity of the cooked paste may be determined immediately after preparation with the Brookfield Viscometer, or after cooling at a prescribed rate to a lower temperature while stirring. Since most starch pastes are non-Newtonian, viscosities may be determined with several spindles at different speeds to obtain data indicating the shear dependence. The same spindle and speed should be employed in all sample comparisons involving a single observation, and the spindle number and speed should be reported with all calculated viscosities.

e. *Other Procedures*

The preceding sections describe the application of only four devices commonly used in the characterization of starch pastes. Three of these are rotational instruments, but a complete list of rotational devices that have been applied to starch pastes would include the Rotovisco, the Ferranti-Shirley Cone-Plate viscometer, the Fann V-G meter, the Stormer and MacMichael viscometers, the Hercules Hi-Shear instrument, and many others. The falling or rolling ball and the falling plunger principles have been employed with some success. These and other commercial instruments are described by Van Wazer and co-workers (66). Still, the simple and unsophisticated flow-through orifice instrument, as represented by the Scott Viscometer, is used most extensively for quality control in the starch processing industry. A variety of glass and metal vessels, of substantially cylindrical geometry to which standard orifices can be attached, have become analytical tools for process viscosity control.

Although a few starch viscosity and consistency measuring devices accomplish paste preparation and property measurement more or less simultaneously, most present day approaches separate preparation and measurement. It must be remembered, however, that the viscometric and/or rheological properties of starch pastes are functions of the method of preparation as well as sample origin and history. Consequently, it is imperative that adequate and reproducible pasting procedures be employed prior to paste characterization.

5. Gel Strength

Gelling tendencies of cooked pastes of native starches vary considerably, the most significant factor being the concentrations of linear and branched polymers (amylose and amylopectin). In addition, gelling tendencies are influenced significantly by the type and degree of starch modification and/or derivatization, and the strengths of starch gels are affected by the gelatinization procedure and by the incorporation of additives. For these reasons, starch gel strength information is relative in character; evaluation of starch modification, derivatization, or the incorporation of additives, requires standardization of gel preparation and examination procedures.

Advances in starch gel strength procedures have been few since the subject was reviewed by Kerr (67) in 1950. The embedded disk method of Saare and Martens (68) and later modifications (67, 69, 70) are employed most frequently. The improved procedure of Hjermstad (71) employs the embedded disk principle and utilizes the Corn Industries Gelometer (Fig. 10; Gaertner Scientific Corporation, 1201 Wrightwood Ave., Chicago, Illinois), an accessory to the Corn Industries Viscometer (refer to Section III,4,b). The Hjermstad procedure is preferred to methods utilizing the plunger (72–74) and torsion (75) principles; it provides data on degree of deformation as well as yield point of starch gels.

Product comparisons and determination of the effects of type and degree of modification or derivatization on starch gel strengths require reproducible preparation of starch pastes and gels. Reproducible cooking is best accomplished in the Scott bath, in the Brabender Amylograph, or in the Corn Industries Viscometer as described in Section III,4; the latter instrument is employed when the Corn Industries Gelometer is available for gel strength determination. Sample concentration will depend on the product type, and it will generally be equal to or greater than that used for hot paste viscosity measurement. Immediately after cooking and after reconstitution with water to the original sample–water slurry weight if excessive evaporation occurs during cooking, the paste is poured into the 150-ml., wide-mouth gel jar (59 mm. I.D. $\times$ 85 mm. tall); it is filled so that the liquid level will be 3.0 cm. above the disk when the disk is supported by the slotted cover. The disk assembly consists of a circular metal disc, 19 mm. in diameter; a 2.2 mm. diameter metal rod is attached to the disk, centrally and perpendicularly. The upper end of the rod is fashioned into a hook, and the distance from the upper end of the hook to the disk is about 80 mm. A small metal washer that is affixed to the metal rod about 25 mm. below the hook rests on the slotted jar cover and supports the disk assembly during gel formation. The disk is inserted in the sample; the slotted cover is placed on the flat lip of the gel jar with the hook projecting through the slot, and the disk is supported in the center of the sample by the washer affixed

FIG. 10.—Corn Industries Gelometer — an accessory for use with the Corn Industries Viscometer.

to the rod of the disk assembly. The surface of the paste is carefully covered with a thin layer of mineral oil to prevent evaporation while aging. The gel jar with sample is placed in a level position in a constant temperature bath at 20° or 25°, the latter being preferred, and the sample is aged at least 2 hr.; longer periods are generally required to obtain maximum gel strengths.

The jar with the conditioned gel is clamped in the Gelometer (Fig. 10), and the cover is carefully removed. The cord from the dynamometer of the Corn Industries Viscometer is attached to the hook of the disk assembly, and the jar height is adjusted so that the pen on the strip-chart recorder rests on the zero line. The jar-lowering and chart drive motors are started simultaneously. Thereafter, the test is performed automatically; the force exerted as the jar is lowered increases until the yield value is reached. The force-time plot increases regularly during the early portion of the test, and levels off or drops sharply when the yield point is reached.

The force in gram-centimeters (g.-cm.) corresponding to the yield value or gel strength can be read directly from the chart, or converted to grams by dividing by the effective radius, in centimeters, of the cable drum in the dynamometer of the Corn Industries Viscometer. The deformation, in centimeters, of the gel at any point during the test or at the yield point can be calculated by subtracting the distance traveled by the disk (a force function) from the vertical distance traveled by the jar.

If the Corn Industries Viscometer and Gelometer accessory are not available, a modification of the method of Saare and Martens (68) requires only a single beam, two-pan balance. The paste and conditioned gel with disk embedded therein are prepared as described in the preceding paragraphs. The jar and gelled sample are placed on an adjustable platform above the left pan of the balance. The jar cover is carefully removed; the jar is positioned so that the disk assembly is vertically below the stirrup hook, and the latter is connected to the disk assembly hook by means of a wire with hooks at both ends. The platform supporting the sample jar is lowered to remove slack from the connecting hooks. The balance beam is released and small shot, or a liquid of suitable density, are added at a slow and uniform rate to a tared dish on the right-hand pan; the addition is stopped at the instant the gel breaks. The weight, in grams, of shot or liquid, less the weight of the disk assembly and wire hook connecting the stirrup hook, is the gel strength. This value is sometimes divided by the disk area, and the gel strength reported as grams per square centimeter for a given starch concentration.

IV. DERIVATIVE METHODS

1. Acetyl

Starch acetates having low degrees of substitution (D.S.) are prepared commercially by treating an aqueous starch slurry with acetic anhydride under mildly alkaline conditions at temperatures substantially below the gelatinization point. High D.S. products are usually prepared by treating a dry, pregelatinized starch, sometimes defatted, with acetic anhydride and pyridine at the reflux temperature (76).

The acetyl contents of these derivatives and of the acetates of other simple sugars and polysaccharides can be determined accurately by the transesterification procedure of Whistler and Jeanes (77). However, since the method requires absolutely anhydrous reaction conditions which are achieved only with meticulous care, the procedure is recommended only for referee work and for the establishment of proper reaction conditions in other methods. Acetyl contents of these derivatives are commonly determined by modifications of the alkali saponification techniques described by Genung and Mallatt (78). Low D.S. products (D.S. below 0.3) encountered most frequently are saponified in an aqueous system and high D.S. products in aqueous alcohol.

Although not absolutely essential, it is generally recommended that the sample be freed of extraneous residual materials prior to analysis. If the sample is a granular, cold-water-insoluble product, this is readily accomplished by washing with distilled water. If the product is soluble in water, a 1–2% solution is dialyzed 30–40 hr. against running distilled water, and the sample is recovered by freeze-drying or by precipitation in several volumes of acetone. The latter precipitate can be recovered by vacuum filtration, and freed of water and acetone by washing with anhydrous ethanol. In either method of preparation, the sample can be dried in a vacuum oven prior to analysis, or the volatiles content can be determined by vacuum oven drying, so as to permit calculation of degree of substitution.

In the analysis of low D.S. products, about 5 g. of finely ground sample, either predried or of known volatiles content, is weighed accurately and placed in a 250-ml. Erlenmeyer flask and suspended in 50 ml. of distilled water. After addition of a few drops of phenolphthalein indicator, the suspension is titrated with 0.1N sodium hydroxide to a permanent pink end point. Then, 25.0 ml. of 0.45N sodium hydroxide solution is added, taking care not to wet the neck of the flask. The flask is sealed tightly with a rubber stopper and shaken vigorously for 30 min.; a mechanical shaker is recommended.

After shaking, the stopper is carefully removed and washed down, together with the walls of the flask, with a fine stream of distilled water. The saponified sample mixture, containing excess alkali, is then titrated with standard 0.2N hydrochloric acid to the disappearance of the phenolphthalein color.

In the analysis of high D.S. starch acetates, about 1 g. of finely ground sample, either predried or of known volatiles content, is weighed accurately and placed in a 250-ml. Erlenmeyer flask, and 50 ml. of 75%

ethanol in distilled water is added. The flask is loosely stoppered, and the contents are warmed to 50° while stirring and held at this temperature for 30 min. After cooling to room temperature, 40 ml. of 0.5N potassium hydroxide solution is added while swirling; the flask is stoppered and allowed to stand 72 hr. at room temperature with occasional swirling. The excess alkali is titrated with standard 0.3N hydrochloric acid using phenolphthalein as indicator. Additional alkali which might leach from the sample is titrated after the mixture is permitted to stand an additional 2 hr.

Starches and their derivatives treated with caustic in either the aqueous or alcoholic systems outlined above undergo minor degradation with consequent caustic consumption. Therefore, it is necessary to treat a portion of the underivatized original starch in the same manner to obtain a blank value. From this and the sample titer, the D.S. is calculated as follows:

Percent acetyl (dry basis) =
$$\frac{(\text{Blank titer} - \text{Sample titer}) \text{ milliliters} \times \text{Acid normality} \times 0.043 \times 100}{\text{Sample weight in grams (dry basis)}}$$

$$\text{Degree of Substitution (D.S.)} = \frac{162A}{4300 - 42A}$$

in which A = percent acetyl (dry basis).

2. Alkoxyl (Methoxyl and Ethoxyl)

Starch can be methylated in a number of ways (79, 80) to produce methyl ethers having properties substantially different from those of the original starch. The degree of change in the physical properties thus altered is a function of the extent of reaction or degree of substitution (D.S.) of the product. The methoxyl content, or the ethoxyl content if the sample is an ethylated starch, is determined by a modification of the basic method of Zeisel (81), which involves cleavage of the ether linkage with hydriodic acid and quantitative formation and determination of the corresponding methyl or ethyl iodides. Many modifications of the original method have been applied to various sample types (82). The technique recommended here is similar in most respects to those recommended by Vieböck and Schwappach (83) and by Clark (84).

Commercial products will not contain significant amounts of alkylating reagent or alcohol residues which would react with hydriodic acid to yield the corresponding alkyl iodides and, therefore, interfere in the determination of combined alkoxyl groups. Products prepared in the laboratory should be purified before analysis by the techniques suggested by Smith and co-workers (79). In general, low D.S. water-soluble products may be purified when necessary by dialyzing a 1–2%

aqueous solution in a cellophane tube against running distilled water for 30–40 hr. The product is recovered by concentrating and freeze-drying. Low D.S. cold-water-insoluble products can be freed of interfering residues by slurrying in and washing with water. High D.S. products which are water-insoluble can be dissolved in chloroform and the solution washed with water. The chloroform solution is then dried over anhydrous sodium sulfate and evaporated to dryness under reduced pressure. The residue is powdered and redried at 100° under reduced pressure before analysis.

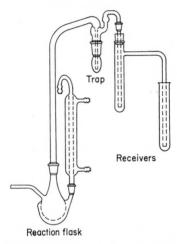

Fig. 11.—Apparatus for determination of alkoxyl groups.

The apparatus shown in Figure 11 consists of a double-boiler-type reaction vessel; capacities of both the inner and outer chambers are about 50–75 ml. The outer chamber or jacket has a single neck to which is attached a small water-cooled condenser. A 1-mm. I.D., heavy-walled gas inlet tube is attached to the inner or reaction chamber, which also has a centrally located neck for attachment of a glass column serving as an air condenser. The column is constructed of 10-mm. I.D. glass tubing and the length is not less than about 30 cm. below the bend. A gas scrubber, bubble trap, and two receivers (150 × 18 mm. test tubes) are connected serially thereto. Gas delivery tubes in the scrubber and receivers are fashioned so that gases flowing through the apparatus are delivered well below the surface of the trapping solutions. With the exception of the rubber stopper connection in the first receiver, all connections should be fashioned with standard-tapered ground glass joints as indicated in the accompanying figure or with ball and socket ground glass joints which give the apparatus greater flexibility and minimize breakage.

In operation, the outer jacket of the reaction vessel is filled about three-fourths full with a solvent mixture composed of 95 parts (by volume) of mixed xylenes and 5 parts of *n*-butyl alcohol (1-butanol). This mixture boils at a temperature causing the hydriodic acid in the inner chamber to reflux at about half the height of the glass column, and the composition of the mixture can be adjusted to achieve this condition. The inner reaction flask is charged with 7.5 ml. of molten phenol and 15 ml. of concentrated (specific gravity 1.7, 57% HI) methoxyl-grade hydriodic acid; the volumes of reagents may be increased proportionately if large samples are analyzed. Two or three small silicon carbide granules should be added to prevent bumping. The scrubber is charged with a solution containing equal parts of 5% aqeuous cadmium sulfate and 5% aqueous sodium thiosulfate in sufficient volume so that the inlet tube delivers the gas stream well below the liquid surface. The apparatus is assembled as shown in the accompanying figure, and a close-fitting heating mantle that is controlled by a variable transformer is placed in position around the lower half of the reaction vessel.

The gas inlet tube is connected to a carbon dioxide source. A convenient supply is a small (1-pint) Dewar flask with a narrow neck filled with solid carbon dioxide (Dry Ice). The flask is closed with a 2-hole rubber stopper fitted with two short lengths of glass tubing. One opening is attached by means of a short length of rubber tubing to a mercury trap serving as a pressure relief valve. The other opening is attached by means of rubber tubing, fitted with a screw clamp, to the gas inlet. The screw clamp is adjusted to give a carbon dioxide flow rate of 70–100 bubbles per minute through the apparatus, as observed in the cadmium sulfate–sodium thiosulfate solution scrubber. The variable transformer controlling the heating mantle is adjusted to bring the solvent mixture in the outer jacket to a gentle boil, and heat is applied in this manner for 30 min. while purging the apparatus with carbon dioxide.

Twelve drops of reagent-grade bromine are added to 15 ml. of glacial acetic acid containing 1.5 g. of potassium acetate dissolved therein. After mixing, 10 ml. of this absorbing solution is poured into the first receiver and the remainder in the last receiver. The receivers are attached to the apparatus as indicated, and the carbon dioxide flow rate is readjusted, if necessary, to 70–100 bubbles per minute.

A portion of the prepared and dried sample containing about 2–4 mg. of methoxyl is weighed accurately in a small glass vial. This may be constructed of a short length (15 mm.) of glass tubing with one end closed and flattened to facilitate weighing. The sample need not be dry if the moisture or volatiles content is known, but it must be free of reagent residues and solvents which react with hydriodic acid giving volatile alkyl iodides.

The heating mantle is removed from the reaction vessel, and the latter is allowed to cool a few minutes. The reaction vessel is disconnected from the apparatus; the glass vial with sample is introduced, and the vessel is quickly reconnected to the apparatus. The heating mantle is repositioned and heat is reapplied so that the solvent mixture refluxes for a period of 40 min. while carbon dioxide flows through the system at a rate of 70–100 bubbles per minute. The reaction is frequently rather vigorous immediately after sample introduction, which requires some adjustment of the carbon dioxide flow rate.

The receivers are removed from the apparatus without interrupting the carbon dioxide flow rate. With the aid of distilled water, the absorbing solutions in both receivers are transferred quantitatively to a 250-ml. flask containing 5 ml. of 25% sodium acetate solution, and the solution is diluted to about 100 ml. with water. Concentrated formic acid is added dropwise until the yellow color of the bromine is discharged, and 12 drops in excess are added. The solution is mixed and allowed to stand about 2 min.

Ten milliliters of 1:9 sulfuric acid solution is added followed by 10 ml. of 15% potassium iodide solution. The liberated iodine is titrated immediately and rapidly with standard $0.1N$ sodium thiosulfate solution. When the end point is approached, as evidenced by nearly complete elimination of the yellow color of the iodine, 1 ml. of starch indicator solution is added, and the titration is completed by dropwise addition of the thiosulfate solution until the characteristic blue starch–iodine color disappears.

A blank determination is performed on all reagents in the same manner.

Percent methoxyl ($-OCH_3$) =

$$\frac{(\text{Sample titer} - \text{Blank titer}) \text{ milliliters} \times \text{Thiosulfate normality} \times 0.031 \times 100}{\text{Dry sample weight in grams} \times 6}$$

$$\text{Degree of Substitution (D.S.)} = \frac{162M}{3100 - 14M}$$

in which M = percent methoxyl (dry basis).

The apparatus described here is ideally suited to a laboratory performing many alkoxyl determinations. When the inner reaction chamber is charged with 10 ml. of molten phenol and 20 ml. of hydriodic acid, as many as four determinations can be performed consecutively without recharging the apparatus with reagents, except the absorbing solution in the receivers. When such procedure is followed, the reaction time is increased 5 min. for each succeeding sample to insure complete reaction, and the contents of the vessel are discarded after the fourth analysis.

A reaction vessel without the outer jacket for temperature control may also be employed; in this case, the reaction chamber must be heated carefully with the heating mantle or a shielded microburner so as to obtain the proper rate of reflux.

Ethyl ethers of starch are analyzed in substantially the same way. The principal difference is the substitution of the milliequivalent weight of 0.045 for the value of 0.031 in the equation for calculation of methoxyl content. Experience will dictate whether the reaction time should be extended to insure complete reaction. The equation for calculating D.S. becomes:

$$\text{Degree of Substitution (D.S.)} = \frac{162E}{4500 - 28E}$$

n which E = percent ethoxyl (dry basis).

3. Hydroxyalkoxyl (Hydroxyethyl and Hydroxypropyl)

Starch can be reacted in several ways with ethylene oxide or propylene oxide to produce the corresponding hydroxyethyl- or hydroxypropylstarch ethers (85). The degree of substitution of these industrially important products is determined by a modification of the hydriodic acid hydrolysis method of Zeisel (81). In studies on hydroxyethylcellulose and other ethylene glycol ethers, Morgan (86) found that reaction with hydriodic acid yielded both alkyl iodide and the corresponding alkene, and the sum of these two products was stoichiometrically equal to the hydroxyalkyl content of the derivatized product. Lortz (87) modified the method for analysis of hydroxyalkylstarch and the method described here has been adapted therefrom.

As in methoxyl analysis, the starch products must be free of residues of ethylene oxide, ethylene glycol, alcohols, and similar materials which react with hydriodic acid to yield volatile alkyl iodides and/or alkenes. Such residues can be removed easily from most commercial derivatives which are granular, cold-water-insoluble products. A 20-g. sample is slurried in about 200 ml. of distilled water at room temperature, and the mixture is stirred for 15 min. The starch is recovered by vacuum filtration on a fritted glass or Büchner funnel and washed with 200 ml. of distilled water. The product is reslurried in and washed with water a second time, and the resulting filter cake is dried in an air oven at 38°–50°.

If the sample is a cold-water-soluble product which cannot be washed free of interferring residues in the same manner, a 1-2% aqueous solution (paste), contained in a cellophane tube, is dialyzed against running distilled water for 30–40 hr. After concentrating the solution, the product is recovered by freeze-drying.

Purified products so obtained may be dried at 100° under vacuum before analysis, or the moisture content may be determined by the method recommended in the preceding section.

The apparatus shown in Figure 12 is similar in many respects to that employed for methoxyl determination. The double boiler type reaction vessel with water-cooled condenser attached to the outer chamber and gas inlet attached to the inner reaction chamber and the

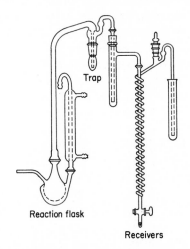

Fɪɢ. 12.—Apparatus for determination of hydroxyalkyl groups.

glass column with attached gas scrubber and bubble trap are identical. The receivers differ because alkene as well as alkyl iodide must be recovered quantitatively. The first receiver which contains the silver nitrate solution for recovery of alkyl iodide is constructed of an 18 × 150 mm. test tube with a side arm. The second or spiral receiver which contains a bromine solution for recovery of the alkene is constructed in the manner indicated so as to provide efficient scrubbing of the gas stream. The spiral section, about 30 cm. long and about 2.5 cm. in outer diameter, contains 20 or 21 spirals constructed of 7 mm. glass tubing. Gas passes down the vertical inlet and enters the bottom spiral. The gas outlet tube contains a bubble trap and a closable opening (standard tapered neck and plug) for introducing the absorbing solution. The last receiver is an 18 × 150 mm. test tube containing potassium iodide solution to recover bromine lost from the spiral receiver.

Gas delivery tubes in the scrubber and receivers are constructed so that gases flowing through the apparatus are delivered well below the surface of the trapping solutions. With the exception of the rubber stopper connection in the first receiver and the standard-tapered, ground glass scrubber connection, all other connections should be made with ball and socket ground glass joints which give the apparatus greater flexibility and minimize breakage.

In operation, the outer jacket of the reaction vessel is filled about three-fourths full with a solvent mixture composed of 95 parts (by volume) of mixed xylenes and 5 parts of n-butyl alcohol (1-butanol). This mixture boils at a temperature causing the hydriodic acid in the inner chamber to reflux at about half the height of the glass column, and the composition of the mixture can be adjusted to achieve this condition. The inner reaction flask is charged with 2 ml. of propionic anhydride, 2 ml. of molten phenol, and 25 ml. of concentrated (specific gravity 1.7, 57% HI) methoxyl-grade hydriodic acid; two or three small silicon carbide granules are added to prevent bumping. The scrubber is charged with a solution containing equal parts of 5% aqueous cadmium sulfate and 5% aqueous sodium thiosulfate in sufficient volume so that the inlet tube delivers the gas stream well below the liquid surface. The apparatus is assembled as indicated in Figure 12, and a close-fitting heating mantle controlled by a variable transformer is placed in position around the lower half of the reaction vessel.

The gas inlet tube is connected to a carbon dioxide source. A convenient supply is a small (1-pint) Dewar flask with a narrow neck filled with solid carbon dioxide (Dry Ice). The flask is closed with a 2-hole rubber stopper fitted with two short lengths of glass tubing. One opening is attached by means of a short length of rubber tubing to a mercury trap serving as a pressure relief valve. The other opening is attached by means of rubber tubing, fitted with a screw clamp, to the gas inlet. The screw clamp is adjusted to give a carbon dioxide flow rate of 70–100 bubbles per min. through the apparatus, as observed in the cadmium sulfate–sodium thiosulfate solution scrubber. The variable transformer controlling the heating mantle is adjusted to bring the solvent mixture in the outer jacket to a gentle boil, and heat is applied in this manner for 30 min. while purging the apparatus with carbon dioxide.

Exactly 10.0 ml. of alcoholic silver nitrate solution is added to the first receiver which is then attached to the apparatus. This absorbing solution is prepared by dissolving 15 g. of reagent-grade silver nitrate in 55 ml. of distilled water acidified with a few drops of conc. nitric acid and diluting the solution to 500 ml. with absolute ethanol.

The second or spiral receiver and the last test tube receiver are attached to the apparatus. A bromine solution for absorbing the alkene is prepared by dissolving 1.0 ml of reagent-grade bromine in 300 ml. of glacial acetic acid saturated with dry potassium bromide; 15.0 ml. is added to the spiral trap. This absorbing solution should be kept in a dark amber bottle and stored away from light when not in use. Finally, 10 ml. of 15% potassium iodide solution is added to the last receiver to recover bromine lost from the spiral receiver.

A portion of the prepared sample containing not more than 1 g. of dry starch and about 25 mg. of hydroxyethyl group (expressed as C_2H_4O) is weighed accurately in a small glass vial. This may be constructed of a short length (15 mm.) of glass tubing with one end closed and flattened to facilitate weighing. Drying prior to analysis is not essential; small amounts of moisture contributed by the sample are not detrimental.

The heating mantle is removed from the reaction vessel, and the latter is allowed to cool a few minutes. The reaction vessel is disconnected from the apparatus; the glass vial with sample is introduced, and the vessel is quickly reconnected to the apparatus. The heating mantle is repositioned and heat is reapplied so that the solvent mixture refluxes, causing the reaction mixture to reflux at about half the height of the glass column. Care should be exercised to insure tight seals at all glass connections so that none of the reaction products are lost. Heating is continued for 1 hr. while carbon dioxide flows through the assembly at a rate of 70–100 bubbles per min. The reaction is usually rather vigorous immediately after sample introduction, requiring some adjustment of the carbon dioxide flow rate.

The receivers are removed from the apparatus in reverse order without interrupting the gas flow rate and before the heat source is removed. Contents of the last receiver (potassium iodide solution) are transferred quantitatively to a 250-ml. Erlenmeyer flask with the aid of distilled water. Contents of the spiral receiver are drained into the same flask and the transfer is made quantitative by rinsing with distilled water. Ten milliliters of 5% sulfuric acid solution is added, and the liberated iodine is titrated immediately with standard $0.05N$ sodium thiosulfate solution. When the end point is approached, as evidenced by nearly complete elimination of the yellow color of the iodine, 1 ml. of starch indicator solution is added, and the titration is completed by dropwise addition of the thiosulfate solution until the characteristic blue starch–iodine color disappears.

Contents of the silver nitrate solution receiver are transferred quantitatively to another flask with the aid of distilled water. The solution is heated to boiling, cooled to room temperature, and titrated with standard $0.1N$ ammonium thiocyanate solution; about 3 ml. of saturated ferric ammonium sulfate solution acidified with a few drops of concentrated nitric acid is used for end point detection.

After completing the analysis, the apparatus is cleaned and dried and recharged with all reagents and absorbing solutions as described in the preceding paragraphs. A blank determination is performed without sample addition.

In the case of methyl ethers, it is customary to report methoxyl content ($-OCH_3$, formula weight = 31) even though the increase in molecular weight is only 14 ($-CH_2-$) per substituent group. In the case of hydroxyethyl ethers, however, it is standard practice to calculate percentage of C_2H_4O, which is equivalent to the molecular weight increase per substituent group, and equivalent to the reagent, ethylene oxide. The percentage of combined C_2H_4O is equivalent to the sum of the ethyl iodide and ethylene produced by hydriodic acid decomposition.

Percent C_2H_4O ($-C_2H_5I$) =

$$\frac{(\text{Blank titer} - \text{Sample titer}) \text{ milliliters} \times \text{Thiocyanate normality}}{\text{Dry sample weight in grams}} \times 0.044 \times 100$$

Percent C_2H_4O ($-C_2H_4$) =

$$\frac{(\text{Blank titer} - \text{Sample titer}) \text{ milliliters} \times \text{Thiosulfate normality}}{\text{Dry sample weight in grams}} \times 0.022 \times 100$$

$$\text{Degree of Substitution (D.S.)} = \frac{162\ HE}{4400 - 44\ HE}$$

in which HE = total percent C_2H_4O (dry basis).

Hydroxypropylstarch is analyzed in the same way but milliequivalent weights of 0.058 and 0.029 are substituted in the two equations for calculating % C_2H_4O (equivalent to the propyl iodide and propylene, respectively). The equation for calculating D.S. becomes:

$$\text{Degree of Substitution (D.S.)} = \frac{162\ HP}{5800 - 58\ HP}$$

in which HP = percent C_3H_6O (dry basis).

4. Carboxyl

Oxidation of aqueous granular starch dispersions with sodium hypochlorite is one of the most commonly practiced methods of starch modification (88). Physical as well as chemical properties are altered, and the extent of the latter is indicated by measuring the carboxyl content. Carboxyl groups may also be introduced by derivatization reactions such as those used to produce carboxymethyl or carboxyethyl starch, but such products are encountered much less frequently than oxidized starches. In either case and particularly with oxidized starches, carboxyl contents are usually less than 1%, and rarely in excess of 3%.

Carboxyl contents of such products are often determined by treatment of demineralized samples with aqueous calcium acetate followed by titration of the liberated acetic acid (89). Mattisson and Legendre modified the procedure specifically for oxidized starches and found that a simplified procedure involving direct titration of a paste of the demineralized sample gave good agreement (90). This latter technique or modifications of it is commonly used in the corn wet-milling industry.

Finishing steps in the commercial processing of oxidized starches are usually in the pH range of 5 to 7, so the end products are usually the sodium salts although they often contain other cations contributed by process waters. These must be removed and the product rendered in the free acid form to permit direct titration of the carboxyl group. A finely ground sample ranging in size between 0.15 g. and 5 g. is weighed accurately, slurried in 25 ml. of 0.1N hydrochloric acid, and stirred occasionally over a period of 30 min. The sample size selected for analysis should not contain more than about 0.25 milliequivalents of carboxyl so that the hydrochloric acid is present in sufficient excess to effect complete removal of cations. The slurry is then filtered through a medium-porosity fritted-glass crucible or small funnel, and the residue is washed with distilled water until the washings are free of chloride as shown by silver nitrate test.

Samples containing high carboxyl contents, particularly derivatives that swell excessively in water at room temperature, are best freed of cations by leaching the sample with about 25 ml. of 2N hydrochloric acid in 70% methanol (v/v). The sample is recovered by filtration through a medium-porosity fritted-glass crucible or funnel and washed with 70% methanol (v/v) until the washings are free of chloride.

The demineralized sample is transferred quantitatively to a beaker and dispersed in about 300 ml. of distilled water. The dispersion is heated in a steam bath or boiling water bath and stirred continuously until the starch gelatinizes; heating is continued for about 15 min. to insure complete gelatinization. The pasted sample is titrated hot, or after cooling, with 0.1N sodium hydroxide solution to a phenolphthalein end point. More dilute alkali solutions are recommended when titrating samples having low carboxyl contents.

Titers obtained by the preceding procedure represent the carboxyl group and other acidity native to the starch. Research has shown that the latter is due largely to fatty acids complexed with the amylose present in common starches (90). Since contributions from this source vary with starch origin and history, the unoxidized or underivatized original starch should be titrated to provide a blank value. The same weight of starch as that used for demineralization should be pasted in about 300 ml. of distilled water and titrated with sodium hydroxide solution in the same manner as outlined above; acid leaching and washing are not required prior to titration.

Percent carboxyl =
$$\frac{(\text{Sample titer} - \text{Blank titer}) \text{ milliliters} \times \text{Alkali normality} \times 0.045 \times 100}{\text{Sample weight in grams}}$$

Recently, Cheung and co-workers (91.) have shown that carboxyl contents of oxidized starches can be determined by reaction with methylene blue. The anionic oxidized starch reacts with the cationic dye to form a complex having spectral characteristics different from those of the dye. This characteristic permits spectrophotometric analysis wherein absorption differences can be related directly to carboxyl contents. Since the procedure is substantially less time-consuming than the commonly used demineralization–titration technique, it may gain favor with processors of oxidized starch.

Carboxymethylstarch is sometimes analyzed by direct titration of the ash resulting from sample ignition (92). The sample may be demineralized by leaching with methanolic hydrochloric acid as outlined in the above procedure. After washing to remove all chlorides, the sample is gelatinized in a minimum quantity of distilled water, and the paste is neutralized with sodium hydroxide solution to a phenolphthalein end point, thus converting the carboxyl groups to the sodium salts. After evaporation to remove excess water, the sample is dried and ignited in a platinum dish at about 500° until the residue is free of carbon. This treatment decomposes the organic material and converts the sodium salts of the carboxylate groups to sodium carbonate; concentration of the latter, which is proportional to the carboxyl content of the original sample, is determined by dissolution of the ash residue in water and titrating with standard hydrochloric acid solution to a methyl orange end point.

$$\text{Percent carboxyl} = \frac{\text{HCl milliliters} \times \text{HCl normality} \times 0.045 \times 100}{\text{Sample weight in grams}}$$

5. Carbonyl

Oxidative modification of starch is most commonly accomplished by treatment with hypochlorite (88). Although such reaction results principally in production of carboxyl groups which alter physical as well as chemical properties, the reaction is nonspecific and produces carbonyl groups as well. Oxidation with periodate is also practiced commercially (93). This reaction is considerably more specific; oxidation occurs principally at the *vic*-glycol structure in the D-glucose moiety (C2–C3). Two carbonyl groups are produced per mole of periodate consumed, producing a product commonly referred to as dialdehyde starch. Carbonyl groups in starch may be obtained by other derivatization and/or oxidative procedures.

Numerous chemical and physical methods have been applied to the determination of carbonyl groups in a wide variety of organic compounds (94), and those most suitable for the analysis of treated cellulose and frequently applied to starch have been detailed by Green (95). Carbonyl contents of oxidized starches, obtained by other than periodate oxidation, are determined only infrequently and then by oximation. The reaction can be achieved without hydroxylamine salt formation and consequent interference from the carboxyl group (96). The cyanohydrin method (97) may be more specific, but the reaction time is prohibitively long, requiring several days for completion. Dialdehyde starch can be analyzed by the borohydride reduction technique (98), but the colorimetric method based on the *p*-nitrophenylhydrazone derivative is preferred because of the speed and excellent precision over a broad range of carbonyl contents (99).

a. *Hydroxylamine Method*

The hydroxylamine reagent is prepared by dissolving 25 g. of reagent-grade hydroxylamine hydrochloride in water and adding 100 ml. of $0.5N$ sodium hydroxide. The mixture is diluted to 500 ml. and mixed. The reagent is unstable and should be discarded when its age exceeds 2 days.

A portion of the powdered or finely ground (60 mesh) oxidized starch, containing not more than 10 g. of dry starch and not more than 40 mg. of carbonyl (expressed as $>$C=O) is weighed accurately and transferred to a beaker. The sample size is selected so that the blank-sample titer difference does not exceed about 15 ml. of $0.1N$ hydrochloric acid solution, so as to provide a substantial reagent excess during the reaction. The sample is gelatinized by the addition of 100 ml. of boiling distilled water; the resultant dispersion is cooled to 40°, adjusted to pH 3.2, and transferred quantitatively to a 500-ml. glass-stoppered flask with the aid of distilled water.

Exactly 60.0 ml. of hydroxylamine reagent is added to the sample solution, and the flask is stoppered and placed in a water bath at 40°.

After 4 hr., the excess hydroxylamine is determined by rapid titration of the reaction mixture to pH 3.2 with standard 0.1N hydrochloric acid solution. End point detection as well as pH adjustment prior to reagent addition is accomplished with the aid of a pH meter. A blank determination on all reagents should be performed in the same manner, and an identical weight of the original unoxidized starch should be included whenever it is available.

$$\text{Percent carbonyl}\ \left(\!\!\diagup\!\!\!\!\diagdown\ \!\!C\!\!=\!\!O\right) =$$

$$\frac{(\text{Blank titer} - \text{Sample titer})\ \text{milliliters} \times \text{Acid normality} \times 0.028 \times 100}{\text{Dry sample weight in grams}}$$

b. *Colorimetric Method*

The p-nitrophenylhydrazine colorimetric method was developed for the analysis of dialdehyde starches (*99*), and it should not be applied to other oxidized starches without preliminary validation. If the product in question contains less than one dialdehyde unit per 100 glucose residues, that is, less than about 0.35% carbonyl, a dry sample weight equivalent to about 0.25 mg. of 100% dialdehyde (1 dialdehyde unit per glucose residue or about 35% carbonyl) starch is taken for analysis. In other words, the dry sample weight selected for analysis should contain about 0.09 mg. of carbonyl group.

The weighed sample is transferred to an 18 × 150 mm. test tube and suspended in 20 ml. of water. The sample is gelatinized by placing the test tube in a steam bath and heating it for 30 min. while stirring with a thin glass rod which is left in the test tube.

The reagent is prepared by dissolving 250 mg. of p-nitrophenylhydrazine in 15 ml. of glacial acetic acid; 1.5 ml. of reagent solution is added to the sample solution, and the mixture is heated 1 hr. in the steam bath with occasional stirring. The reaction mixture is cooled to room temperature; 0.4 g. of analytical-grade Celite filter aid is added, and the insoluble p-nitrophenylhydrazone is recovered on a 3.5-cm., medium-porosity, fritted glass funnel by vacuum filtration.

The precipitate is washed with two 5-ml. portions of 7% acetic acid solution, followed by two 5-ml. portions of water. The washing solutions are used first to rinse the test tube to insure quantitative transfer of the precipitate. Washings are discarded and the receiver is replaced with a clean and dry 500-ml. filter flask. The filter cake is then washed repeatedly with hot 95% ethanol until all p-nitrophenylhydrazone has been dissolved and collected in the receiver.

The alcohol solution is transferred quantitatively to a 250-ml.

volumetric flask and diluted to volume with 95% ethanol. After mixing, a portion of the solution is transferred to a 1- or 2-cm. cuvette. A reagent blank is run in the same manner, using an identical weight of the original unoxidized starch, and a matching cuvette is filled with the blank solution. The absorbance of the sample solution is determined at 445 mμ against the blank.

In the analysis of more highly oxidized samples, a dry sample equivalent to about 50 mg. of 100% dialdehyde starch, that is, a sample containing about 17 mg. of carbonyl group, is weighed accurately and transferred to a 200-ml. volumetric flask along with about 180 ml. of water. After mixing, the sample is gelatinized by heating 2–3 hr. in a steam bath with occasional stirring. The solution is cooled to room temperature and diluted to volume with water. A 20.0-ml. aliquot is pipetted into an 18 $\times$ 150 mm. test tube. To this 3 ml. of the p-nitrophenylhydrazine reagent is added, and the mixture is heated 1 hr. in a steam bath. The p-nitrophenylhydrazone derivative is recovered, washed, and dissolved in 95% ethanol as described previously. A 5.0-ml. aliquot of the 250-ml. sample solution is diluted to 100 ml. with 95% ethanol for determination of absorbance at 445 mμ.

Calculation of carbonyl content or the number of dialdehyde units per 1 or per 100 D-glucose residues, from the sample absorbance value, requires preliminary calibration with dialdehyde starch samples of known composition. In the case of periodate-oxidized starches containing less than 1 dialdehyde unit per 100 D-glucose residues, periodate consumption during oxidation is the best measure of dialdehyde content; 1 mole of dialdehyde is produced per mole of periodate consumed. The same technique may be applied in the preparation of more highly oxidized products, or the product itself can be characterized by sodium borohydride reduction (98).

Absorbances of the alcoholic p-nitrophenylhydrazone solutions deviate slightly from Beer's law, particularly at absorbance values above 0.7. For this reason, samples and standards should be analyzed at equivalent concentrations, preferably at levels producing absorbances smaller than 0.7.

6. Phosphorus

Native starches often contain combined phosphate groups; for example, the anionic properties of potato starch are the result of substituent phosphate ester groups. Starch can also be reacted with phosphorus oxychloride, orthophosphate, and tripolyphosphate to form phosphate esters. Phosphation with phosphorus oxychloride produces cross-bonded mixtures of mono-, di-, and trisubstituted starch phosphates, whereas reaction with ortho- and tripolyphosphates results in formation of monosubstituted phosphoric acid esters (*100*).

Determination of phosphorus in these products requires preliminary destruction of organic matter and conversion of phosphorus to orthophosphate. Organic matter may be destroyed by digestion (wet-ashing) in sulfuric acid with the acid of nitric acid or hydrogen peroxide, by digestion with nitric acid using the Carius method, by fusion with sodium peroxide in a Parr bomb, or by dry-ashing with a suitable fixative to prevent loss of phosphorus. The last decomposition method is preferred in the analyses of starch phosphates because samples of adequate sizes can be ashed with ease.

Following sample preparation by dry ashing, the residue containing phosphorus is dissolved in dilute acid and heated to hydrolyze pyrophosphates to orthophosphate. The latter, if present in significant quantities, may be precipitated as magnesium ammonium phosphate and determined gravimetrically, or it may be precipitated as ammonium phosphomolybdate and determined either gravimetrically or volumetrically (*101, 102*).

Gravimetric techniques are time-consuming and often not suitable for the analysis of samples containing little phosphorus, and volumetric procedures frequently lack precision. These disadvantages are overcome by colorimetric or spectrophotometric methods which are particularly well-suited to the analysis of small amounts of phosphates in digests of organic samples. Procedures based on reduced heteropolyphosphomolybdic acid (molybdenum blue) are exceptionally sensitive, and recent improvements (*103, 104*) in the reduction reaction provide color stability and good precision. Although somewhat less sensitive, the spectrophotometric method based on the molybdovanadophosphoric acid complex (*105*) is not affected adversely by many ions which interfere in other colorimetric techniques (*106*). It has been used extensively for the analysis of organic materials (*107, 108*), and it is preferred for the analysis of starches and starch phosphates.

The product may contain soluble phosphate salts which are not combined with the starch, and it should be analyzed without pretreatment if the total phosphorus content is desired. When the combined phosphate value is required, the sample is freed of soluble phosphates by washing or dialysis prior to analysis.

If the starch is a granular cold-water-insoluble product, a 20-g. portion is slurried in about 200 ml. of distilled water at room temperature, and the mixture is stirred for 15 min. The starch is recovered by vacuum filtration on a fritted glass or Büchner funnel and washed with 200 ml. of distilled water. The product is reslurried in and washed with water a second time in the same manner, and the resulting filter cake is dried in an air oven at a temperature below 50°.

If the starch sample is soluble in water, a 1–2% aqueous solution (paste) is prepared. This solution is placed in a cellophane tube and dialyzed against running distilled water for 30–40 hr. The starch is then precipitated by pouring the solution into 4 volumes of acetone (per volume of paste) while stirring. The precipitated product is recovered on a fritted glass or Büchner funnel, deyhdrated by washing with absolute ethanol, and dried in an air or vacuum oven prior to analysis. A dry product can also be recovered from the dialyzed paste by freeze-drying.

A representative portion of the prepared sample, not more than 20 g. and containing not more than 40 mg. of phosphorus, is weighed accurately into a 100-ml. Vycor dish. Ten milliliters of 10% zinc acetate solution is added, distributing the solution uniformly through the sample by adding water if necessary. The sample is evaporated to dryness on a steam bath, heated on a hot plate until thoroughly charred, and then ignited 2 hr. in a muffle furnace at 550°. The dish is cooled to room temperature, and the residue is wetted by cautious addition of 3 ml. of 29% nitric acid. The sample is again evaporated to dryness on a steam bath and dehydrated completely by brief heating on a hot plate, and the dish is returned to the muffle furnace at 550° for about 30 min. This process assures complete decomposition of organic material in the shortest time.

After cooling to room temperature, the sides of the dish are washed down with 10 ml. of 29% nitric acid followed by 15 ml. of distilled water. The dish is covered with a watch glass; the residue solution is heated to incipient boiling and held 10 min. at that temperature to insure complete hydrolysis of pyrophosphate to orthophosphate. After cooling to room temperature, the solution is quantitatively filtered through Whatman No. 1 paper into a volumetric flask of a size selected to provide a final concentration of 1–4 mg. of phosphorus per 25 ml. The transfer is completed by washing the dish and filter paper with small portions of distilled water, and the solution is diluted to volume and mixed thoroughly.

An aliquot selected to contain not more than 2.5 mg. of phosphorus is pipetted into a 100-ml. volumetric flask, and 25 ml. of water is added to another 100-ml. volumetric flask serving for the reagent blank. The following reagents are added to both flasks, in the order stated, mixing after each addition: 10 ml. of 29% nitric acid, 10 ml. of 0.25% ammonium vanadate solution (prepared by dissolving 2.5 g. of ammonium metavanadate in 600 ml. of boiling water, cooling to 60°–70°, adding

20 ml. of conc. nitric acid, cooling to room temperature, and diluting to 1 liter with water), and 10 ml. of 5% ammonium molybdate solution. Both solutions are diluted to volume with water, mixed thoroughly, and allowed to stand 10 min. Using the reagent blank in a 1-cm. cuvette as the reference at zero absorbance, the absorbance of the sample solution at 460 mμ is determined in a 1-cm. matching cuvette. The phosphorus concentration (milligrams per 100 ml.) of the sample solution is read from the calibration curve.

The calibration curve is prepared with the aid of a standard solution of potassium dihydrogen phosphate. Aliquots containing 0.5, 1.0, 1.5, 2.0, and 2.5 mg. of phosphorus are pipetted into separate 100-ml. volumetric flasks, and 25 ml. of water is added to another flask serving for the reagent blank. The following reagents are added to each flask, in the order stated, mixing after each addition: 10 ml. of 29% nitric acid solution, 10 ml. of 0.25% ammonium vanadate solution (preparation described in preceding paragraph), and 10 ml. of 5% ammonium molybdate solution. All solutions are diluted to volume with water, mixed thoroughly, and allowed to stand 10 min.

Using the reagent blank in a 1-cm. cuvette as the reference at zero absorbance, the absorbances of the standard solutions are determined at 460 mμ in matching 1-cm. cuvettes. A calibration curve which is reproducible, but which should be checked when fresh reagents are used, is obtained by plotting standard solution absorbances (at 1 cm.) versus phosphorus contents (milligrams per 100 ml.) on linear coordinates. Phosphorus contents of sample solutions are ascertained by reference thereto.

Percent phosphorus =

$$\frac{P \times \text{Dilution volume, milliliters} \times 100}{\text{Aliquot volume in milliliters} \times \text{Sample weight in grams} \times 1000}$$

in which P = phosphorus content (milligrams/100 ml.) from calibration curve.

Percent phosphate (PO$_4$) = Percent phosphorus $\times$ 3.065

7. Sulfur

Sulfur contents of native starches are small and of no particular consequence, but the determination of sulfur in derivatives such as starch sulfates (109) and sulfonates (110) permits calculation of the extent of derivatization or degree of substitution (D.S.). Determination of sulfur in these compounds usually requires decomposition of the organic material and conversion of the sulfur to sulfate. Oxidative decomposition of the sample may be accomplished in many ways: by wet-ashing, by the Carius method, by fusion with sodium peroxide, or by combustion in a Parr oxygen bomb (*111*). The decomposition method selected depends to a certain extent on the ultimate procedure for sulfate determination, and the oxygen bomb technique is preferred because the digest is free of inorganic additions.

Sulfate contents of oxygen bomb digests are determined infrequently by gravimetric means because the low concentrations do not afford good precision. More frequently, interferring cations in the oxygen bomb digests are removed by ion-exchange treatment, and then sulfate contents are determined colorimetrically with barium chloranilate (*112*) or barium chromate (*113*), or titrimetrically with barium chloride, barium perchlorate, or lead nitrate using absorption indicators (*114*) such as dithizone (*115*). The lead nitrate titration method in conjunction with dithizone indicator gives good precision in the analysis of samples containing as little as 0.2% of sulfur.

The sample, for example, a sulfur-containing starch derivative, must be free of sulfur-containing reagents which may have been used in its preparation. If the starch is a granular cold-water-insoluble product, a 20-g. sample is slurried in about 200 ml. of distilled water at room temperature and stirred about 15 min. The starch is recovered by vacuum filtration on a fritted glass or Büchner funnel and washed with 200 ml. of distilled water. The product is reslurried in and washed with water a second time, and the resulting filter cake is dried in an air oven at 38°–50°.

If the starch sample is soluble in water, a 1–2% aqueous solution (paste) is prepared. This is placed in a cellophane tube and dialyzed against running distilled water for 30–40 hr. The product may be recovered by concentrating and freeze-drying, or, alternatively, it may be precipitated by pouring the solution into 4 volumes of acetone (per volume of paste) while stirring. The precipitated product is collected on a fritted glass or Büchner funnel, dehydrated by washing with absolute ethanol, and dried in an air or vacuum oven prior to analysis.

A representative portion of the finely ground or powdered sample of known moisture or volatiles content, not more than 1.2 g., is weighed accurately and wrapped in a half circle of 9-cm. Whatman No. 1 filter paper. The wrapped sample is placed in the ignition cup of a Parr oxygen bomb; the fuse wire is attached and positioned so that it touches the wrapped sample. Twenty milliliters of 6% hydrogen peroxide solution is pipetted into the base of the bomb. The cover is placed in position and tightened, and oxygen is added carefully to a pressure of 29 atm. The oxygen inlet should be modified if necessary so that the oxygen stream is directed horizontally toward the interior wall of the bomb rather than toward the base. The charge is then ignited as directed in the manufacturer's instruction manual (*116*).

One minute or more after ignition, the bomb is fixed horizontally in a shaker, and the contents are agitated vigorously for 15 min. to complete the oxidation of the lower oxides of sulfur to sulfate. The bomb is then placed in an upright position and allowed to stand a minute or two; residual pressure is carefully released, and the cover is removed and rinsed with a fine stream of water delivered from a wash bottle. Contents of the bomb are transferred quantitatively to a 250-ml. beaker; the transfer is completed by washing the bomb with about 30 ml. of distilled water in small portions.

Reagent-grade silver oxide powder, 0.4 g., is slowly added to the sample solution which is then heated to boiling and boiled 5 min. with continuous stirring. This treatment may be omitted if the sample is free of chlorides and phosphates which interfere in the subsequent titration with lead nitrate. The solution is cooled to room temperature, transferred quantitatively to a 100-ml. volumetric flask, and diluted to volume with water. The solution is mixed thoroughly, and the precipitate is allowed to settle; if settling does not yield a clear supernate, the solution should be gravity filtered.

Fifty milliliters of the supernatant sample solution is pipetted into a small glass ion-exchange column (15 × 150 mm.) with a glass reservoir (25 × 70 mm.) at the top, having a capacity somewhat in excess of 50 ml. The lower end is constricted and a short length of rubber tubing and screw clamp are attached thereto for adjustment of flow rate. The column contains 10 ml. (wet settled volume) of Nalcite HCR(H^+) cation-exchange resin, freshly regenerated with 60 ml. of 10% nitric acid and washed with water until the effluent is essentially neutral. The sample solution is allowed to flow as rapidly as the column will permit, and the effluent is collected in a 100-ml. volumetric flask. Flow is continued until the solution meniscus reaches the upper surface of the resin bed; the column reservoir is rinsed with a fine stream of water delivered from a wash-bottle, and the washings are allowed to drain to the upper surface of the resin bed. The sample solution in the column is displaced by adding 10 ml. portions of water, allowing each portion to drain to the upper surface of the resin bed prior to addition of the next portion. Washing is continued until 100 ml. of effluent has been collected, and the effluent is mixed thoroughly.

An aliquot of the effluent, preferably not more than 20 ml., containing 0.1–1.5 mg. of sulfur, is pipetted into a 250-ml. beaker, and water is added to give a minimum volume of 10 ml. Two drops of bromophenol blue indicator solution (0.1% in ethanol) is added, and *N* ammonium hydroxide solution is added dropwise until the solution color is distinctly blue. Sufficient $0.16N$ nitric acid is added to discharge the blue color, and 1 ml. of 20% acetic acid solution is added. The sample solution is then diluted with 5 volumes of A.C.S. reagent-grade acetone, and 4 drops of freshly-prepared dithizone indicator solution (0.1% in acetone) is added for each 60 ml. of total volume. The green solution is then titrated, while stirring continuously, with standard $0.01N$ lead nitrate solution until a pale pink end point persists. The standard lead nitrate solution should be prepared from reagent-grade material, and it can be standardized by titrating a 10.0-ml. aliquot of standard $0.01N$ sulfuric acid solution in the manner described above.

Percent sulfur =

$$\frac{(\text{Pb(NO}_3)_2 \text{ milliliters}) \times (\text{Pb(NO}_3)_2 \text{ normality}) \times 0.016 \times 100 \text{ ml.} \times 100 \text{ ml.} \times 100}{\text{Dry sample weight in grams} \times 50 \text{ ml.} \times \text{ml. of Aliquot}}$$

Degree of substitution values for sulfate and p-toluenesulfonate derivatives of starch are calculated as follows:

$$\text{Degree of Substitution (D.S.)(Sulfate)} = \frac{162 \, S}{3200 - 102 \, S}$$

$$\text{Degree of Substitution (D.S.)(p-Toluenesulfonate)} = \frac{162S}{3200 - 154S}$$

in which S = percent sulfur (dry basis).

V. References

(1) "Official Methods of Analysis," W. Horwitz, ed., Association of Official Agricultural Chemists, P.O. Box 540, Benjamin Franklin Station, Washington 4, D.C., 9th Ed., 1960, pp. 169, 282.

(2) Standard Analytical Methods of the Member Companies of the Corn Industries Research Foundation, Inc., R. J. Smith, ed., Corn Industries Research Foundation, Inc., 1001 Connecticut Ave., N.W., Washington 6, D.C., 1st Ed., 1952.

(3) L. Sair and W. R. Fetzer, *Ind. Eng. Chem., Anal. Ed.*, **14**, 843 (1942).

(4) M. Ulmann and F. Shierbaum, *Staerke*, **9**, 23 (1957).

(5) W. R. Fetzer, *Anal. Chem.*, **23**, 1062 (1951).

(6) K. Fischer, *Angew. Chem.*, **48**, 394 (1935).

(7) J. Mitchell and D. M. Smith, "Aquametry. Application of the Karl Fischer Reagent to Quantitative Analyses Involving Water," Interscience Publishers, Inc., New York, N. Y., 1948.

(8) C. M. Johnson, *Ind. Eng. Chem., Anal. Ed.*, **17**, 312 (1945).

(9) Technical Bulletins 308 and 308-B, "Operating and Maintenance Instructions," Beckman Instruments, Inc., Fullerton, California; see also, H. A. Frediani, *Anal. Chem.*, **24**, 1126 (1952).

(10) J. D. Neuss, M. G. O'Brien, and H. A. Frediani, *Anal. Chem.*, **23**, 1332 (1951).

(11) M. B. Jacobs, "The Chemistry and Technology of Food and Food Products," Vol. 1, Interscience Publishers, Inc., New York, New York, 2nd Ed., 1951, p. 317.

(12) "Cereal Laboratory Methods," E. C. Swanson, ed., American Association of Cereal Chemists, Inc., University Farm, St. Paul, Minnesota, 6th Ed., 1957, p. 40.

(13) Reference 1, p. 282.

(14) Reference 2, Method B-10.

(15) J. Patton and W. Reeder, *Anal. Chem.*, **28,** 1026 (1956).

(16) F. J. Welcher, "The Analytical Uses of Ethylenediamine Tetraacetic Acid," D. Van Nostrand Company, Inc., Princeton, New Jersey, 1958, p. 110.

(17) Reference 1, p. 400.

(18) J. B. Thompson and E. Toy, *Ind. Eng. Chem., Anal. Ed.*, **17,** 612 (1945).

(19) L. F. Burroughs and A. H. Sparks, *Analyst*, **89,** 55 (1964).

(20) Reference 1, p. 401.

(21) A. H. Bennet and F. K. Donovan, *Analyst*, **68,** 140 (1943).

(22) A. N. Prater, C. M. Johnson, M. F. Pool, and G. M. MacKinney, *Ind. Eng. Chem., Anal. Ed.*, **16,** 153 (1944).

(23) J. D. Ponting and G. Johnson, *Ind. Eng. Chem., Anal. Ed.*, **17,** 682 (1945).

(24) F. S. Nury, D. H. Taylor, and J. E. Brekke, *J. Agr. Food Chem.*, **7,** 351 (1959).

(25) A. Steigmann, *J. Soc. Chem. Ind.*, **61,** 18 (1942).

(26) Recent examples: D. C. Udy, *Cereal Chem.*, **33,** 190 (1956); *ibid.*, **34,** 389 (1957); J. Bunyan, *J. Sci. Food Agr.*, **10,** 425 (1959); L. Feinstein and J. R. Hart, *Cereal Chem.*, **36,** 191 (1959); P. C. Williams, *J. Sci. Food Agr.*, **12,** 58 (1961); O. J. Banasik and R. A. Gilles, *Cereal Sci. Today*, **7,** 28 (1962).

(27) Reviews: R. B. Bradstreet, *Chem. Rev.*, **27,** 331 (1950); R. B. Bradstreet, *Anal. Chem.*, **26,** 165 (1954); C. D. Neill, *Cereal Sci. Today*, **7,** 6 (1962).

(28) J. T. Kjeldahl, *Z. Anal. Chem.*, **22,** 366 (1883).

(29) "Quantitative Organic Microanalysis," J. Grant, ed., J. & A. Churchill, Ltd., London, England, 5th English Ed., 1951, p. 78.

(30) G. M. Gustin, *Microchem. J.*, **1,** 75 (1957); *ibid.*, **4,** 43 (1960); I. K. H. Otter, *Nature*, **182,** 656 (1958).

(31) T. J. Schoch, *J. Am. Chem. Soc.*, **64,** 2954 (1942).

(32) T. J. Schoch and C. C. Jensen, *Ind. Eng. Chem., Anal. Ed.*, **12,** 531 (1940).

(33) T. J. Schoch, in "Methods in Carbohydrate Chemistry," Vol. 4, R. L. Whistler, ed., Academic Press Inc., New York, N. Y., 1964, p. 61.

(34) C. A. Browne and F. W. Zerban, "Physical and Chemical Methods of Sugar Analysis," John Wiley and Sons, Inc., 3rd Ed., 1941, p. 828.

(35) P. Bernfeld, in "Methods in Enzymology," Vol. 1, S. P. Colowick and N. O. Kaplan, eds., Academic Press Inc., New York, N. Y., 1955, p. 149.

(36) R. L. Bruner, in "Methods in Carbohydrate Chemistry," Vol. 4, R. L. Whistler, ed., Academic Press Inc., New York, N. Y., 1964, p. 67.

(37) M. J. Blish and R. M. Sandstedt, *Cereal Chem.*, **10,** 189 (1933).

(38) H. C. Gore and H. K. Steele, *Ind. Eng. Chem., Anal. Ed.*, **7,** 324 (1935).

(39) T. J. Schoch, in "Methods in Carbohydrate Chemistry," Vol. 4, R. L. Whistler, ed., Academic Press Inc., New York, N. Y., 1964, p. 64.

(40) "Cereal Laboratory Methods," M. M. MacMasters, ed., American Association of Cereal Chemists, Inc., 1955 University Ave., St. Paul, Minnesota, 7th Ed., 1962, Methods 14–10, 14–20.

(41) D. B. Judd, "Color in Business, Science, and Industry," John Wiley and Sons, Inc., New York, N. Y., 1952, p. 191.

(42) R. J. Smith and C. R. Colburn, *Pittsburgh Conf. Anal. Chem. Appl. Spectry.*, Pittsburgh, Pennsylvania, 1958, Paper No. 83.

(43) C. R. Colburn, in "Methods in Carbohydrate Chemistry," Vol. 4, R. L. Whistler, ed., Academic Press Inc., New York, N. Y., 1964, p. 218.

(44) Reference 2, Methods E-16 and F-14; see also, Method B-14.

(45) A. C. Hardy, "Handbook of Colorimetry," The Technology Press, Cambridge, Massachusetts, 1936.

(46) National Bureau of Standards, "Letter Circular LC 547."

(47) National Bureau of Standards, "Letter Circular LC 929."

(48) T. J. Schoch and H. W. Leach, in "Methods in Carbohydrate Chemistry," Vol. 4, R. L. Whistler, ed., Academic Press Inc., New York, N. Y., 1964, p. 101; see also H. W. Leach and T. J. Schoch, *Cereal Chem.*, **38**, 40 (1961).

(49) W. J. Remington and R. Pariser, *Rubber World*, **138**, 261 (1958).

(50) W. F. Ulrich, *The Analyzer*, **2**, No. 1 (Jan. 1961), published by Beckman Instruments, Inc., Fullerton, California.

(51) R. J. Joyce, *The Analyzer*, **2**, No. 4 (Oct. 1961), published by Beckman Instruments, Inc.; see also, "Air Comparison Pycnometer," Bulletin No. 786-A, Beckman Instruments, Inc., Fullerton, California, 1961.

(52) H. Buel, *Intern. Congr. Appl. Chem., 8th, Orig. Comm.*, **13**, 63 (1912).

(53) W. R. Fetzer and L. C. Kirst, *Cereal Chem.*, **36**, 108 (1959).

(54) Reference 2, Method B-61.

(55) M. R. Cannon, R. E. Manning, and J. D. Bell, *Anal. Chem.*, **32**, 355 (1960).

(56) H. W. Leach, L. D. McCowen, and T. J. Schoch, *Cereal Chem.*, **36**, 534 (1959).

(57) J. R. Katz, M. C. Desai, and J. Seiberlich, *Trans. Faraday Soc.*, **34**, 1258 (1938).

(58) R. R. Myers, C. J. Knauss, and R. D. Hoffman, *J. Appl. Polymer Sci.*, **6**, 659 (1962).

(59) W. R. Fetzer, *Anal. Chem.*, **24**, 1129 (1952).

(60) M. J. Mason and W. R. Fetzer, in "Starch and Starch Products in Paper Coating," TAPPI Monograph Series—No. 17, Technical Association of the Pulp and Paper Industry, 155 East 44th Street, New York, N. Y., 1957, p. 65.

(61) E. G. Mazurs, T. J. Schoch, and F. E. Kite, *Cereal Chem.*, **34**, 141 (1957).

(62) C. A. Anker and W. F. Geddes, *Cereal Chem.*, **21**, 335 (1944).

(63) C. C. Kesler and W. G. Bechtel, *Anal. Chem.*, **19**, 16 (1947).

(64) Suggested Method T 637 sm-53, April 1953, "Tentative and Official Testing Methods—Recommended Practices—Specifications," Technical Association of the Pulp and Paper Industry, 155 East 44th Street, New York, N. Y.

(65) W. G. Bechtel, *Cereal Chem.*, **24**, 200 (1947).

(66) J. R. Van Wazer, J. W. Lyons, K. Y. Kim, and R. E. Colwell, "Viscosity and Flow Measurement. A Laboratory Handbook of Rheology," Interscience Publishers Inc., New York, N. Y., 1963.

(67) R. W. Kerr, "Chemistry and Industry of Starch," Academic Press Inc., New York, N. Y., 2nd Ed., 1950, p. 134.

(68) O. Saare and P. Martens, *Z. Spiritusind.*, **26**, 436 (1903).

(69) W. J. Hamer, *J. Res. Natl. Bur. Stds.*, **39**, 29 (1947).

(70) W. G. Bechtel, *J. Colloid Sci.*, **5**, 260 (1950).

(71) E. T. Hjermstad, *Cereal Chem.*, **32**, 200 (1955); see also E. T. Hjermstad, "Methods in Carbohydrate Chemistry," Vol. 4, R. L. Whistler, ed., Academic Press Inc., New York, N. Y., 1964, p. 148.

(72) E. J. Saxl, *Ind. Eng. Chem., Anal. Ed.*, **10**, 82 (1938).

(73) F. L. DeBeaukelaer, J. R. Powell, and E. F. Bahlmann, *Ind. Eng. Chem., Anal. Ed.*, **2**, 348 (1930).

(74) G. L. Baker, *Ind. Eng. Chem.*, **18,** 89 (1926).

(75) B. Brimhall and R. M. Hixon, *Ind. Eng. Chem., Anal. Ed.*, **11,** 358 (1939).

(76) O. B. Wurzburg, in "Methods in Carbohydrate Chemistry," Vol. 4, R. L. Whistler, ed., Academic Press Inc., New York, N. Y., 1964, p. 286.

(77) R. L. Whistler and A. Jeanes, *Ind. Eng. Chem., Anal. Ed.*, **15,** 317 (1943).

(78) L. B. Genung and R. C. Mallatt, *Ind. Eng. Chem., Anal. Ed.*, **13,** 369 (1941).

(79) G. W. Hay, B. A. Lewis, and F. Smith, in "Methods in Carbohydrate Chemistry," Vol. 4, R. L. Whistler, ed., Academic Press Inc., New York, N. Y., 1964, p. 306.

(80) E. F. Degering, in "Starch and Its Derivatives," Vol. 1, J. A. Radley, ed., John Wiley and Sons, Inc., New York, N. Y., 3rd Ed., 1954, p. 326.

(81) S. Zeisel, *Montash.*, **6,** 989 (1885).

(82) A. Elek, in "Organic Analysis," Vol. 1, J. Mitchell, Jr., I. M. Koltoff, E. S. Proskauer, and A. Weisberger, eds., Interscience Publishers, Inc., New York, N. Y., 1953, pp. 67–126.

(83) F. Vieböck and A. Schwappach, *Ber.*, **63,** 2818 (1930).

(84) E. P. Clark, *J. Assoc. Offic. Agr. Chem.*, **15,** 136 (1932).

(85) C. C. Kesler and E. T. Hjermstad, in "Methods in Carbohydrate Chemistry," Vol. 4, R. L. Whistler, ed., Academic Press Inc., New York, N. Y., 1964, p. 304.

(86) P. W. Morgan, *Ind. Eng. Chem., Anal. Ed.*, **18,** 500 (1946).

(87) H. J. Lortz, *Anal. Chem.*, **28,** 892 (1956).

(88) C. H. Hullinger, in "Methods in Carbohydrate Chemistry," Vol. 4, R. L. Whistler, ed., Academic Press Inc., New York, N. Y., 1964, p. 313.

(89) E. C. Yackel and W. O. Kenyon, *J. Am. Chem. Soc.*, **64,** 121 (1942).

(90) M. F. Mattisson and K. A. Legendre, *Anal. Chem.*, **32,** 1942 (1952).

(91) H. C. Cheung, B. Carroll, and C. E. Weill, *Anal. Chem.*, **32,** 818 (1960).

(92) R. W. Kerr, "Chemistry and Industry of Starch," Academic Press Inc., New York, N. Y., 2nd Ed., 1950, p. 685.

(93) C. L. Mehltretter, in "Methods in Carbohydrate Chemistry," Vol. 4, R. L. Whistler, ed., Academic Press Inc., New York, N. Y., 1964, p. 316.

(94) J. Mitchell, Jr., in "Organic Analysis," Vol. 1, J. Mitchell, Jr., I. M. Koltoff, E. S. Proskauer, and A. Weisberger, eds., Interscience Publishers, Inc., New York, N. Y., 1953, p. 243.

(95) J. W. Green, in "Methods in Carbohydrate Chemistry," Vol. 3, R. L. Whistler, ed., Academic Press Inc., New York, N. Y., 1963, p. 49.

(96) H. J. Roberts, personal communication.

(97) J. Schmorak and M. Lewin, *Anal. Chem.*, **33,** 1403 (1961).

(98) J. C. Rankin and C. L. Mehltretter, *Anal. Chem.*, **28,** 1012 (1956).

(99) C. S. Wise and C. L. Mehltretter, *Anal. Chem.*, **30,** 174 (1958).

(100) E. F. Paschall, in "Methods in Carbohydrate Chemistry," Vol. 4, R. L. Whistler, ed., Academic Press Inc., New York, N. Y., 1964, p. 294.

(101) Scott's "Standard Methods of Chemical Analysis," Vol. 1, N. H. Furman, ed., D. Van Nostrand Company, Inc., Princeton, New Jersey, 1962, Chapter 35.

(102) Reference *1*, pp. 84, 160.

(103) G. Telep and R. Ehrlick, *Anal. Chem.*, **30,** 1146 (1958).

(104) D. N. Fogg and N. T. Wilkinson, *Analyst*, **83,** 406 (1958).

(105) G. Misson, *Chem. Ztg.*, **32,** 633 (1908).

(106) R. E. Kitson and M. G. Mellon, *Anal. Chem.*, **16,** 379 (1944).

(107) R. A. Koenig and C. R. Johnson, *Ind. Eng. Chem., Anal. Ed.*, **14,** 155 (1942).

(108) J. J. Cincotta, *J. Agr. Food Chem.*, **8,** 145 (1960).

(*109*) R. L. Whistler and W. W. Spencer, in "Methods in Carbohydrate Chemistry," Vol. 4, R. L. Whistler, ed., Academic Press Inc., New York, N. Y., 1964, p. 297.

(*110*) H. J. Roberts, in "Methods in Carbohydrate Chemistry," Vol. 4, R. L. Whistler, ed., Academic Press Inc., New York, N. Y., 1964, p. 299.

(*111*) J. J. Bailey and D. G. Gehring, *Anal. Chem.*, **33**, 1760 (1961).

(*112*) R. J. Bertolacini and J. E. Barney, II, *Anal. Chem.*, **29**, 281 (1957).

(*113*) J. Iwasaki, S. Utsumi, K. Hagino, T. Tarutani, and T. Ozawa, *Nippon Kagaku Zasshi*, **79**, 32 (1958); *ibid.*, **79**, 38 (1958); *ibid.*, **79**, 44 (1958); *Anal. Abstr.*, **5**, 4079 (1958).

(*114*) J. S. Fritz and M. Q. Freeland, *Anal. Chem.*, **26**, 1593 (1954).

(*115*) E. E. Archer, *Analyst*, **82**, 208 (1956).

(*116*) "Oxygen Bomb Calorimetry and Combustion Methods," Manual No. 130, Parr Instrument Company, 211 53rd Street, Moline, Illinois, 1960.

CHAPTER XXVI

INDUSTRIAL MICROSCOPY OF STARCHES

By Thomas J. Schoch and Eileen C. Maywald

Moffett Research Center, Corn Products Co., Argo, Illinois

I. Introduction

The producer of refined cereal starches in the United States is concerned primarily with corn and sorghum starches and their waxy counterparts, and to a somewhat lesser degree with wheat starch. However, these starches may be chemically or physically modified in numerous ways, and the microscope provides a versatile and unique method of detecting or monitoring these modifications. In addition, the world markets supply a variety of other starches, including normal and waxy rice, arrowroot, tapioca, potato, sweet potato, sago, and canna. Each of these varieties may be modified or admixed with other starches, and frequently the microscope is the only possible method of analytical identification.

II. Granule Aggregation

Most commercial starches are "simple" single granules; that is, they are not associated in clumps or "compound" granules. However, the mode of factory drying may sometimes cause extensive clumping of the granules into large aggregates, perhaps by a very slight surface gelatinization of the granules which causes them to cohere to one another. These products obviously will give poor coverage if used for dry-dusting purposes, as in cosmetic powders or for the dusting of bread or chewing gum. On the other hand, when a non-dusting starch is required, as a brewing adjunct, for example, the commercial starch is deliberately aggregated by the manufacturer, usually by slight overheating of the wet starch to produce incipient gelatinization. In general, starches dried in kilns or on continuous belt dryers are not aggregated, while flash-dried starches may frequently be aggregated into large clumps of 25–100 granules.

In testing for aggregation, starch is mounted first in glycerol and examined under the microscope to determine whether the granules are single or clumped. The extent of aggregation is determined next in water. Usually the adhesive bonding between granules is very weak and the clumps dissociate in water. Sometimes, however, the aggregates will persist even when the aqueous starch slurry is warmed to 50°; these products may give "microlumps" on cooking, resulting in a gritty and nonhomogeneous paste.

III. IDENTIFICATION OF STARCH SPECIES

Most of the common starches are readily and unequivocally identifiable under the microscope, using the criteria of granule size and shape, presence of lamellations, form and position (centric or eccentric) of the "hilum" or botanical center of the granule, and brilliance of the interference cross under polarized light. Kerr (1), Radley (2), and particularly Reichert (3) provide excellent photomicrographs of various species; however, it is far preferable to maintain authentic samples of the various starches in order to make side-by-side comparisons with an unknown sample. Corn and sorghum starches are virtually indistinguishable under the microscope. While the granules of sorghum and its waxy counterpart are slightly larger than those of corn and waxy maize, this difference cannot be appraised with any certainty by the eye, and consequently actual measurements of granule dimensions must be made, either manually or with such mechanical means as the Coulter particle size counter. Early reports suggested that sorghum starch could be distinguished from corn starch by the presence of numeours small granules or by traces of adherent protein on the surface of the granule. However, present methods of centrifugal separation remove protein and small-granule starch in the overflow. One Canadian manufacturer claims to market a wheat starch composed of the large-granule fraction presumably obtained by centrifugal removal of the smaller granules. A source of frequent confusion is the improper application of the term "arrowroot" to starches of the *Arum*, *Curcuma*, and *Tacca* genera, rather than limitation to the West Indian *Maranta*.

IV. GELATINIZED GRANULES

When the starch granule commences to swell, it loses the bright interference cross visible under polarized light. This is by far the simplest and best criterion of the presence of gelatinized granules in a starch sample; it is readily applied merely by examining a 0.2–0.3% water suspension under the microscope with crossed polarizers. Any gelatinized granules are invisible on the resulting dark field, and the proportion of such granules may be readily counted in a hemacytometer. The presence of a small proportion of pregelatinized starch may be intentional on the part of the manufacturer. For example, the addition of 2–3% of pregelatinized corn starch to granular corn starch gives a "soft-settling" product which is easily stirred into water and which does not settle to a firm compact cake. Congo red has been suggested as a preferential stain for gelatinized starch granules, but the authors have had no success with this technique.

V. Incipient Gelatinization

Gelatinization normally commences at the hilum which is located at the center of the interference cross seen under polarized light. The initial stage of gelatinization appears as a darkened hilum. This effect may be accentuated by mounting the dry starch in clove oil, which has the same index of refraction as starch; the granule disappears under normal lighting, and the gelatinized hilum shows up as a strongly contrasting dark area. Incipient gelatinization is usually caused by overheating of the wet starch during processing or drying, particularly in a flash dryer. It does not in any way impair the properties of the starch.

VI. Kofler Gelatinization Temperature

When heated in water to progressively higher temperatures, the granules first gelatinize and lose their polarization crosses, and thereafter undergo a continued swelling. For present purposes, gelatinization is defined as the loss of the interference cross visible within the granule under polarized light, and the gelatinization temperature is that point at which this transition occurs. While each individual granule gelatinizes quite sharply, not all the granules in a starch sample gelatinize at the same temperature, but rather over a range of some 8°–10°. This reflects differences in the internal bonding forces within individual granules. The resulting gelatinization range is a specific characteristic of each starch species or variety of modified starch.

The use of a heated water bath is not recommended for determination of gelatinization temperature. Even if the system is heated slowly with good agitation, the wall of the vessel containing the starch slurry is necessarily at a higher temperature, and hence will cause pregelatinization of granules in that vicinity. Instead, the Kofler hot stage is preferred for continuous observation of the heated starch slurry under the polarizing microscope (4). This instrument was originally designed for determination of the melting points of organic substances and it provides precise and replicable gelatinization temperatures of starches. In practice, a 0.1–0.2% suspension of the starch is made in the appropriate medium, usually water. A droplet of this suspension is placed on a short microscope slide; the droplet is ringed with a circle of light mineral oil, and a cover glass is placed on top in such fashion that no air bubbles are enclosed and the droplet is completely surrounded by a contiguous oil barrier. The purpose of the oil is twofold: (a) to prevent the escape of steam during heating and consequent fogging of the field, and (b) to prevent the entry of air channels into the sample and resultant displacement of the starch granules during observation. The slide is placed on the hot stage and covered with a glass baffle, and a glass cover is placed over the entire assembly. A special objective with a long focal distance must be used, and the resulting low magnification is counter-balanced by the use of a 20× ocular. The hot stage is heated at a rate of 2° per minute by a variable transformer, and the field is continuously watched under normal illumination. The point at which the first few granules commence to swell, as confirmed by loss of their polarization crosses when viewed under polarized light, is recorded as the initiation of gelatinization. The midpoint is likewise determined when approximately half the granules have lost their polarization crosses as judged by rapid alternate inspection under normal and polarized light. Finally, the completion point is recorded when only two or three granules in the field still retain their polarization crosses. Thus the gelatinization temperature range of corn starch would be given as 62°–67°–72°. Two or three determinations should be made on each sample and the results averaged. With moderate practice, the temperatures can be determined to a precision of ±0.5°.

A refinement of this procedure is to plot the percentage of gelatinized granules, as estimated visually, against the temperature, as shown in Figure 1. With practice, good visual estimates of the proportion of gelatinized granules can be made at the following points: initiation, 10%, 25%, 50%, 75%, 90%, completion. An unmodified starch should give a fairly symmetrical sigmoid curve. If the sample is a blend of two starches of markedly different gelatinization ranges, it will give a double sigmoid curve, and the proportion of components can be approximated from the transition point. If the starch is derivatized with a chemical group such as a hydroxy-ethyl ether group which lowers the gelatinization temperature, the entire sigmoid curve should be displaced uniformly toward a lower temperature. Sometimes the gelatinization curve of such a product is attenuated, with a greatly reduced initiation point, but with the termination point substantially the same as the parent unmodified starch. Such a curve is evidence of nonuniform derivatization, whereby some of the granules are over-derivatized and other granules are virtually untouched. The gelatinization curve provides the only known method by which this situation can be diagnosed.

When the last granules are gelatinized, heating should be continued toward 100°, since this provides useful visual information on the swelling behavior of the starch. Those starch products that have been extensively modified to give low-viscosity high-soluble pastes, such as acid-modified or oxidized starches and some white dextrins, show extensive granule dissolution as the temperature is raised. Chemically cross-bonded (inhibited) starches will have essentially the same gelatinization range as the parent starch, but granule swelling will obviously be limited at higher temperatures. Quantitative confirmation of cross-bonding may be obtained by determining the swelling power and solubility at 95°, using the method of Leach and co-workers (5).

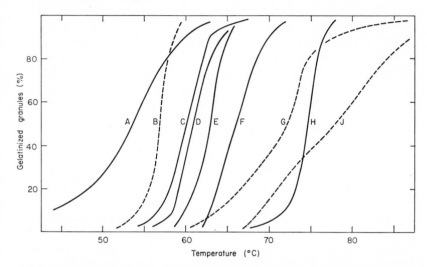

Fig. 1.—Kofler gelatinization temperature ranges of various starches: A, sulfodicarboxylic ester of corn starch; B, barley starch; C, cationic corn starch, 0.05 D.S.; D, potato starch; E, hydroxyethyl sorghum starch, 0.1 D.S.; F, corn starch; G, cationic high-amylose corn starch; H, sorghum starch; J, high-amylose corn starch, 55% amylose.

Occasionally, a food-grade potato starch may be encountered with a gelatinization temperature substantially higher than normal. When heated above the gelatinization range, the granules do not swell freely but show a restricted lobe-type of swelling. Individual granules may open up by a radial split, and then contort into shrimp-like shapes. If the swelling power (5) is determined gravimetrically at 95°, it will be restricted far below normal. Such products are "heat-moisture" treated, probably by maintaining high humidity during the drying operation. This causes a rearrangement in the crystalline pattern within the granule, similar to the heat-moisture treatment of Sair (6) or the hot digestion in 70% diacetone alcohol (4-hydroxy-4-methyl-2-pentanone) described by Leach and co-workers (5). The purpose of heat-moisture treatment is to restrict granule swelling and thus stabilize the paste viscosity. While most starches will undergo some increase in gelatinization temperature on heat-moisture treatment as shown in Table I, marked alteration in paste properties is obtained only with the high-swelling root and tuber starches, such as tapioca and potato.

Table I also shows the gelatinization temperatures of various chemically modified starches. The following significant features will be noted:

1. Lower degrees of acid modification, as with commercial 40- and 60-fluidity thin-boiling starches, do not significantly alter the gelatinization temperature. Acid modification to the 80-fluidity level surprisingly increases the gelatinization temperature.

2. Oxidized starches show a progressive decrease in gelatinization temperature with increasing oxidation. Similarly, the introduction of hydroxyethyl ether groups lowers the gelatinization temperature by decreasing the intermolecular bonding within the granule.

3. Introduction of ionizable groups, such as cationic ether groups, into granular starch greatly decreases the gelatinization temperature. Mutual repulsion between similarly charged ionic sites within the granule may even induce gelatinization at room temperature.

4. Chemical cross-bonding does not significantly alter the gelatinization temperature of the starch.

The Kofler hot stage can likewise be used to determine gelatinization temperatures in aqueous solutions of sugar and various salts. Depending on their position in the Hofmeister lyotropic series, salts may greatly decrease the gelatinization temperature (thiocyanate, iodide) or may increase it (sulfate, carbonate). As shown in Table I, low concentrations of sucrose do not hinder the gelatinization of corn starch although high concentrations greatly increase the temperature of gelatinization.

VII. Iodine Staining

Iodine staining of granular starches is used routinely to distinguish between the red-staining waxy varieties and the blue-staining normal starch. The percentage of each variety in a mixture can be readily determined by lightly staining the sample with iodine and counting the proportion of red and blue granules in a hemacytometer. For qualitative inspection of starch samples, over-staining with iodine should be avoided since it obliterates certain pertinent features of the granules. In such cases, the procedure recommended by MacMasters (7) is employed whereby the sample is mounted in water medium, a drop of dilute iodine solution is placed at the outside edge of the cover glass, and this iodine solution is then drawn through the sample by touching the opposite edge of the cover glass with a piece of dry filter paper. The advancing iodine boundary is

Table I
Kofler Gelatinization Temperatures of Various Starches
(Initiation, Mid Point and Completion, in °C)

Unmodified Starches			
Corn	62–67–72	Waxy maize	63–68–72
Sorghum	68–73.5–78	Waxy sorghum	67.5–70.5–74
Wheat	58–61–64	Barley	51.5–57–59.5
Tapioca:		Rye	57–61–70
Brazilian	49–57–64.5	Pea (green garden)	57–65–70
Siamese	62–68–73	Rice	68–74.5–78
Dominican	58.5–64.5–70	High-amylose corn	67–80–?[a]
Potato	59–63–68		

Modified Starches			
Acid-modified corn starch:		Hydroxyethyl sorghum starch, thick-boiling:	
40-fluidity	62–67–72	0.06 D.S.[b]	61–66–68
60-fluidity	63.5–69–73.5	0.1 D.S.	58.5–63–67
80-fluidity	68–72–77		
		Heat-moisture treated starches:	
Oxidized corn starch:		Potato:	
low-converted	55–64–73	untreated	56–61–67
medium-converted	54–60–69.5	treated[c]	65–71–77
high-converted	52–59–68	Tapioca:	
		untreated	51–58–66
Cross-bonded starches:		treated[c]	62–65–69
waxy sorghum	67–75–77	Corn:	
waxy maize	63–70–76	untreated	62–65–69
corn	62–69–74	treated[c]	68.5–72–76
Cationic corn starch, high-viscosity:			
0.046 D.S.[b]	52–58–65		
0.11 D.S.	room temperature		

Corn Starch in Various Aqueous Media[d]			
Water	62–66–72	NaOH, % 0.2	55.5–64–69.5
		0.3	49–59–65
Sucrose, % 5	60.5–67–72.5		
10	60–67–74	NaCl, % 1.5	67.5–72–77
20	65.5–72–78	3.0	69.5–74–78.5
30	69.5–74–81	6.0	75–79.5–82.5
40	72–79.5–85		
50	76–85–90.5	Na₂CO₃, % 5	64–70–75
60	84–90.5–96.5	10	67–72–76
		20	77.5–82–87
		30	92–98–103

[a] Complete gelatinization of high-amylose corn starch is not effected in boiling water.

[b] D.S. = degree of substitution.

[c] Heat-moisture treated by refluxing in 70% diacetone alcohol, according to Leach and co-workers (5).

[d] The same sample of corn starch was used in these tests in various aqueous media.

examined microscopically to show all gradations of staining. Light staining does not obscure the interference cross under polarized light, and a mixture of waxy and normal starches then appears as red and blue granules on a dark field. This permits the detection of any incipient or extensive gelatinization of either or both of the components.

VIII. DYE STAINING

Anionic starches stain with positively charged organic dyes, and conversely cationic starches stain with negative dyes (4). The degree of staining is a qualitative indication of the ionic charge on the starch. For example, potato starch, a natural ionic starch phosphate, stains a uniform moderately dark blue with methylene blue. The preferred practice is to add 25–50 mg. of the starch to 0.1% aqueous methylene blue solution in a small test tube, mix by shaking, and centrifuge. The supernatant dye solution is decanted; the sedimented starch is washed once by shaking with distilled water followed by centrifugation, and the stained sample is then examined under the microscope. Among the more common anionic starches are the oxidized products, various phosphate ester derivatives, and in Europe, carboxymethylstarch. An important point is the uniformity of staining. If some of the granules are strongly stained and the remainder unstained, either a deliberate blend or accidental contamination is indicated. If all degrees of staining are observed in a single sample, the method of modification has not been uniform and homogeneous. For example, oxidized starch produced by a semi-dry process shows a wide range of staining due to nonuniform reaction between the individual granules and the oxidizing agent.

Cationic starches are never encountered in food use, but they are becoming increasingly important for the sizing of paper. The preferred stain for these products is "light green SF yellowish," obtainable as a certified biological stain. The same considerations apply with respect to depth and uniformity of staining as with methylene blue.

IX. PREGELATINIZED STARCHES

Pregelatinized starches are convenience products, precooked and dried by the manufacturer, which reconstitute to give viscous pastes on the addition of water. They have practical importance as constituents of packaged pre-mixes and as thickening agents for users who do not have the facilities for cooking starches. The latter category includes such widely varied applications as bodying agents for oil well drilling muds, adhesives in foundry cores for metal casting, and thickeners for pie fillings and sauces.

The mode of drying can usually be determined by mounting the sample in glycerol and examining under low-power magnification (100–200×).

1. *Spray-dried.*—These products consist of hollow spheres, with an air cell at the center. In production, the starch is cooked first in water, and the hot paste is sprayed into a drying chamber or tower.

2. *Roll-dried.*—These appear as flat irregular platelets quite similar to broken shards of window glass. In production these products are generally simultaneously cooked and dried on heated rolls, using either a closely set pair of squeeze rolls or a single roll with a closely set doctor blade. In either case, a paper-thin flake is obtained which is then ground to the desired screen size.

3. *Drum-dried.*—The individual particles are much thicker and more irregular in dimensions than roll-dried starches. The process of production is similar to roll-drying, except that a thicker coating of paste is applied to the heated rolls and the dried product is then ground to size. Similar products are likewise produced by recent extruder processes whereby moistened starches are forced through a superheated chamber under very high shear, then "exploded" and simultaneously dried by venting to atmospheric pressure.

One of the most important characteristics of a pregelatinized starch is the particle size. Finely ground products generally give the highest viscosity when reconstituted with water, and properly prepared pastes show a good surface gloss. However, such products are difficult to disperse in water since they tend to hydrate too rapidly, giving lumps and clots which may contain unwetted starch in the center. Coarsely ground products reconstitute much more readily in cold water, but the pastes are of lower viscosity and may have a grainy surface.

To be effective as a thickening agent, substantially all the granules of a pregelatinized starch should be well gelatinized. This can be qualitatively evaluated by slurrying the product in cold water and examining under the polarizing microscope. There should be no significant number of ungelatinized granules showing polarization crosses. Yet commercial products have actually been encountered containing 25% or more of granules that still retained their polarization crosses; obviously these materials have poor efficiency as cold-pasting products.

The species of a pregelatinized starch can frequently be identified by the fact that a very few granules may escape gelatinization during manufacture. However, these cannot be distinguished in the mass of pregelatinized starch. If the sample is treated with a strong solution of a liquefying alpha-amylase for 30–60 min. at 30°–40°, the pregelatinized material is dissolved leaving the ungelatinized granules intact. The mixture can then be centrifuged, and the trace of insoluble sediment examined under the polarizing microscope. The enzyme solution should be carefully filtered before use to remove any insoluble material. This procedure will readily detect one part per thousand of ungelatinized granules and thus identify the starch origin. However, the method must be used with considerable discrimination; for example, if the manufacturer processes several species of pregelatinized and granular starches, trace contamination by the latter may occur, either air-borne or by common use of bagging equipment. The sediment may also show honeycomb-like structures; these are empty cellwall residues from which the starch granules have been removed. Since these structures do not survive a wet-milling operation, their presence is indicative of a dry-milled cereal.

The identity of a pregelatinized starch, or of a physical mixture of several pregelatinized starches, can sometimes be determined by iodine staining. A few milligrams of the dry material is placed on a microscope slide, moistened with a droplet of water, and covered with a cover glass. A drop of very dilute iodine solution is allowed to seep in from the edge of the cover glass, and the advancing stained boundary is examined microscopically. Particles of waxy starch will stain red or brownish-red, corn or wheat particles a blackish or purplish-blue, and potato or tapioca a strong bright blue. If the starch particles swell too much under these conditions, it may be feasible to dust some of the dry finely powdered material on a microscope slide, cover with a cover glass, focus on an appropriate field, and then seep very dilute iodine solution into the sample. In this manner, the color of the particles at the advancing wet boundary can be observed before excessive swelling occurs. The method is applicable only to single pregelatinized starches, or to dry-blended mixtures of several pregelatinized starches. If a mixture of several starches, such as corn and potato, is roll-dried, the identity of the composite particle cannot be determined. It is not generally recognized that carboxymethylcellulose will stain blue with iodine under these conditions; however, this material can be recognized easily as brilliantly birefringent fibrils when the sample is mounted in glycerol and examined under the polarizing microscope. Amylose-complexing agents such as monoglyceride are sometimes added to pregelatinized starches to slow hydration and thus improve dispersibility in water. Since such adjuncts interfere with iodine color, a small portion of the sample should be extracted several times in a test tube with hot ethanol, then dried, and tested with iodine under the microscope.

Occasionally useful information can be obtained by staining a pregelatinized starch with methylene blue or with light green SF. The technique is the same as for iodine staining, except that excess dye should be subsequently removed by drawing a droplet of distilled water through the sample with a piece of filter paper. For example, this technique can be used to distinguish between pregelatinized potato and tapioca starch, since the latter does not bind the stain.

X. Microexamination of Enzyme-Liquefied Bread

Enzymic liquefaction has been employed to facilitate microscopic examination of bread. This technique is suggested as a possible supplement to micro-examination of sectioned samples. When bread crumb is digested with a filtered solution of alpha-amylase, as previously described for the examination of pregelatinized starches, the crumb structure is rapidly and completely liquefied to give a fluid system that can be readily examined under the microscope, either with or without staining. Rather surprisingly, the gelatinized wheat starch granules are not attacked, or are only very slowly attacked, even after 24-hr. digestion. Probably the starch substance is so thoroughly retrograded within the granule that it resists enzyme digestion.

It is suggested that this technique may be useful in showing the influence of emulsifiers on the state of dispersion of the fat, using suitable fat-soluble stains. However, such an application requires more definite establishment by competent experts. The method has been useful in showing that dusting the dough with starch is not a cause of subsequent rifts or breaks in the crumb structure. Thus waxy sorghum starch was used for dusting, and the bread baked. The surfaces of the internal rifts were scraped off, liquefied with enzyme, and tested with iodine. The proportion of red-staining starch was no higher than in the rest of the crumb structure, showing that there was no localization of the dusting starch in these rifts.

XI. References

(1) R. W. Kerr, in "Chemistry and Industry of Starch," R. W. Kerr, ed., 2nd Ed., Academic Press Inc., New York, N. Y., 1950, pp. 18–25.

(2) E. Young, in "Starch and Its Derivatives," J. A. Radley, ed., 3rd Ed., Chapman and Hall, Ltd., London, Vol. 2, 1953, p. 443ff.

(3) E. T. Reichert, "The Differentiation and Specificity of Starches in Relation to Genera, Species, etc.," Carnegie Institution of Washington, Washington, D. C., Publication 173, Parts 1 and 2, 1913.

(4) T. J. Schoch and E. C. Maywald, Anal. Chem., 28, 382 (1956).

(5) H. W. Leach, L. D. McCowen, and T. J. Schoch, Cereal Chem., 36, 534 (1959).

(6) L. Sair and W. R. Fetzer, Ind. Eng. Chem., 36, 205 (1944).

(7) M. M. MacMasters, in "Methods in Carbohydrate Chemistry," R. L. Whistler, ed., Academic Press Inc., New York, N. Y., Vol. 4, 1964, p. 237.

CHAPTER XXVII

PHOTOGRAPHS OF STARCHES

By Gerald P. Wivinis (Technical Photographer) AND
Eileen C. Maywald

Moffett Technical Center, Corn Products Co., Argo, Illinois

I. INTRODUCTION

The starches shown in the accompanying plates were chosen primarily for their diversity of granule appearance. Their sizes range from the almost submicroscopic granules of taro to the enormous granules of canna. Hilum position varies from centric (wheat) to extremely eccentric (banana), and polarization crosses from very brilliant (potato) to relatively weak (wheat). In most starches, the granules are single or simple; however, those of alstroemeria and of high-amylose pea are compound, and the granules of lentil and other legume starches are frequently twinned. Figures 1–31 are at a magnification of exactly 700 diameters; Figure 32 of potato cells is of lower magnification. Reichert's monograph (*1*) contains excellent photomicrographs of over 300 starches under normal and polarized light.

II. PHOTOMICROGRAPHIC METHODS

Microscope equipment.—A Zeiss polarizing microscope (Model WL) was used, fitted with Zeiss 25× planapochromat objective (N.A. = 0.65) and Zeiss 10× Komplan ocular. This optical system, or its equivalent from another manufacturer, is essential for a flat "in-focus" field and good definition.

Filter.—A green filter (Kodak No. 58-B) was employed to provide monochromatic light for improved detail.

Magnification.—By means of a stage micrometer slide (1 mm. graduated in 0.01 mm. divisions), the bellows of the camera was adjusted to give exactly 400× magnification on the ground-glass viewing plate. Prints were then enlarged to a final magnification of exactly 700×. To ensure against error, a photomicrograph of the micrometer slide was processed in the same fashion as the starch samples.

Film, exposure and development.—Kodak 5 × 7 inch panchromatic Tri-X film was used (ASA rating = 320). Illumination was determined with a Gossen Lunasix exposure meter with both normal and polarized light. To improve contrast, exposure was decreased to one-quarter the calculated time, and the film was then overdeveloped in Kodak Polydol (13.5 minutes at 20° instead of the normal 8 minutes' development). Exposure time was approximately 0.2 second with normal lighting, and 0.5–2 seconds with polarized light.

Photography of samples.—To minimize evaporation and movement of granules in the field, the powdered starches were suspended in 1:1 glycerol–water mixture. Brownian movement was observed with several of the small-granule starches; this was minimized by dissolving a trace of sodium chloride in the medium. With each starch, the same field was photographed with both normal and polarized light merely by inserting or withdrawing the polaroid analyzer in the body tube of the microscope.

III. DESCRIPTION OF STARCHES

Alstroemeria starch is obtained from the tubers of South American *Alstroemeria chilensis*, that is related to the amaryllis family. Granules are round or oval, sometimes with deep fissures. Most granules are compound and show multiple hila under normal light and brilliant multiple interference crosses under polarized light. A similar starch from *Alstroemeria ligtu* has been marketed commercially under the name of Chilean or Talcohuano "arrowroot" (Figs. 1, 2).

Banana starch is obtained from the green fruit of *Musa paradisiaca* var. *sapientum*. Granules are irregular, oval or pear-shaped, with extremely eccentric hila and pronounced lamellations. Polarization crosses are of moderate to strong brightness (Figs. 3, 4).

Barley starch, obtained from the seed of *Hordeum vulgare*, is a mixture of very small granules (1–2 microns) and large round or round-oval granules. No hilum is visible. Polarization crosses in large granules are centric and of moderate to low brightness. Small granules show little or no birefringence (Fig. 27).

Canna starch obtained from the tubers of *Canna edulis* is also termed "tous-les-mois" starch and (improperly) "Australian arrowroot." Granules are the largest of any commercial starch. The shape is a broad oval, with pronounced lamellations around a very eccentric hilum. Polarization crosses are very strong (Figs. 5, 6).

Corn or maize starch, obtained from the seed of *Zea mays* var. *indentata*, is a mixture of rounded granules from the floury endosperm and angular granules, usually 4- or 5-sided, from the horny endosperm; the latter show pronounced pressure facets from field-drying. The hilum is centric, and polarization crosses are of moderate to strong brightness (Figs. 7, 8).

High-amylose corn starch, obtained from the seed of maize varieties containing 55–70% of linear fraction, has deformed, lobed, or greatly elongated (rod-like) granules, with little or no birefringence (Figs. 9, 10).

Lentil starch from the seed of *Lens esculenta* (or *L. culinaris*) is one of the most ancient cultivated foods (possibly the biblical "mess of pottage" of Esau). Granules are oval or kidney-shaped, with fairly pronounced lamellations. Some compound granules may be observed. The hila are centric and sometimes deeply fissured. The polarization crosses are strong (Figs. 11, 12).

Maranta starch is true St. Vincent arrowroot starch from the rootstock of West Indian *Maranta arundinacea*. The granules are irregularly oval with a moderately eccentric and frequently fissured hilum. The polarization crosses are strong (Figs. 13, 14).

Oat starch, obtained from the seed of *Avena sativa*, has small, usually angular granules, frequently associated in natural aggregates. Polarization crosses are generally centric and relatively weak (Fig. 28).

High-amylose pea starch was obtained from the seed of wrinkled-seeded garden peas, *Pisum sativum* var. "Laxton's Progress," which contains 75% of linear fraction. Most of the granules are compound, in the form of rounded rosettes. Birefringence is low, and most granules show no distinct polarization cross (Figs. 15, 16).

Potato starch, obtained from tubers of *Solanum tuberosum*, consists mostly of large oval granules, with highly eccentric hila and pronounced lamellations ("oyster-shell" striations) and very bright polarization crosses (Figs. 17, 18).

Potato starch granules within the cells of the tuber are shown at a lower magnification in Fig. 32.

Rice starch is obtained from the seed of *Oryza sativa*. The granules are the smallest of the common commercial starches. They are very angular (usually 5-sided) and frequently aggregated into large clusters owing either to inadequate steeping or to improper drying during manufacture, and have a centric hilum and a relatively low birefringence (Fig. 29).

Rye, obtained from the seed of *Secale cereale*, is a mixture of large and small granules, round or lens-shaped, with centric hila sometimes fissured and moderate birefringence. (Figs. 19, 20).

Sago starch is obtained from the stem piths of various East Indian and Malaysian palms, including *Sagus rumphii*, *Metroxylon sagu*, and *Cycas revoluta*. It has oval and truncated oval granules, with eccentric and frequently fissured hila, and strong polarization crosses (Figs. 21, 22).

Sweet potato starch is obtained from the root of *Ipomoea batatas* (or *Batatas edulis*) and is sometimes termed batata starch. The photographed sample was a white Japanese variety. Most granules are polyhedral, with some rounded and faceted-round granules. The hilum is usually centric, and polarization crosses vary from strong in rounded granules to low in polyhedral granules (Fig. 30).

Tapioca starch, obtained from the root of *Manihot utilissima*, is also known as cassava or manioc starch and (improperly) as "Brazilian arrowroot." Granules are of various types: round, truncated egg-shaped, and cap-shaped. Hila are centric, sometimes slightly fissured. Polarization crosses are of moderate to strong brightness (Figs. 23, 24).

Taro starch is obtained from the tubers of Polynesian *Colocasia antiquorum* var. *esculenta* (*Caladium esculentum*) and is also known as dasheen and eddo starch. Granules are 1 micron or less in diameter, probably the smallest authentic starch. Birefringence is extremely low (Fig. 31).

Wheat starch, obtained from the seed of *Triticum aestivum* (*T. sativum*), contains two distinct granule types: (*a*) large round granules that are actually lens-shaped, and (*b*) small spherical granules. The hilum is not visible. Polarization crosses are centric and of low to moderate brightness. However, large lens-shaped granules show very bright polarization crosses when viewed edgewise. Commercial starches may contain a substantial number of damaged granules due to dry-milling of the grain (Figs. 25, 26).

IV. Reference

(*1*) E. T. Reichert, "The Differentiation and Specificity of Starches in Relation to Genera, Species, etc.," Carnegie Institution of Washington, Washington, D.C., Publication **173**, Part 1, 1913.

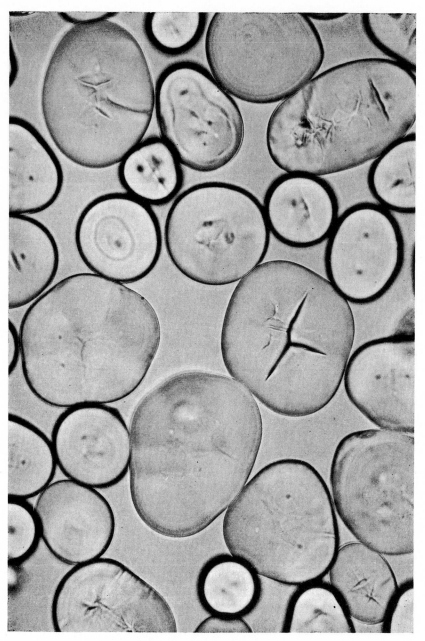

Fig. 1.—Alstroemeria starch.

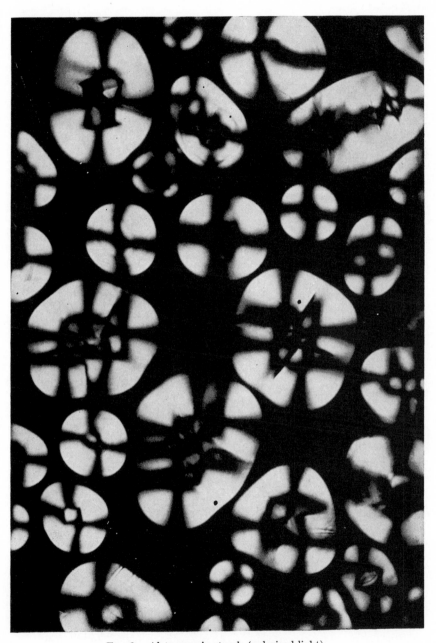

FIG. 2.—Alstroemeria starch (polarized light).

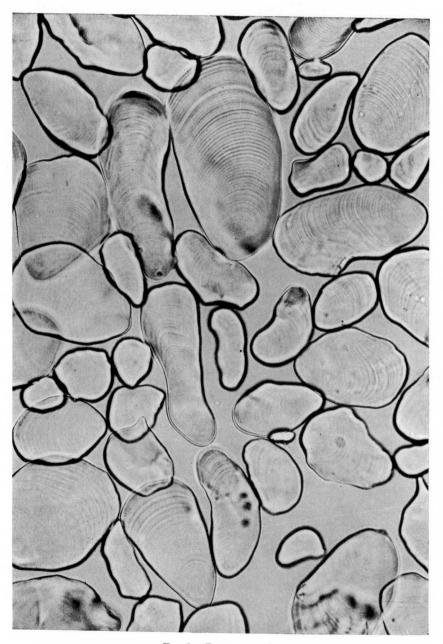

FIG. 3.—Banana starch.

FIG. 4.—Banana starch (polarized light).

FIG. 5.—Canna starch.

FIG. 6.—Canna starch (polarized light).

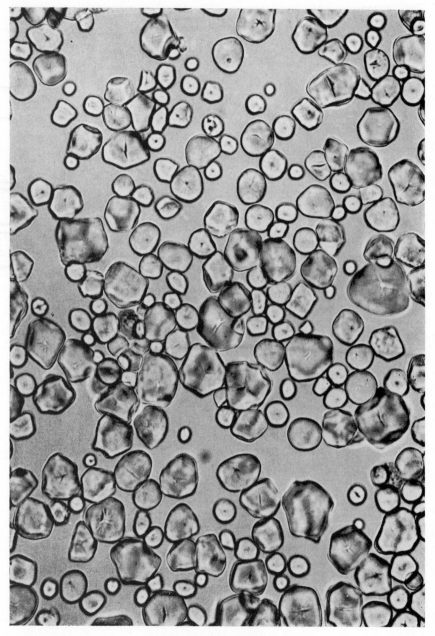

FIG. 7.—Corn starch.

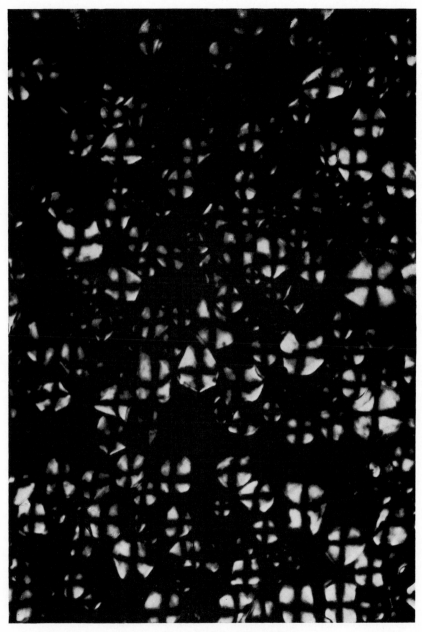

FIG. 8.—Corn starch (polarized light).

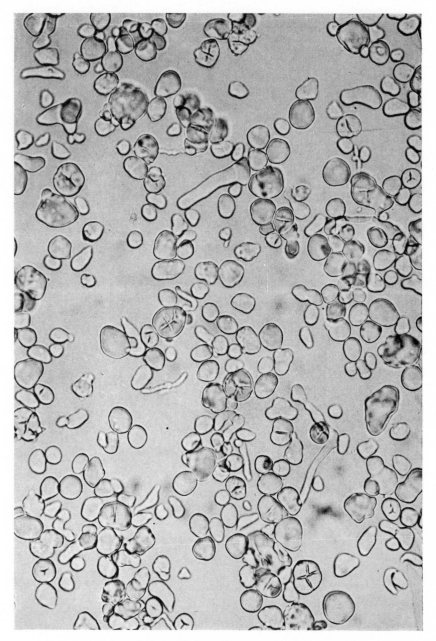

FIG. 9.—High-amylose corn starch.

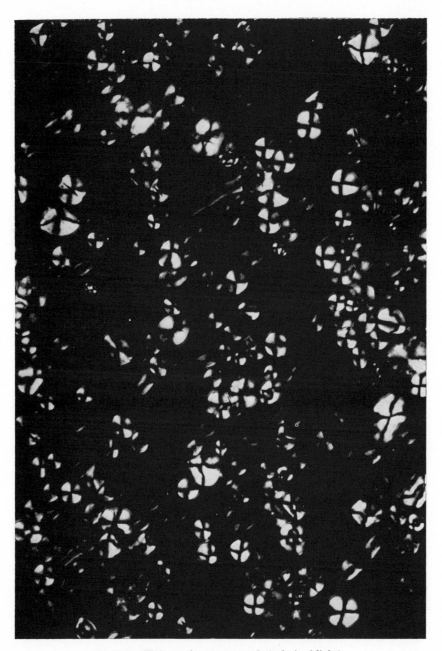

FIG. 10.—High-amylose corn starch (polarized light).

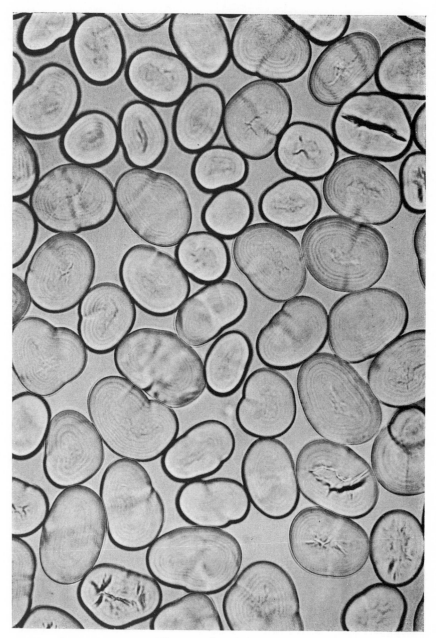

Fig. 11.—Lentil starch.

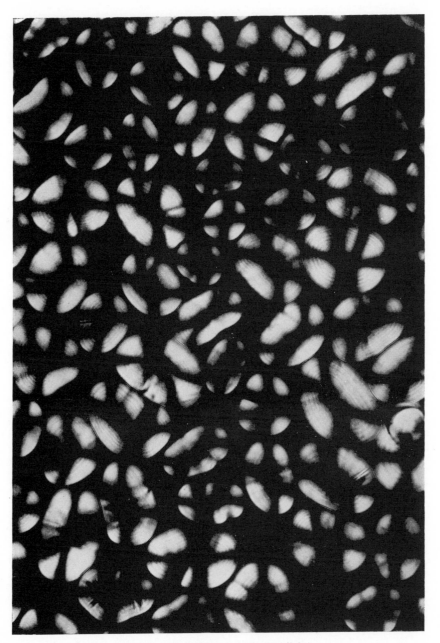

FIG. 12.—Lentil starch (polarized light).

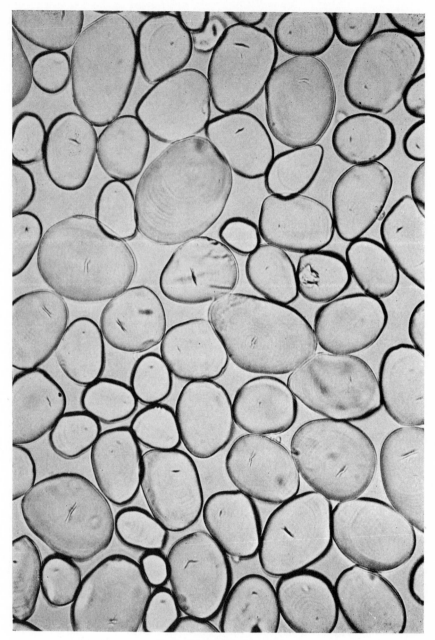

FIG. 13.—Maranta starch.

Fig. 14.—Maranta starch (polarized light).

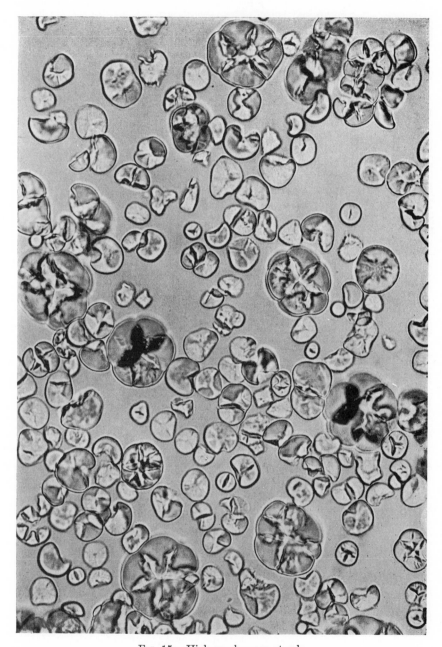

FIG. 15.—High-amylose pea starch.

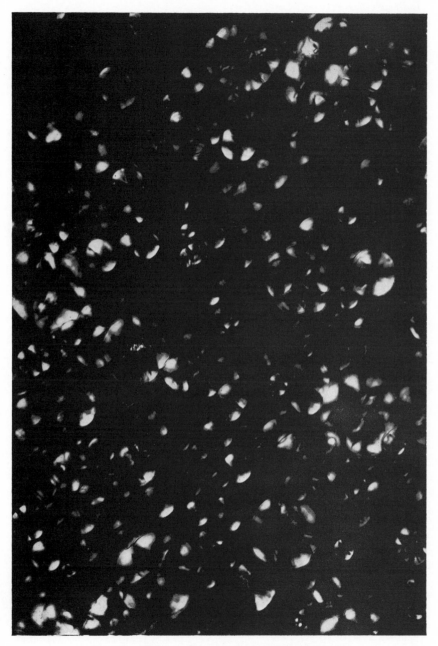

Fig. 16.—High-amylose pea starch (polarized light).

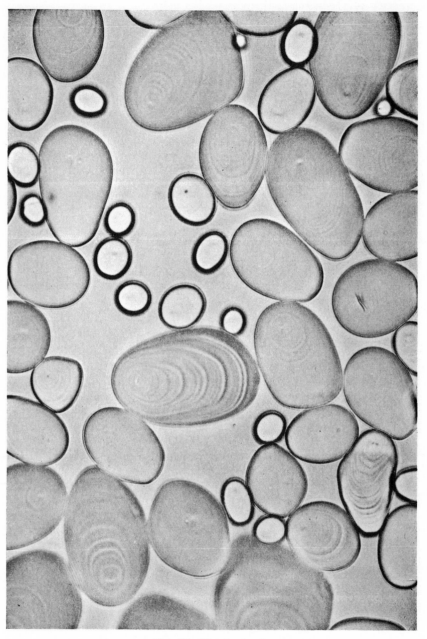

FIG. 17.—Potato starch.

FIG. 18.—Potato starch (polarized light).

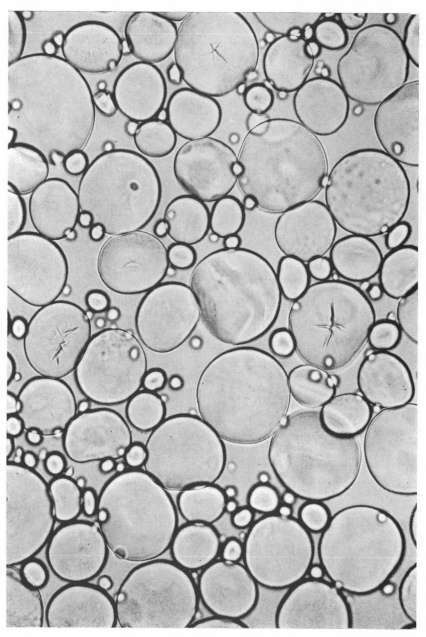

Fig. 19.—Rye starch.

FIG. 20.—Rye starch (polarized light).

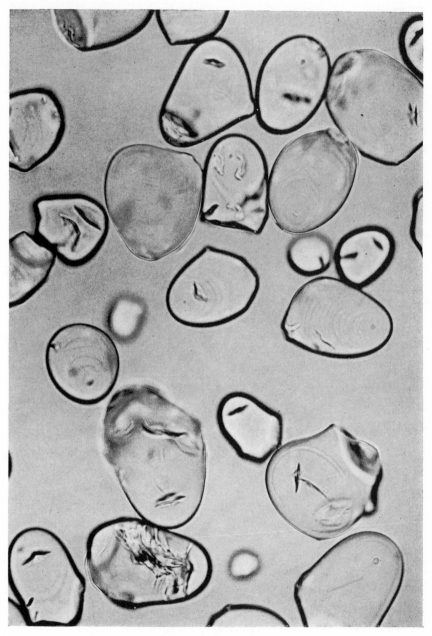

FIG. 21.—Sago starch.

Fig. 22.—Sago starch (polarized light).

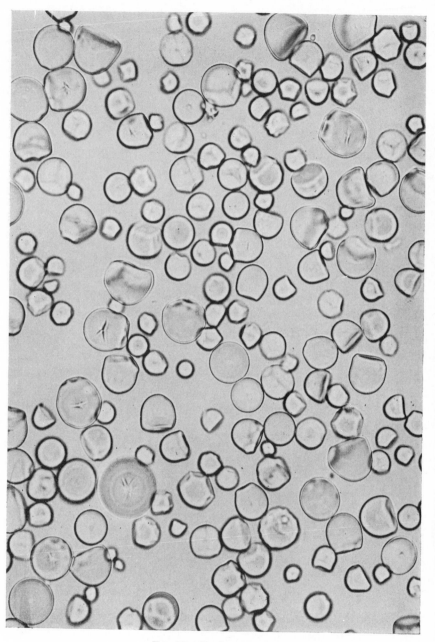

FIG. 23.—Tapioca starch.

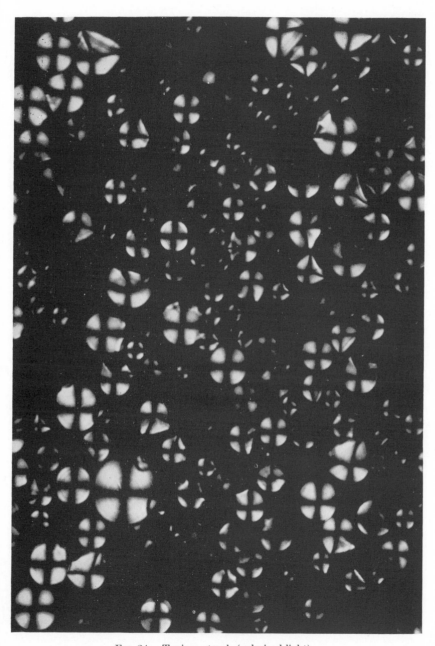

Fig. 24.—Tapioca starch (polarized light).

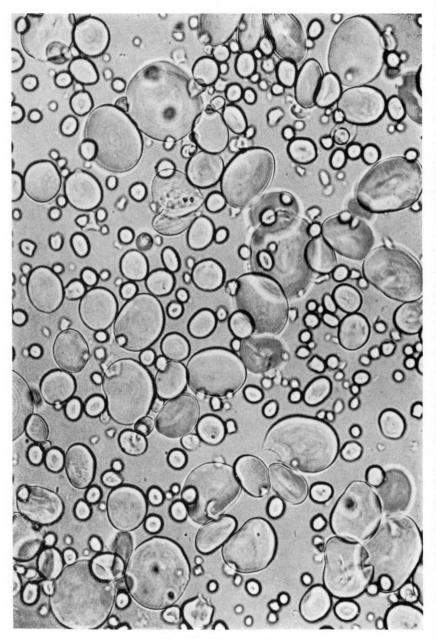

FIG. 25.—Wheat starch.

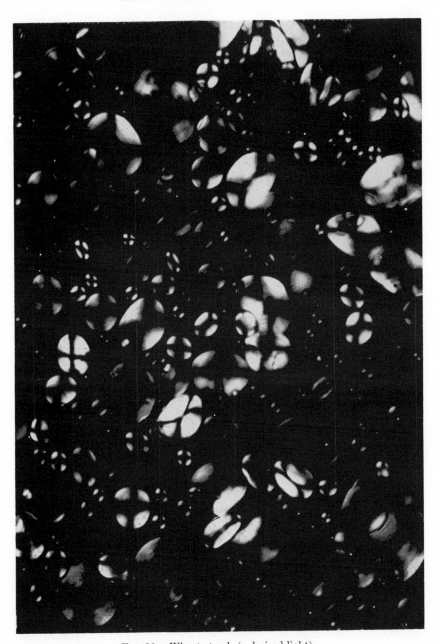

FIG. 26.—Wheat starch (polarized light).

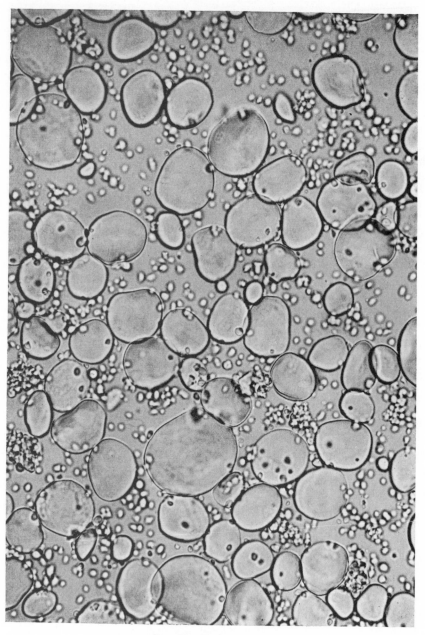

FIG. 27.—Barley starch.

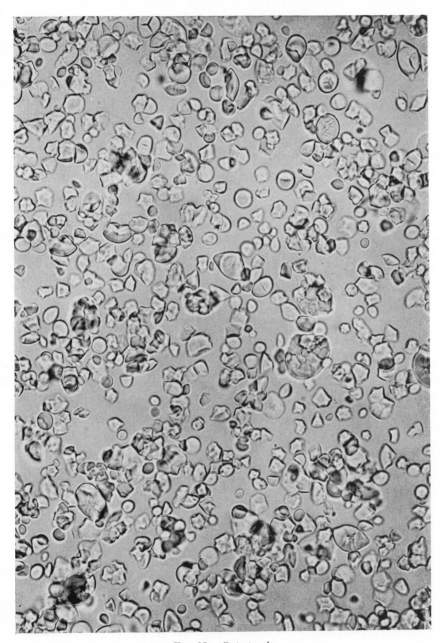

Fig. 28.—Oat starch.

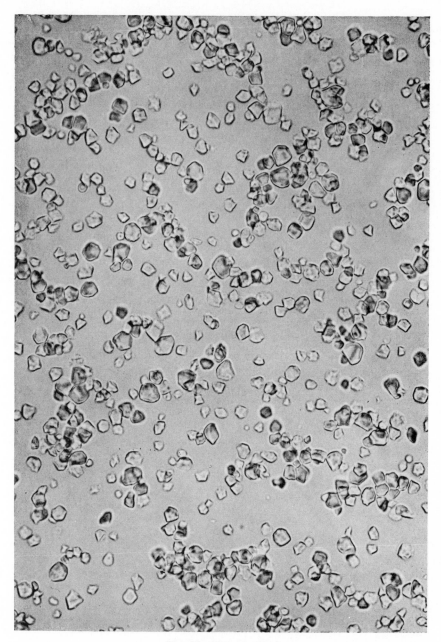

FIG. 29.—Rice starch.

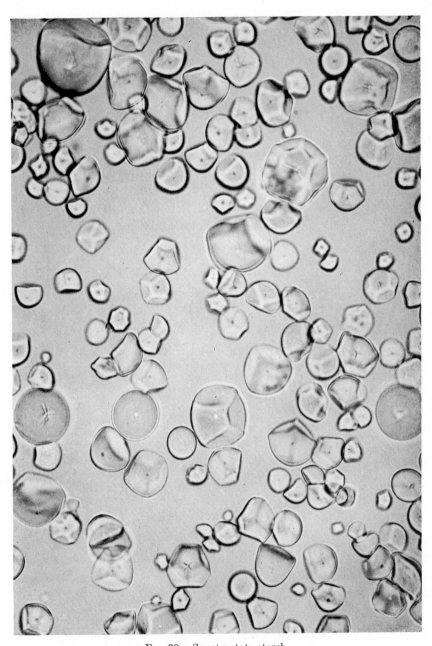

FIG. 30.—Sweet potato starch.

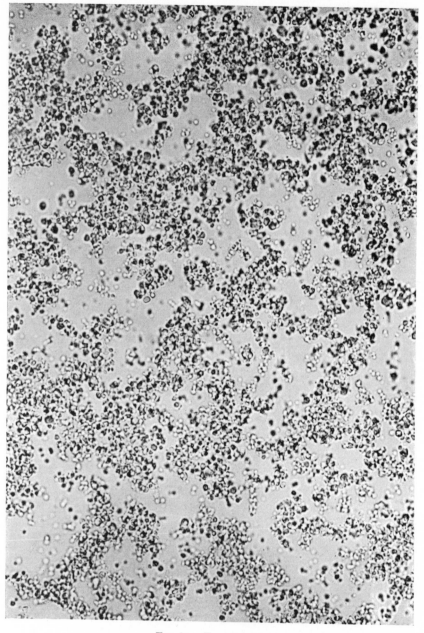

FIG. 31.—Taro starch.

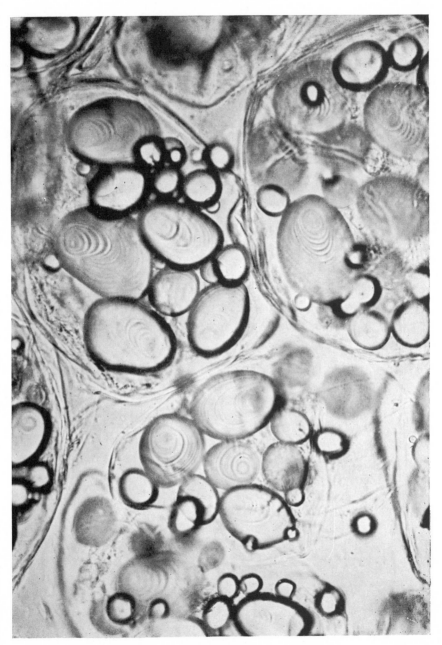

Fig. 32.—Potato starch granules within tuber cells.

AUTHOR INDEX

Numbers in parentheses are reference numbers and indicate that an author's work is referred to although his name is not cited in the text. Numbers in italic show the page on which the complete reference is listed.

A

Abbott, R. C., 187(91), *213*, 510(22), *521*

Abdel-Akher, M., 328(465), *348*, 438(29), *443*, 458(25), *494*

Abdullah, M., 556(25), *567*

Adams, G. A., 55(7), *62*

Adamek, E. G., 311(202, 204), 312(202), 325(202), *340*

Adamo, G., 298(26), 303(26), 304(88), 307(26), *334*

Adams, R., 323(389), *345*

Afanas'eva, E. M., 464, *495*

Agness, B., 303(78), *336*

Airy, J. M., 10(28), *48*

Ajichi, T., 317(307), *343*

Ajinimoto, K. K., 316(283), *342*

Akiyama, V., 316(277), *342*

Albert, C. G., 137, *144*

Albrecht, J. J., 177(71, 72), *212*, 357, *367*

Alsberg, C. L., 194(105), *213*, 222(38), *234*

Alverson, L. H., 561(54), *568*

Altschul, A., 14(43), *49*

Altschul, A. M., 67(8), *78*

Anastasi, A., 36(122), *51*

Anderson, D. M. W., 82(7), *86*, 456(16), *494*

Anderson, E., 23(95), *50*

Anderson, J. R., 299(46), 304(46), 314(46), *335*

Anderson, J. S., 556(22), *567*

Anderson, R. A., 28(108), 29(109), *51*, 56(17), 57(24, 25), 58(25), 59(25), 60(25a), *62*, 501(5–9), 502(13), 503(13), 504, 505(5, 6, 7), 514, *521*

Ando, T., 556(19, 20), 558, *567*

Andreasen, A. A., 558(35), *567*

Andrianou, K. A., 324(423, 424), *347*

Angel, T. H., 551, *552*

Angier, D. J., 329(490), *349*

Anker, C. A., 184(86), *213*, 600, *633*

Apple, R. S., 317(292), *317*

Appleman, C. O., 202, 204, *214*

Arakawa, M., 322(386), *345*

Archer, E. E., 629(115), *635*

Armbruster, F. C., 559(41), *567*

Arnold, K. A., 138, *145*

Asahina, T., 324(422), *347*

Asdell, B. K., 137, *144*, *145*

Ashby, M. L., 416(63), 439(33), *422*

Ashford, W. R., 311(184), *339*

Aslett, M. J., 89(2), *101*

Astbury, W. P., 455(13), *494*

Astrup, T., 309(162), *339*

Aszalos, A., 381(41, 42), *400*, *401*, 411(40), *421*

Aten, A., 67(9), *78*, 104(2), *119*

Atkinson, R. W., 556(12), *566*

Augustat, S., 457, 481(22), *494*

Autrey, H. S., 67(8), *78*

Avery, G. S., Jr., 19(70), *50*

Axtmayer, A. J., 166(7), *211*

B

Babcock, G. E., 328(472), *348*

Badenhuizen, N. P., 254, *276*, 507, 510, *521*

Bahlmann, E. F., 608(73), *633*

Bailey, J. J., 629(111), *635*

Bailey, L. H., 171(36), *211*

Baird, D. K., 453(5), *493*

Baird, P. D., 21(83), 34(83), *50*

Baker, D., 407(25), *421*

Baker, G. L., 608(74), *634*

Baker, M. H., 324(412)

Balassa, L., 428(65), *432*

Balassa, L. L., 314(258), 315(273), 316(273), *341*, *342*

Baldinus, J. G., 309(172), *339*

Baldwin, A. R., 16(52, 54), 28(54), *49*

Baldwin, R. R., 463, 465(35), *494*

Ball, E. M., 559(38), *567*

Balle, G., 375(32), *400*

Banasik, O. J., 581(26), *632*

Bandel, D., 439(39), *443*

Banks, W. H., 546, *552*

Barber, E. J., 425(35, 36), *431*

687

SUBJECT INDEX

A

Acetals, 330
Acetates, 333, 369–399
  determination of, 332, 399, 610–612
  effect on gelatinization, 386
  low degree of substitution, 384–389
  paper, in, 388–389
  preparation, 371–387
  properties, 390–399
  uses, 387–389
  viscosity, 385, 391
Acetylation, acid catalyst, effect on, 373
Acetyl determination, 332, 399, 610–612
Acetylsalicylate, 304
Acidity determination, 579, 580
Acid-modified starch, *see also Thin Boiling*, 217–234
  alkali number, 227
  candy, in, 232, 234
  formation, 222, 223
  gelatinization, 223–227
  gel strength, 224–227
  highly depolymerized, 389–399
  history, 218, 219
  hydrolysis, 222–227
  industrial uses, 230–234
  laundry, 233, 234
  molecular weight, 227–230
  paper, in, 233
  production, 219–222
  properties, 223–230
  size, in, 231
  solubility, 223, 224
  textiles, in, 230–232
  uses, industrial, 230–234
  viscosity, 222, 224–227
  wheat starch, 286
Acrylic latices in paper, 135
Acrylonitrile, 320, 321
Adhesion, size, 152
Adhesives, 538–552
  amylose, 491
  bags, in, 547–549
  borax, in, 275
  British gums, in, 276
  classification of, 539, 545–547

corrugated board, in, 549–550
cross-linked starch, in, 449
defoamers, 544
dextrins, in, 274–276
dry, 540
envelope, 287
law, 545
liquid, 540
  starch, 541, 542
manufacture, 538–545
mineral fillers, 545
packaging of, 545
plasticizers, 544
potato starch, 100
pregelatinized starch, 532
preservatives, 544
sacks, in, 547–549
uses, 547–552
viscosity, 545, 546
water resistant, 543, 544
wetting agents, 544
wheat starch, 281, 284, 285
Adipate, 333
Aging, *see Retrogradation*
Agriculture, *see Culture*
Air knife coating, paper, 141
Aleurone layer, corn, 11, 12, 34
  milo, 25, 26
Alkali degradation, oxidized starch, 246, 247
  lability, starch dextrins, 267–269
  number, acid-modified starch, 227
    determination, 587–589
  process, rice, 73–80
    wheat starch, 55
Alkoxides, 330, 331
Alkoxyl determination, 612–616
Alkyl, determination, 332
  ether, 322, 324
Alsatian process, wheat starch, 54
Alstroemeria starch, description, 650
  photograph, 654, 655
Alternaria, milo, in, 28
Alum, paper, in, 128
Alumina, paper, in, 128
Amaranthus, 79

715